Multivariate Analysis and Psychological Theory

D1477028

Multivariate Analysis and Psychological Theory

edited by JOSEPH R ROYCE

The Center for Advanced Study
in Theoretical Psychology,
The University of Alberta,
Edmonton, Canada

The Third Banff Conference on Theoretical Psychology

1973

ACADEMIC PRESS . London . New York

A subsidiary of Harcourt Brace Jovanovich, Publishers

ACADEMIC PRESS INC. (LONDON) LTD.
24/28 Oval Road,
London NW1

United States Edition published by
ACADEMIC PRESS INC.
111 Fifth Avenue
New York, New York 10003

An Leabharlann
Leitir Ceanainn
Ceard Choláiste Réigiúin
A 150.1

Copyright © 1973 by
ACADEMIC PRESS INC. (LONDON) LTD.

All Rights Reserved

No part of this book may be reproduced in any form by photostat, microfilm, or any other means, without written permission from the publishers

Library of Congress Catalog Card Number: 72-12278
ISBN: 012 600750-0

PRINTED IN GREAT BRITAIN BY
C. TINLING & CO. LTD, LONDON AND PRESCOT

Participants

In the Third Banff Conference on Theoretical Psychology

JOHANN C. BRENGELMAN.† *Department of Psychology, Max Planck Institute of Psychiatry, Munich, Germany.*

DESMOND S. CARTWRIGHT.* *Department of Psychology, University of Colorado, Boulder, Colorado 80302, U.S.A.*

R. B. CATTELL. *The Department of Psychology, University of Illinois, Champaign, Illinois, U.S.A.*

WILLIAM CLAEYS.*† *Department of Psychology, University of Louvain, Louvain, Belgium.*

D. W. FISKE.*† *Department of Psychology, University of Chicago, Chicago, Illinois 60637, U.S.A.*

B. FRUCHTER.*† *Department of Psychology, The University of Texas, Austin, Texas, U.S.A.*

JEFFREY A. GRAY.*† *Department of Experimental Psychology, University of Oxford, 1 South Parks Road, Oxford OX1 3PS, England.*

J. P. GUILFORD.*† *Department of Psychology, University of Southern California, Los Angeles, U.S.A.*

JOHN L. HORN.*† *Department of Psychology, University of Denver, Denver, Colorado 80201, U.S.A.*

KATHERINE HOWARD.* *Department of Psychology, University of Colorado, Boulder, Colorado 80302, U.S.A.*

GEORGE W. KAWASH.*† *The Center for Advanced Study in Theoretical Psychology, The University of Alberta, Edmonton, Canada T6G 2E9.*

H. LANSDELL.*† *Neuropsychology Section, Clinical Center, National Institute of Health, Bethseda, Maryland, U.S.A.*

S. MESSICK.*† *Educational Testing Service, Princeton, New Jersey 08540, U.S.A.*

KURT PAWLIK*†. *Psychologisches Institut, 2 Hamburg 13, Von Melle Tark 6, Germany.*

WAYNE POLEY.*† *The Center for Advanced Study in Theoretical Psychology, The University of Alberta, Edmonton, Canada T6G, 2E9.*

JOSEPH R. ROYCE.*† *The Center for Advanced Study in Theoretical Psychology, The University of Alberta, Edmonton, Canada T6G 2E9.*

WM. W. ROZEBOOM.*† *The Center for Advanced Study in Theoretical Psychology, The University of Alberta, Edmonton, Canada T6G 2E9.*

SAUL B. SELLS.*† *Institute of Behavioral Research, Texas Christian University, Fort Worth, Texas 76129, U.S.A.*

HERMAN TENNESSEN.† *The Center for Advanced Study in Theoretical Psychology, The University of Alberta, Edmonton, Canada T6G 2E9.*

STEVEN G. VANDENBERG.*† *Department of Psychology, University of Colorado, Boulder, Colorado 80302, U.S.A.*

PHILLIP E. VERNON.*† *Department of Psychology, University of Calgary, Calgary 44, Alberta, Canada.*

T. E. WECKOWICZ.*† *The Center for Advanced Study in Theoretical Psychology, The University of Alberta, Edmonton, Canada T6G 2E9.*

KELLOG, V. WILSON.* *The Center for Advanced Study in Theoretical Psychology, The University of Alberta, Edmonton, Canada T6G 2E9.*

* Contributor to this volume. † Discussant.

Preface

This is the third of our Center-sponsored conferences on theoretical psychology. The proceedings of the first and second conferences appear in "Toward Unification in Psychology" (edited by Joseph R. Royce, University of Toronto Press, 1970) and "The Psychology of Knowing" (edited by Joseph R. Royce and Wm. W. Rozeboom, Gordon and Breach, 1972).

Banff conferences on theoretical psychology are held every few years as a culmination of the Center's program of work on a particular theme. Under the Distinguished Visiting Scholars Program, each year leading contributors to theoretical-philosophical psychology are invited to the Center for seminar visits lasting from a week to as long as a month. A Banff conference provides for a final series of meetings on a particular topic with all relevant Center visitors brought together. The recent theme of Center work responsible for the present conference is "Contributions of Multivariate Analysis to Psychological Theory". Of those presenting papers, R. B. Cattell, University of Illinois; J. P. Guilford, University of Southern California; J. Horn, University of Denver; S. J. Messick, Vice-President, Research, Educational Testing Service; S. G. Vandenberg, University of Colorado; and P. E. Vernon, University of Calgary, have recently visited the Center. A grant from the North Atlantic Treaty Organization permitted the invitation of the following European psychologists: Johann C. Brengelmann, Director, Department of Psychology, Max Planck Institute of Psychiatry, Munich, Germany; Willem Claeys, Department of Psychology, University of Louvain, Louvain, Belgium; Jeffrey A. Gray, Department of Psychology, Oxford University, England; and Kurt W. Pawlik, Department of Psychology, University of Hamburg, Hamburg, Germany.

Drs. Claeys and Brengelmann served as discussants, and Dr. Gray and Professor Pawlik also gave papers. In addition, D. S. Cartwright, University of Colorado; D. W. Fiske, University of Chicago; and Saul Sells, Texas Christian University, were invited to present papers through the Center's conference collaboration with the Society of Multivariate Experimental Psychology. The Center staff had, of course, been hard at work on this theme over a period of several years prior to the conference. Thus, papers were also presented by Center Staff members Joseph R. Royce, T. E. Weckowicz, and K. V. Wilson. Staff members Wm. W. Rozeboom and Herman Tennessen served as discussants. In the case of this particular theme local activity was particularly augmented by a Center Sub-Group working on grants* in support of the Individuality Project. This group consisted of Center Research Associates George W. Kawash and Wayne Poley, and Graduate Research Assistants Allan Buss, David Johnson, and Douglas Wardell. Drs. Kawash and Poley also served as discussants for selected sessions of the conference.

The conference was held over a period of six days, September 27 – October 2, 1971, at the Banff School of Fine Arts in the Canadian Rockies. However, because of our cooperative arrangement with the Society of Multivariate Experimental Psychology, there were modifications of our usual procedure. For the first four days we followed essentially the same format as our previous conferences—namely, pre-distributed invited papers, seminars-in-the-round, and highly compressed commentary following each paper. Participants in a given seminar were limited to around 250 words for the printed version of the discussion material. The official discussant, however, was allowed up to 1000 words, and each author was allowed around 1000 words in rebuttal. In general, the chief discussant's comments are presented first, followed by other comments and the rebuttal. However, due to an embarrassment of riches both in the available talent and in the number of papers, we eliminated the auditors' hours, and we limited each participant to no more than two-thirds of the sessions. This was a welcome procedure as our heavy program (fifteen papers in four days) forced us to double up for some seminars and to schedule three seminars per day for two of the four days. The last two days of the conference followed the standard format of the annual meeting of the Society of Multivariate Experimental Psychology, namely, presentation by SMEP members of thirty to sixty minute papers followed by a typical

* Canada Council Grant Nos. 68–0137, S70–0433 and a grant from the Province of Alberta Human Resources Research Council allocated to Joseph R. Royce.

round table discussion. One advantage to this arrangement was that all participants could attend the sessions of both groups.

Informal evaluations from some of the hundred or so participants confirm our belief that we are engaged in a significant enterprise, both in terms of content and format. The content for this particular conference, although overwhelming, was not quite as broad in scope as our previous two conferences. Perhaps partly for this reason but mostly because of a commonality of prior commitment, it seemed to me that this was the best conference we have held so far. For the quality of intellectual content, and the degree of communication of ideas combined with practically no *ad hominem* irrelevancies, was at an unusually high level. For this we are primarily indebted to the invited participants. What we strive for at Banff conferences can be characterized as "intellectual happenings" which require considerable improvisation on the part of each participant. Thus, the trick is to have a good cast, provide a proper atmosphere, and then turn the actors loose. The key contributor to providing the "proper atmosphere" was the Center Administrative Officer, Hinton Bradbury. Hinton put in months of preparation, and full time at the conference itself as the Conference Manager. But no amount of effort can capture the special something that Hinton provided. Whatever it was (I think it was care combined with unobtrusiveness), it is clear that Hinton's efforts were not in vain.

There were others behind the scene as well. These include Mrs. Leola Roth, Secretary to the Director, who provided her usual pleasant and efficient "general assistance", and later coordinated the collation of manuscript material for this volume; Mr. Paul DeGroot, Department Technician, who, once again, supervised the audiotape and videotape recordings, and the staff of the Banff School of Fine Arts, Banff, Alberta, who provided physical facilities and related services for the conference.

We are also grateful to Henry Kreisel, Academic Vice-President, University of Alberta; John R. McGregor, Dean of Graduate Studies and Research, University of Alberta; W. A. S. Smith, President, University of Lethbridge; each of whom took time away from pressing administrative duties in order to chair one of our seminars-in-the-round.

For the second time we have received very generous financial support from the North Atlantic Treaty Organization. It is clear that a conference of this quality simply would not have been possible without NATO, for their funds provided expenses for all the major participants. Our European colleagues deserve much credit for the academic success of the conference.

We were also financially supported by the University of Alberta.

This consistent funding for each of our conferences allows us to provide extras, such as student stipends to cover living expenses so that University of Alberta graduate students can attend as auditors.

Finally, we are grateful, to Douglas Wardell for the care and work which he put into compiling both the indexes for this book.

JOSEPH R. ROYCE
May 1973

Contents

Introduction and Overview

JOSEPH R. ROYCE*

The Center for Advanced Study in Theoretical Psychology

The Present Situation in Multivariate Theoretical Psychology

The focus of this book is on substantive theory from the perspective of multivariate analysis. Our ultimate goal is to provide a better understanding of behavior, particularly human behavior. We are concerned with the full spectrum of psychological phenomena, whether it be molecular events, such as a reflex or the conditioned response, or molar events, such as a person's life style or international warfare.

In principle, we are open to any method, bivariate or multivariate, which provides us with insight. However, it is our view that there is especially great potential in the combination of multivariate research and theory construction. We base this view on the generally agreed observation that behavior is the most complex system of events to come under scientific surveillance. The ideal of complete scientific control of all variables except one appears to us unlikely of realization in the field of behavior, especially for intact and freely exploring organisms, and especially for the human species. While theory commonly seeks to comprehend an underlying pattern in explaining the flurry of natural events, multivariate techniques are designed precisely to trace as many of the separately varying sources of influence as possible within a given set of data. In short, it is our view that there has been insufficient awareness within psychology of the potential for multivariate theory. Thus this book was stimulated into being out of a concern for the present multivariate–theoretic vacuum, and it is our hope that it will provide a platform on which to build.

Historians of the future, with the advantage of hindsight and per-

* The writer is indebted to his conference colleagues for critical review of this chapter, particularly in providing minor revisions of my brief descriptions of their papers. In addition I wish to thank Henry Kaiser for his gracious and helpful suggestions in the final revision of the section entitled Technical Problems Indigenous to Factor Analysis.

spective, might well ask why their twentieth century colleagues were so blind to the obvious point that psychology is a multivariate domain in need of multivariate method and thought. It is possible to offer some insights on the matter, even though they will suffer from the distortions of a viewpoint which is necessarily non-historical and idiosyncratic (i.e. primarily those of one person, the editor). I will offer this perspective in terms of three sub-headings, which can be referred to as (1) technical problems indigenous to factor analysis, (2) issues indigenous to the psychology zeitgeist and (3) the role of theory in psychology. Before we launch into these issues, however, a word of clarification regarding our usage of the key words "multivariate" and "theory".

The Meaning of Multivariate and Theory

While both terms are meant to be all-inclusive in principle, our coverage is selective in this book. Thus, the word multivariate refers to a wide range of research strategies which deal with many variables simultaneously. This includes such correlational methods as multiple and partial correlation and canonical correlation, such extensions of fundamentally bivariate techniques as multiple analysis of variance and multiple discriminant function, as well as such diverse approaches as latent structure analysis, diallel analysis, path analysis, pattern and profile analysis, multidimensional scaling, multitrait-multimethod matrices, cluster analysis, and multiple factor analysis (see Cattell, 1966, for a comprehensive coverage of multivariate strategies). While we allude to many multivariate strategies in the text, our attention is focused primarily on factor analysis. Hence, my commentary below on technical problems is similarly selective.

The word "theory", while not used in any prescribed, selective sense, has, however, tended to be similarly selective because of the heavy commitment of conference participants to the factor approach. However, I find myself unable to adequately characterize the exact nature of this selectivity for the simple reason that so little is explicitly known regarding theory construction via factor analysis. What I can say is that commitment to the factor approach carries with it a peculiar, and possibly even a paradoxical, scientific problem solving style. This involves a commitment to a highly formal rationalism on the one hand—that is, the mathematical model aspects of factor analysis—and an extremely high respect for data, that is, a serious empiricism, on the other hand. It follows, therefore, that the factor analyst tends to reject both reductionistic, hypothetico-deductivism, and a simple-minded super-empiricism. What he wants is a highly developed formal model whose empirical imperative is that we come up with what we can call "low level" empirical regularities. Why is this paradoxical? For the simple reason that most formal models call for comparable "high level" empirical findings.

How can we account for this rational–empirical paradox? I think it arises out of the essentially pre-scientific, and therefore pre-theoretical, character of the factor analytic enterprise. That is, factor analysis *per se* cannot provide us with full-blown substantive theory. It can provide us with some potentially powerful theoretical constructs, and possibly some clues regarding how these constructs are taxonomically arranged (Royce, 1963), but the building of theoretical structures which elaborate on relationships between variables and otherwise "explain" observables is an extra-factorial enterprise. In this book the reader will be confronted with the spectacle of tough minded concern for both method and data and, in my opinion, a well founded scepticism concerning non-data based substantive theory. The kind of theory presented in this volume has been characterized by the philosophers of science as "low level"—meaning empirically based conceptualizing. While the future holds exciting prospects for a more abstract, high flying, a more comprehensive, unified, multivariate theory, this first summary statement must be limited to a more mundane picture.

Technical Problems Indigenous to Factor Analysis

Putting aside issues concerning the misuse of factor analysis—such problems as assembling poor test batteries, factoring weak raw data, factoring a correlation matrix *post hoc*, and following erroneous procedures as a result of ignorance—there are methodological difficulties at each phase of the factoring process. Most of these problems arise from the fact that empirical data are necessarily fallible. For example, let us take the interrelationships between communality estimates, the rank of the matrix, and criteria for when to stop factoring. On purely algebraic grounds there is no problem here. One simply plugs in communality estimates which are consistent with the rank of the R matrix, adopts any reasonable criterion for the number of common factors, and iterates until there is convergence of communalities. Problems arise in practice, however, because there is no guaranteed method for discriminating between true common factor variance and unique variance.

There are also technical–methodological difficulties in regard to the transformational problem. The essence of this problem is to find a unique position for the factor reference frame. Since the location of the reference axes after factoring is essentially arbitrary (i.e. depends upon the method of factoring), the problem now arises as to what rotated position would not be arbitrary. In principle there are an infinity of possible positions. Thus, what is required is a set of criteria which provide constraints for location of the reference frame. Several such criterion sets have been suggested, the most powerful being the set of criteria for simple structure.* Before the last decade transformations to simple structure had to be done entirely visually, and by hand calculators. With the advent of the computer we have been inundated with an array of pharmaceutical-sounding mathematical solutions such as varimax, quartimax and quartimin, oblimax and oblimin, covarimin, biquartimin, binormamin, promax, parsimax, equamax, maxplane and orthoblique. It is now possible to closely approximate various subsets of simple structure criteria via appropriate computer programs, usually followed by a relatively small number of mopping up graphic rotations (blind rotations constitute the most stringent requirement) to either oblique or orthogonal simple structure. However, there is some indeterminacy in all this. It is not certain, on either empirical or theoretical grounds, to what extent different solutions would converge on the same oblique or orthogonal simple structure. When there are serious *divergencies* in solution criteria (e.g. orthogonal versus oblique solutions), we get different solutions. A reasonable summary of the situation is that, given similar mathematical constraints, there will be convergence on the same solution to the extent there is overdetermined, "clean", simple structure. However, since there is no way to predetermine the nature of the underlying simple structure, it is apparent that we are stuck with some degree of uncertainty about the adequacy of existing mathematical solutions to provide a fit to empirical simple structures.

The current crucial issue in factor methodology is the problem of factor invariance—that is, factor similarity despite shifts in investigators, subjects and tests. Although there are some dozen or two quantitative solutions in the literature, and although some classes of invariance are relatively easy to establish, the really interesting ones, such as the classes of invariance involving different tests or/and different subjects, have not yet been convincingly dealt with. And the extreme case of invariance for different tests and different subjects may actually be unresolvable in principle (i.e. due to insufficient available information).

Other methodological difficulties also arise from deficiencies of sampling—such as the sampling of tests and factors of a given behavioral domain. Finally, we have the problem inherent in failure to follow

* Thurstone's statement contains five criteria. One reason for variations in analytic simple structure solutions is that different classes of mathematical solutions maximize or minimize different subsets of these five criteria.

standardized procedures—that is, different investigators use different methods of factoring, different methods of rotation, and some rotate to orthogonal simple structure and others rotate to oblique simple structure.

However, none of the problems considered above constitutes a truly serious deficiency in method. The practitioner of factor analysis can conduct exciting and fruitful research in spite of these problems because there are reasonable answers for each of them. For example, the factoring problem is hardly an issue any more, with the availability of iterative procedures such as principal axes or alpha factoring, combined with an appropriate index, such as the Guttman-Kaiser eigenvalue criterion, or the Rao-Maxwell-Lawley significance test. Furthermore, even if such a procedure overestimates the number of common factors, the risk involved in rotating a few extra factors is not devastating.* That is, since they will contain so little common factor variance they will eventually be identified as residuals. And the indeterminacy inherent in the rotational problem is also resolvable in practice, but it requires that investigators actually plot their computerized solutions, and follow up with graphic rotations where needed. (N.B. in addition, there is increasing elegance available via mathematical solutions, such as the Harris-Kaiser, 1964 "orthoblique" solution.) Even invariance has been demonstrated in practice, but it must be admitted that it is the weakest link in the factor analytic chain. It is also, in my opinion, the most crucial requirement, as it provides a way to specify the boundary conditions of factors. But it appears that invariance will have to remain essentially qualitative until the more mathematically oriented factor methodologists come up with a more adequate solution. However, we should not forget that bivariate, experimental manipulations of factors also constitute an independent (i.e. extra factor analytic) means of determining the boundary conditions (i.e. invariance) of factors.† With the gradual solution of invariance and related problems,

* It should be pointed out, however, that overestimation of the number of common factors is a more serious problem with current analytic oblique methods. In principle, resolution of the factor invariance problem would provide corrective feedback for a more adequate solution to the number of factors problem.

† I have come to the conclusion that the invariance problem needs to be reconceptualized in terms of boundary conditions. I say this because the present conception imposes an impossible scientific demand, namely, that a factor be completely invariant. But such universality is highly improbable for any scientific phenomenon, and even less so for context-dependent phenomena such as behavior. If we look at factors in terms of boundary conditions, on the other hand, we will have stated the problem in a more manageable form, for then we would merely specify the limits (i.e. in terms of time and space) within which a given factor functions. (N.B. even a phenomenon as universal as gravity has specifiable limits—that is, outside those limits, gravitational pull between physical bodies is inoperative.)

it will eventually be possible to move to a more rational basis for a standardized set of procedures. In the meantime, we should keep in mind that present procedures, although not yet completely standardized, nevertheless lead us to replicable constructs which have considerable theoretical potential. In this connection the reader is referred to Kaiser's (1971) Jiffy III computerized program, which sets out a pragmatic standard operating procedure from initial factoring to the final factor matrix, including a crude index of adequacy of simple structure.

Issues Indigenous to the Psychology Zeitgeist

It was uniquely appropriate for the Society of Multivariate Experimental Psychology to co-sponsor this particular conference because SMEP was founded in the spirit of providing a rapprochement between the traditional bivariate experimental psychology and the more recent multivariate, correlational psychology (e.g. see Royce, 1950; Cronbach, 1957; Cattell, 1966). It is, of course, well known that the bivariate tradition has dominated the early history of our discipline as part of a scientific methodology borrowed from the older sciences. It was natural for the new discipline of psychology to latch on to whatever scientific method it could find in order to gain acceptability in the scientific fraternity and in order to make headway in solving problems. However, it soon became apparent that many problems would not succumb to the traditional bivariate approach. In short, such inadequacies constituted the necessity for such multivariate inventions as multiple and partial correlation, pattern analysis, and factor analysis. However, the early experimental tradition continued to have its successes in the major substantive domains of perception and learning and despite the growth of the testing movement and applied psychology, commitment to the myth of what was "truly scientific" continued to revolve around the magic words "experimental control" and "laboratory research".

Besides, by this time behaviorism had taken the field, along with the implicit philosophy of science known as logical positivism. Thus, the combination of an S–R psychology and a radical empiricistic philosophy left little room for concepts such as traits or other not directly observed (i.e. inferred) constructs.* In short, the behavioristic stranglehold on psychology has just begun to be broken, and we are still suffering from the effects of an outmoded philosophy of science. While it seems reasonable to say that a more flexible cognitive psychology has already

* There are exceptions, of course, such as Hull's intervening variables. But the basic thrust of *radical* behaviorism (e.g. Skinner) is to exorcise unobservables.

begun to replace the previously restrictive behavioristic psychology, our discipline seems to be floundering in a philosophic vacuum at present, torn between the irrationality of existentialism at one extreme, and attempting to break loose from the shackles of operationalism and positivism at the other extreme. Psychology needs to embark on a self-conscious search for a philosophy which emerges from its own problems (Royce, 1970; Wolman, 1971), just as it needs to pay more attention to its indigenous methodology. When this happens, multivariate analysis will be firmly integrated with other approaches within the discipline.

The Role of Theory in Psychology

Advanced scientific disciplines typically go through four stages of development (Royce, 1957): (1) pre-scientific speculative philosophy, (2) empirical exploration, (3) experimental sophistication and (4) rational-mathematical unification. It can be shown that psychology is somewhere between stages (2) and (3), although it has tapped in on stage (4) in a minor way in relatively minute segments of the total discipline. In short, overall, psychology is in a relatively primitive state as a theoretical science. To sum up the matter quite bluntly and inelegantly, we have tons of data which make little or no sense, and whatever sense there is has been provided by a type of conceptualizing which, in general, is more accurately referred to as a point of view rather than substantive theory (what Krech has called "e.g." rather than "i.e." theory). Furthermore, there are a large number of viewpoints and theories, not just one or two. However, because of the enormous complexity of our subject matter, and because of misconceptions concerning what can be accomplished via theory (e.g. see Rozeboom, 1970), the meaning of our multi-theoretic situation is not at all clear and it must be analyzed with great care. For example, Naess, the philosopher (1971), takes the position that, since we cannot escape an underlying pluralistic ontology, pluralism in scientific theory is inevitable. Thus, at least two analysts of the current scene in theoretical psychology, Royce (1970) and Scriven (1969), are of the opinion that psychology can best be described as a multi-paradigmatic science (see Kuhn, 1962, concerning the concept of paradigm).

The relatively low level of sophistication in theory construction within the psychology community also applies to multivariate theory, but it has been exacerbated by the fact that approaches such as factor theory have not been part of mainstream psychology. While there have been notable exceptions (e.g. Thurstone), in much of its history factor analysis has been the esoteric plaything of converted engineers and mathematicians who were not primarily interested in psychological problems. Part of this commitment to pure formalism was both justifiable and necessary, as there were (and still are) serious methodological–technical problems which required solution before factor analysis could move into the theoretical–empirical world with sufficient reliability and validity. However, the result of all this has been a fundamental ignorance and mistrust of factor analysis on the part of the general psychology community. Since a minimal technical proficiency in factor analysis is limited to a small proportion of the professional community, it should come as no surprise that it has had relatively little impact on mainstream psychology. Moreover, factor analysts themselves have not adequately pursued the role of the factor approach in theory construction. The invited participants represented in this volume, for example, probably represent the bulk of the major contributors to substantive, multivariate psychological theory *c* 1970. To my knowledge, this is the first multivariate theory conference to be held. The point is that we have just begun to look seriously at what multivariate strategies can do for theoretical psychology. Thus, we may all be in for a surprise, both the participants and the readers. It seems reasonable, for example, to predict an upsurge in substantive multivariate theory because of the backlog of data which is screaming for meaningful interpretation. Also the logic of factor analysis, largely untouched, is in need of proper analysis. As an empirico-inductive-hypothesis-generating method, factor analysis constitutes a "for instance" of what the philosophers of science refer to as the "context of discovery" (e.g. see Reichenbach, 1938; Hanson, 1961; Rozeboom, 1972). Thus, we can also anticipate a more sophisticated use of factor analysis in theory construction as we become more aware of its underlying philosophical characteristics.

An Overview of Conference Papers

My review of the present situation in multivariate theoretical psychology indicated a need for a more self-conscious focus on substantive theory. Thus, the call went out for papers which were to meet three criteria: multivariate, substantive, and theoretical. While the degree of emphasis on each of these criteria was left to the individual, we did insist that each paper pay attention to all three. However, since we were not explicit (by design) concerning how to interpret these criteria, there was considerable variation in the papers produced. The least variation occurred in connection with the first criterion—multivariate. While the number of dimensions considered varies with the questions being asked as well as the domain, there is fundamental agreement that organized complexity is the real issue, and that traditional bivariate approaches to such problems are just too simplistic! What about the second criterion—substantive? While all the papers kept behavior and/or experience in focus, we can sum up the situation by saying there is considerable variation in the extent to which substantive issues are dealt with directly. They range from the highly substantive papers of Part II to the formal–methodological papers by Wilson and Pawlik in Part I. But the widest range of interpretation occurred in the case of the third criterion—theoretical. Some contributors, possibly reflecting an empirical bias, felt that a literature review with running commentary and/or some degree of synthesis was as theoretical as they could get. At the other extreme we have contributions which are essentially philosophical in nature. While the writer is aware of the fact that it is frequently impossible to separate empirical, theoretical, and philosophical issues, it was decided, nevertheless, to group the papers into two large categories—theoretical and metatheoretical. Thus, those papers whose focus is more metatheoretical, methodological or pretheoretical (i.e. pretheoretical meaning fundamentally empirical or minimally substantive-theory oriented) have been assembled in Part I. Those papers whose focus is primarily substantive-theoretical (i.e. going beyond the data, but not to metatheoretical issues), on the other hand, have been organized as Part II.

The first four papers are primarily concerned with methodological and metatheoretical issues. Pawlik and Wilson, for example, are concerned with the underlying assumptions of the factor analytic and other linear regression models. They point out that such models are limited to the compensatory case, and further, that we must at least be aware of the fact that underlying relationships of behavior are more likely to be interactive (i.e. context dependent) than non-interactive, and nonlinear rather than linear. Thus, they are focused on various technical–methodological aspects of multivariate methods which have implications for how we can use such methods in theory construction. Fiske, on the other hand, although speaking primarily at a metatheoretic level, approaches the problem from a more substantively-based perspective. He is fundamentally disenchanted with our progress in "personology" to date, and he puts the blame squarely on our failure to pay sufficient attention to concepts. Thus, his paper serves as a reminder of why we called this conference into being. He also brings out potential pitfalls so mercilessly that it points up the sheer difficulty of the task before us. While Sells' paper moves in the direction of substantive theory in spirit, its content is primarily metatheoretical. He provides us with metaconcepts which are consistent with multivariate theory, and he also calls our attention to the importance of situational variance in addition to the more extensively investigated person variance.

The remaining papers in Part I are more clearly substantively oriented, but are, in general, less metatheoretical. Vernon gives us a contemporary and historical review of the status of cognitive styles. He recommends caution because there are so few style constructs which will survive empirical scrutiny. The other three papers are concerned with the nature of intelligence. Both Vandenberg and Horn take a strong empirical stance, not venturing far afield from the data, but attempting to firm up the data base for a multi-factor theory. Vandenberg's pre-theoretical review of the empirical literature is very broad, covering seven categories of findings which are relevant to potentially invariant factors. Horn, on the other hand, is interested in a multidimensional perspective which might transcend sensory modality. Thus, in this paper he has particularly focused on those cognitive abilities which are manifested via audition. Guilford looks at relationships between his well known operational–informational approach and five historical–theoretical issues. These are: mental powers versus mental operations, mental contents versus mental acts, the problem of behavioral units, the limitations of associationism (including behaviorism), and objective versus subjective approaches to behavior. While he begins with the Structure of Intellect model, he is pointing to a general theory of behavior.

Messick's paper, the first in Part II, makes a plea for going beyond mere dimensional taxonomy to a better understanding of complex psychological processes such as problem solving and creativity. Messick is in agreement with the need for understanding structure first, but he wants to get on with dynamics. He suggests a component–sequential approach as the best way to do this. Subsequent contributors are in essential agreement with Messick's stance, but the authors doubt that this can be achieved in the near future. Royce, for example, concerned with a general theory of individual differences, takes the view that we have a long way to go before we will have evolved an adequate dimensional taxonomy. As a first approximation he has put forward a hierarchical model for cognitive, affective, and style structures. He then takes some steps toward process by elaboration of how factors behave over the life span, an analysis of hereditary and environmental sources of factor variation, and speculations concerning the neural mechanisms of cognitive and affective dimensions. Gray carries the concern for process still further in the direction of biological explanation. Working at the level of such higher-order Eysenckian dimensions as introversion-extraversion and anxiety, he elaborates a three-system basis for temperament-emotionality: the hypothalamic approach system, the septo-hippocampal stop system, and the amygdala fight/flight system. Among other things, his model requires that the neural correlate for introversion-extraversion be modified to include the septo-hippocampal structure of the limbic system in addition to the reticular activating system.

The reader may have noticed that there are two crude logics guiding the sequence of papers in this volume. We have already alluded to the first one, namely the grouping into Parts I and II on the grounds of metatheoretical versus theoretical focus. Thus, Guilford's paper, while it is focused on metatheory,* is firmly grounded in substantive theory, thereby constituting an appropriate bridge from Part I to Part II. Messick's paper, while not explicitly substantive, provides an appropriate bridge to Part II because of its explicit concern for theory on the one hand and its explicit unconcern for metatheory on the other hand. Cattell's paper provides a similar bridge in terms of the second crude logic—namely, a progression within Part II away from the cognitive and the static to the non-cognitive and the dynamic. Thus, while others in this volume deal with process in one way or another, Cattell zeros in explicitly on the most dynamic of process variables—motivation. The paper consists of an elaboration of the motivational term of Cattell's extended specification equation, namely $\Sigma b_{hjz} s_{kd} D_{zc}$, where D subsumes the several dynamic traits, b is an index of trait increment with respect to a particular behavior and s is a modulating index due to situational determinants. Cattell conveys the flavor of his model via the following six key issues: (1) the motivational components, (2) conflict in terms of motivational factors, (3) relationships between personality factors and dynamic factors, (4) the nature of reward, (5) relationships between learning and the dynamic calculus and (6) the concept of mental energy.

The last two papers, by Weckowicz and Cartwright and Howard, constitute forays into psychopathology and social psychology. For Weckowicz offers us the beginnings of a multidimensional theory of depression, and Cartwright and Howard take on the age-old problem of delinquency. Weckowicz suggests that an understanding of pathological depression will include the following three dimensions: (1) somatic symptoms such as insomnia and loss of appetite, (2) involutional, obsessional, and mildly paranoid symptoms and (3) self-

* Since Guilford's paper is a mixture of theory and metatheory, its placement in Part I is somewhat arbitrary. The editor's reasons for this decision are elaborated in the text.

depreciation and guilt feelings. The total Cartwright-Howard model includes consideration of the source of delinquent behavior, recent contributing causes, type of causal condition and social context. In the present report, the authors are focused on the relevance of peer group factors (as distinct from adult group and other influences). Examples of such factors are Peer Facilitation, Peer Instigation, Peer Permission, Aggravation, "Cool" Leadership, Desire to Outwit Peers and Felt Anonymity. Regardless of its adequacy as theory, it is doubtful that previous attempts to unravel delinquency have been as multivariately sophisticated or as comprehensively conceptualized.

Perhaps it is not inappropriate to conclude this introduction to our conference proceedings with the observation that one of the virtues of multivariate analytic theory is the ease with which it can move into the practical arenas of life (e.g. personnel selection, education, testing and counselling, psychopathology, delinquency etc.) as well as the more esoteric domains of academic psychology.

REFERENCES

Cattell, R. B. (ed.) (1966). "Handbook of Multivariate Experimental Psychology." Rand McNally, Chicago.

Cronbach, L. J. (1957). The two disciplines of scientific psychology. *Am. Psychol.* **12,** 671–684.

Hanson, N. R. (1961). Is there a logic of scientific discovery? *In* "Current Issues in the Philosophy of Science." (Feigl, H. and Maxwell G. eds) Holt, Rinehart and Winston, New York.

Harris, C. W. and Kaiser, H. F. (1964). Oblique factor analytic solutions by orthogonal transformations. *Psychometrika* **29,** 347–362.

Kaiser, H. F. (1971). Little Jiffy, Mark III. Unpublished manuscript.

Kuhn, T. S. (1962). The structure of scientific revolutions. "Foundations of the Unity of Science," (Neurath, O. ed.) Vol. II, No. 2. University of Chicago Press, Chicago.

Naess, A. (1971). "The Pluralist and Possibilist Aspect of the Scientific Enterprise." Allen and Unwin, London.

Reichenbach, H. (1938). "Experience and Prediction." University of Chicago Press, Chicago.

Royce, J. R. (1950). A synthesis of experimental designs in program research. *J. gen. Psychol.* **43,** 295–303.

Royce, J. R. (1957). Toward the advancement of theoretical psychology. *Psychol. Rep.* **3,** 401–410.

Royce, J. R. (1963). Factors as theoretical constructs. *Am. Psychol.* **18,** 522–528.

Royce, J. R. (1970). The present situation in theoretical psychology. *In* "Toward Unification in Psychology. First Banff Conference on Theoretical Psychology." (Royce, J. R. ed.) University of Toronto Press, Toronto.

Rozeboom, W. W. (1970). The art of metascience, or, what should a psychological theory be? *In* "Toward Unification in Psychology, The First Banff Conference on

Theoretical Psychology." (Royce, J. R. ed.) University of Toronto Press, Toronto. (N.B. Also see other papers in this volume.)

Rozeboom, W. W. (1972). Scientific inference: The myth and the reality. *In* "Science, Psychology and Communication: Essays honoring William Stephenson." (Brown, S. R. and Brenner, D. J. eds) Teachers College Press, New York.

Scriven, M. (1969). Psychology without a paradigm. *In* "Clinical-cognitive Psychology: Models and Integrations." (Breger, L. ed.), pp. 9–24. Prentice-Hall, Englewood Cliffs, N.J.

Wolman, B. (1971). Does psychology need its own philosophy of science? *Am. Psychol.* **26,** 877–886.

Part I

Methodological, Pre-theoretical, and Meta-theoretical Issues

Right Answers to the Wrong Questions? A Re-examination of Factor Analytic Personality Research and its Contribution to Personality Theory

KURT PAWLIK

University of Hamburg

When he invited me to this conference, Professor Royce asked for a paper of primarily theoretical orientation rather than a data-centered piece of research. I shall abstain, therefore, from discussing empirical work to any great extent. Instead, I shall develop some more fundamental issues in multivariate personality research which seem to fit in properly with the central theme of this conference: to what extent and in what way can factor analytic personality research contribute and be pertinent to personality theory? More specifically, this paper seeks to identify the type of questions originating in personality theory which factor analytic personality research has attempted to answer and conversely, the type of questions hitherto left unattended to by the multivariate personality researcher.

To this end, the model and current state of factor analytic personality research will be briefly reviewed and subsequently evaluated with respect to several criteria: theoretical "power" and relevance; semantic structure restrictions and social-psychological limitations; restrictions originating in the mathematical model; psychological restrictions to the model. Thereby it is sought to answer those critics who maintain that basically, multivariate research is furnishing right answers to the wrong questions. As will be shown below neither are the questions that wrong nor are the answers that right.

The Factor Analytic Model

As will be recalled, the basic equation of factor analysis is given by

$$X = AF + A_u F_u \qquad (1)$$

where X is an $m \times n$ score matrix (data matrix) in m variables and n

subjects, A is the $m \times k$ factor pattern matrix in k common factors and F denotes the $k \times n$ common factor score matrix; A_u is the $m \times m$ unique factor matrix, F_u the $m \times n$ unique factor score matrix. Then the factor analytic model states that a given data matrix X can be analysed according to Eq. (1), with $k < m$, the rows of the supermatrix

$$F \equiv \left(\frac{F}{F_u}\right) \tag{2}$$

being linearly independent (i.e. F of rank $k+m$), and A_u being a diagonal matrix. In this case the Gramian matrix of the row vectors of X is solely a function of the k common factors. Thus, if the row vectors of F in Eq. (2) are normalized and of length n, for the case of mutually orthogonal unique factors the generalized Garnett equation

$$\frac{1}{n} XX' = AC_f A' + A_u^2 \tag{3}$$

is obtained, with $C_f \equiv \frac{1}{n} FF'$. The model can be applied to data matrices X regardless of the way the variables are scaled. If the scores are standard scores the left-hand side of the equation (3) becomes the matrix of test intercorrelations, C_f, the matrix of common factor intercorrelations, and $I - A_u^2 = H^2$ denotes the diagonal matrix of test communalities.

Although developed by psychologists for data reduction problems encountered in psychology, this model is in no way limited in its applicability to psychological data. Formally, the model is an extension of the classical true score theory of psychological tests, in that the one true score component is decomposed into $k < m$ linearly independent "common factors". Notice, however, that whereas Spearman's (1904) general-factor model originated in a substantive psychological theory (of mental tests and intellectual functioning), the multi-factor model stated above has been introduced, not for reasons of psychological theory, but in an attempt to achieve a better statistical approximation of intercorrelation matrices of psychological tests. Later on hierarchical factor models were also considered a suitable operationalization of the traditional trait concept of individual differences theory. In heuristic terms, at this point the factor model turned into a psychological factor theory (of mental tests, personality structure etc.) as has been recognized, e.g., by Bischof (1964) and Hall and Lindzey (1957).

It is important to keep in mind, however, that a set of m linearly independent variables can always be analysed according to the model given above, regardless as to whether or not its "true" component

19679161 19679161

structure is of the type stated in equation (1). Thurstone's (1947) well known box and cylinder problems are good examples of this point. They show that variables generated according to non-linear functions are still amenable to decomposition into linear components or factors. This leads us to conclude that, from a logical point of view, a factor theory of behavior will be difficult to disprove formally; as a matter of fact, its formal "refutability" will be next to nil. This is not a happy affair, as many a philosopher of science will tell us. As a consequence we have to resort to various auxiliary criteria for evaluating such a theory. This will be done below. In order to do so it is necessary to briefly delineate the current state of empirical research based upon the factor model.

The Current State of Factor Analytic Personality Research

In quantitative terms, factor analytic personality research has been largely a post-1950 affair, mainly as a result of the growing availability of advanced computing facilities. However, the major lines of approach, both methodological and in substantive respects, have already been set out in the classical studies of the Thurstones, of Cattell and Guilford. A systematic review of the results of factor analytic psychological research, employing the best possible objective evidence on cross-studies factor identification and aiming at a convergent synthesis of results in this vastly expanding field, has been given by the present author elsewhere (Pawlik, 1971). For the present purpose it will be sufficient to summarize some major points from this source:

(1) Contrary to some widely held criticism, factor analytic personality research does not "split up" personality into innumerable, atomistically unrelated "splinter" factors of no apparent psychological meaning. Nor would it be correct to maintain that results in this field of research cannot be meaningfully interrelated between different studies and/or schools of research. It is true though, that a considerable portion of published factor analytic studies (between approximately 20 to 50%, depending on the nature of variables under investigation) cannot be adequately integrated; but I would seriously doubt that this proportion differs significantly from comparable proportions to be obtained from other fields of psychology. What is more important, methodologically well designed studies yield converging results despite differences in schools of thought, variables, subject populations, and sampling strategies. Furthermore, these replicated factors of ability, temperament and motivation appear to be readily interpretable psychologically and, judging from the evidence we have on their interrelation-

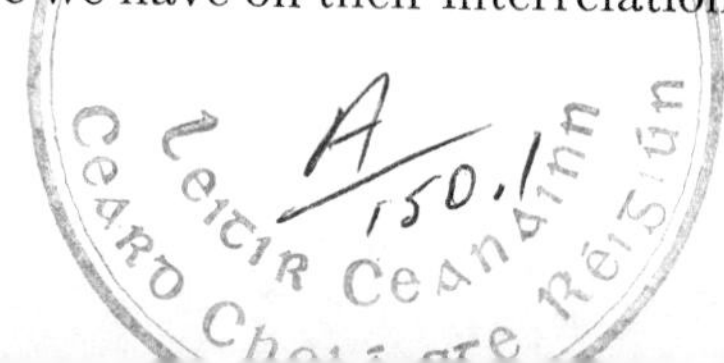

ships, their intercorrelation is consistent and psychologically meaningful. This becomes obvious also from the corresponding higher-order factorizations.

(2) On present empirical evidence some 7–10 psychomotor proficiency factors, 5 factors in perceptual tests, 4–5 memory factors, about 15 to 20 "intelligence" factors, about an equal number of "temperament" factors ("personality" factors *sensu strictiore*) and some 5 to 8 motivation factors seem adequately cross-identifiable and replicated, the numbers varying in accordance with how conservatively the limits are to be set. Empirical intercorrelations are consistently non-zero for most of the primary intelligence factors, giving rise to several clusters or higher-order factors. A similar situation obtains for primary factors isolated from personality questionnaires and objective personality tests (cf. Hundleby *et al.*, 1965), the majority of the questionnaire primaries clustering in two high-variance second-order factors (extraversion–introversion, emotionality) and two smaller factors (sensitivity and independent-mindedness). It can be shown that these second-order factors can be conceived of as clustered covariation subspaces (out of the total personality variable space) or "sectors of personality".

(3) Substantial *criterion correlations* have been consistently found for a number of factors, including clinical–psychological validities of various temperament (esp. questionnaire) factors. As would be expected in view of the psychological complexity of most criteria, pure factor validities are lower than complex test validities. However, multiple correlations between criteria and several selected primaries typically do not fall short of respective raw score validities while, at the same time, allowing for a psychological analysis of the criterion in terms of primary factors substantially involved. In addition to the issue of external validation, questions of *age development* (cf. the Burt–Garrett factorial differentiation theory of intellectual development, Burt, 1954; Garrett *et al.*, 1935), of *psychopathology* (e.g. Cattell and Scheier, 1961; Eysenck, 1957), *genetics* (e.g. Vandenberg, 1968) and other more special problems have been studied for selected groups of primary factors.

(4) Genuine progress in recent years has become (and will continue to be, for some time to come) a function of inventiveness on the measurement side, be it methodological or substantive or both. Examples are Guilford's (1967) extension of ability factors research into the new area of behavioral content or "social intelligence" tests or Cattell's (1959) analysis of motivation test items constructed according to a facet–type theory of attitudes and motives.

(5) Past research has been impeded by various methodological pitfalls, a few of which will be discussed further below, and too little

attention has been given to integrative empirical studies investigating, for example, the cross-relationships *between* factors of different personality domains in different natural subject populations. As a result of this, integration of results is possible only on a factor by factor basis rather than across factors and variable domains.

(6) Finally, only in rare instances has factor analysis been extended to the dimensional study of behavioral *process* variables, such as learning and practice data (cf. Tucker, 1960; Pawlik, 1965, and in preparation). This has put factorial research into a relatively isolated position in relation to conceptualizations in general psychology, clinical work, and developmental psychology. A valuable exception to this rule is for example, the theory of intelligence factors presented by Ferguson (1954).

Theoretical "Power" and "Relevance" of Factor Analytic Personality Research for Personality Theory

A research is considered "theoretically relevant" if it contributes to the construction, extension, or clarification of a theory or to its testing with respect to logical or experiential criteria. The term "theoretical power" as used here is equivalent to what Feigl (1949, 1970) has called the "level of scientific explanation" in his structure of scientific theories: a theory is the more powerful, the larger the number of hypotheses which can be deduced from it and the larger the number of empirical observations it explains.

If one wishes to assess the power and relevance of factorial research for personality theory we shall have to begin by clarifying the term "personality theory". Obviously there is no such thing readily available as "*a* theory of personality", at best one can identify various theories of personality, although some of them may not even be admissible scientific theories when subjected to Popper's (1959) criterion of falsifiability.*

For our present purpose any set of interrelated postulates put forward to explain:

(1) the reliably observable behavior differences, their interrelations and relations with non-behavioral organismic variables,
(2) the origin and causes, development and effects of these behavior differences, and/or
(3) the reaction of a person to the experience of his own and/or other persons' behavioral characteristics

* See the discussion of psychoanalysis by Meehl (1970), for example.

is considered a "personality theory". Few personality theories attempt all three goals. Theories confined to (1) are generally called *structural theories of personality*, those confined to (2) *dynamic* or *process theories of personality*, and those confined to (3) *social* or *stimulus theories of personality*.

With these distinctions in mind we shall re-approach our problem. Obviously, factor analytic personality research is relevant to structural personality theory in that it provides a structural stratification of individual difference variables on the basis of their intercorrelations and correlations with other organismic variables. However, there has been little impact of factor analytically derived concepts on dynamic and on stimulus theories of personality. For structural or taxonomic purposes, factor analytic research has succeeded in representing many thousands of items and several hundreds of tests as linear functions of as few as about 50 to 60 well replicated primary factors of individual differences. Typically, these factors have been understood in terms of "inner" traits of personality. Compared to other kinds of trait constructs they have the extra advantage of fully explicit operational definitions (given by the factor matrix!) which link them to the observational variables.

Can one, then, speak of a "factor theory of personality"? Only in the limited sense that the results of factor analytic personality research *can be utilized for* the construction of a structural (e.g. trait) theory of personality. Examples of such factor analytically derived structural

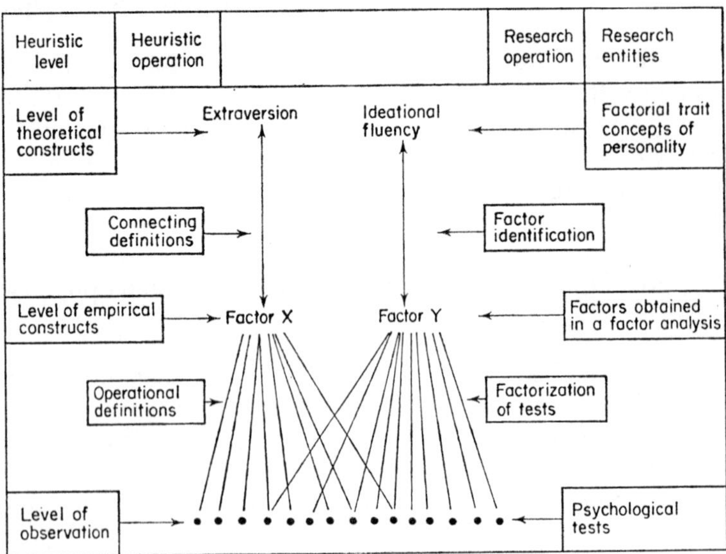

Fig. 1. Heuristic scheme of a factorial trait theory of personality.

personality theories are Guilford's (1967) S–I (structure of the intellect) model or Cattell's (1963) alternative theory of fluid and crystallized intelligence. Other than that the results of a factor analysis are no more "theoretical" than a χ-square value or an F-ratio. The mere fact that the primary factors are fewer in number than the variables does not lend them any special explanatory or causal status other than that of a variable X in the first-order correlations r_{xy} and r_{xy}. From a logic of science point of view personality factors are *empirical constructs* ("constructed" according to the rules of the factor analytic methodology). A "factor theory of personality", on the other hand, is a set of postulates in terms of *theoretical constructs* (e.g. visualization ability, anxiety, superego strength) which are linked to the results of factor analyses by way of *connecting definitions*. For example: The factor *U. I. T.* 24—Anxiety (empirical construct), as obtained by Cattell (1959), is connected to a *trait* concept of anxiety (theoretical construct) which is considerably wider in meaning than the former. Figure 1 illustrates this point.* A factorial trait theory of personality differs formally from alternative trait theories to the extent that the factor analytic model, which enters into the theory via the operational definitions, differs from the formal properties underlying these alternative theories. Thus, a factor theory of personality presupposes general traits, for example, whereas idiographic trait theories would presuppose traits which are qualitatively unique for each individual.

Apparently, in the past a lot of confusion has arisen on this very issue, either because primary factors were erroneously regarded as theoretical constructs which "explain" the observations† or because researchers overlooked the distinction between a factor (as an empirical finding) and its interpretation (as a definition connecting this factor to a theoretical construct from a particular factor theory of personality, cf. Fig. 1). Such misunderstanding of the logical nature of factor concepts

* This scheme also covers the distinction between so-called *exploratory factor analysis* and *confirmatory factor analysis*. The former simply "explores" the factor structure of a given (fixed or sampled) set of variables, the latter aims at testing a factorial trait theory of personality or parts thereof. In exploratory factor analysis the process of factor identification means connecting the obtained factors to existing or newly constructed trait concepts. In confirmatory factor analysis typically connecting definitions are hypothesized between certain theoretical trait concepts and expected factors; one then evaluates the factorial results in terms of goodness of fit between the factors obtained and the factors expected on the basis of the hypothesized connecting definitions.

† The misunderstanding may relate to (i) the factor extraction rule of aiming at $k < m$ and/or to (ii) an unjustified causal way of reading a multiple regression equation. Notice that in other multivariate methods, e.g., canonical correlation, the factors are represented as linear functions of the variables. By the same token, in canonical correlation analysis the variables would have to be considered "causes" of the factors.

may be the basis for the relatively small influence factor analytic research has had on personality theory construction, particularly if one takes into account the massive body of empirical evidence put forward by this research approach. Too often factor analysts seem to have been satisfied with a study once they succeeded in working out psychological interpretations for the factors obtained—hardly ever realizing that these interpretations are in fact part of miniature theories from which proper hypotheses still have to be developed and which still have to be properly tested in due course (cf. 1st footnote on p. 23). Undoubtedly multivariate personality research ought to be encouraged to reflect upon its own relationship to theoretical psychology.

Turning to the question of theoretical power of factor theories of personality we have to recognize two obvious restrictions:

(1) A factor theory of personality can be no more general (in terms of variable and subject populations) than the model underlying the method of factor analysis.
(2) The generality of a factor theory of personality is limited to the extent that the instruments of behavior measurement, which are "fed" into the analysis, are of limited generality themselves.

The first restriction states that the theoretical power of a factor theory of personality is limited by the generality of the underlying model. Applying the model anywhere beyond this boundary line will in fact yield a right answer to a wrongly put question. The second restriction is more general and applies to any personality research. It maintains that the (formal or substantive) rationale underlying the construction of measurement instruments defines the generality of subsequent analyses employing these behavior measures.

Below three such restrictions to the theoretical power of factor theories of personality are discussed.

Semantic Structure Restrictions and Other Social-psychological Limitations

A large portion of personality research, in particular research on temperament and interests, still relies upon self-report data, questionnaires, rating scales, and similar (heavily verbal) instruments. In these language of scientific research is to be kept uncontaminated by that of the theoretical constructs under study. Here the *language of observation* and the *language of theory* intermix. Obviously studies of this type are in a heuristically weak position when it comes to theory testing and the logical consistency of theories originating in research of this kind seems difficult to ascertain.

But there is a second semantic restriction operating as well. If the language of observation is in turn identical to everyday-life language (as is the case in ratings and questionnaires), dimensional analyses of such instruments necessarily reflect the dimensional characteristics inherent in the latter (e.g. what has been called implicit personality theory or logical error in ratings; cf. Guilford, 1959). Very little is known as to what extent factor analysis of rating and questionnaire data reveals the "true inner" trait organization of the subject or rather mirrors the pre-scientific stereotypes prevalent within a given culture and embedded in its language habits in the use of a behavior-descriptive vocabulary. Studies by Becker (1960) and Mulaik (1964), for example, have to be interpreted in the latter direction—much the same as the literature on the semantic differential which shows that the typical three-factor-solution is descriptive of the semantic structure inherent in the rating scales rather than being characteristic of the concepts, persons, images etc. which are rated along these scales.

One possible way in which these and other social-psychological factors may get superimposed onto the diagnostically intended variance in rating data is illustrated by the following finding from a yet unpublished study of the present author on rater-trait-ratee interaction. In one experiment the subjects were 11–12 year old elementary-school children who knew each other for at least two years. Each subject had to rate himself and each of his classmates on six traits (reliable, obedient, industrious, helpful, honest, and courageous), each on a five-point scale. In addition, a complete matrix of sympathy ratings was obtained. For each subject the correlation was computed between his sympathy ratings and the similarity of his self-ratings and peer-ratings. (For a subject A the absolute differences between his self-ratings and his ratings of peer B were summed over the six traits, yielding the discrepancy score A–B. Similarly discrepancy scores A–C, A–D etc. were calculated for his peers C, D etc. Finally these discrepancy scores were correlated with A's sympathy ratings of his peers B, C, D etc. This procedure was followed for all subjects A, B, C etc.) The correlations obtained in this one sample varied between −0·34 and +0·85 (each of $df = 16$), as shown in Fig. 2. These results are fairly typical and do not seem to depend on age or educational level of the subjects. Thus, for a class of 18–19 year old high-school students the correlations varied again between −0·20 and +0·80. These results illustrate once again that different subjects differ considerably in their mechanism of person perception, with sympathy perhaps being but one out of a whole series of important variables operating on and modifying rating data correlations. Too little is known about the systematics of such *moderator effects* although an appropriate statistical methodology has been available for quite some time. Results of this type impose a clear limitation on traditional factor analytic methodology which assumes completely uniform regressions throughout a population and does not include any moderator search.

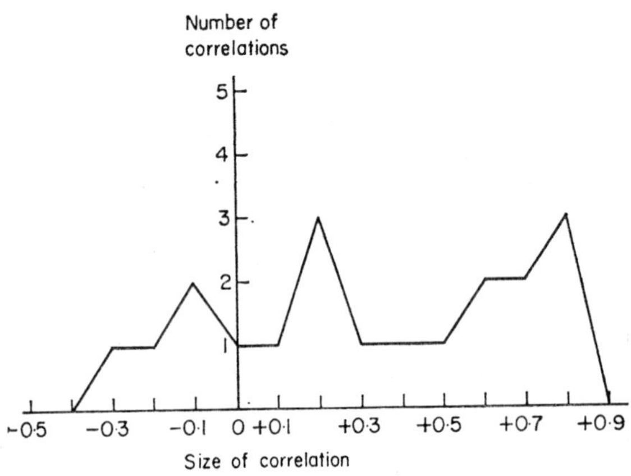

Fig. 2. Frequency distribution of sympathy—discrepancy correlations in self-ratings and peer-ratings of 19 elementary school children.

The semantic structure restriction is paralleled by a similar one operating through various still broader cultural determinants. An example: It is a well-replicated result that the ability factors *V* (verbal comprehension) and *N* (numerical facility) are positively correlated. Pawlik (1971, p. 357) reported a correlation of +0·23, averaged across many studies. How can one account for this correlation? The factors are quite distinct in task content and make-up of marker variables—but they closely resemble the elementary school subjects English and Arithmetic. Since individuals will differ considerably in the amount, quality and intensity of schooling, a positive correlation between the factors could be explained from a common environmental component operating upon both in the same direction—that is, a learning situation common to both factors. If Ferguson (1954) is right in his interpretation of aptitude and ability factors in terms of sources of asymptote variance in learning curves, the hypothesis is suggested that the obtained aptitude and ability factor structure also mirrors the structural organization of the different learning situations (and opportunities) within a given culture—much the same as the positive correlation between N and V may be due to a common learning element.

The *trait approach to personality study* has been criticized repeatedly and from several different angles. To the traditional factor analyst the trait concept seems fully justified and indispensable. How else could he conceive of the obtained primary factors as "underlying" the observed variables? The foregoing discussion should have made it obvious that, as an alternative to trait theory, cross-studies consistency of factor structure can be explained equally well in terms of consistent common molding "from the outside", i.e. in terms of recurrent reinforcement strategies operating upon the individual and thus generating correlations between behaviors of similar reinforcement value.* In the end it is an empirical question to what extent these semantic, social-psychological and cultural determinants actually operate upon factor analytic results. It is a question of great importance, however, and ought to be given priority before far-reaching factor theories of personality are entertained.

Restrictions Originating in the Underlying Mathematical Model

The factor analysis model set out in equations (1)–(3) presumes that a set of m variables can be decomposed into k common factors and m unique factors, all $k+m$ factors being linearly independent vectors, the k common factors in addition being orthogonal to the m unique factors.† Few researchers employing factor analysis seem to be fully cognizant of these model restrictions. On the other hand, it is this very feature of the factor analytic model which, together with the error axioms of classical test theory, makes the common factors formally uncontaminated by error of measurement. This property of the common factors is lost if the aforementioned restrictions are violated. The

* Alternatively a thorough revision of the traditional trait concept would seem required, giving up the notion of stable "inner dispositions". To illustrate this point consider the following hypothetical example: A given culture is characterized, among other things, by giving positive reinforcement to people nodding their head, walking slowly, and not underlining their talk by lively gesture. Assume further that people will differ in the extent to which they seek and/or have access to social reinforcement. As a result of this, positive correlations are to be predicted for the 3 variables in question, perhaps giving rise to a "personality factor" or "subdued agreeableness". One may still prefer to call this pattern a "trait", although actually it is but an instrumental aggregation of habits due to the particulars of a reinforcement strategy, resembling the Hullian concept of a "habit hierarchy".

† As presented by Thurstone, the model actually entails k common factors, m error factors, and m specific factors, making a total of $k+2m$ linearly independent vectors. For sake of simplicity the unique factor variance will not be further subdivided here.

present author suspects that this, in fact, is the case in many factor analytic studies. The argument leading to this proposition is twofold:

(1) The model is violated whenever the row vectors of X cease to be *linearly independent* as unique factor variance is thus shared by two or more variables. This will be the case if algebraically derived variables are included, such as sums or differences or ratios derived from scores already entered into the matrix (cf. Pawlik, 1964). A lot of this seems to happen in research on personality tests.

(2) A second kind of violation of the model is possible despite intact linear independence of the rows of X: if *unique variance components* are *correlated between variables*. In this case again both common factors and unique factors will show up in the test intercorrelations, and consequently the "common factors" extracted from these correlations will be contaminated with unique variance, e.g. error variance. This is exactly what will happen with correlated experimental errors. For example, tests given within one testing session are likely to share those errors of measurement (such as loss of interest or slow warming-up) which are of a duration exceeding the administration time of a single test. Or tests of similar format, instruction, response mode etc. are likely to elicit experimental errors (cheating, type of test-taking attitude, increased or lowered attention etc.) to a comparable extent.

This is clearly a source of error not included in the classical test theory definition of error, and it is difficult to ascertain empirically what the chances are that tests will show correlated errors of this kind. Some answer seems possible to this question from work of the present author with artificial variables of known factor structure.*

In recent years one approach to estimating the number k of common factors has become more and more popular among factor analysts: Guttman's (1954) criterion 1. It says that the number s of eigenvalues of the correlation matrix (with unities in the principal diagonal) equal to or greater than one is mathematically a lower bound to the number k of common factors:

$$s \leqslant k \tag{4}$$

if s is the number of eigenvalues λ of R fulfilling

$$\lambda \geqslant 1. \tag{5}$$

* The author is grateful to Mr. B. Heinze for the computational work involved in this study.

Let us assume that all m eigenvalues of R are known and distinct. They can be ordered by size, such that

$$\lambda_1 > \lambda_2 > \ldots > \lambda_p > \ldots > \lambda_m. \tag{6}$$

Plotting λ_p against p will be called the *eigenvalue plot* of a given R matrix. As can be easily shown with artificial data of known factor structure (cf. Pawlik 1971, p. 127 f.) this eigenvalue plot will be *discontinuous* in the point λ_k if k is the correct number of common factors and if the data is constructed according to the factor analysis model set out in equations (1)–(3). In this exact case the following inequalities always hold:

$$\lambda_k \geqslant 1, \ \lambda_{k+1} < 1. \tag{7}$$

Figure 3 is illustrative of such a "theoretical" eigenvalue plot.

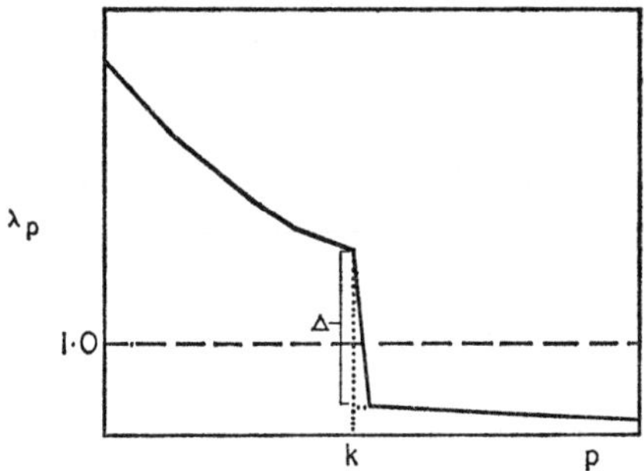

Fig. 3. Eigenvalue plot obtained from the analysis of artificial data generated from k common factors.

The puzzling thing though is the very fact that eigenvalue plots of empirical correlation matrices almost without exception are smooth, either exhibiting no discontinuity at all or exhibiting minor discontinuities at much later points $\lambda_p < 1$ (cf. Pawlik, 1971). Figure 4 illustrates this point.

What is the reason for this marked discrepancy between theory and data? In Table I the *discontinuity measure*

$$\Delta \equiv \lambda_k - \lambda_{k+1} \tag{8}$$

is studied as a joint function of the average communality $\bar{h}^2$ of the variables and of the true number k of common factors. The data is from 15 factor analyses, each one for $m = 40$ artificial variables of known factor structure differing in $\bar{h}^2$ and true k. Notice that Δ approaches zero only for very low values of $\bar{h}^2$ and if k approaches $m/2$. It can be

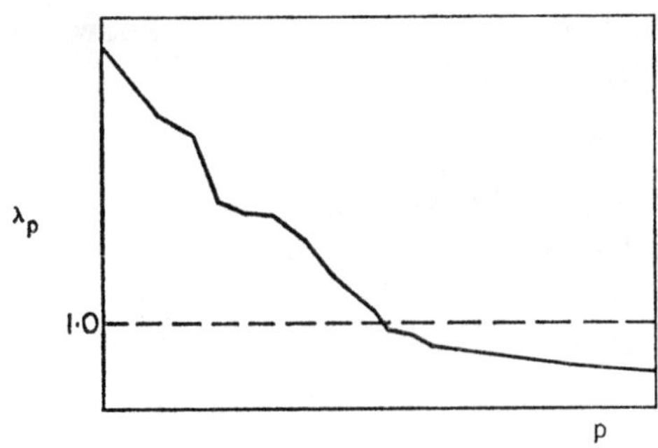

Fig. 4. Typical eigenvalue plot obtained from empirical data.

shown that Δ (like λ_1) is a linear function of $\bar{h}^2$. Obviously the lack of a marked discontinuity near $\lambda_1 = 1{\cdot}00$ in empirical eigenvalue plots cannot be explained from insufficient communality of the tests because, for the typical range of empirical communalities, Δ still should differ markedly from zero.

Table I. Δ as a function of true k and $\bar{h}^2$—uncorrelated unique factors ($m = 40$)

	$\bar{h}^2$				
	0·125	0·275	0·525	0·775	0·875
$k = 6$	0·43	1·08	2·15	3·20	3·62
$k = 12$	0·04	0·15	0·34	0·53	0·60
$k = 20$	0·01	0·03	0·09	0·15	0·18

Next Δ was investigated under sampling conditions. Again a marked discontinuity of the eigenvalue plot was obtained as long as h^2 was 0·3 or greater and k stayed well below $m/2$. Finally, the same sets of variables as analysed in Table I were recomputed under the assumption that the unique factors would be correlated to the extent of 1/3 of the total unique variance. This drastically changed the picture, as the reader can judge from Tables II and III. Table II is set up parallel to Table I, Table III gives the "jumping height" of the eigenvalue plot in the interval of $\lambda_s \geqslant 1$, $\lambda_{s+1} < 1$. Both tables exhibit the same general picture: the eigenvalue plot is drastically "smoothed" if unique factors are partially correlated and this is true both in the point λ_s and in the point λ_k.

To summarize: the eigenvalue plot of empirical correlation matrices appears to be evidence either of correlated unique variance or of very

Table II. Δ as a function of true k and $\bar{h}^2$—correlated unique factors ($m = 40$)

	$\bar{h}^2$				
	0·125	0·275	0·525	0·775	0·875
$k = 6$	0·01	0·08	0·32	0·59	0·70
$k = 12$	0·02	0·04	0·04	0·11	0·15
$k = 20$	0·01	0·02	0·01	0·03	0·02

Table III. Δ_s as a function of true k and $\bar{h}^2$—correlated unique factors ($m = 40$)

	$\bar{h}^2$				
	0·125	0·275	0·525	0·775	0·875
$k = 6$	0·01	0·08	0·32	0·59	0·70
$k = 12$	0·01	0·02	0·04	0·13	0·16
$k - 20$	0·01	0·01	0·03	0·06	0·06

large true numbers of common factors ($k > m/2$) or both. In either case, the factor analytic model is severely violated. Requiring both a parsimonious factor solution ($k < m/2$) and uncorrelated unique factors seems to be incompatible with the majority of empirical data, at least with almost all empirical eigenvalue plots the present author has ever seen. Consequently, one of these two restrictions will have to be dropped if the factor model is to be retained for a broad range of empirical data. (Presumably it will be preferable to drop the requirement of uncorrelated unique factors.) In any case, it would seem that "common factors" obtained and interpreted in past research are very likely contaminated to a certain degree with errors of measurement.

While I am on this point I might as well draw attention to the fact that the parsimony issue in factorial research may need some reconsideration for other reasons too. The parsimony requirement goes back to Thurstone's restriction that the number k of common factors is to be the "minimal rank" (more precisely: the minimal *off-diagonal* rank) of the correlation matrix. Extensive literature has accumulated on the problem of how to obtain a suitable estimate of this minimal rank k. Apparently preference has been given to Guttman's index s as an estimate of k because this index is easily obtained with modern computing facilities. And since s is the lowest of the three lower bounds to k given by Guttman, factor analysts felt they were using a conservative estimate of k. However, some authors have suggested taking some value larger than s as an improved estimate of the number of common factors. On this important point, Guttman has been misinterpreted: the index s is a lower bound to k in *algebraic* terms, although not necessarily in a *statistical* sense. In the aforementioned analyses of artificial variables the present author also studied the behavior of the s-index under conditions of sampling errors. Monte-Carlo estimates of the sampling distribution of s were obtained as a function of (1) sample size, (2) number of variables analysed, (3) true number of common factors, and (4) average communality of the variables in the population. Samples were drawn from an artificial raw score population matrix (10000 "subjects") of known factor structure which was modified according to the conditions of the design. The figures given below are from a total of 875 factor analyses performed according to this design, with 35 independent random samples analysed per "experimental condition". Table IV summarizes the results for three levels of average test communality (0·275, 0·575, and 0·775), three sample sizes (80, 120 and 250) and two values of true k (6 and 12). The entries for two of the cells of this design are left blank because the results could not be completed in time for this conference. In each cell, the upper figure is the mean s-index obtained for a given condition, the lower figure the standard deviation of the s-index.

Table IV. Arithmetic mean (upper figures) and standard deviation (lower figures) of the obtained sampling distribution of the s-index as a function of true k, $\bar{h}^2$, sample size n, and number of variables m.

		$\bar{h}^2$								
		0·275			0·575			0·775		
		$n =$			$n =$			$n =$		
		80	120	250	80	120	250	80	120	250
$k = 6$	$m = 20$	7·9	7·7	6·9	6·0	6·0	6·0	6·0	6·0	6·0
		0·6	0·6	0·6	0·2	0	0	0	0	0
$k = 6$	$m = 40$	14·4	13·9	12·4	8·8			6·0	6·0	6·0
		0·7	0·6	0·7	0·9			0	0	0
$k = 12$	$m = 40$	15·5	15·5	14·6	12·1	11·7	11·1	10·9	11·0	11·0
		0·7	0·5	0·6	0·5	0·5	0·3	0·3	0	0

The results show that, statistically, s tends to overestimate k under conditions of medium to low average communality. If the standard deviation of s is also considered it will become obvious that the number of common factors must be overestimated rather drastically in small sample studies (n around 100) employing tests of medium to low reliability. For fixed k, the bias in the direction of overestimating the number of common factors increases also with increasing numbers of variables. Thus, in a study of 40 variables and 80 subjects the number of common factors would be overestimated on the average (!) by a factor of 2·5, if the average communality is in the neighbourhood of 0·3. Only for high communalities and larger numbers of variables and factors does s tend to show a statistical bias in the opposite direction.

These findings cast some doubt on factor analytic work of recent years as far as the number of factors extracted is concerned; since the chances are that the aforementioned restrictions imposed by the model will have been violated repeatedly, the two errors will add to each other. A factor theory of personality based upon these results will have to be scrutinized most carefully as to the very parsimony criterion of factor analysis. After all, the critic who maintains that too many factors have been retained may not be all that wrong, and his criticisms cannot be "debated away" by simply replying that the parsimony criterion of factor analysis has been adhered to. Thus, the 70 or so personality factors referred to above require a population of approximately $576 \cdot 10^{30}$ individuals if only 3 levels of factor endowment are distinguished for each factor and if it is required that each "quadrant" in hyperspace be occupied by at least one individual. Under similar assumptions Guilford's structure-of-intellect model presupposes a subject population of 10^{59} individuals—more than 10^{50} times as many people as there are living in the U.S.A. And similar reasoning, incidentally, will apply to individual factor analyses as well. If 40 tests have been factored to yield say 10 common factors, a minimum of 2^{10} or 1,024 subjects would be needed if factors are dichotomized and each "quadrant" of the hyperspace is to be occupied by at least one individual. However, in a typical application of factor analysis, the number of subjects will hardly exceed 150–200. As a result at least 800–850, or approximately 80 to 85% of all possible "quadrants" in hyperspace will not have a single person occupying it. Are we sure this is a parsimonious representation of the data?*

Psychological Restrictions to the Model

Several critics have questioned the usefulness of the factor analytic model on the grounds that it would be psychologically unrealistic to work on the assumption that the trait composition of a given item of behavior is constant over all individuals. However, this argument is

* The fact that most of the factor space is empty space as far as subjects is concerned will be dealt with in more detail in a forthcoming paper by the present writer. It has some bearing, for example, on rotations following the approach of McDonald (1967).

wrongly put. Although it is correct that individual differences show up in the factor score matrix F only, with the factor loadings of the tests (elements of the factor pattern matrix A) being constant over all subjects, the factor analysis model nevertheless allows for variation in the way a given measure of behavior is brought about in the individual case. If the (reduced) specification equation of a given variable in 2 common factors is

$$x = 0 \cdot 2 f_1 + 0 \cdot 5 f_2$$

then two subjects A and B with factor scores given by

	f_1	f_2
A	+1·0	0·0
B	0·0	+0·4

will both yield a score of $x = +0 \cdot 2$, as can be easily verified. Notice, however, that one and the same test score is "earned" via factor 1 in the one case (subject A), and via factor 2 in the other (subject B). This is due to the *compensatory model* implicit in the multiple regression approach and therefore implicit in factor analysis too. Low scores in one predictor (factor) are compensated for by high scores in other predictors (factors) of corresponding regression weights (factor loadings).

Actually the opening remark of this section has to be turned around 180 degrees: the very fact that factor analysis does imply a compensatory model of behavior sets a major psychological restriction on its generality, simply because it may be inappropriate with many items of behavior following a different model. Two examples follow. Success as a salesman seems to depend, among other things, on good social intelligence *or* technical knowledge.* Success in navigating an airplane, however, depends upon low susceptibility to vertigo *and* good spatial orientation. The first is an example of a *disjunctive* item, the second of a *conjunctive* item. If our "theories" of salesmanship and pilot performance are right, applying a compensatory multiple regression model would distort the true state of affairs in each case. Of course, this does not only apply to criterion scores but also to test items. Thurstone's flags test, for example, may follow the disjunctive model, since it can be solved equally well either by inductive reasoning *or* by spatial thinking. Con-

* Assuming that there are several *alternative* ways and means of reaching an equivalent performance.

versely, mechanical aptitude tests seem to be of the conjunctive item type because a certain test score will require both a certain degree of mechanical knowledge *and* a certain degree of spatial visualization ability, for example.

The differences between the three models are illustrated in Fig. 5 by way of a simple example: Let us assume that a test x is a function of two factors only, f_1 and f_2, and the respective weights are again $+0{\cdot}2$ and $+0{\cdot}5$. Each score in x can be represented by a "score trace line" in the f_1–f_2 plane. A score trace line is the subspace of all subjects carrying that particular score in variable x. These score trace lines are straight lines in the compensatory model, and right-angles of the same origin but different opening in the other two models. All trace lines shown in Fig. 5 are for a test score of $x = +0{\cdot}2$. The trace lines for other scores in the same tests are straight lines and right-angles, respectively, parallel to the ones shown in the figure.

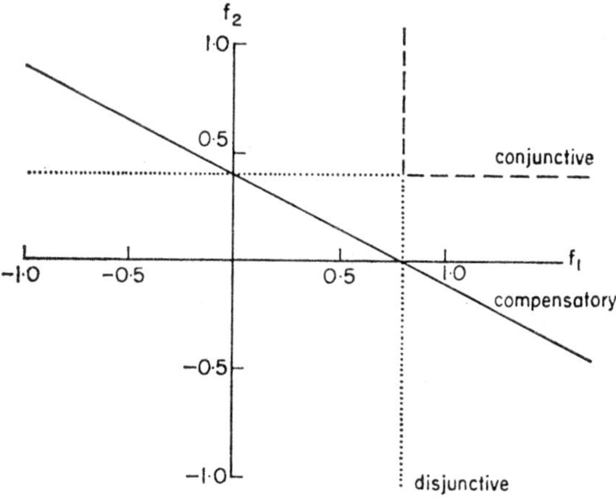

Fig. 5. Score trace lines for three alternative item models: conjunctive, compensatory, and disjunctive.

Past factor analytic personality research has failed to recognize this problem. On intuitive grounds it seems very likely that for many behavior measures a conjunctive or a disjunctive model is more justified than the compensatory one. In these cases the compensatory factor analysis model would have been applied inappropriately. It is conceivable, for example, that Cattell's cases of "cooperative factors" are indicative of such conjunctive behavior items. Certainly the generality of a factor theory of personality must be limited to that subsample of instances of behavior for which a compensatory model will be appropriate. Empirical work which would tell us the limits of this subsample and the degree of distortion resulting from inappropriate application of factor analysis beyond these limits is urgently needed.

Summary and Conclusions

1. The basic factor analytic model is briefly reviewed. It is explained that, as a behavior theory, the model is of low formal "refutability". Therefore auxiliary criteria are introduced for evaluating its theoretical relevance and "power" or "explanatory level".
2. A schematic outline of the current state of factor analytic personality research is given in order to indicate major lines of approach, principal results and possible extension of past research strategies.
3. The results of a factor analysis, the primary factors, are to be regarded as empirical rather than theoretical constructs (which form part of a theory). A system of postulates about personality based upon factor analytic results is called a factor theory of personality. Its concepts have to be linked to the empirical concepts by proper connecting definitions which form part of the factor interpretation. It is argued that a good deal of confusion has existed in the past regarding this heuristic nature of factor concepts and their interpretation. The theoretical power of a factor theory of personality is limited both by restrictions inherent in the model of factor analysis and by restrictions originating in the instruments of behavior measurement.
4. Personality research through questionnaires and rating scales necessarily suffers the shortcomings of research in which the language of observation and the language of theory intermix. Furthermore, the factor analytic results are likely to reflect to a yet unknown extent both the semantic structure (the implicit everyday-life personality theory) and the biotopical organization of situations of psychological stimulation, motivation, and learning in a given culture. This casts some doubt on the traditional interpretation of factorial results solely in terms of "underlying inner traits".
5. The factor analysis model imposes restrictions on the data (concerning linear independence and mutual orthogonality of common and unique factors) which do not seem to be met in the typical factor analytic study. Judging from the distribution of eigenvalues of empirical correlation matrices as compared to artificial data

matrices (which follow the model exactly), factorial research seems to have violated the model frequently with respect to

(i) the requirement that the true number of common factors be considerably smaller than the number of variables and/or
(ii) the restriction of mutually orthogonal unique factors (especially: errors).

It is shown, furthermore, that, given either one of these violations of the model, the number of common factors will be overestimated if Guttman's criterion 1 is employed. The same index will often lead to an overestimation of k also as a result of sampling errors.

6. It is stressed that the model of factor analysis only holds for behavior items of the compensatory type. Items of the conjunctive or disjunctive type will thus be analysed inappropriately.

Implications of these results for a factor theory of personality are indicated.

COMMENT ON PAWLIK'S PAPER

WM. W. ROZEBOOM

What Pawlik seeks to promote here, some cold-eyed scrutiny of the suppositions and methodological bases of applied factor analysis, is something which has my strongest possible endorsement. For reasons which have never been clear to me, psychologists are extraordinarily reluctant to think critically about the conceptual foundations of their work, almost as though they dread that Lovecraftian horrors lurk therein. If factor analysts have been no worse than average in this respect, neither have they been a notably shining exception, and there are so few of us philosophical gadflies to service the entirety of our profession that I am delighted by the vigor and enthusiasm with which Pawlik wields his stinger.

Even so, much as it embarrasses me to defend orthodoxy, I cannot agree that current factorial practices are quite so maladroit as are alleged here. Since Pawlik clearly relishes controversy, I trust that he will approve my choosing to disagree with him in my short time allocation rather than reiterating those points with which I quite agree.

One objection I have to Pawlik's argument is in fact a deeply serious one. It is evident from his dislike for the inrefutability of the factor-analytic model (Pawlik, this volume p. 19), his esteem for Popperian falsifiability (Pawlik, this volume p. 21), and his poor-mouthing of factor interpretations which stop short of "proper hypotheses" which can in due course be tested (Pawlik, this volume p. 29), that Pawlik wishes us to live by the textbook maxim that good scientific theory is developed hypothetico-deductively. In a similar vein, he denies explanatory significance to the primary-factor outputs of factor-analytic algorithms on grounds that these are merely empirical abstractions from the data (Pawlik, this volume pp. 22–23). Philosophers of science are finally coming to realize that the classic hypothetico-deductive model of scientific inference is epistemologically vacuous and that it tells nothing whatsoever about theory confirmation which is not trivial. (cf. Skyrms, 1966; Hesse, 1970; Rozeboom, 1970, p. 93ff.). Moreover, I have argued elsewhere (Rozeboom, 1961, 1966b, 1972) that the way we really learn about the explanatory sources of observed events is through inductive inference forms which algorithmically interpret the distinctive features of data patterns and that factor analysis, in particular, is a paradigmatic instance of explanatory induction in this sense even if only one species under its factorial-decomposition genus (Rozeboom, 1966b, p. 203). The common factors* implied by a particular factoring of a given correlation matrix—and I say "implied" rather than "defined" because, Pawlik notwithstanding (Pawlik, this volume p. 23), common factors are *not* operationally reducible to the data variables, neither are they logically guaranteed to be nomic sources (causal or logical) common to the data variables, nor even to span a space which contains such sources. However, pending further information, they are our best bet in this regard and a pretty plausible one too if the factor pattern is strongly simple-structured.

Obviously a lot more needs to be said on this point, with more space I would not sound quite this sanguine about factor interpretations; but it is important to insist that even if common-factoring often yields spurious source variables, it is nonetheless this kind of data analysis and interpretation which generates hard knowledge (contra hypothetico-deductive speculations) about the underlying determinants of our data. Pawlik is, of course, entirely correct in desiring that factor-analytically grounded personality theory broaden the scope of its data variables and especially that it get on with the study of psychological change insomuch as our understanding of any phenomenon remains superficial until we know something about its process dynamics.† However, without factor

* Common factors, i.e. those obtained under a rank-reducing communalities solution, are importantly unlike descriptive factors (e.g. principal components and canonical factors) in this respect, insomuch as they do not lie in data space (see Rozeboom, 1966a, p. 264f.).

† One important reason for the absence to date of factor-analytically based dynamic theories of personality has been a lack of decent factor-analytic models of multivariate process data. However, a family of such models which appear to be both conceptually natural and astonishingly powerful analytically has now become available (Rozeboom, unpublished).

analysis and other methodologically comparable multivariate methods or their less efficient counterparts in everyday intuition, this enriched data base would profit us little, simply because we would have no epistemologically creditable way to interpret it.

My other main dispute with Pawlik, this time a matter of technicalities rather than of methodological principle, concerns the factor-analytic model's vulnerability to violations of assumptions. I am surprised, for example, by Pawlik's claim that factor analysis cannot appropriately handle data whose factorial composition is conjunctive or disjunctive rather than compensatory for I am sure that he knows as well as I (Rozeboom, 1966a, p. 523ff.) that nonlinear determinations of the data variables by their sources can often be well approximated by equations which are *parameterized* linearly and whose nonlinear components, if shared by several data variables, are recovered by common-factoring just as readily as are the linear components. (To be sure, this still leaves factor-analytic problems, notably, determining which factors are nonlinear functions of which others, but these are problems of practical detail, not limitations in principle.) It is also cheating to act as though the orthogonal-unique assumptions can be so easily dis-assumed. It is stipulated that, with sampling errors excepted, unique factors are orthogonal to the common factors and to each other. Residual correlations other than zero between the data variables is manifest evidence, according to the model, that at least one common source remains yet unextracted.* These two points—that nonlinearities appear as extra factors and that correlated residuals are not genuinely unique—effectively discount the possibility that the number of factors common to m logically independent data variables could ever be considerably less than m. However in practice that matters little. What is important is only that the number of common factors which account for an *appreciable* amount of data variance be considerably less than m. There is probably no such thing as overfactoring in the strict sense that Pawlik has emphasized; the real how-many-factors problem is to find that stopping point in the extraction sequence where the space spanned by the accounted–for parts of the data variables optimally approximates the space spanned by a scientifically significant *subset* of the data variables' common factor.

Finally, on the number of common factors issue, I think that Pawlik has exaggerated the strength of Guttman's $\lambda_k \geqslant 1 > \lambda_{k+1}$ criterion (where k is the estimated number of common factors and λ_i ($i = 1, \ldots, m$) is the ith eigenvalue of the data correlation matrix) for this.

* Note that were we to allow correlated unique factors, then each data variable could be accounted for by exactly one factor, namely, itself.

Even in the ideal case where each unique factor is orthogonal to all the other common and unique factors, the k which satisfies this criterion is indeed only a lower bound on the number of common factors, not an identification thereof as Pawlik suggests (Pawlik, this volume p. 28), nor is it necessary that a break in the smooth decrease of eigenvalues occur at this point. This can be appreciated most easily in the special case where all the m data variables have the same communality h^2; for then, given ideal unique-factor orthogonalities,

$$\begin{aligned} \lambda_i &= h^2\mu_i + (1-h^2) \\ &= 1 + h^2(\mu_1 - 1) \end{aligned} \qquad (i = 1, \ldots, m),$$

where μ_i is the ith eigenvalue of the correlation matrix for the common parts of the data variables.* This shows that, given equal communalities and ideal uniqueness orthogonalities, $\lambda_i > 1$ if and only if $\mu_i > 1$. Now, if there are k common factors, $\mu_{k+1}, \ldots, \mu_m$ are all zero while the average of $\mu_1, \ldots, \mu_k$ is m/k. Consequently, if k is considerably smaller than m and if the common-factor variance is rather diffusely distributed, i.e. if all the common factors account for roughly the same amount of data variance, then it may well occur that μ_k exceeds unity and hence brings it about that $\lambda_k > 1 > \lambda_{k+1}$. However, when k is not much smaller than m, or when the first few common factors are fairly strong, μ_1 and hence λ_1 can easily sink below unity for i less than k. Further, regardless of how greatly m exceeds k, there is no particular reason why μ_1 cannot approach zero smoothly as i approaches $k+1$, in which case there will be no discontinuity in the data-eigenvalue plot between λ_k and λ_{k+1}. Neither is there any reason, when $\mu_k < 1$, to anticipate a discontinuity at the point where the data-eigenvalue plot drops below unity, though to be sure a later discontinuity at λ_k is not implausible even if not at all inevitable.

In short, while I agree with Pawlik that Guttman's eigenvalue criterion for when to stop factoring has no special merit in applied factor analysis and that it may well be generally best to stop sooner than this criterion dictates, I would prefer that his arguments for these conclusions were a bit stronger.

* If $\mathbf{R}_X$ and $\mathbf{R}_H$ are respectively the correlation matrices of the data variables and of their common parts, while $\mathbf{I}$ is the m by m Identity matrix, $\mathbf{R}_X = h^2\mathbf{R}_H + (1-h^2)\mathbf{I}$ in this special case. Hence any eigenvector of $\mathbf{R}_H$ corresponding to eigenvalue μ_i is also an eigenvector of $\mathbf{R}_X$ corresponding to eigenvalue $h^2\mu_i + (1-h^2)$.

REJOINDER TO DISCUSSANT'S COMMENTS

K. PAWLIK

Perhaps a word or two will be in order on the general intent of my paper before I go into specifics: What I intended to do is to draw attention to several psychological, methodological, and heuristic fallacies which have become apparent in past applications of factor analysis to problems of structural psychological research. At the same time, these turn out to be issues which have been given little attention, if any, in the past and which, I believe, may be held at least partially responsible for the fact that factor analytic research has not been as influential on concept, model, and theory construction in psychology as it may have otherwise deserved. Thus, no matter how positive I generally (cf. Pawlik, 1971) prefer to be with respect to the use of multivariate techniques in psychology, here I deliberately meant to undertake a tough-minded re-evaluation of our research behavior in this field. I should regret it, therefore, if Rozeboom's "sanguinity" should detain the reader from trying out a similar critical attitude himself.

In his discussion of my paper, Rozeboom essentially raises three points: the heuristic status of factor concepts, the question of the vulnerability of the factor model to violations of its assumptions and my discussion of Guttman's criterion for estimating the number of common factors. I shall take them up briefly in this order.

1. I find myself in agreement with Rozeboom on the relative merits of hypothetico-deductive versus inductive reasoning in research. I disagree with him, however, in his enthusiastic acceptance of current factor interpretation practices. While I am aware (cf. Pawlik, 1971, Chapter 5) of the fact that in common factor analysis the factor space cannot be mapped onto the test space, I am, at the same time, afraid that a good simple structure will not get us off the hook either. Simple structure is an appropriate rotational rationale if the variables are sampled in a few "packages" of tests each, different packages comprising tests from different domains of variation (in terms of test content, format, method and/or style). As a matter of fact, factors may emerge in a given study which simply reflect the peculiarities of the given strategy of subject and/or variable sampling. I wonder if Rozeboom would not agree with me that his portrayal of the matter would, in fact, presuppose ideal population data, both variable-wise and subject-wise.

2. I agree with my discussant's remark that nonlinearly deter-

mined variables still are open to linear analysis, as long as one does not mind that the factors obtained may differ *drastically* (cf. Pawlik, 1971), both in number and in content, from the true factors the tests were derived from. Whether we wish to restrict the term "uniqueness" to what Rozeboom calls "genuine uniqueness" or not is a matter of terminology. What is important, though, is the fact that so-called "common factors" may have nothing more "common" to them than common error once the assumption of uncorrelated errors of measurement, which underlies the factor model, is violated—and as I tried to indicate, both psychological evidence and intuition do lend support to this correlated error notion. Incidentally, the third footnote in Rozeboom's comments section will no longer be true if the restrictions implied in the various factor extraction methods (principal axes, centroid, etc.) are taken into account.

3. I was aware (cf. my equation 4, for example) that Guttman's criterion is a lower bound to k. As to strength of argument, I felt our evidence from representative analyses of artificial variables to be rather strong. Certainly it is aimed at *applied* factor analysis i.e. factor analysis as applied to questions arising in psychological research. However, that is what my whole paper is about.

REFERENCES

Becker, W. C. (1960). The relationship of factors in parental ratings of self and each other to the behavior of kindergarten children as rated by mothers, fathers and teachers. *J. consult. Psychol.* **24,** 507–527.

Bischof, L. J. (1964). "Interpreting Personality Theories." Harper and Row, New York.

Burt, C. (1951). The differentiation of intellectual abilities. *Br. J. educ. Psychol.* **24,** 76–90.

Cattell, R. B. (1957). "Personality and Motivation Structure and Measurement." World Book Co., Yonkers, New York.

Cattell, R. B. (1963). Theory of fluid and crystallized intelligence: A critical experiment. *J. educ. Psychol.* **54,** 1–22.

Cattell, R. B. and Scheier, I. H. (1961). "The Meaning and Measurement of Neuroticism and Anxiety." Ronald Press, New York.

Eysenck, H. J. (1957). "The Dynamics of Anxiety and Hysteria." Routledge and Kegan Paul, London.

Feigl, H. (1949). Some remarks on the meaning of scientific explanation. *In* "Readings in Philosophical Analysis." (Feigel, H. and Sellars, W. eds) Appleton-Century-Crofts, New York.

Feigl, H. (1970). The "orthodox" view of theories. *In* "Analyses of Theories and Methods of Physics and Psychology." (Radnor, M. and Winokur, S. eds), Vol. IV, pp. 3–16. University of Minnesota Press (Minnesota Studies in the Philosophy of Science), Minneapolis, Minnesota.

Ferguson, G. A. (1954). On learning and human ability. *Can. J. Psychol.* **8,** 95–112.

Garrett, H. E., Bryan, A. I. and Perl, R. E. (1935). Age factor in mental organization. *Archs. Psychol.* **176,** 1–31.

Guilford, J. P. (1959). "Personality." McGraw-Hill, New York.

Guilford, J. P. (1967). "The Nature of Human Intelligence." McGraw-Hill, New York.

Guttman, L. (1954). Some necessary conditions for common-factor analysis. *Psychometrika* **19,** 149–161.

Hall, C. S. and Lindzey, G. (1957). "Theories of Personality." Wiley, New York.

Hesse, M. (1970). Theories and the transitivity of confirmation. *Philosophy Sci.* **37,** 50–63.

Hundleby, J. D., Pawlik, K. and Cattell, R. B. (1965). "Personality Factors in Objective Test Devices." Knapp, San Diego, California.

McDonald, R. F. (1967). Nonlinear factor analysis. *Psychometric Monogr.* **15.**

Meehl, P. (1970). Some methodological reflections on the difficulties of psychoanalytic research. *In* "Analyses of Theories and Methods of Physics and Psychology." (Radner, M. and Winokur, S. eds), Vol. IV, pp. 403–416. University of Minnesota Press (Minnesota Studies in the Philosophy of Science), Minneapolis, Minnesota.

Mulaik, S. A. (1964). Are personality factors raters' conceptual factors? *J. consult. Psychol.* **28,** 506–511.

Pawlik, K. (1964). Experimentelle Untersuchungen zur Faktorenanalyse algebraisch abgeleiteter Variabler. *Biometr. Z.* **6,** 42–44.

Pawlik, K. (1965). Elementarfunktionen ("Faktoren") einfacher Lernverläufe. *In* "Bericht über den 24. Kongress der Deutschen Gesellschaft für Psychologie." (Heckhausen, H. ed.), pp. 349–356. Hogrefe, Göttingen.

Pawlik, K. (1971). "Dimensionen des Verhaltens." (Dimensions of Behaviour.) 2nd Edn. Huber, Bern-Stuttgart-Wien.

Pawlik, K. Übung als qualitativer Prozess. (Practice as a Qualitative Process.) (In preparation.)

Popper, K. R. (1959). "The Logic of Scientific Discovery." Basic Books, New York.

Rozeboom, Wm. W. (1961). "Ontological Induction and the Logical Typology of Scientific Variables." *Philosophy Sci.* **28,** 337–377.

Rozeboom, Wm. W. (1966a). "Foundations of the Theory of Prediction." Dorsey Press, Homewood, Illinois.

Rozeboom, Wm. W. (1966). Scaling theory and the nature of measurement. *Synthese* **16,** 170–233.

Rozeboom, Wm. W. (1970). The art of metascience, or, what should a psychological theory be? *In* "Towards Unification in Psychology." (Royce, J. R. ed.) Toronto University Press, Toronto.

Rozeboom, Wm. W. (1972). Scientific inference: The myth and the reality. *In* "Science, Psychology and Communication: Essays Honoring William Stephenson." (Brown, S. R. and Brenner, D. J. eds) Teachers College Press, New York.

Rozeboom, Wm. W. (Forthcoming) "Linear Analysis of Multivariate Process Data."

Skyrms, B. (1966). Nomological necessity and the paradoxes of confirmation. *Philosophy Sci.* **33,** 230–249.

Spearman, C. (1904). "General intelligence," objectively determined and measured. *Am. J. Psychol.* **15,** 201–293.

Thurstone, L. L. (1947). "Multiple Factor Analysis." University of Chicago Press, Chicago.

Tucker, L. R. (1960). Determination of generalized learning curves by factor analysis. "Technical Reports." Educational Testing Service, Princeton, New Jersey.

Vandenberg, S. G. (1968). The nature and nurture of intelligence. *In* "Biology and Behavior: Genetics." (Glass, D. C. ed.), pp. 3–58. Rockefeller University Press, New York.

Linear Regression Equations as Behavior Models*

KELLOGG V. WILSON

The Center for Advanced Study in Theoretical Psychology
University of Alberta

Classes of Behavior Models

In a previous paper (Wilson, 1970), the author distinguished between three important classes of behavior models which correspond to the three major classes of formal grammars described by Chomsky (1963). These classes of behavior models are briefly characterized below.

Linear Generators

Behavior is generated in a serial order in which the last response generated provides at least some of the stimuli for the next response. All other relevant stimuli are environmental.

Context-Free Models

Behavior is generated by a hierarchical arrangement of units in which the higher units make major decisions which are sent to lower units which make a set of subdecisions within the limits of the more major decisions. There is no feedback from lower to higher units and no interconnection between units on the same level. Information is transmitted in one direction only—from higher to lower units.

Context-Dependent Models

Behavior is generated by a network of interconnected and interactive units which operate in parallel.

These three classes are arranged in order of increasing generality (i.e. each class includes the preceding one as a special case) and decreasing

* This paper was written while on sabbatical leave at Stanford University.

compatibility with S–R models.* There are few context-dependent models in psychology and those mentioned in the previous paper are in early stages of development. However, context-dependent thinking about behavior has been part of the tradition of psychology for some time. The analyses of perception by the Gestalt psychologists were a reaction against introspective "analysis" of sensation into elements—an enterprise which had a context-free flavor. These analyses emphasized that configurations comprise functional unities in which the "meaning" of any part of a configuration depends on the configurational context. Similar considerations seem to be involved in discussion of personality and social "dynamics".†

Thinking about behavioral phenomena in context-dependent or configurational terms necessarily involves analysis of the interrelationships of a number of variables. Such analyses might appear to be the concern of what has recently been called *multivariate psychology* (Cattell, 1966) and what is known as *multivariate analysis* in statistics (Morrison, 1967). However, nearly all of the structural models basic in these areas, as well as many models in the area of artificial intelligence (i.e. computer simulation of cognition), have a distinctly context-free quality due to their common dependence on the linear regression equation. The purpose of this paper is to discuss this equation as a model of behavior and to analyse some of the consequences of this model in particular areas of application of interest to psychologists.

The Linear Regression Equation

The general form of the linear regression equation is as below.

$$Y_c = w_{c1}X_1 + w_{c2} + \ldots + w_{cn}X_n = \sum_{m=1}^{n} w_{cm}X_m$$

where Y_c is the value of the dependent variable c (or the c'th component of the vector dependent variables), X_1, X_2 through X_n are the n independent variable values, w_{c1}, w_{c2} through w_{cn} are the corresponding regression weights and w_{cm} and X_m represent any one of these sets (or vectors) of regression weights and independent variables.‡

* It was not asserted that either context-free or context-dependent models are incompatible with S-R principles but that some rather drastic extensions of such principles would be required, especially in the context-dependent case.

† The use of the term "dynamics" in such contexts seems puzzling and one wonders what personality and social "statics" might be.

‡ There should be a constant added to the equation above which would be the value of Y_c when all X's are zero but it was omitted for the sake of simplicity.

In effect, this equation "rewrites" or "recodes" a set of n independent variable values into a single dependent variable value. This equation is both linear and non-interactive and because of its non-interactive property, is similar to a context-free grammar since the contribution of each term of the relation does not depend on the value of more than one independent variable.* To make this point clear, consider the four equations below in which a dependent variable Y is related to two independent variables X_1 and X_2.

(i) Linear and Non-Interactive Relationship
$$Y = 0{\cdot}3X_1 + 0{\cdot}5X_2$$

(ii) Non-Linear and Non-Interactive Relationship
$$Y = 0{\cdot}3X_1 + 0{\cdot}2X_1^2 + 0{\cdot}5X_2 + 0{\cdot}4X_2^2$$

(iii) Linear and Interactive Relationship
$$Y = 0{\cdot}3X_1 + 0{\cdot}5X_2 + 0{\cdot}6X_1X_2$$

(iv) Non-Linear and Interactive Relationship
$$Y = 0{\cdot}3X_1 + 0{\cdot}5X_2 + 0{\cdot}2X_1^2 + 0{\cdot}4X_2^2 + 0{\cdot}6X_1X_2$$

The non-linear relations have terms which contain the square of the independent variable values and the interactive relations contain a term which involves the product of the two independent variables. In Fig. 1, the relations between Y and X_1 are shown for various values of X_2 for the four relations. In the case of the two non-interactive relations the curves for the various X_2 values are additive while in the interactive relations they are not. The term "interaction" here is used in the same sense as in the linear hypothesis or fixed effects model for analysis of variance (Hayes, 1963) in which absence of interaction corresponds to additivity of effects. In the non-interactive relations above, each term is a function of one variable only so these "effects" are additive. The similarity of the non-interactive relations to context-free grammars corresponds to this additivity of effects, i.e. the effect of one variable does not depend on the value of any other variables.

Computer Programs for Pattern Recognition

A considerable number of proposed pattern recognition programs for computers have used the linear regression equation in the stage of analysis involving assigning an unknown pattern to one of two or more

* The regression equation is a rewriting rule which generates one symbol from n symbols and so violates the property not reducing the number of symbols which is characteristic of context-free and Type 1 context-dependent grammars (Wilson, 1970).

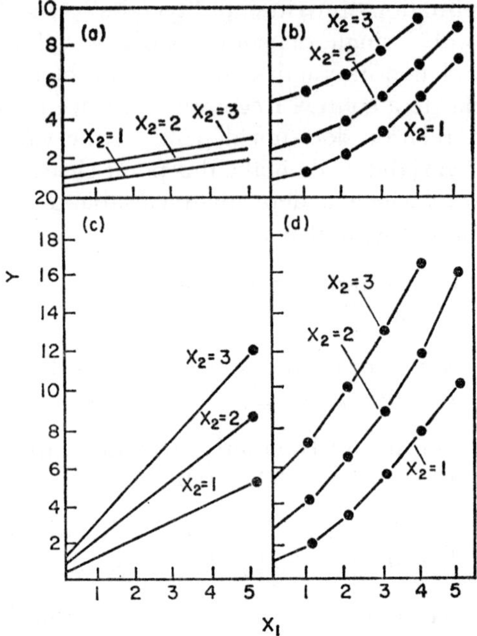

Fig. 1. Four types of relations between Y and X_1 and X_2.

(a) Linear and Non-Interactive
$Y = \cdot 3X_1 + \cdot 5X_2$

(b) Non-Linear and Non-Interactive
$Y = \cdot 3X_1 + \cdot 2X_1^2 + \cdot 5X_2 + 4X_2^2$

(c) Linear and Interactive
$Y = \cdot 3X_1 + \cdot 5X_2 + \cdot 6X_1 X_2$

(d) Non-Linear and Interactive
$Y = \cdot 3X_1 + \cdot 2X_1^2 + \cdot 5X_2 + \cdot 4X_2^2 + \cdot 6X_1 X_2$

classes. The common aspects of such programs are summarized below.

1. An unknown pattern, nearly always a single letter or figure (rather than a picture containing several objects), is approximated by filling in squares on a grid with "ones" in filled squares and "zeros" in unfilled squares and the resulting binary matrix read into the computer.*

2. The binary matrix is "scanned" by a number, n, of feature analysers which detect such "features" as corners, straight and curved line segments or broken line segments. The output of the n feature

* This coding is usually done by hand but could be made automatic if a threshold were established for the amount of light reflected from areas corresponding to unfilled squares.

analysers (which may be binary with 1 corresponding to "feature present" and 0 to "feature absent") constitute the set of independent variables $X_1, X_2, \ldots, X_n$.

3. If there are but two classes to which the unknown pattern is to be assigned, there will be but one set of regression weights, $w_1, w_2, \ldots, w_n$ and one value of the dependent variable Y. If the calculated Y value is above a given critical threshold, θ, the pattern is assigned to one category and if below, to the other category.

During the "learning" phase for such devices, they are informed whether their decisions are correct or incorrect and the values of the regression weights, the w's, or the threshold, θ, are adjusted to improve performance. The exact method of making these adjustments differs from one model to another but, if this procedure will work in principle (a problem to be discussed below), the parameters will sooner or later converge to appropriate values (providing the method of making these adjustments is reasonable). Also, the various models differ in the method of selecting the feature analysers. In the Perceptron (Rosenblatt, 1958 and 1962), they were assigned to random combinations of squares of the binary input matrix.

In the Uhr and Vossler pattern recognizer (Uhr and Vossler, in Feigenbaum and Feldman, 1963), the feature analysers were deliberately chosen but the program was provided with a method of discarding feature analysers which were not useful and for forming new analysers randomly or from combinations of analysers already being used. Also, the pattern recognizing device is potentially capable of classifying into more than two categories. In Pandemonium (Selfridge and Neisser, in Feigenbaum and Feldman, 1963), there was a different set of weights and a different Y_c value calculated for each category to which a pattern might be assigned and the assignment is made to the category for which Y_c is the largest. A more general review of such devices is given by Uhr (1963) and Gyr *et al.* (1966).

In the formal analysis of such devices made by Sebesteyen (1962) and extended by Nillsson (1965), the criterion of linear separability was proposed. For each pattern in the population of patterns to be classified, there corresponds a set of n values of the X's corresponding to the feature analysers and a point in n dimensional space for which the X values are coordinates. If the patterns corresponding to different categories can be separated from each other by lines, planes or hyperplanes in this n dimensional space, the categories of patterns are said to be linearly separable. If this criterion is satisfied, then in principle, it should be possible to adjust the regression weights and threshold values during the learning phase so the patterns can be classified without error.

Sebesteyen and Nillsson discuss algorithms for this process which are essentially sequential* versions of multiple discriminant analysis of multivariate statistics (Morrison, 1967, Chapter 4). Thus, if the "right" set of feature analysers is selected so the populations of patterns can at least approximately satisfy the linear separability criterion, it should be possible for a pattern recognizing device with adjustable weights and thresholds to learn to perform with a high probability of correct decisions after sufficient training. Sebesteyen and Nillsson also consider other than linear methods but these are beyond the scope of this paper.

In their penetrating analysis of such pattern recognizing devices, Minsky and Papert (1969) analyse a number of limitations imposed by feature analysers of particular types. If feature analysers are confined to a limited region of pattern, it will not be possible to correctly classify patterns according to properties of the "whole" pattern—a conclusion which is strongly implied by Gestalt psychology as well. One of their examples concerns the patterns in Fig. 2 which are to be classified according to whether or not they contain a closed region, i.e. patterns (a) and (d) which contain a closed region and are to be distinguished

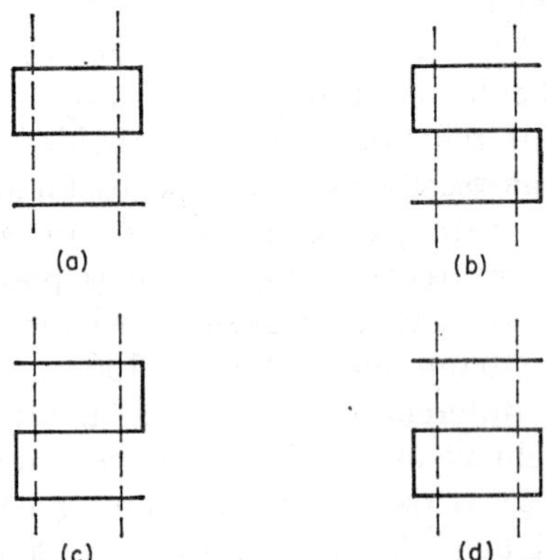

Fig. 2. Example from Minsky and Papert (1969, p. 13).

from (b) and (c) which do not. Each of the patterns is divided in Fig. 2 by vertical broken lines into three regions, left, center and right, and it is assumed that the feature analysers can be divided into three mutually exclusive sets according to area of the patterns to which the analysers are sensitive. The outputs of the feature analysers for the middle regions of all four figures will be the same since these regions are identical. On the basis of the left ends of the figures, (a) and (b) would be distinguished

* This means that the parameter estimates are adjusted after each member of the sample is taken rather than the usual practice of calculating the estimates only after the entire sample is taken.

from (c) and (d), and on the basis of the right end, figures (a) and (c) would be distinguished from (b) and (d). However, there can be no weighting of features from the left and right ends that would distinguish figures (a) and (d) from (b) and (c). Such weighting would be possible only if some feature or features were to be sensitive to both ends of the figure and, in particular, to whether a closed contour on one end is continued on the other.

In terms of the analysis of this paper, the only way to correctly classify patterns of a "wholistic" property such as "closure" or "connectedness", is either on the basis of features which are sensitive to combinations of aspects of the figure or some terms in the equation for Y must be functions of more than one feature. In other words, the necessary contextual dependencies must be built in at the level of the feature analysers or into the computing algorithm for classifying the patterns. Uhr and Vossler (in Feigenbaum and Feldman, 1963) have chosen to modify the set of feature analysers and it is possible to combine feature analysers in their system. Another possibility would be to inspect the figure sequentially so that preliminary analysis can select what aspects of a configuration are analysed. This is suggested by Minsky and Papert in the following quotation.

> "It is our conviction that the deterioration of the perceptron's ability to recognize patterns embedded in other contexts is a serious deterrent to using it in real, practical situations. Of course, this deficiency can be mitigated by embedding the perceptron in a more serial process—one in which the figure of interest is isolated and separated from its context in an earlier phase" (Minsky and Papert, 1969, p. 113).

Such central determination of attention is discussed by Norman (1969), and Spinelli and Pribram (1966, 1967) describe experimental evidence which indicates that activity in the so-called visual association areas of the cortex can determine differential patterns of activity elicited by flashes.

Of course, it is a moot question if such pattern recognizing devices should be considered as psychological models. It should be appreciated that work in this area can at least be suggestive for models of perception, and work on such devices has been done by many psychologists and reviewed in the psychological literature (Rosenblatt, 1958; Uhr, 1963; Gyr *et al.*, 1966; Neisser, 1967). The point of this discussion is that any general model of human perception must consider contextual dependencies at some level.

Models of Decision Making and Judgment

The linear regression model has been characterized by Edwards and Tversky (1967) as the "one idea" which "so completely dominates the literature on riskless choice that it has no competitors". In addition to its linear and non-interactive properties, the linear regression equation as a model of decision making has the additional property of being *compensatory*.* In the case of two dimensions of utility, X_1 and X_2, which are to be combined by a regression equation using weights w_1 and w_2 into a composite measure Y, this means that some entities with a lot of X_1 but little X_2 can be as "desirable" (i.e. have the same Y value) as entities with little X_1 but a lot of X_2 or with moderate amounts of both X_1 and X_2 (assuming the pairs of X's and w's are not grossly unequal). In other words a deficiency in one utility dimension can be "compensated for" by an extra amount of another utility dimension. In contrast, a *conjunctive* model would require that an entity would require beyond a minimum amount of each utility dimension to be acceptable.

As a model for decision making, the linear regression equation would seem to have similar limitations to those noted above for pattern recognition. In games like checkers or chess, it is easy to imagine situations in which particular combinations or arrangements of pieces on the board would have properties which could not be adequately inferred from some sort of linear combination of the values of individual piece positions. In the features he selects for computing what is, in effect, the utility of anticipated moves in checkers, Sammuels (in Feigenbaum and Feldman, 1963) seems to select some features which are sensitive to combinations of positions of pieces so the interactive aspects of piece positions are captured at the feature level.†

Einhorn (1970) has reviewed the use of noncompensatory, nonlinear, and to some extent, interactive models in decision making, so little of what he says shall be repeated here. Hammond and his associates (Hammond, Hursch and Todd, 1964; Hammond and Summers, 1965; Hursch, Hammond and Hursch, 1964) have extensively used the linear regression equation as a model for judgment and have shown that experimental subjects can learn in terms of regression weight values. Einhorn (1970) points out that the index of nonlinearity proposed by Hursch *et al.* (1964) does not distinguish between nonlinear and error variance. In addition, it does not account for interactive relations between cues and the subjects' judgments and between the distal event and cues. If the Gestalt psychologists and the previous analysis of the relations of limited features to "wholistic" properties of patterns above is correct, a linear relation between distal visual events and proximal cues is not to be expected as a general rule.

Finally, the issues of clinical versus statistical prediction should be

* The terms *compensatory* and *conjunctive* are taken from Coombs (1964).

† An example is the feature which Sammuels calls "cramp".

examined. Again, the linear regression equation is frequently used to carry out the statistical predictions, so the problem can be analysed into two sub-problems; one concerning the adequacy of the linear regression model for the relations between objective information and the clinical diagnostic categories, and the other concerning the computing capabilities of human judges. The studies of Hammond *et al.* (1964) and Hammond and Summers (1965) indicate that judges use linear models to a considerable extent but can use nonlinear cues as well. *A priori* it seems reasonable to conclude that human judges will never be able to perform better than some statistical algorithm in making judgments in situations where the relevant information can be given to the computing device and where the computing algorithm is general enough to be sensitive to the relations between the information and the optimum judgment. As before, if the relations are linear and noninteractive, the linear regression equation should work well, but if the relations are nonlinear, and especially if they are interactive, either another equation should be used as a model or the information transformed or recodified so the relations will be linear and noninteractive. However, an argument can be made for the judgment of the clinician where the information on which the judgment is based is not codified in an objective form. On the basis of speculation described in another paper by this author (Wilson, 1970), such judgments are most likely to be made intuitively using context dependent rules which the judge cannot explicitly state.* This sounds mysterious but is probably no more mysterious than the judgments we all make in processing visual, perceptual or semantic information.

The Factor Analytic Model

Factor analysis has been used for some time by psychologists as a technique for inferring what factors are basic to the generation of a larger set of measures such as measures of personality or intellectual functioning. While the results of factor analysis can be regarded as merely descriptive, there have been claims for central theoretical status of such results (e.g. Royce, 1963; Cattell, 1966, esp. Chapters 1, 2 and 3).

The basic structural assumptions in factor analysis are stated in the pattern equation (Harman, 1967, Chapter 2) which is also a linear regression equation.† Neglecting the contribution of specific and error

* This conclusion seems essentially in agreement with the recent paper by Holt (1970).

† In matrix form, the pattern equation for the common factor portion of variance is $X = A.F$ where X is the n by N, observed variable by subject data matrix, A is the n by r, observed variable by factor loading matrix and F is the r by N, factor by subject factor score matrix. As a general rule, $r < n < N$.

factor variance, the Y's in this application are the observed variables (in standard score form), the X's are values of the underlying factors (also in standard score form) and the w's are factor loadings. As before, the model is linear and non-interactive.

One common practice among factor analysts of the Thurstone-Cattell persuasion is to rotate factors to an oblique simple structure position. The set of criteria for simple structure will not be given here (see Harman, 1967, pp. 97–99) but they will always be satisfied if there are several observed variables corresponding to each factor (i.e. several large loadings with the remaining loadings close to zero) and if each variable corresponds to no more than one factor (i.e. has a large loading on only one factor).* Thus, in this case, the measures would be divided into disjoint subgroups with each subgroup corresponding to a factor. If we proceed to factor analyse the intercorrelations of the oblique factors of the first solution to obtain a second order factor analysis, as is customary in the Thurstone-Cattel school, and if the rotation had the happy result of dividing the first order factors into disjoint subgroups, as described for the first order analysis, we would have obtained two levels of a hierarchical classification system. If this were continued until only one common factor remained, we would have the observed measures at the lowest level of a hierarchical scheme in which each entity at a lower level would correspond to no more than one entity at the next higher level.† The structure thus generated resembles the familiar schemes of biology for taxonomic classification of organisms. This is the result of the generative schemata of context-free grammars as well (Wilson, 1970). The results of several higher order factor analyses with oblique rotation to simple structure can approximate this result although the lower level entities may be associated with two or three higher order entities as the figures in the paper by Royce (1963) imply. Thus, the generative schemata of higher order factor analyses has an approximately context-free character which is a not too surprising result of the assumptions of the pattern equation. (Also see Cattell, 1966, Chapter 9 for a further discussion of taxonomic classification in a factor analytic context.) While those favoring oblique simple structure rotation correctly claim that such solutions are more general than ortho-

* This is essentially the independent clusters criterion proposed by Harris and Kaiser (1964) which is simpler and somewhat stronger than the simple structure criteria. The author prefers the name disjoint clusters criterion since the clusters are disjoint and are, in fact, not independent in that membership in one cluster precludes membership in another as well.

† If the correlations were converted to distance measures, the hierarchical clustering procedure of Johnstone (1967) would in principle produce the same hierarchy.

gonal rotations, all types of factor analytic solutions are limited by the assumptions implicit in the pattern equation.

Before proceeding further, it would be well to consider the results of applying a factor analysis to a set of relations which are linear and interactive functions of two known "factors" or generative independent variables. The two variables, designated X and Y, take on the entire range of integer values of 0 through 9 and the set of the 100 combinations of X, Y values can be regarded as a population (as distinguished from a sample) in which X and Y have rectangular distributions and are independent. The relations between X and Y selected for the factor analysis are given in the left column of Table I. Relations 1 through 4 are all linear functions of X and Y (including X and Y which are "markers") and so satisfy the linear pattern equation. Relations 5 through 7 are interactive in a technical sense but were selected as monotone functions of X and Y which should have substantial correlations with X and Y over a limited range of values.* Relations 8 through 11 were selected as more "context dependent" in that the nature of the relation involving one variable depends on the value of the other variable and the relations were deliberately balanced so the correlations with X and Y were zero.

The correlations were factor analysed using a Principal Axes solution (ones in diagonal) and three factors selected for subsequent rotation. The eigenvalues corresponding to these factors were 4·18, 3·40 and 2·54 which account for 92·1 % of the variance (which is all reliable variance). The remaining eigenvalues were all 0·39 or less so three is the number of factors to be rotated according to the eigenvalues of one or more criterion of Guttman and Kaiser or the Scree criterion of Cattell.

Since X, Y, and the set of relations 8 through 11 are all mutually orthogonal, an orthogonal rotation was attempted in the hope that the resulting factors might correspond to these mutually orthogonal sets. Rotation using Varimax, Equimax and Quartimax criteria was carried out with similar results so only the Varimax rotation is reported here in Table I. While the data is obviously quite artificial, the analysis reported here conforms to fairly standard practices (with the possible omission of an oblique rotation).

While the rotated solution in Table I does not correspond to the expected result, they are quite interpretable and illustrate how interactive relations can affect a factor analysis. Factor I corresponds to the interactions with moderate loadings for the interactive relations with

* This indeed was the case. Relation 5 has a correlation of +0·64 with X and Y separately while relation 6 and 7 have correlations of +0·51 with the variable in the numerator and of −0·58 with the variable in the denominator.

Table I
Rotated factor solution for factor analyses of various relations between X and Y

Relation	Factor I	II	III	h^2
1. X	−0·03	+0·71	+0·69	0·97
2. Y	−0·03	+0·71	−0·69	0·97
3. $2X+Y$	−0·04	+0·95	+0·31	0·99
4. $X+2Y$	−0·04	+0·95	−0·31	0·99
5. XY	+0·32	+0·94	+0·00	0·98
6. $\frac{X}{Y+1}$	−0·32	−0·07	+0·84	0·81
7. $\frac{Y}{X+1}$	−0·32	−0·07	−0·84	0·81
8. X if $Y \geqslant 5$; $9-X$ if $Y \leqslant 4$	+0·92	+0·05	+0·01	0·85
9. Y if $X \geqslant 5$; $9-Y$ if $X \leqslant 4$	+0·92	+0·05	−0·01	0·85
10. 9 if $X \geqslant 5$, $Y \geqslant 5$ or $X \leqslant 4$, $Y \leqslant 4$; 0 otherwise	+0·97	+0·03	0	0·95
11. 9 if $X \geqslant 5$, $Y \leqslant 4$ or $X \leqslant 4$, $Y \geqslant 5$; 0 otherwise	−0·97	−0·03	0	0·95

correlations with X and Y (relations 5 through 7) and high loadings for interactive relations uncorrelated with X and Y (relations 8 through 11). The positive loadings correspond to relations which increase with both X and Y (relations 5, 8, 9 and 10) and the negative loadings to relations which increase with one variable and decrease with the other (relations 6, 7 and 11). Factor II corresponds to those relations which are either linear in either X or Y alone (relation 1 and 2) or in both X and Y (relations 3, 4 and 5) and so is positive for relations positively correlated with the sum of X and Y. The status of relation 5 is peculiar since it is both linear in X and Y and also interactive since the value of one variable determines the slope of the linear relation with the other.* Factor III corresponds to variables which are correlated with the difference between X and Y (the sign of the relation corresponding to the sign of the correlation) in the same sense that Factor II corresponds

* The interpretation of Factor II is not quite exact since it has near zero loadings for relations 6 and 7 which are linear in one variable but not the other.

to relations which are positively correlated with the sum of X and Y.*

Regarding factor analysis as a descriptive technique, the results of this analysis are not particularly unsatisfactory. The communalities of all relations is fairly high and only 8% of the total (and total reliable) variance is lost by the linear approximation. Rather than expressing the eleven relations as five types of relations† of two variables, the factor analysis results in an approximate description of the relations as one type of relation of three variables. In regard to the discovery of the nature of the "true" relations (a quite possibly naive goal for real scientific problems), these results might be disappointing to those who might regard factor analysis as a sort of Royal Road to Truth. If k variables are basic to the generation of a set of relations, then there are $(2^k - k - 1)$ potential interactions which can correspond to factors.‡ If k is two, as in the above example, this number of potential additional factors is only one but if k is six the number of potential additional factors is 57, and if k is ten the number is 1013. To pick a somewhat familiar example, let us consider the set of measures of autonomic reactivity which are often measured in connection with studies of human emotional reactivity (e.g. heart rate, blood pressure, galvanic skin response). If we assume that this set of measures is under the control of the autonomic nervous system only (disregarding the fairly well documented contribution of the limbic system—see Wright and Taylor, 1970, Chapter 6), then the measures can be regarded as generated by k variables which correspond to the level of activity of k independently responding centers in the autonomic nervous system. The autonomic nervous system contains two antagonistic divisions, the sympathetic and parasympathetic, and while the sympathetic division can be regarded as acting as a whole (and hence having only one center), the parasympathetic division cannot be so regarded and it may not be unreasonable to assume there are five. Since the autonomic nervous system is

* Further rotation was not attempted since it seemed not likely to make more than minor improvements in the factorial complexity of the relations. Relations 1 and 2 could be made to corrlespond to one factor only by an approximate 45 degree rotation of Factors II and III but reations 3, 4 and 5 would remain factorially complex. Also, it seems virtually impossible to decrease the factorial complexity of variables 5 through 7 without increasing the complexity of other relations.

†The relation types correspond to the following bracketed sets of relations: (1, 2, 3, 4), (5), (6, 7), (8, 9) and (10, 11).

‡ The reasoning behind this statement starts by analogy with the linear hypothesis model for k dimensions of classification for analysis of variance (Hayes, 1963). This model contains 2^k terms (aside from error) in an additive equation each of which could correspond to a term in the pattern equation except for the mean of the dependent variable which is removed, in effect, in calculating covariances or correlations. Of the remaining $(2^k - 1)$ terms, k corresponds to main effects which are already included in the pattern equation. Therefore, there are $(2^k - k - 1)$ potential interactions.

highly integrated with the endocrine system, it is reasonable to assume there are chemical effects accompanying activity of at least some autonomic centers (and some effects are already familiar). Since chemical effects are dependent on the chemicals in the mixture to which a chemical is added, we have the necessary conditions for context dependency and the dimensions of autonomic reactivity could be as many as the number of combinations of autonomous centers.*

The preceding discussion implies that factor analysis may frequently need supplementation or extension using other techniques, or that models specific to the domain being studied need to be considered after initial exploration using factor analysis. While users of factor analytic techniques may acknowledge such strategies, the ratio of such supplementation to the total number of factor analytic programs is remarkably small. Guilford's, Cattell's and Gray's papers in this Conference can be regarded as praiseworthy exceptions to the general tendency.

Detection of Interaction Effects

The best defense of the pervasive use of the linear regression equation as a behavior model is that it leads to algorithmic solutions and is supported by an impressive body of mathematical theory. Quite general interactive models are simply not practical because the potential number of interactive factors (discussed above) is far in excess of the measures which can be reasonably taken for any number of generative variables (k). However, the situation is not entirely hopeless because there are some techniques which can be applied even though they lack the generality one might hope for. Some of these are discussed below.

Guttman's Facet Analysis

Facet analysis (Guttman, in Cattell, 1966, Chapter 14; Foa, 1968) provides a method for ordering factors as interactions of generative variables. However, the analysis is heavily based on *a priori* considerations in the selection of the dimensions of the facet. At this conference, Messick interpreted Guilford's Structure of Intellect model as a Facet representation in which the factors in the cells correspond to the triple

* This example was suggested by Royce's comment on Gray's paper in this volume which indicated that the number of dimensions of emotional reactivity is considerably in excess of the three emotional response systems described by Gray. A very similar argument could be made from Gray's hypothesized interconnections between the sub-systems involved to explain why this ought to be expected.

interactions of the various levels of the three dimensions of the model.

Hunt, Stone and Marin's Concept Learning System

The Concept Learning System (Hunt *et al.*, 1966) is capable of inferring a rule for assigning entities to one of two categories on the basis of a vector of quantized characteristics of a sample of objects known to be in each of the two categories. The Concept Learning System could be regarded as an alternative to the pattern recognition and learning algorithms of Nillsson (1965) and Sebesteyen (1962) since it can also revise its decision rule when it is incorrect. Also, it could be used to infer a decision tree structure used by, say, a personnel manager to accept or reject candidates for positions based on a vector of quantized characteristics. It is capable of detecting a considerable variety of logical rules including "biconditional relations" which correspond to the relations like 10 and 11 in Table I. However, the Concept Learning System requires that an entity which has a particular vector always be assigned to one category which, in effect, precludes measurement error.*

The Concept Learning System has been programmed in a variety of forms but all depend on the Wholist Algorithm which can be stated as follows in a very much simplified form:

Step 1. Search for a characteristic shared by all known entities in one class and none of those in the other. If one is found, that characteristic can be used to classify the entities. If none is found, proceed to Step 2.
Step 2. Find the characteristic which is more useful than any other in distinguishing the classes. (Various criteria have been used to determine this.) Divide the samples in each class into sub-samples on the basis of this characteristic and return to Step 1, treating each sub-sample as a separate problem.

The Wholist Algorithm will generate a decision tree structure which has branches corresponding to the characteristics selected in Step 2 and eventually terminating on a decision based on a characteristic found in Step 1.

* Dawes (1971) argues that the linear regression equation is a good approximation to more complex models when measurement error is present or relations between criterion and predictor variables are less than perfect. This implies that a stochastic version of the Concept Learning System may be no better than the Nillsson-Sebesteyen algorithms and, more generally, that the linear regression model may be all that is needed when relationships are strictly stochastic.

Sonquist-Morgan Interaction Effect Detector (1964)

The Sonquist-Morgan (1964) program was designed to detect and use interaction effects among predictor variables (discrete or continuous) in predicting a criterion variable (ordinarily continuous) and so is an alternative to the multiple correlation coefficient which is based on the same linear regression equation as the models described above. The mode of operation of this program is similar to the Concept Learning System and, in a considerably simplified form, proceeds as follows:

Step 1. Carry out a one-way analysis of variance with the criterion variable in the role of the dependent variable and using a partition (ordinarily binary) of each of the predictor variables as the dimension of classification. The sample is divided into sub-samples on the basis of the partition of a predictor variable associated with the largest between groups variance.
Step 2. Step 1 is repeated for each of the remaining partitions of the predictor variables in each of the sub-samples. This process is repeated until no appreciable between groups variance can be obtained and/or sizes of the sub-samples are too small.

The Sonquist-Morgan program generates a prediction tree much like the decision tree of the Concept Learning System where the highest node corresponds to the single most important variable and subordinate nodes correspond to variables which are the most important for each level of the variable of the superordinate node. If there are interactions, the nodes under the different levels of a superordinate node will be different. For example, an analysis of average hourly earnings indicated that college graduation (yes or no) was the most important single variable. For the college graduates the most important variable was whether or not the individual was over 35, while for the non-college graduates the most important variable was whether or not the individual grew up on a farm or in the southeastern United States. In other words, college graduation effectively eliminates place of origin in determining income since this variable does not appear at any of the lower nodes for the prediction of income for college graduates. Also, level of achievement motivation appears as a node only in the branch for college graduates over 35, which implies that it is effectively related to income for a relatively limited class of individuals. In addition to being more appropriate for interacting predictor variables than the multiple linear regression equation, this method of analysis yields information which is directly useful in the interpretation of the processes involved.

One limitation of the Sonquist-Morgan program is that it is a heuristic interaction finding device and not an algorithm, but an algorithm is an unrealistic expectation for reasons discussed above. Aside from limitations of the size of sub-samples, which must inevitably become small, and the errors which are inevitable with the use of any statistical method, the main limitation of the Sonquist-Morgan program is in the detection of interactions of variables which are exactly balanced (like relations 8 through 11 in Table I) so that the variables involved in such interactions are in no way involved in main effects or lower order interactions.

The author of this paper had been considering the development of a procedure similar to that of Sonquist and Morgan, before he had learned of their work,* which was based on his experiences in the application of analysis of variance to designs with a substantial number of independent variables (usually about six). The significant main effects and interactions involved in such analyses can nearly always be arranged in one or two hierarchies whose highest member is a main effect and whose lower members are interactions which involve the term of the main effect (or the terms of a lower order interaction) and an additional term. To interpret the entire set of effects, a Duncan Multiple Range or Newman-Kuhls test will be carried out for the entire set of sample means associated with all combinations of terms in the highest order significant interaction in the hierarchy. The results of this post-mortem comparison can be used to generate tables or a tree structure like that of Sonquist and Morgan which can explain the interaction in a fairly easily interpreted form. The point of this seeming digression is that the hierarchies of main effects and interactions which the Sonquist-Morgan program is sensitive to are fairly common since interactions are rarely so exactly balanced that none of the variables involved appear in main effects in analyses of variance. Also, the preceding observations imply that the Sonquist-Morgan program would be primarily sensitive to only one such hierarchy but that this limitation could be easily removed by permitting it to start the development of decision trees from several of the partitions associated with large between groups sums of squares.

In closing, there is an implication of the Sonquist-Morgan program for users of factor analysis. If factors do interact, the user of factor analysis can expect to find that, after rotation, there will be no more

* The author is grateful to Dr. J. Paul Johnston of the Department of Political Science, University of Alberta, for introducing him to the work of Sonquist and Morgan.

than a small number of factors (probably, three at most) which have a substantial number of nonzero loadings on distinct sets of measures while there are many remaining factors which have nonzero loadings for small numbers of measures and that these sets of measures overlap substantially with the sets for other factors—a state of affairs somewhat like that in Table I. If this is the case, and sample sizes permitting, the factor scores for the major and clearly distinct factors could be used to select sub-samples for separate factor analyses. If the less well defined factors in the initial analysis emerge more clearly as distinct factors associated with particular levels of the major factors, then the initially less well defined factors will be better defined as interactive factors. The problem of sample size is severe for extensive pursuit of this strategy, but it could be eased by confining analyses to sub-sets of measures suggested by the initial analysis or by collecting further samples of individuals with extreme scores on the main factors. It should be noted that the strategy suggested here is much in the spirit of Guttman's facet analysis discussed above.

Conclusion

The linear regression assumption is made in a good many models of interest to psychologists but the title of this paper is somewhat misleading since it implies that the linear regression *is* a model and even that there is a "school" which might be called "linear regression psychology". Since it is a common and a strong assumption, however, its effects in a variety of contexts are worth examining and this has been the aim of this paper. It ought to be obvious that the author believes that the noninteractive and context-free properties of this equation are quite critical and that users of models which embody this equation as part of its assumptions should be aware of the potential limitations of such models and consider some of the alternatives suggested in the final portion of this paper.

COMMENT ON WILSON'S PAPER

JOHN L. HORN

I have not found much to criticize in Wilson's paper. This is unfortunate, for a critical tack is often most useful in sharpening issues and etching the strengths and weaknesses of a position. Nevertheless, rather than criticize sharply, I will simply emphasize, elaborate and question. While this is not likely to be the best form of discussion, it may help to focus some of the issues raised by Wilson's paper.

The major point of the paper is well taken: a linear, noninteractive, compensatory model* truly is a Procrustean couch. Relatively few psychological processes can be expected to fit on this couch without first being maimed by procedures which force a fit (of sorts).

It is probably true, as Wilson acknowledges, that most investigators who have gone through the apprenticeship training which enables one to become accepted as a multivariate psychologist are aware of this fact. At least they recognize it as a fact. But this recognition does not seem to register very convincingly in the behavior involved in building a science of behavior. It seems that the habit of thinking in terms of a LNC model is so well ingrained that to think in other ways is uncomfortable and therefore something to be avoided. Reminders of the form provided by Wilson's examples are thus well calculated to have a therapeutic effect.

In my own case, for example, I can occasionally recognize that the habit of thinking in terms of a LNC model is so well practised that I use it, almost as a reflex, not only when dealing with problems in psychology, but also in matters having little to do with psychology. I catch myself advising my adolescent son that in making points with the opposite sex he can make up for what he lacks in money and automobile

* Hereafter I will refer to LNC model (to represent linear, noninteractive, and compensatory, respectively) rather than use the term "regression model". This latter often connotes a least-squares solution for weights and neither the least-squares quality nor the quality of weighting is of particular interest in this discussion (or in Wilson's paper). Indeed, in a sense these two qualities of the linear regression model define a context-dependent characteristic of this model, although the dependence in this case is different in noteworthy respects from that which Wilson is mainly concerned in his paper.

Dependence in the regression model results by virtue of the fact that in selecting beta weights by use of the least-squares procedure the magnitude of each weight is a function of the way in which the corresponding variable predicts (on an average over subjects) relative to the prediction provided by the other independent variables in the set. The weight is the part correlation between the predictor and the criterion, scaled by the inverse of the part standard deviation, where the part in each case represents the variance of the predictor which is not accounted for (linearly) by other predictors. Thus the weight represents the contribution to prediction which is made by a variable when it is in the context of particular other variables. As is well known, the weight can change drastically as the context changes—as variables which correlate with the variable in question are added to or subtracted from the predictor set. It is in this sense that the LNC model is not context free. But, of course, this is not the idea of context free to which Wilson refers in emphasizing that the LNC model does not contain features which enable one to give explicit recognition to interaction terms.

In fact, the maximization process which is accomplished by a least squares solution for weights yields a solution in which the variance which might be represented in cross-products (interactions) is often represented in the weights for the single variables. In particular, the linear components of the cross-product terms are absorbed in the weights for the single variables. This is a kind of mathematical efficiency and parsimony but it needn't be a good model for a psychological (or other) process.

with good humor and athletic ability. I am also sure that my "luck" at the race track attests to the fact that too often I combine the elements of the racing form in a simple linear manner when winning strategies call for configural models. Similarly, although Hoffman (1960) emphasized the para in referring to a paramorphic model for clinical diagnosis, I suspect that for me—as for many others raised in the traditions of connectionist, SR psychology—the model often better fits what I am doing (or trying to do) in diagnosis than does a more complex model. These examples from outside the realm of science no doubt are indicative of the thinking which is implicit in my scientific work.

It seems, therefore, that it is worthwhile for persons to forcefully remind us, as has Wilson (as Meehl, 1950, before him), that thinking in terms of an LNC model sometimes will not enable us to solve even very simple problems or problems as important as those represented by an attempt to describe the perception of closure of simple figures.

We need to keep Wilson's reminders in perspective, of course. For it is true, also, that the LNC model has proven to be useful for dealing with a surprising number of problems in the behavioral sciences, including problems for which the ideal (error free) solution requires another model. The recent summaries and analyses of Dawes (1971) and Goldberg (1970) illustrate this point beautifully and also indicate some of the reasons why the LNC is as hardy as it is.* It may be, as Dawes' analyses indicate, that when any substantial portion of error enters into observations, the LNC model will often provide the most representational and for this reason, the most valid representation of reality. There is however, danger in unreflective acceptance of this perspective, partly because it can condition researchers to learn to live with substantial portions of error when scientific advance requires that error be drastically reduced and partly because there no doubt are instances, perhaps numerous and important, in which uncritical application of an LNC model will lead to unreliable results even when one is working in a noisy, error-ridden world.

For a simple example illustrating this last point we may think of a bivariate relationship (riddled with measurement error) which, however, is nonlinear, as depicted in Fig. 1, and in respect to which sampling error is introduced in researchers' attempts to characterize the relationship. If a linear model is used and one researcher selects a sample in the range between A and B along the X-axis, the relationship will be characterized by a line having positive slope. A second researcher using

* In several earlier papers (e.g. Horst, 1954; Humphreys, 1957; Hoffman, 1960; Horn, 1963) some of the points made by Dawes and Goldberg were adumbrated and other virtues of the LNC model were discussed.

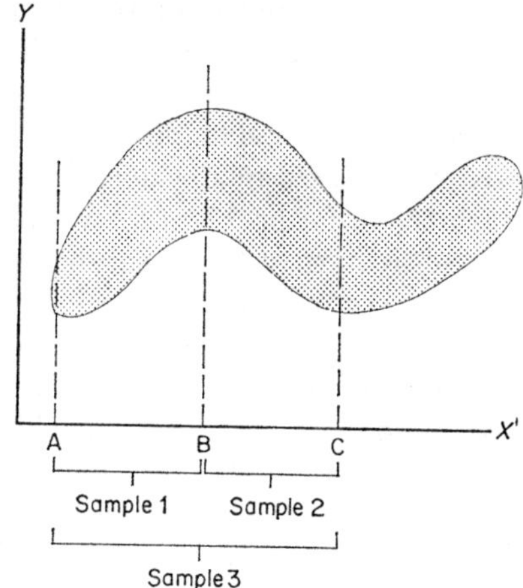

Fig. 1. A relationship between *X* and *Y* in which there is sampling in different parts of the continua.

a linear model and selecting a sample in the range between B and C along the X-axis would not replicate the first researcher's findings and, indeed, would report that the relationship was characterized by negative slope. A third researcher selecting a sample in the range between A and C along the X-axis might well conclude that both previous researchers obtained unreplicable results because there is no noteworthy relationship between X and Y. This conclusion could follow from uncritical acceptance of the idea that a linear model provides the best fit to observations when substantial portions of error (measurement and sampling) obtrude. The example is overly simple, of course, so one can readily see how in practice he would not be fooled in this instance, but it illustrates the kind of thing that can occur in more complex cases even when the conditions to which Dawes refers are operating.

This example illustrates, also, as do the examples of Wilson's paper, that contrary to an oft-heard argument, the LNC model need not provide a good first approximation to the model that will accurately represent reality. None of the linear equations suggested in the example really give a first approximation to the cubic function indicated in Fig. 1 unless it is recognized that the findings do *not* represent failure to replicate, and this requires acceptance of the idea that the linear component need not be prominent. Similarly, a LNC model does not provide a first approximation to a conjunctive categorization unless it is accepted that a surplus in one variable need not compensate for a dearth in another variable. Thus, recognition of the fact that the LNC model can provide a good first approximation when a more complex model ultimately is needed, and an awareness that this model often seems to work fairly well in actual applications, can lull us into a belief that we are making progress in a particular area when, in fact, we are not. The assumptions of the LNC model need to be considered carefully in respect to each scientific problem for which the model can be used, and this, of course, is part of the lesson of Wilson's paper.

Having aroused us to reconsider the limitations of the LNC model, Wilson's paper must then provoke us to consider alternatives, and there's the rub. For it is one thing to recognize the limitations of the LNC model when one chooses a problem on which there is already enough known to make it evident that the model will not provide a fully adequate representation, and it is quite a different matter, in areas where little is known and we are searching for order and for models with which to represent this, to specify procedures which will enable us to do the following:

1. To know when a simple model is not likely to provide a good first approximation or lead to an adequate representation in the long run or not likely to lead away from a truly adequate representation, and,
2. to select from an immense number of possible models that one which is most likely to lead to the most accurate solution in the long run.

The procedures which Wilson suggests are steps in the direction of dealing with these issues, but they are only halting initial steps. Much more must be done, as Wilson recognizes.

With regard to this and with particular reference to Wilson's expression of the opinion that it is virtually impossible to develop general algorithmic procedures for finding context-dependent relations, I wonder if perhaps we have not been overly concerned about the degrees of freedom problem which is raised by use of empirical search for nonzero terms in a general polynomial model? If we have been overly concerned and the empirical search procedure using the general polynomial* can be shown to lead to replicable results, then this approach provides an alternative which in several respects is more powerful than the approaches which Wilson mentions. In what follows I will attempt to summarize some of the reasons why I think we may have been overly concerned about the loss of degrees of freedom which may accompany use of the general polynomial model and along the

* For brevity's sake I will refer to this as the ESGP approach or model.

way, consider some specific features of the alternatives suggested by Wilson.

Perhaps I am wrong, but it seems to me that most of our empirical basis for the belief that the ESGP approach is unproductive, derives from work in which the aim was to find pattern scoring procedures for the items of personality inventories. We now pretty well understand that the reasons why this research on patterns has not worked is because responses to specific stimuli (items) are so intrinsically trivial, idiosyncratic, unreliable and invalid that there simply are too many patterns that are not stable under the conditions of replication which can be arranged in most behavioral science researches. If, however, the variables involved are not trivial items, what then? Are there likely to be many stable patterns arising, in fact, in large samples of subjects? If in relatively large samples of subjects only a relatively small number of patterns appear for substantial numbers of subjects, then can it not be reasonably concluded that the patterns which appear for only a few subjects are either the result of error, in which case the patterns can be classified with those that they resemble most closely, or represent anomalous occurrences of the influences which produce the more normal patterns? The problem in this respect is the same in principle as one of specifying adequate subsample size for interaction groupings formed by the multiple branching procedures which Wilson describes.

The astronomical number of patterns which can arise for consideration in applications of the ESGP approach result in part because of the large number of categories (magnitudes) which may be represented in each of several variables and in part because of the large (infinite) number of powers (and geometrically corresponding numbers of cross-product terms) which may be used in the general polynomial. These problems also appear, although in somewhat different guises, in the approaches which Wilson describes.

In the methods discussed by Wilson there is an implicit suggestion that the first of these problems may be kept within manageable bounds by dichotomizing the variables. This, however, can mean that a high price is paid for simplifying the search for patterns. *A priori* and statistical divisions of variables (e.g. at the median) need not provide a sound basis for revealing interactions which may characterize phenomena and similarly, it is not unreasonable to suppose that some of the more important interactive relationships characterizing "wholes", say, will be found only if variables appear as trichotomies or, in general, multichotomies. Nevertheless, if the number of variables to be considered in an empirical search is at all large, the number of categories of each variable must be kept small if the number of interactive possibilities is not to get out of hand. This need not imply, however, that all of a set of variables should be dichotomized. Perhaps some should be trichotomized and others represented in terms of four categories.

With regard to this, as in consideration of the power to be tried in the general polynomial, and generally all attempts to apply an empirical search for patterns, probably the most effective and valid way to narrow the interactive possibilities, thus maintaining a requisite number of degrees of freedom, is to employ strong theory—i.e. theory based upon good logic and as many relevant findings as one can put together. For example, if there is sufficient knowledge of the phenomena under consideration to ensure that the variables may be dichotomized without gross distortion, and that all but two-variable interactions are illogical or unlikely then assuming 10 variables to be under consideration; this need involve only 55 terms in the general polynomial. These 55 terms, with proper choice of weights, can represent all of the 1024 distinct patterns which can be represented among 10 dichotomous variables.* In this case each of the 45 cross-product terms, as well as the 10 variables considered separately, might be treated as a predictor and examined by bivariate, partial and multiple correlational† procedures to determine which interactions were contributing unique and valid variance in the prediction of a valid criterion. Similarly, in using factor analytic approaches, if a strong enough substantive theory is adopted, a small enough number of equations may be written in order to discover whether or not one or the other of the several possible nonlinear structures emerges in sufficiently overdetermined data.

In contrast to this particular application of the ESGP approach, the successive branching procedures which Wilson proposes force consideration of higher order interactions or interactions within interactions. Of course the ESGP model can be made to include such interactions by making the power for the polynomial larger or simply including desired terms in the expanded form of the polynomial. But to step-up systematically to successively higher powers for the polynomial is to expand greatly the number of possibilities to consider, whereas in Wilson's proposals there is a step-down which is limited by subsample size.

* Representing the $2^k - k - 1 = 1024 - 10 - 1 = 1013$ potential interactions to which Wilson refers.

† Since the interactive components are not linearly dependent upon the separate components, but are nonlinearly related to these, and are not mutually dependent, the inverse for such a solution will exist. Actually, a step-wise multiple correlational analysis (with perhaps rational–theoretical, rather than statistical choice of the variable for inclusion at each step) might often be the better way to augment and refine a model in areas where strong theory can guide the search for patterns.

What is mainly lacking to make the ESGP approach generally applicable in the behavioral sciences is the presence of strong substantive theories. However a potentially salubrious influence of Wilson's paper is that it provides some promising approaches for yielding mathematical representations which can mesh with logical understanding of phenomena. It thus may encourage those who have a fairly good understanding of the phenomena in their research area to try to specify the more complex models which will adequately represent the phenomena they understand.

One thing that worries me a bit about Wilson's branching analysis of variance procedure (adapted from Sonquist and Morgan, 1964) is that this, like the multiple regression model and other procedures based upon least-squares estimation, implicitly assumes that because one classification (variable) has more variance than another, it should be given first consideration in developing the model which will ultimately provide the best representation of the data. The relative standings of variables with respect to variance usually reflect such things as subject sampling and the reliability of measurement and (given that reliabilities and sampling influences are constant) scientific importance, as represented by a term being indispensable in a thoroughly adequate model, does not necessarily stand in a one-to-one relation to variance contribution. Short of using a strong substantive theory however, I know of no solution to this problem.

I am intrigued and not a little puzzled by the factor analysis which Wilson provides. It seems to me that, in part, it represents what one should strive not to do if he wants to use factor analysis as a road (Royal or otherwise) to truth. That is, if one had the idea that there were five types of relations of two variables in Wilson's data and these were supposed to be indicated by the results from a factor analysis based upon conventional methods for limiting the number of factors, then he would want to be sure to over-determine each factor by representing each type of relation with four or more* of the kinds of combinations which constitute the variables in Wilson's analyses. The simple interaction type of relation would not be expected to be represented by a factor in Wilson's analysis, for example, because it is represented in only one variable and a solution in which the root-one criterion limits the number of factors would not be expected to have a factor defined by only one variable.†

* As argued by Horn in his contribution to this symposium.

† If more factors were allowed, such a factor might appear. I am not sure of this, however, because I have not worked with factoring under conditions where such factors would be postulated.

Be this as it may, Wilson's factor analysis is indeed useful in indicating how interactive relations can operate in a factor analytic solution. I think, also, that his proposals for searching out interactive effects by first classifying with respect to factor scores derived from disjoint factors and then factoring within these classifications are promising. We have tried something similar to this in our attempts to build diagnostic categories for persons who enter a hospital for treatment of problems associated with excessive use of alcohol (Horn *et al.*, 1972). What we find is that symptoms which are not unifactorial with respect to primary-level factors will often prove to be good measures (i.e. unifactorial measures) of second order factors. Relative to Wilson's proposal, what the factorially complex variables seem to represent is the fact of interaction among influences represented by primary-level factors. I intend to look into this matter a bit more carefully in response to Wilson's analyses.

In conclusion, I think that Wilson's paper has several interesting and provocative implications which should be followed up in research on issues of theoretical importance in the behavioral sciences.

COMMENT ON WILSON'S PAPER

J. R. ROYCE

During the discussion the point was made that the factor model is a compensatory, context-free model, and is, thereby, limited to linear and noninteractive relations of factors. Further, in his paper Wilson raises the issue of whether factors should be regarded as merely "descriptive" or whether they might be regarded as more "explanatory" (e.g. see p. 53 ". . . there have been claims for central theoretical status of such results.)" The major thrust of the discussion seemed to be that current factor procedures are inadequate or limited since most relationships among psychological variables are probably non-linear and interactive (i.e. context dependent).

I suspect we have a straw man issue here and if so, I would like to lay the issue to rest. My understanding of factor analysis *c* 1970 is that it is, indeed, a linear model etc., and that it makes no claim whatsoever to identify the equations which functionally relate factors, whether these equations are linear or nonlinear, interactive or noninteractive. My guess regarding how science gets done is that no algorithm, including factor analysis, will be able to do that for us. In short, constructing such equations is a post-factorial business. It is, in fact, an important aspect of the construction of nomological nets or theoretical structures, of which factors can be a very potent part. While it is true that a single factor analytic study, or factor findings at an early stage of investigation of a given domain may be merely descriptive, it is also true that a linked series of investigations, involving anchor variables and invariant factors, can lead to factors which lie deep within the nomological net. Such factors, properly embedded in the context of other constructs (i.e. either factorially or non-factorially derived) carry the same kind of pervasive explanatory potential which has been attributed to non-factorially derived constructs.

REJOINDER TO DISCUSSANTS' COMMENTS

KELLOGG V. WILSON

Since Horn was in such substantial agreement with my paper, I find little I could say in rejoinder.

My main point of disagreement is his discussion of the factor analysis in Table I. There were only three major classes of relations: linear in X and/or Y (relations 1 through 4), interactive but correlated with X and Y (relations 5 through 7), interactive and uncorrelated with X or Y. (The five types of relations mentioned in footnote 17 refer to more specific mathematical forms.) The interactive relations which were uncorrelated with X or Y (8 through 11) correspond to a factor (I). The other three interactions (5 through 7) were factorially complex, loading either on the "interaction" factor (I) or one of the factors associated with X and Y (II or III). While this class of interactions was not "overdetermined" by Horn's criterion of four or more, factorial complexity was virtually inevitable by virtue of the substantial correlation of this class with X and Y. The point of this example was that interactive relations can produce additional factors even though the factor analysis does indicate a good "fit" to a linear model by virtue of a large proportion of reliable variance accounted for. The only indicator of the presence of interactive factors in this example was factorial complexity for the interactive relations which had substantial correlations with the relations which were linearly related to the factors. While this class of interactions is *a priori* more likely than the "balanced" interactions, such as relations 8 through 11, the factorial complexity would occur only if both noninteractive and interactive relations were incorporated in the measures. Also, of course, factorial complexity can occur for reasons other than the interaction of factors.

The bulk of Horn's discussion was concerned with the desirability of considering alternatives to the standard modes of factor analysis and to better utilize knowledge of the domain in selecting such alternatives. These were themes of my paper and I hope that more imaginative consideration of alternatives will occur in factor analysis and the other applications of the linear model. While most users of multivariate methods "know" the assumptions of the linear model, it is not clear they are aware of the strength of these assumptions and that there are—potentially at least—alternative modes of analysis. The latter observation is my reply to Royce's comments—the assumptions are known but their implications are not generally appreciated.

REFERENCES

Cattell, R. B. (ed.) (1966). "Handbook of Multivariate Experimental Psychology." Rand-McNally, Chicago, Illinois.

Chomsky, N. (1963). Formal properties of grammars. *In* "Handbook of Mathematical Psychology." (Luce, R. D., Bush, R. R. and Galanter, E. eds) Wiley, New York.

Coombs, C. (1964). "A Theory of Data." Wiley, New York.

Dawes, R. M. (1971). Why linear models work in a noisy, non-linear world. Paper presented at the Annual Meeting of the Society of Multivariate Experimental Psychology. Banff, Alberta, Canada.

Edwards, W. and Tversky, A. (eds) (1967). "Decision Making." Penguin Books, Baltimore.

Einhorn, H. J. (1970). The use of nonlinear, noncompensatory models in decision making. *Psychol. Bull.* **73,** 221–230.

Feigenbaum, E. A. and Feldman, J. (eds) (1963). "Computers and Thought." McGraw-Hill, New York.

Goldberg, L. R. (1970). Man versus model of man: A rationale, plus some evidence, for a method of improving clinical inferences. *Psychol. Bull.* **73,** 422–432.

Gyr, J., Brown, J. S., Willey, R. and Zivian, A. (1966). Computer simulation and psychological theories of perception. *Psychol. Bull.* **65,** 174–192.

Hammond, K. R., Hursch, C. J. and Todd, F. J. (1964). Analyzing the components of clinical inference. *Psychol. Rev.* **71,** 438–456.

Hammond, K. and Summers, D. A. (1965). Cognitive dependence on linear and nonlinear cues. *Psychol. Rev.* **72,** 215–224.

Harman, H. (1967). "Modern Factor Analysis" (2nd Edn). University of Chicago Press, Chicago, Illinois.

Harris, C. W. and Kaiser, H. F. (1964). Oblique factor solutions through orthogonal rotations. *Psychometrika* **29,** 347–362.

Hayes, W. (1963). "Statistics for Psychologists." Holt, New York.

Hoffman, P. J. (1960). The paramorphic representation of clinical judgment. *Psychol. Bull.* **57,** 116–131.

Holt, R. R. (1970). Yet another look at clinical and statistical prediction. *Am. Psychol.* **25,** 337–349.

Horn, J. L. (1963). Equations representing combinations of components in scoring psychological variables. *Acta Psychol.* **21,** 174–217.

Horn, J. L., Wanberg, K. W. and Foster, F. M. (1972). "The Alcoholism Symptoms Scale." Fort Logan Mental Health Center, Denver, Colorado.

Horst, P. (1954). Pattern analysis and configural scoring. *J. clin. Psychol.* **10,** 3–11.

Humphreys, L. G. (1957). Characteristics of type-concepts with special reference to Sheldon's typology. *Psychol. Bull.* **54,** 218–228.

Hunt, E. B., Murin, J. and Stone, P. J. (1966). "Experiments in Induction." Academic Press, New York and London.

Hursch, C. J., Hammond, K. R. and Hursch, J. L. (1964). Some methodological considerations in multiple-cue probability studies. *Psychol. Rev.* **71,** 42–60.

Johnson, S. C. (1967). Hierarchical clustering schemes. *Psychometrika* **32,** 241–254.

Meehl, P. E. (1950). Configural scoring. *J. consult. Psychol.* **14,** 165–171.

Minsky, M. and Papert, S. (1969). "Perceptrons: An Introduction to Computational Geometry." M.I.T. Press, Cambridge, Massachusetts.

Morrison, D. F. (1967). "Multivariate Statistical Methods." McGraw-Hill, New York.

Neisser, U. (1967). "Cognitive Psychology." Appleton-Century-Crofts, New York.

Nillsson, N. J. (1965). "Learning Machines: Foundations of Trainable Pattern-Classifying Systems." McGraw-Hill, New York.

Norman, D. A. (1969). "Memory and Attention." Wiley, New York.

Rosenblatt, F. (1958). The perceptron: A probabilistic model for information storage in the brain. *Psychol. Rev.* **65,** 386–408.

Rosenblatt, F. (1967). "Principles in Neurodynamics." Spartan Books, New York.

Royce, J. R. (1963). Factors as theoretical constructs. *Am. Psychol.* **18,** 522–528.

Sebesteyen, G. (1962). "Decision Making Processes in Pattern Recognition." Macmillan, New York.

Sonquist, J. A. and Morgan, J. N. (1964). "The Detection of Interaction Effects." Monograph No. 35, Survey Research Center, Institute of Social Research, University of Michigan, Ann Arbor.

Spinelli, D. N. and Pribram, K. H. (1966). Changes in visual recovery functions produced by temporal lobe stimulation in monkeys. *Electroencephalography and Clinical Neurophysiology* **20,** 44–49.

Spinelli, D. N. and Pribram, K. H. (1967). Changes in visual recovery functions and unit activity produced by frontal and temporal area stimulation. *Electroencephalography and Clinical Neurophysiology* **22,** 143–149.

Uhr, L. (1963). "Pattern recognition" computers as models far from perception. *Psychol. Bull.* **60,** 40–73.

Wilson, K. V. (1970). "Grammars and Behavior Models." Unpublished manuscript.

Wright, D. S. and Taylor, A. (1970). "Introducing Psychology." Penguin Books, Baltimore.

How Shall We Conceptualize the Personality We Seek to Investigate?

DONALD W. FISKE*

University of Chicago

The psychological study of individual differences has come a long way. We have a substantial body of test theory and sophisticated techniques for analysing data. We know something about the behavior of subjects while they are taking tests and about how ratings and clinical judgments are made, though we need to know a lot more. What we have done least adequately is the investigation of the relationships between our data and the constructs at which our measuring instruments are aimed. Measurement is always a means to an end. More attention must be devoted to specifying that end, to understanding how the goal of any research activity should guide the selection and application of the measuring procedures used.

This paper is concerned primarily with problems in conceptualizing and measuring personality. Its purpose is to identify and examine some critical problems. It will propose steps toward resolving some of these, but will leave others as issues to be settled later. Many of these problems seem to be present in other parts of psychology, and also in other behavioral sciences. The reader may determine for himself the appropriate limits to such extensions.

The exposition is based on the premise that the aim of a science is to develop theory which enables us to understand a body of phenomena. Such theory contains concepts which are constructed by scientists; the term "construct" can be employed to call attention to this important fact. Within the body of a mature science, there is consensus among the qualified workers on the basic constructs. Such consensus is just as necessary as consensus among scientists on each observation and on each "fact". But on how many terms in personality is there such

* This paper is based on work supported by the National Science Foundation under Grant Nos. GS 1060, 1998, and 3127.

consensus? More particularly, on how many personality variables is there essential agreement? Few, if any. In spite of dictionaries and glossaries (e.g., Verplanck, 1957), the picture is little better in the rest of psychology: occasionally, the agreement may be fairly good but it is rarely precise.

The Substance of Personality

Conceptualizations

How do we observe and conceptualize personality? Personality phenomena are all around us. Throughout our lives, we have experienced them in others and in ourselves and have conceptualized them more or less explicitly. Personologists (those engaged in the scientific study of personality) have frequently taken over these concepts from everyday life. As an unfortunate consequence, when they use such terms, they and their readers have the feeling that they know to what the terms refer. Our common experiences lead us to believe that these words mean the same thing to all of us. In fact, however, we do not agree exactly on these meanings. In addition, a cursory examination of the literature reveals that the same term is often used by several theorists even though each theorist appears to have a somewhat distinct personal definition. We should write not about anxiety, but about anxiety-Freud, anxiety-Cattell, anxiety-Taylor, etc.

We must go even further and identify explicitly the referents of each such construct in terms of the theory in which it is embedded. The specifications of each construct should include several facets. One facet is behavioral: what are the several manifestations of the construct? Another is situational: in what contexts does it appear? It may be necessary to have more than one situational facet, each with its several elements. (These and other guidelines for specifying personality concepts are discussed in Fiske, 1971a.) The purposes of such explicit formulations are to clarify and pin down the construct in the thinking of the conceptualizer and his colleagues and to provide a definite target at which measuring instruments can be aimed.

To return to the illustration of anxiety, this term is so broad that it identifies a large area within personality, not a distinct variable. McReynolds (1968) identifies three dimensions or dichotomies which in combination yield eight anxiety variables. Of the 88 formal anxiety measurement procedures he reviews, some assess one of these variables, some another: he identifies the IPAT Anxiety Scale with characteristic, overall, existent anxiety and the Test Anxiety Questionnaire with characteristic proneness to a specific anxiety. But for research on some current psychoanalytic proposition involving anxiety, it is doubtful that any questionnaire would closely fit the construct in that theoretical context.

As another example, consider drive. Murray (1938) uses it synonymously with need. Certainly his meaning is not identical with that of Hull, Spence, or Dollard and Miller. As English and English (1958) say, "Drive is currently used in innumerable contexts, often quite loosely." Impulsivity also has modified meanings in different theories. While speed of response is a common theme, Allport conceives impulsivity as deficiency of control and lack of coordination, Murray brings in inability to inhibit an impulse, Sanford and his colleagues are concerned with gratifying impulses, and G. Kelly with a short period of circumspection. Since the definitions are in terms of the theories, the corresponding ways of measuring the variable, though correlated, are not interchangeable.

Observations

In the natural sciences, there is implicit agreement on how observations will be made. Phenomena are observed by a trained scientist in such a way that other scientists can agree with him. Any one of them can read the dial and record the observation. There is only one perspective for such scientific work. In personality, we also use dial-readers or data-producers, but all too often we allow the observer to decide which dial he will read, and how he will read it and interpret it. For example, in ratings by self or by others, the content to be observed or reviewed is indicated only in general terms, the relative weights to be assigned to the frequency and the intensity aspects of the behavior are not stated, and the rating form permits the rater to express his personal response style in making his ratings.

More generally, there is no consensus in the personality field on a single perspective for observing the relevant phenomena. Personologists are trying to understand how a person sees himself and develops his self concept, what his immediate experience is like, how he is perceived by peers, and how personality phenomena are related to psychophysiological functioning. Types of personality theories differ in their major emphases, which may be on the self, phenomenology, social perception, psychophysiology, or intra-psychic processes. Recently, a conception based on response potentialities has been proposed (Wallace, 1966). This heterogeneity becomes understandable when we realize that there are several kinds of phenomena which personologists seek to understand. One may or may not choose to view these as perspectives for approaching that which people call personality. In terms of research strategy, however, these kinds of phenomena provide separate but related areas to be investigated. In personology, the object of study is not just behavior, but behavior as viewed from some particular vantage point. This qualification may apply to other parts of psychology and other behavioral sciences.

Somewhat corresponding to those several perspectives are several modes of observation which are used in studying personality. One is self-description as typified by the questionnaire. Another is current experiencing as in reports of perceptions, stated preferences between presented stimuli, and fantasy productions. A third is evidence of capabilities as in tests of ability and also in tests of cognitive styles. Prior behavior may be utilized in ratings by associates or judgments about products. Psychophysiological observations may be based on skin resistance, heart rate, or pupil size. There is, finally, the observation of ongoing behavior. This mode includes several important subvarieties: observation in a natural or simulated setting (the playground or the situational test), interviewing, and projective testing. These vary in the extent of the inferences made by the observer in producing his ratings or other indices. (See Fiske, 1971a.)

This particular classification is not neat. It is based on such diverse criteria as who produces the data, who produces the index, whether the subject knows he is being measured, and what task is given the observer. While this analysis has proved useful, more fruitful ones may be conceived. In any case, the simple fact remains that the observations used to study personality are made in a variety of ways. It is not surprising that these ways yield somewhat independent indices. To date, the observed relationships between data from different modes of observation are too low to permit us to consider them as interchangeable. Although the physicist can measure temperature by more than one means and can transform data from one instrument so that it reproduces data from another kind of instrument, the personologist cannot make such calibrated transformations. As long as instruments contribute unique variance, he will not be able to do so.

Some theorists make clear the mode of observation appropriate for the empirical investigation of their theory. The dynamic theorists usually rely on expert judges, diagnosticians or others who make inferences about intrapsychic processes. The personal construct theory of Kelly (1955) requires self-report as in responses to his REP Test. In other cases, it is up to the investigator to determine which mode or modes are consistent with the perspective of the theory being studied.

Personality phenomena as processes

Personality involves functioning and behaving. The variables of interest to personologists are not fixed attributes like height or eye color but rather refer to aspects of processes. When a person encounters a stimulus, does he attend to it or not? If he attends, how does he perceive it? How does he cognize it? What feelings does he have toward it? What change in his interaction with it does he intend to make? How does he make such a change? Is the change successful? Thus the characteristics of perceptual tendencies, cognitive styles, feelings, valuing, motivations, instrumental acts, and achievements refer to particular phases in processes. The study of personality is exceedingly difficult because it is concerned with aspects of processes in active, functioning people.

Each datum used in personality research is a fixed record of the experience or behavior of a person at some stage in a process. Each such observation is of course selective: it records one aspect and ignores others. We often note the location of the subject's mark on the answer sheet while ignoring the latency of his response and the graphological features of his mark. Our observations are also intrusive. We ask the subject to imagine that he is crawling along a ledge high on a mountain side and then interrupt his fantasy to ask him whether he has an uneasy feeling.

When taking a test or being measured in some other way, the subject is still the locus of psychological processes. There is the general process of coping with the test as a whole, to which subjects typically react by trying to complete it as rapidly as possible. Within that process, there are shorter processes associated with each stimulus-item. Testing procedures vary in the kind of relationship between such test-processes and the processes associated with the variable that the experimenter seeks to measure. A test of reasoning ability attempts to provide a work-sample of the subject's reasoning processes by inducing him to reason about a problem. A test of field independence determines how rapidly and accurately the subject can determine whether a simple figure is embedded in a more complex one. In such procedures, the experimenter observes the subject's processes as he reacts to stimuli, both the stimuli and the task being more or less representative of corresponding parts of the conceptualization for the construct being assessed.

In another test design, the experimenter induces in the subject some process which is taken *a priori* as related to the construct being measured. The subject's demonstration that he possesses certain information (such as knowledge of vocabulary or generally known facts) is seen as evidence that he has had the capacity to acquire such information and since he remembers it today, it is concluded that he still has the capacity to function as the construct specifies. In using questionnaires, we assume that a person who reports affiliative activities has been and still is affiliative.

A third test design is used in the Strong Vocational Interest Blank and in the MMPI. The experimenter interprets the number of a subject's answers which resemble those of a known criterion group as indicating the degree of similarity of that subject to that group. Since such tests are constructed empirically, the experimenter need not have any rationale about the processes involved in taking the test. Practically speaking, his only concern is that the characteristics of the testing situation be similar to the conditions in which the criterion responses were obtained, sufficiently similar to permit him to make the judgment about the strength of the construct in his subject.

These three designs are, in the order presented, increasingly indirect: by large steps, the testing processes depart more and more from those specified in formulating the construct. While economic and practical considerations often dictate the choice of measuring instrument, the experimenter must recognize the risks involved when basing his measurements on behavior, observed in his testing room, which is different in kind from that encompassed by his construct.

Unresolved Issues

Personology today faces many difficulties in coordinating its concepts and its measuring operations. Only a few can be mentioned here.

The phenomena of personality are multiply determined and are so complex that they are exceedingly difficult to dissect analytically or experimentally. Those phenomena of most interest are the ones which differentiate one person from another. Standard, common reactions, like being startled by an unexpected noise or greeting a friend in passing on the street, do not attract our research efforts. Instead of the responses whose variance is determined primarily by one stimulus, we are intrigued by responses influenced jointly by the several different stimuli provided by the given setting.

When we select a construct for investigation, we try to study it in a way which will be minimally affected by confounding influences. While we can, to some extent, control external conditions, we have little or no control over internal determinants. To mention only one consideration, the study of a single motive usually involves focusing on just one component of an interactive set of motives. The need for Achievement must be studied in conjunction with the fear of failure. The need for Affiliation must be viewed as involving expectations of both positive and negative reinforcements in interpersonal relationships (Mehrabian and Ksionzky, 1970). (These oppositional forces remind one of the pairings of excitatory and inhibitory functions in biology.) However, beyond these general linkages, there is the matter of the differing role of the motive in personality structures. Achievement may be central to the personality of one person, while fear of failure is central for others (cf. Sanford, 1956). While centrality is undoubtedly related to the strength of the motive, it may also involve qualitative differences in the motive. We simply do not know yet how to determine objectively the centrality of motives.

The specificity of procedures

The multiple determination of personality phenomena is a frustrating fact. Theory tells us that behavior varies not only with the stimulus but also with the characteristics of the situation and with the state of the organism. The findings of experimental studies support this conclusion. While there are few systematic studies of behavior over extended periods outside the laboratory, there is reason to believe that everyday behavior is more or less specific to its conditions. Responses in a testing situation are just a particular kind of behavior; they too vary with the setting, the reason the subject is there, the task, the format of the test, and the stimuli. The total effects from such sources, together with those associated with the mode of observation, are what is meant by method (as in "method factor" or "method variance").

We all know that most pairs of questionnaires aimed at the same trait-label yield scores which intercorrelate substantially below the limit set by their internal consistencies, simply because the tests have different content. The implicit conceptualization of each test constructor leads him to select items with a somewhat distinctive emphasis. This problem can in principle be resolved by more complete explication of the conceptualization held by each test designer, so that we can see to what extent the designers are defining the common trait-label differently. We can then judge the face validity of each instrument and can also decide which instrument is best for testing any given theoretical proposition.

More disturbing are the less readily understood effects associated with apparently small changes in procedure. For examples, reviews of the Water-Jar Test (Levitt, 1956) and of the Prisoner's Dilemma (Nemeth, 1970) note the influence of administrative conditions on scores. An unpublished study by Goldberg and Hettema finds that, although total score on the Rod and Frame Test did not correlate with several outside measures, certain subscores did. Does the construct of field independence or psychological differentiation vary psychologically as a function of initial frame and rod positions, of sequence, and of their interaction?

In applied work, this specificity of tests and procedures may not be serious. One can fairly readily determine which instrument works best in the given application. In basic research, however, this specificity poses a fundamental problem. How can we test propositions relating one construct to others if the empirical correlations vary with the particular instrument selected to represent the construct of interest? (We are not considering the total problem here—we are ignoring the fact that every point raised about our measures of the target construct will also apply to the measures of any other psychological construct which we correlate with our target construct.)

Extrinsic convergent validation

One approach to this specificity problem is to determine the extrinsic convergent validity of each measure. That is, given two or more measures of our construct, how close is the agreement between their profiles of relationships with other measures? I have examined several of the limited number of studies reporting such sets of correlations for more than one measure of a given construct. As one instance, in the assessment of clinical psychology students (Kelly and Fiske, 1951), we had staff, team mate, and self ratings on the same personality variables.

For 22 variables, the ratings from all three sources were intercorrelated, yielding a 66 × 66 matrix. Consider the ratings on one variable, Depressed–Cheerful. The correlations of the staff ratings on this variable with self ratings on each of the other 21 were compared with the corresponding profile of correlations for team mate ratings of Cheerful against the same self ratings. The pairs of correlations in the profiles showed no major differences. However, we also compared the two profiles for team mate ratings and for self ratings on Cheerful as correlated with staff ratings on the other 21 variables. This time, there were a number of discrepancies. The team mate ratings of Cheerful correlated more highly with staff ratings of Assertive and Unshakable Poise than did the self ratings for Cheerful. In contrast, the self ratings of Cheerful had higher correlations with staff ratings of Talkative, Adventurous, and Adaptive than those for team mate ratings of Cheerful. Thus the results suggest that the staff and team mate ratings of Cheerful are functionally equivalent in terms of their correlations with these self ratings, while the team mate and self ratings are differentiated from each other when correlated with staff ratings on other variables. These findings occurred in spite of the fact that these three sources yielded sets of ratings with fairly similar factorial structures (Fiske, 1949).

The picture is further complicated when we look at correlations with 112 scores from questionnaires and other tests. Even when ratings from two sources agree reasonably well on their profiles with ratings from the third source, they may show appreciable discrepancies in their profiles of correlations with test scores. Finding agreement between two measures in terms of their correlations with one kind of outside variable offers no assurance that similar agreement will be found between profiles for another kind.

Some comments on these analyses must be added. The comparisons between profiles were made by inspection, using an arbitrary difference between correlational values as a criterion, an obviously crude approach. It is also true that the reliability of the ratings presumably affects the overall height of the profile of correlations. As a function of reliability or of similarity in mode of observation, staff and team mate ratings generally showed higher intercorrelations than either did with self ratings. Lastly, it appeared that the higher the observed correlation in a profile, the more likely were large absolute differences.

In other data, an examination of extrinsic convergent validation was also made at the item level, with highly discouraging results. Probably as a function of unreliability, high convergence of profiles with test scores was rarely found. In addition, male and female subjects produce somewhat different pictures. It does not look as though more homogeneous tests could readily be built by finding items with congruent profiles of correlations with outside variables. Comparisons of item clusters from Comrey's work showed more convergence than that seen in these item data, but not sufficient to consider most pairs of clusters from the same factor as conceptually interchangeable.

Other studies have made it possible to analyse data from tests of intelligence and from personality instruments other than questionnaires (Fiske, 1971a, Chapter 11). The general findings remain the same: two measures aimed at the same construct will typically correlate with each other well below the limit set by their reliabilities; while that intercorrelation provides a very rough estimate of the observed similarity between their profiles of relationships with outside measures, the two profiles will rarely show high extrinsic convergent validation except in those exceptional cases in which that intercorrelation is close to its theoretical limit. Each measure can be expected to differ psychometrically, and therefore conceptually, from other measures of the same target construct.

What is the value of determining the extrinsic convergent validation of a test? Comparing the profile for a given test with those for other tests enables us to learn how the meaning to be attributed to that test is the same as and how it differs from the meaning for each of the other tests. Given such information, we have some idea to what extent we can generalize from the interpreted findings for that test to expected findings for other tests. More generally, the observed departures from convergence with alternative instruments for assessing the same target-construct point out areas where judgments about construct validity must be most cautious.

Alternative Resolutions

How can we resolve the various problems and issues discussed above? The answers are not at all clear at this time. There are several possible strategies, each with its strengths and limitations.

As indicated earlier, the abandonment of the individual difference or correlational approach in favor of the experimental does not provide an escape. Subjects in experimental conditions also react, showing evaluation apprehension (Rosenberg, 1969) which is related to test anxiety. Varying the instructions or other aspects of experimental conditions affects the observations obtained. It is doubtful that a science of personality phenomena in the laboratory can substitute for personology as a whole.

Yet it may be possible to produce significant phenomena in the laboratory which help us to understand basic personality processes. For example, Holzman and Rousey (1970) have demonstrated that vocal productions (TAT stories) are monitored when a person hears his own voice as he speaks; when a person speaks without being able to hear himself, there is an increase in expression of impulse and a decrease in effective defending.

A return to more natural observations may prove fruitful. By reliable field observation, Zinner (1963) has demonstrated situational dependencies in specific behaviors. As Sells (1969) notes, however, such ecological work must cope with the still unresolved difficulty of encoding the person's environment, of identifying and measuring its major attributes. The availability of videotape recordings will permit intensive investigation of aspects of non-verbal communication not previously amenable to objective study. And Luborsky (1970) has shown how such dynamic phenomena as symptom formation can be studied systematically under non-experimental conditions.

Levels of conceptualization and measurement

From a psychometric point of view, a personality variable can be classified at several levels of abstraction or generality. All too often, we confuse our conceptual work by using the same label for several or all levels. Within any one mode, such as self-report or ratings by others, there are levels ranging from the single observation to the global trait. The response to the single stimulus is obviously of very limited conceptual interest. At higher levels, there are the scores or indices from clusters and scales. Each measuring operation yields a score for item, cluster, or scale and each such score can be viewed as a low-level concept. Unfortunately, this approach gives us an enormous number of concepts to be studied and understood. For example, at the test level alone, there are dozens for anxiety (cf. McReynolds, 1968).

At a still higher level, there are scores based on several tests or sets of observations. The strategy of obtaining a trait-composite, proposed some years ago by Vernon (1953), has not received the systematic study it deserves. Once the domain of a personality trait has been adequately specified, one could develop a set of procedures representing that domain, sampling all areas of the trait's manifestations. In combining the subscores, however, it is not immediately apparent how to weight each area, even within a single mode of observation. Also, the theoretical justification for any composite involving several modes has not been worked out. Here is one of the instances in which some composition model (Coombs, 1964) other than the compensatory may be most appropriate. For example, the disjunctive mode may be more suitable: assigning each subject a standard score on each measure of the trait, we could take his highest standard score as best estimating the strength of the trait in his personality structure. Whatever formal model is used, it should be selected for explicit reasons which take into account the substantive conceptualization of the trait.

The conceptual level for a composite score based on diverse tests must be carefully distinguished from the level for a test score or a cluster score. The same label should not be used for identifying the concepts associated with these scores differing in generality. Perhaps subscripts or other modifiers are needed to keep straight our terminology and our thinking.

Traits, qualities, and salience

The author believes that the difficulties considered earlier in this paper will eventually have to be resolved at a conceptual level. Those of us interested in measurement have done the best we can, given the loose theorizing about the nature of personality which has been available to us. Thus, it may be that the conventional concept of trait is of little scientific utility. Originating in lay experience, it is useful in everyday life as a way of reducing or construing the amorphous mass of daily impressions. Yet the vast body of scientific measurements of personality indicates that conceptualizing persons as possessing traits of various strengths is a crude over-simplification. Personality is concerned with processes, with behaving. For all people, behaving varies with the situation. Even within a situation, the behaving of each person varies over time. Perhaps, instead of attempting to locate each person at a point on each trait dimension, we should classify him as falling within some range, an approach which would require us to modify our statistical procedures for determining degrees of relationships between dimensions.

Still another possible strategy, a radical and disruptive one for most of us, would be to give up the assumption that personality phenomena are best analysed into nomothetic trait dimensions applicable to all persons. In every research program in personology, we study a sample from a population which is restricted on age, sex, cultural group, or some other variable. Why should we not study groups formed on the basis of the presence, the quality, or the function of some characteristic in the subjects' personalities? For instance, it may be conceptually inappropriate to see every variable as an attribute of every person. Positive strength may be qualitatively different from zero strength. For example paranoia might best be viewed as applying to some people and not applying at all to others. Less radical would be the alternative principle that a variable is qualitatively different at different strengths. Some people may experience few paranoid feelings during their lifetime, and these may be transitory and trivial. Others may occasionally experience some paranoid feelings, these forming significant secondary aspects of their personalities. For only a few people is paranoia a major aspect of their personality. Is it conceptually sound to measure all these people by a single test and see them as differentiated only quantitatively, in terms of intensity or frequency? If a variable takes qualitatively different forms in people, we have to investigate each form within those people manifesting it, looking for variables related to it within that subgroup of the population and also studying how that subgroup as a whole differs from those subgroups in which the variable takes other forms or is functionally not present at all.

One form of this strategy might be based on the view that each person is differentiated from others most clearly in terms of a few predominant features of his behaving and experiencing. The approach need not be completely idiographic. From a standard list of major characteristics of people, we might identify the few (one, two, or perhaps half a dozen) which were most salient in the personality make-up of each person. People would then be classified on each characteristic, with the majority falling in the group of those for whom it was of little or no relevance. Within the selected group for whom it was highly pertinent, the functioning of the characteristic could then be studied. Such research would probably require additional classifications based on the presence or absence of other salient characteristics or on the particular interrelationships of such characteristics with the one being investigated.

If personality were construed in this way, we would need to revise our theories and our experimental designs. For example, the propositions tested in an experimental study might be of this form: persons for whom the fear of personal rejection is central will manifest defensiveness when introduced into a group of strangers; persons for whom such fear is weak or unimportant will not; furthermore, the form of defensiveness manifested by a subject in the first group will vary according to his subgroup membership as determined by the subjects' independently assessed defensive strategies. As an example of this approach, Fiedler (1970) has obtained empirical support for differential predictions for the behavior of a leader as a function of his motivational hierarchy in interaction with the nature of the situation.

Master concepts?

One final strategy deserves consideration. Related to the preceding one is the possibility that personality has been construed too atomistically, that to understand most functioning of people, we need to identify, measure, and study a few master constructs. These may provide focal points around which other dimensions of personality phenomena can be conceptually organized. Loevinger (Loevinger and Wessler, 1970) has proposed ego-development as the one master concept, and she may prove to be correct. Certainly the one or more master concepts should be construed with a developmental emphasis. It does seem likely that there should be separate major constructs for each of several domains, including the interpersonal, the moral, and the cognitive.

At the moment, we have little empirical knowledge about such master concepts: Kohlberg (1963) and Loevinger have each worked primarily with a single measuring procedure whose specificity may be distorting the inferences drawn from the empirical findings. Their master concepts involve ordered stages. The assignment of a person to his stage is still rather arbitrary and a matter of judgement. For any such classification procedure, a conceptual rationale based on the substantive nature of the construct should be developed.

A master concept dealing with the capacity for information-processing might be developed from the Structure of Intellect model proposed by Guilford (1967), a model which is potentially the core of a general psychological theory. This possible master concept suggests, of course, that the strategy of master concepts may not escape some of the difficulties discussed earlier: Guilford's tests for any one combination of a content, an operation, and a product still seem to have considerable individuality, and of course some overlap with tests for other combinations. What is true for one master concept, however, may not hold for others since they may apply to quite dissimilar aspects of psychological functioning. At the least, intensive efforts to operationalize separate manifestations of a master concept will be a more valuable contribution to the field than similar concentration on one of the many dozens of currently named personality traits.

In general terms, the theoretical question might appear to be this: after removing from the variance of behavior the major contributions associated with age, sex, subculture, and social status, what personality concepts account for the largest portions of the small amount of the remaining, unexplained variance? In fact, the question should be posed without such restriction. Age, sex, etc. are not appropriate psychological explanations of individual differences. For example, while age is an objective measure which happens to indicate very roughly the person's stage in the life-cycle, his developmental stage in Erikson's terms may have much more explanatory power.

Although the direction that will lead to progress in our scientific measurement and study of personality is not obvious, it seems clear that some reconceptualization of the domain is required. The armchair theorizing which has more or less guided prior work in personality measurement has not been sufficiently precise to serve as the foundation for a science of personology. The theorists have not modified their formulations to be congruent with the hard data showing great specificity of observations as a function of stimulus, conditions, and state of the subject. We must have a conceptualization of personality which is compatible with current empirical observations. In complementary fashion, measuring procedures must be designed to be coordinate with explicit conceptual models of the target variables.

Summary

For personology to become a mature science it must have constructs on whose conceptualization there is intersubjective agreements, constructs which are represented by standard measuring procedures. In such specifications of constructs within a theoretical context the perspectives and the pertinent modes of observation must be indicated. Personality variables refer to aspects of processes. The relationship between such processes and those utilized in measuring procedures varies with the rationale used in devising the test.

Since personality phenomena are multiply determined, each test or measuring procedure has some specificity in its scores. The extrinsic convergent validity of a test may be examined by comparing its profile of correlations with other variables to the profile for another test of the same concept: there are usually one or more discrepancies of such size that the tests cannot be considered interchangeable because they lead to different conceptual conclusions. Such specificity is not restricted to measures of individual differences.

Some new ways of construing personality functioning seem necessary. Perhaps the variables should be investigated by devising composite scores combined by a rationale congruent with the conceptualization of the construct, using a disjunctive rather than compensatory composition model. Perhaps personality should be construed in terms of two to five master concepts with developmental orientations. Perhaps the centrality or hierarchical status of each variable within each personality must be introduced into our conceptual and operational work. Whatever the conceptualization of personality, ways must be found to integrate measuring procedures into that theoretical framework since it provides their prime reason for being.

COMMENT ON FISKE'S PAPER

RAYMOND B. CATTELL

Two main virtues impress me in Fiske's approach. First he brings to the task a patient, realistic and shrewd approach to the phenomena of personality as such—unlike the grandiose theorizing remote from measurement or subtle observation which grievously characterized so much of personality writing in the last generation. Secondly, he brings an extremely open-minded "market of discussion" to the conceptual suggestions of all and sundry.

With regard to the second, however, it has been recognized in all sciences that the cost of a large bibliography may be a descent into the chaos of eclecticism. Too ready an abandonment of critical demands in method produces a psychological junk yard or flea market, or a mere alignment with pervading fashions, in a sycophancy of the largest crowd—though the latter has never been a part of Fiske's philosophy.

The neurosis of current society and its values centers on a terror of being labelled narrow minded, and since this has extended also to psychology, we see many genuine attempts to assert the necessity of scientific standards castigated by the crowd as bigotry. The fact remains that there are standards of scientific evidence and concept formation which need constantly to be asserted. For example, the indispensable preliminary to causal laws is the demonstration of covariance—in one design or another. A younger reader would get no sense of this imperative from Fiske's paper, and no indication of the relative methodological firmness of the various concepts on which he is asked to lean. If I am asked what touchstone of "science" I have in mind I can only reply that there are several fine works today on scientific method; but specifically in psychology I would refer to the article by Dr. Gregory and Sir Cyril Burt in the *British Journal of Statistical Psychology* (1958). By these standards I would say that definitely two-thirds of the "concepts" which Dr. Fiske finds it necessary to refer to in the interests of an "unbiased", "democratic" survey of the field could be advantageously cut off. It is on this issue of uncluttering the field and concentrating on more subtle and disciplined models that I find myself impatient with some things he has said.

Open-mindedness is thus a virtue of which one can unquestionably have too much. Parenthetically I think it is the better type of student who leaves psychology for the physical sciences on account of our toleration of muddle. But the groundwork of theory—the patient, close, and faithful observation, in which Dr. Fiske's work excels—is a prerequisite that I would not sacrifice for any precision of mathematical model. Even so, I say "prerequisite". In the sixteenth century such sciences as botany and chemistry were at this descriptive stage. Psychology, as I have often drummed into students, autistically tried to abort this phase, and to jump into personality theory drawn from thin air. That battle has, however, been won. Personality research is now acceptedly observational and quantitative in its basis. So the time has come to move beyond our sixteenth century phase.

In the description and evaluation of currently appearing superstructures of empirical constructs and mathematical models I have to confess that I find this presentation impoverished. There is no systematic reference to what factor analysis has done for personality structure concepts; no examination of the concept of source trait "orders", as in Royce's, Eysenck's and the present writer's systematic findings; nothing about the dynamic calculus model and its potential impact on clinical psychology; nothing about Miller's systems theory; nothing about an effective model for handling state and trait relations, and so on.

Nevertheless, the sensitive, broad observational perspective which Dr. Fiske maintains has ensured that important topics—awkward, substantive issues all too frequently squeezed out of mathematical models as intrusive nuisances, are brought into a due importance in the total picture. Thus, for example, the importance of studying states as well as traits is fully illustrated, even if no model is discussed; the effect of the observer upon trait assessment is mentioned, as an inescapable reality, and the need for a taxonomy of environment is mentioned. But the listener, at least this listener, is left with a sense that Dr. Fiske regards them as hopelessly beyond precise operational research formulation when, in fact, exact models, and even extensive findings with them, are one of the most encouraging features of the present scene. A scholarly treatment would require these at least to be mentioned and then demolished if Dr. Fiske thinks that they should be. For example, the state-trait difference has been very positively handled by P- and dR-technique concepts (Harris, 1965), and by the model of modulators of factor level (Cattell, 1971). Observer effects have been caught in instrument factors and trait view theory, beginning in the paper on perturbations in observation by Digman.

I can best provide the reader with a brief review of instrument factor theory via Table I. This says that with two source traits and two instrument factors a design will appear as shown, in which the reality of the source trait's variance—as something independent of the instrument or source of observation, is shown by the first two columns, and the "perturbations" of the source trait pattern by the instrument factors are shown in the third and fourth columns. (Parenthetically, these solutions are difficult to get in rotation because there is danger of singularity.)

As Dr. Fiske has recognized in some earlier discussions we have had there are some advantages in the "source trait-instrument factor" formulation of the "multi-trait-multi-method" formulation, notably in that the former finds, rather than imposes—the concept of what is an instrument.

Table I

	Factor Pattern Matrix*			
	Trait 1	Trait 2	Instrument 1	Instrument 2
Trait 1 by Device 1	X		X	
Trait 1 by Device 2	X			X
Trait 2 by Device 1		X	X	
Trait 2 by Device 2		X		X

However, let us note that it was Fiske's and Campbell's insistence on the multi-trait-multi-method phenomenon that has powerfully helped, from a new angle, in getting the classical psychometrist to recognize the falsity of the standard dictum in psychometry that high homogeneity is the first condition of a good test. Humphreys had cast doubt on this twenty years ago, and Tsujioka and the present writer (1964) had shown in precise formulae what was lost in dependable validity by making high homogeneity a prime consideration. It has, however, been Fiske's pointed examples that have brought understanding of the point among most psychologists. (I say most, not all, because this very year Howarth and Browne have published an article (1971) "discovering" as a flaw in the 16 P.F. the low homogeneity that was deliberately built into its scales.) Doubtless the rear guard of itemetric psychometrists will take time to absorb the implications of the multi-trait-multi-method or instrument factor theory.

As regards a taxonomy of environment a cluster search procedure operating upon behavioral indices and leading to objective typing of situations in vector statements has been developed (Sells, 1963). These are tangible, experimentally tried answers to the question "How should we conceptualize personality?" and "How should we conceptualize the situation?" which Fiske still raises without a word about their existence. If for some reason the answers to these three domains of conceptualization seem wrong to him, surely we should hear about it. For example, he raises the issue of "the relative importance of personality and environment in behavior" as if it were some ineffable question with a still more ineffable answer. But the psychological meaning of situations (Sells, 1963, p. 63) can be precisely stated by a vector of behavioral indices, and the relative contribution of individual variance on a particular source trait to the variance over situations

* Only four variables are shown where there would need to be eight. Loadings of non-zero value are shown by X's.

precisely stated as a variance ratio—once the population of persons and stimulus situations is defined.

Some years ago the present writer introduced the concept of a dichotomy of validation into direct and indirect (or circumstantial) validity. The former corresponds to the usually accepted practice of correlating a supposed test for trait X with the pure factor score for trait X. The second took a column of correlations of test X with factor measures of a dozen other source traits and compared (by correlation) these correlations with those existing between the pure factor X and this series of source traits. It was demonstrated that when the direct validity of a measure of X is high the indirect (circumstantial) validity is also high. Indirect validity was thus proposed as an hitherto unused source of independent evidence on the validity of a trait measure. Fiske reintroduces essentially the same notion under what seems to the writer the unnecessarily barbarous terminology of "extrinsic convergent validation". Actually his example from earlier work (correlating estimates of the same trait from different sources of observation) seems inconsistent with his definition, and is actually an example of direct validation (correlating several test measures of X with the factor common to them) so one is left uncertain what the new expression means.

However, returning to what appears certainly to be indirect validity he says: "Finding agreement between two measures in terms of their correlations with one kind of outside variable offers no assurance that similar agreement will be found between profiles for another kind." If this means that two circumstantial (indirect) validity coefficients calculated from two different sets of source trait (factors) are not equal except for sampling, it is incorrect. Of course, if one has no conception of, or operation for, trait sampling—and Fiske's failure to mention the personality sphere or the concept of primary, secondary and tertiary factors would lead the reader to suppose that he prefers to operate in a conceptual vacuum here—then admittedly strange things may happen. But if we take the correlation of the correlations of test X and factor *X* with primary factors *A*, *B*, *C*, *D*, etc. and the same with primaries *P*, *Q*, *R*, *S*, *T*, etc. they should approach the same value. Indeed, on a small scale, it can be shown that they do so when applied to individual 16 P.F. scales directly and indirectly validated on two sets of other factors (Cattell *et al.*, 1970).

If this "reviewer" of Fiske's paper is expected to take the liberty of historical explanation of what he regards as certain inconsistencies in the dedicated and important contributions which this leader in the field of personality research has made, he would find it in the attempt of

Fiske (and other students of Allport, such as Michel) to combine Allportian—verbally sensitive but non-operational—concepts with multivariate experimental approaches. Like Fiske, Allport was a subtle and catholic observer, but he proceeded directly from these observations with the naked eye to conceptual developments that had no methodological fiber. (It was an old joke of Emerson Hall that the only figures in his books were those at the top corners of the pages.) Fiske's feeling for the necessary foundations of personality concepts has moved beyond this, and inasmuch as he has moved to a blend which insists that good qualitative observation and local quantification must precede the more general mathematical model it is one which this commentator heartily endorses. For example—a point on which I comment belatedly—he has stressed that the right type of variable for studying personality is often a process not a stimulus-response act. This has actually been thoroughly heeded in the construction of behavioral situations for our Objective-Analytic Personality Factor Battery—and in the reduction of a process to parameters that can be used in calculation ("Handbook of Multivariate Experimental Psychology", p. 395).

But for the rest—and here the writer must speak for his own approach—the multivariate and the Allportian approach mix like oil and water. University teachers who have started with the ideal of "balancing" a course in personality by using two texts—Allport's and my own "Scientific Analysis of Personality"—report to me that the more serious students have had a neurosis. This I interpret as a tribute to their intellectual integrity. My impression is that only Fiske's superior level of frustration tolerance has saved him from the same fate.

COMMENT ON FISKE'S PAPER

K. PAWLIK

Fiske's recommendations regarding what he has termed "extrinsic convergent validity" (ECV) should be taken with great caution and understanding of the necessary assumptions. Let me point out a very crucial one first: Fiske's ECV method has to assume that the variables $y_1, y_2, \ldots$, whose ECV is to be evaluated in terms of their correlations with the reference variables $x_1, x_2, \ldots, x_n$, contain no source of variation other than that underlying these reference variables. If this condition is not fulfilled, two variables y_1 and y_2 may be uncorrelated despite satisfactory results in terms of Fiske's ECV. This will become obvious from a simple example as the one which follows:

Consider a set of reference variables $x_1, x_2, \ldots, x_n$ which are functions of k factors so they can be represented in k-space. Assume two variables y_1, y_2 of identical projections onto this k-space which, in addition, have non-zero projections of opposite sign onto a further $(k+1)^{\text{th}}$ axis or factor. In this case y_1 and y_2 will have identical (!) correlations with the reference tests and still can be orthogonal to each other in the test space and thus uncorrelated.

Another problem with the ECV approach relates to the fact that, in general, the reference tests will be intercorrelated. Consequently, the row vectors of reference variable correlations of y_1 and y_2 respectively, must not be understood as analogous to a regression equation. As a matter of fact, these correlations do not express the y variables as functions of the x's! This is a situation similar to the one in ordinary factor analysis where the columns of the factor pattern matrix do *not* express the factors as linear combinations of the variables.

All this leads to the conclusion that ECV as defined by Dr. Fiske should not be regarded a proper substitute for regular, direct validity correlation. ECV is a necessary, but not a sufficient condition, for test validity.

COMMENT ON FISKE'S PAPER

J. R. ROYCE

Fiske's paper focuses on a wide range of methodological and meta-theoretical difficulties involved in conceptualizing personality. As such, he performs a valuable service. However, several of his conclusions and/or suggestions regarding the concept of trait (see Fiske, p. 86) lead me to ask for his reaction to the factor model as a way to get a handle on this problem. I ask this because it seems to me that factor analysis has, in fact, come up with at least partial answers to many of the questions raised about traits (e.g. "... the conventional concept of trait is of little scientific utility", "Personality is concerned with processes ...", "... give up the assumption that personality phenomena are best analysed into nomothetic trait dimensions applicable to all persons" etc.). While I agree that the answers provided by factor work to date are limited, it seems to me that substantive theory is evolving; and further, the formal model itself is peculiarly relevant to the problem of trait dimensions and that a wholesale rejection of the trait approach at a time of imminent breakthrough simply does not make good sense.

While factor analysis *per se* is not mentioned in your paper, Fiske, I sense that you are not overwhelmed by what it might do for us. Since so much of the content of this conference is factor orientated, it would be of value to obtain your explicit views on the adequacies and inadequacies of factor analysis for conceptualizing personality.

REJOINDER TO DISCUSSANTS' COMMENTS

DONALD W. FISKE

One objective of my paper was to stimulate some examination of where our theorizing about personality stands today and some reexamination of both our basic assumptions about personality and our current methods for measuring it. Although this objective was partially achieved in the Conference discussion and in the preceding comments, I feel that some of my colleagues are still not facing the underlying issues regarding substance or content which my paper raised. Do they agree with me that we have scientific consensus on the identification and meaning of few, if any, personality variables? If so, this lack presents a much more fundamental problem than such questions as how extrinsic convergent validation can most profitably be assessed.

Much of my paper is concerned with what comes before and underlies the testing and the test data with which my colleagues are concerned. They seem to ignore the behavior we see in the real world outside the testing room and even the behavioral process which leads to a response in the special situation of being tested. They seem sometimes to treat data derived from such responses as that which they want to understand, as the end in itself. Do we want a theory of test data—or a theory of personality phenomena? Actual behavior varies with S's perception of the situation, as we all know from general psychology (cf. Sells, this volume). Test behavior, and that is all that many of us study, occurs in a single kind of situation and is determined in large part by S's perceptions of that situation. We must put aside the simple, unrealistic attribute model, where so often the trait dimensions are equated with factors from a restricted set of test responses, and take up the challenges presented by the analytic model, including the interactions of person with item, method, and general context (cf. McReynolds, 1971, pp. 5–10).

While the relative contribution of the situation to behavior has not been adequately estimated in empirical work (see my remarks on Sells' chapter, this volume), everyday observation suggests that it is comparatively large. It simply will not help the field to say, as Cattell does in his Comments, that "the psychological meaning of situations . . . can be precisely stated by a vector of behavioral indices". We must go beyond an abstract model to a substantive theory which takes fully into account the individual differences in such meaning. The work of my project on how subjects react to being tested and how they arrive at their responses to such apparently simple things as questionnaire items suggests that such meanings are highly individualistic, even in this one, particular, objectively standardized situation. Kuncel (in press) and other authors have shown clearly that the same response can come from different perceptions and interpretations of the stimulus-item.

In his comments about situations, as in other comments, Cattell seems to feel that basic problems have been solved because a methodological matter has been formulated in a set of constructs or has even been incorporated into a model. I cannot accept that judgment. Granted that these formulations make contributions by recognizing, analysing, and structuring fundamental problems, each has its limitations. Models for data often omit consideration of how the data came into existence. What was going on in the particular subject while he was responding to the total situation as he experiences and interprets it? Until this question has been answered, we make a large inferential leap in any attribution of psychological meaning to the subject's responses to measurement stimuli. Other models resolve issues in principle but either have not or cannot now be put into practical application.

Several of my colleagues place great faith in the capacity of the factor analytic model to solve our basic problems. Many of the comments, both those preceding this reply and those at the Conference, defend factor analysis as the method for obtaining the constructs of personality that will permit the needed advances in personality theory. Cattell has high scientific confidence in his factors and in his measures for these factors. He often seems to see his factors as absolutes, as fundamental variables. I see them (and the factors developed by other investigators) as abstractions from current instruments which are important today but only temporary: they are certain to be replaced when our future Mendeleev has done his work. For the most part, our factors are still method-bound. Even if factor scores from different observer-viewpoints (such as self-ratings and ratings by others) are found to be moderately correlated with each other, this shared variance does not establish the reality of any general factor in nature but rather demonstrates the similarity of the perceptual frameworks in the heads of our observers, be they subjects or raters of subjects.

Confidence in future applications of factor analysis does not seem warranted by the limited record of its past contributions to substantive concepts which are embodied in generally accepted theoretical frameworks. See Royce's discussion of the factor method in the introduction to this volume; Fiske (1971b); and the papers on which the latter comments. In the absence of explicit theory, rigorous research may generate many factors, but such work has not produced any major breakthroughs accepted by consensus in the qualified scientific community. A factor is an empirical finding or, as Cattell has recently written (1972, p. 10), "an abstraction from observable variables." Like Premier Construct, Emperor Factor has no clothes except those in which the scientist sees him. A factor may be the stimulus for someone's construct. If so, it can then be treated, developed, tested and modified like a construct from any other source. A field steps ahead when someone gets a very bright idea which is later supported by empirical research. The refining and polishing of factors does not seem likely to facilitate the generation of such ideas in the factor analyst or in the readers of his reports.

Factor analysis has its place in the scientific investigation of a domain. In spite of the developments in factor analysis since Thurstone's classic work, I agree with his view that the primary place for factor analysis is in the early, exploratory stages. For example, in the personality domain, we must go beyond first or even higher order factors to constructs which are more fruitful than mere verbal or descriptive labels. Factors have usually been equated with simplified trait constructs. The hope for the future lies not in traits as attributes averaged over some unspecified set of situations but in those conceptualizations that seek to understand response regularities associated with particular subjects interacting with designated situational complexes.

One danger in preoccupation with factor analyses of personality items or tests lies in the implicit and unwarranted assumption that the subjects' responses are representative of the phenomena outside the testing room which we wish to understand. Instead, such responses should be viewed as one of several kinds of observations (as proposed in my paper). Even if such responses do relate to general dispositions we choose to postulate for our subjects, there may be another danger: the pattern of covariation observed in the particular context of testing may not hold in other contexts. Does the factor pattern for capabilities as rated by an ego-involved judge correspond with that for tests? Would such ratings of skill in various activities have a pattern like that for more objective and independently assessed indices?

It has been suggested that factor analysis can provide a more informed view of the similarity between two tests than that given by examining their patterns of correlation with other indices, i.e. by extrinsic convergent validation. My view is that we should not accept similarity of factor patterns within any one analysis as establishing interchangeability unless the analysis includes all pertinent variables as measured by varied methods. (Such a study must get around the difficulties that standard factor analysis faces when utilizing data from several methods.)

While I heartily concur with Cattell's feeling that terminology should not be unnecessarily barbarous or foreign, we do need labels and it was hoped that the phrase, extrinsic convergent validation, would stress the norm of convergence and the importance of using conceptually distinct variables. A major reason for examining this approach may have been lost in the discussion of details. I intended to stress the specificity of our measurements from any single procedure. The demonstration that two profiles of correlations have themselves a substantial correlation with each other is but one step forward. Unless that correlation is perfect, the two measures cannot be taken as interchangeable indices of the same variable. It is for the future to show us whether the field can advance much further when each of its measuring operations has its share of unique variance and no measuring procedure gives us indices which can be mathematically transformed into those from any other. For the present, as Pawlik concludes, extrinsic convergent validation can be taken as a necessary but not sufficient condition for test validity. I also agree with him that the outside variables used in such validation should be as diverse as possible. As the example in my paper indicates, the degree of this validity determined for variables from one source may not agree with that for variables from a different source.

I am happy to have Cattell point out to the reader a number of related contributions which were not mentioned in my short paper. Many of these omissions were simply due to lack of the space necessary to indicate that these valuable contributions did not resolve the issues I was raising. Cattell's "younger reader" should certainly consider these issues in the light of discourses on scientific method in psychology and especially in personality. But more pertinent than his citation of Burt and Gregory is the earlier paper by Burt (1958) on "Definition and scientific method in psychology" which notes that ". . . the theory of the concept is prior to the operation for measuring the concept, not vice versa (pp. 57–8)" and that ". . . in any branch of empirical science the fundamental problem is to determine what concepts are most appropriate (p. 32)".

The serious reader should pursue Cattell's references to these other approaches and evaluate their relevance for himself. In my opinion, many of those highly sophisticated descriptions and analyses are schematic, are inventor's sketches of developments not yet in production, not yet ready for the consumer. While some of them indicate recognition of critical problems, they do not provide applicable techniques with demonstrated capacity to cope with the problems. In particular, they do not take care of the critically confounding effects associated with the particular nature of the measuring procedure and the specific viewpoint of the observer who produces our data for us. These sources produce much greater obstacles for our field than they do for any other science and we must recognize this fact. At this point in time, we do not need more mathematical models as much as we need models which will enable us to understand the processes in responding to measurement stimuli, i.e. the behavior which occurs during the measuring operations from which our data are derived, so that we can understand the substantive, psychological meaning and the theoretical relevance of our data.

Cattell suggests that he and others have solved many of the issues in my paper. If time does prove him to be correct, the field is now much further advanced than I view it to be. Perhaps the "truth" lies between his optimistic overview and my pessimistic portrayal.

REFERENCES

Burt, C. (1958). Definition and scientific method in psychology. *Br. J. statist. Psychol.* **11,** 31–69.

Burt, C. L. and Gregory, W. L. (1958). Scientific method in psychology II. *Br. J. statist. Psychol.* **11,** 105–128.

Cattell, R. B. (1966). "Handbook of Multivariate Experimental Psychology." Rand McNally, Chicago.

Cattell, R. B. (1971). Estimating modulator indices and state liabilities. *Multivar. behavior. Res.* **6,** 7–33.

Cattell, R. B. (1972). Real base true zero factor analysis. *Multiv. behavior. Res.* Monograph No. 72–1.

Cattell, R. B., Eber, H. W. and Tatsuoka, M. M. (1970). "Handbook for the 16 PF Questionnaire." Institute for Personality and Ability Testing, Champaign, Illinois.

Cattell, R. B. and Tsujioka, B. (1964). The importance of factor-trueness and validity, versus homogeneity and orthogonality, in test scales. *Educ. psychol. Measur.* **24,** 3–30.

Coombs, C. H. (1964). "A Theory of Data." Wiley, New York.

English, H. B. and English, A. C. (1958). "A Comprehensive Dictionary of Psychological and Psychoanalytical Terms." Longmans, Green, New York.

Fiedler, F. E. (1970). Personality, motivational systems, and behavior of high and low LPC persons. University of Washington, Organizational Research Technical Report 70–12.

Fiske, D. W. (1949). Consistency of the factorial structures of personality ratings from different sources. *J. abnorm. soc. Psychol.* **44,** 329–344.

Fiske, D. W. (1971a). "Measuring the Concepts of Personality." Aldine, Chicago.

Fiske, D. W. (1971b). Strategies in the search for personality constructs. *J. Expl. Res. Personality* **5,** 323–330.

Guilford, J. P. (1967). "The Nature of Human Intelligence." McGraw-Hill, New York.

Harris, C. H. (ed.) (1965). "The Measurement of Change." Wisconsin University Press, Madison, Wisconsin.

Holzman, P. and Rousey, C. (1970). Monitoring, activation, and disinhibition: Effects of white noise masking on spoken thought. *J. abnorm. Psychol.* **75,** 227–241.

Howarth, E. and Browne, J. A. (1971). Investigation of personality factors in a Canadian context: I. Marker structure in personality questionnaire items. *Can. J. behavior. Sci.* **3,** 161–173.

Kelly, E. L. and Fiske, D. W. (1951). "The Prediction of Performance in Clinical Psychology." University of Michigan Press, Ann Arbor. (Greenwood Press, New York, 1969.)

Kelly, G. A. (1955). The psychology of personal constructs. (Vol. 1) "A Theory of Personality," Vol. 1. Norton, New York.

Kohlberg, L. (1963). The development of children's orientations toward a moral order. I. Sequence in the development of moral thought. *Vita Hum.* **6,** 11–33.

Kuncel, R. B. (In press). "Response processes and relative location of subject and Item. *Educ. Psychol. Measur.*

Levitt, E. E. (1956). The Water-Jar Einstellung Test as a measure of rigidity. *Psychol. Bull.* **53,** 347–370.

Loevinger, J. and Wessler, R. (1970). "Measuring Ego Development." (Vol. 1) Construction and use of a sentence completion test. Jossey-Bass, San Francisco.

Luborsky, L. (1970). New directions in research on neurotic and psychosomatic symptoms. *Am. Sci.* **58,** 661–668.

McReynolds, P. (1968). The assessment of anxiety: A survey of available techniques. *In* "Advances in Psychological Assessment," (McReynolds, P. ed.), Vol. 1. Science and Behavior Books, Palo Alto, California.

McReynolds, P. (1971). Introduction. *In* "Advances in Psychological Assessment." (McReynolds, P. ed.). Vol. 2. Science and Behavior Books, Palo Alto, California.

Mehrabian, A. and Ksionzky, S. (1970). Models for affiliative and conformity behavior. *Psychol. Bull.* **74,** 110–126.

Murray, H. A. *et al.* (1938). "Explorations in Personality." Oxford University Press, New York.

Nemeth, C. (1970). Bargaining and reciprocity. *Psychol. Bull.* **74,** 297–308.

Rosenberg, M. J. (1969). The conditions and consequences of evaluation apprehension. *In* "Artifact in Behavioral Research." (Rosenthal, R. and Rosnow, R. L. eds) Academic Press, New York and London.

Sanford, N. (1956). Surface and depth in the individual personality. *Psychol. Rev.* **63,** 349–359.

Sells, S. B. (1963). "Stimulus Determinants of Behavior." Ronald Press, New York.

Sells, S. B. (1969). Ecology and the science of psychology. *In* "Naturalistic Viewpoints in Psychological Research." (Willems, E. P. and Raush, H. L. eds) Holt, Rinehart and Winston, New York.

Vernon, P. E. (1953). "Personality Tests and Assessments." Methuen, London.

Verplanck, W. S. (1957). A glossary of some terms used in the objective science of behavior. *Psychol. Rev.*, Part 2. **64** (6).

Wallace, J. (1966). An abilities conception of personality: Some implications for personality measurement. *Am. Psychol.* **21,** 132–138.

Zinner, L. (1963). "The Consistency of Human Behavior in Various Situations: A Methodological Application of Functional Ecological Psychology." Unpublished doctoral dissertation, University of Houston.

Prescriptions for a Multivariate Model in Personality and Psychological Theory: Ecological Considerations

S. B. SELLS

Institute of Behavioral Research
Texas Christian University

Although the quantity of multivariate research on personality has been extensive, the status of theory in this area is less than impressive. The major emphasis remains at the level of description and measurement of significant traits. Such efforts are focused mainly on the delineation of trait structures; systematic attention to some of the principal sources of variation and concern with problems of the functioning personality are not yet firmly on the agenda. By contrast with the preoccupation of the multivariate approach those major and less theoretical approaches that have concentrated on the functioning personality have either ignored quantitative measurement, as in the case of Freudian and other dynamic theories, or have handled it casually, as illustrated by several perceptually based theories that have employed special apparatus (rod and frame), paper and pencil performance tests (embedded figures), and various projective techniques. Unfortunately, the psychometric sophistication of the multivariate workers in the personality field has not yet produced a breakthrough for which we can claim superiority over the clinicians. At best our factor structures are more comprehensive and are reported with mathematical precision, frequently including geometric space projections, estimates of reliability, corrections for numerous response biases, and other hallmarks of our guild. Regrettably, however, invariance over sample variations and external evidence of validity have been elusive. Fiske's plea on this program for new approaches is hardly surprising and reminds us that scientific rigor and fertile conceptualization are not always compatible goals.

Conceptualization and measurement are interdependent in the context of the scientific method. Concepts put forth as essential to a personality model and the model itself must be capable of representation in the languages of data if they are to result in more than a literary exercise. At the same time, there are numerous problems of measurement *per se* that are beyond the scope of this theoretical essay. These include the different measurement strategies required in relation to Person variations in age, sex, language, socioeconomic level, and other characteristics and in varying life situations, the frustrating problems of coping with rules concerning privacy and with realistic time pressures, as well as others. For the present discussion it is assumed, with optimistic faith, that valid measures can be developed to represent the theoretical constructs involved and that these will vary in content and format in accordance with measurement requirements. Perhaps the contemporary preoccupation with such problems is a realistic index of the state of our enterprise. Even so, theoretical notions are imperative to guide the direction of measurement research.

Preliminary Considerations and Definitions

The focal concepts that appear essential to an ideal model for Personality are indistinguishable from those that one might require to model the integrated behavior of the organism. This is not regarded as a problem, however, since the distinction reflects at most a matter of emphasis. Although trait concepts have become intrenched in multivariate personality formulations, and they are used in the present development, a taxonomy of traits falls short of the requirements for a personality model. The two major organizing concepts in the ideas presented below are Persons and Events. The problem is to develop a theoretical model of a Person that can explain or account for his Behaviors in the real world, defined by Events.

Persons

It is believed that most Person variance can be accounted for by two classes of characteristics which are consistent within Persons, but not necessarily between or across persons. Persons are represented as unique sets of Behavior Repertoires, consisting of patterns of Traits and Behaviors in Settings, representing actual behaviors in settings in which Persons function. Trait patterns may be interpreted as dispositions to manifest particular Behaviors in particular Settings and can be regarded as probability functions of patterns of Behaviors in Settings. As discussed below, traces of Behaviors in Settings are stored and affect subsequent Trait probability functions.

Consistency across Persons is the polar opposite of uniqueness. Both are of concern in the understanding of personality. In view of the endless variation in genetic endowment, environmental circumstances, and cumulative change throughout life, Person uniqueness is inevitable in the sense that identical patterns of all characteristics in any two Persons are precluded. Perhaps more important than statistical idiosyncracy, however, are selectivity, on one hand, and similarity, on the other. Selectivity, which is the essence of individuality, reflects the specific variance of individuals not shared with others, as a result of the idiosyncratic experience defined by individual patterning of Behavior Repertoires and Events, as described below. Similarities in Trait patterns (usually referred to as general or common traits) reflect common variance due to familial, social, organizational, geographic and other shared factors in background and experience. Uniqueness, individuality, and selectivity are of principal concern in the clinical method, while the scientific study of personality focuses more on common patterns observable in definable subgroups of the species.

Behavior Repertoires–Trait Patterns

The Behavior Repertoire is conceptualized as representing a continually changing set of Traits which may pattern differently in relation to different Settings. Traits are defined as dispositions to manifest particular Behaviors in particular Settings and are determined by two subsets of Person Characteristics, identified as Structures and Stored Traces of Experience and Behavior.

Structures

Anatomical structures constitute the constitutional component of the personality. They originate in the genetic process and undergo change throughout an individual's life. Maturational processes and other changes are affected cumulatively by chromosome patterns, prenatal Events, and by the entire history of subsequent Events in each Person's unique and selective continuing stream of life. Such structures, including sensory, neural, muscular, glandular, skeletal, vascular, and other tissues, organs, and organ systems of the organism, influence behavior directly and indirectly in many ways that have been described in the vast literature of personality and that will continue to challenge the ingenuity of experts in experimental psychology and human behavior genetics.

Personality psychologists have looked at Structures primarily as direct or indirect substrata of traits or dispositions, some quite narrow, as in the case of contribution to a specific trait, such as dominance, and others quite broad, such as Adlerian compensatory life style, field dependence, and various somatotypes. A common feature of all concepts implied by these examples is that they are descriptive of varying components of personality structure even though they each have obvious implications for functioning. However, they all fall short of describing a functioning model.

A step toward a functioning model, using structures as components, was taken by Saunders (1961) who described a simulated personality in terms of seven major components of a computer, each of which could take any of a wide range of values of its particular capacity in the total system. The seven components in his Zodiac model were analogous to major structural components of Persons. Saunders approached the problem as a conceptualized computer simulation and described several different Behavior Repertoires in terms of differing configurations of these seven structural components. The result was an ingenious, although grossly oversimplified, personality typology, represented as a functioning system. Saunders' model is distinctive in that it constructed a system out of hardware (structural) components conceptualized as abilities, and described expected variations as a function of interactions of these components. Loehlin (1963) developed a working computer model of a personality named Aldous in which quantitatively defined traits (software) rather than structures were programmed, but which also incorporated variables representing environmental factors. The Aldous program was also endowed with (learning) capacity to modify itself by storing Traces of Experience and Behavior. Such models represent preliminary, but important steps in the direction advocated in the present discussion.

Stored Traces of Experience and Behavior

Although not a *tabula rasa*, the organism at birth is comparatively simple and plastic. Its plasticity is expressed in the use of diverse feedback mechanisms, such as sensitization, adaptation, accommodation, and learning, that have effects comparable to continual adjustment of homeostatic settings, programming, and both short and long-term information storage.

In behavioral terms, stored traces of experience and behavior are of less interest than the trait dispositions in which they are incorporated and expressed, such as tastes, interests, attitudes, aptitudes, abilities, and the like. Nevertheless an adequate model of personality must provide for the feedback and storage processes in order to reflect the continually changing (developing) nature of the organism. Traces of experience and behavior are influenced by the state of the organism at any moment, which includes existing structures and storage, as well as by the Event structure of Behavior Settings and Action Contexts in which Behaviors occur. It is assumed that the organization of Stored Traces is lawful and that the principles involved depend on the organization of Events in the lives of individual Persons as well as on biopsychological principles.

Behaviors in Settings

Taxonomies of Behaviors are required for the systematic study of behavior. The term, Behaviors in Settings is used to emphasize the obvious, although too often neglected, point that significant differences in the nature and frequency of many behaviors may be expected as a result of variation in the linguistic, technological, cultural, geographic, and personnel characteristics of Settings. Comparable differences may also be attributed to other variations, in Action patterns, in Structures, and in the organization of Stored Traces. The interdependencies among the conceptual sets outlined here reflect these interlinked sources of differences in the organization of Behaviors. Much of this conceptual territory is yet to be explored. Indeed, normative data have been collected only in restricted areas (Barker, 1965; Sells, 1963b, 1966a).

In the personality model Behaviors are considered as dependent variables in the sense that they are predicted by antecedent sets of variables, although, as noted earlier, Behaviors leave Traces which affect subsequent Behaviors. In a personality model conceived as a system, Behaviors represent system output.

Events

The major components of Events are Settings and Actions. Although both define the environmental context of Behaviors, Settings represent the general surrounds, while Actions describe the ongoing action contexts. An Event is thus an Action that occurs in a Setting. Behavior Settings and Actions have distal as well as proximal aspects, corresponding to the Gestalt figure and ground. They may be viewed objectively, independently of the perspective of a participant, or phenomenally, in relation to the participant's perspective. However, if Settings and Actions are described with appropriate attention to their nested and sequential organization, as exemplified in the work of Barker and his associates (1963), the distinction between objective and phenomenal orientations becomes less troublesome. Actions and Settings are not independent; Settings limit the Actions that can occur and influence their occurrence. Of all the factors considered in this discussion these have received the least systematic attention.

Behavior Settings

Behavior Settings are finite in time and space and defined in terms of variables related to language, technology, customs (folkways, values and belief systems, social norms and practices), locales (climate, terrain and other aspects of the physical environment), human organizations, and Persons involved. This abbreviated outline refers to the major components of stimulus situations that account for behavior variance. More extensive and systematic taxonomic and analytic discussions of such "stimulus determinants of behavior" have been presented elsewhere by the writer (Sells, 1963a, 1963b, 1966a, 1966b, 1968), while important related contributions have been made by Barker (1968), Barker and Wright (1955), Barker and Gump (1964), and others associated with the Midwest Field Station, at the University of Kansas; also by Murdock and others responsible for the Human Relations Area Files at Yale (Murdock *et al.*, 1961).

In recent years the isolation of psychology from human ecology and indeed from sociology and the other social sciences has gradually given way to a serious development of research focused on the environment. A new journal (*Environment and Behavior*) was founded in 1968 and the volume of publications in this area, both articles and books, has increased. As a result the prospects for a serious attack on the problems of definition and measurement of Behavior Settings are now more favorable than at any previous time.

Perhaps the most important problem in relation to Behavior Settings is that encoding the environment. Even apparently simple environmental factors, such as weather, require careful study before their effects can be understood. Furthermore, these effects, as analysed in recent investigations by Sells and Will (1969, 1971), involve different principles when viewed sociologically, at the level of a population (as of a city), and psychologically, at a level where the unit of observation and analysis is an individual. Sells and Will found that a weather factor in which temperature and atmospheric pressure were salient was the most prevalent weather correlate of police activity, measured by frequency of calls for police response over the Police Department radio transmitter.

When temperatures were high and pressures low the level of police activity was generally on the high side. However, as the study showed, this involved many activities (for example, vacation checks of residences) which were tied to institutional social arrangements, such as the scheduling of vacations during the summer season. Individual situations were not represented in the data.

The encoding of the environment as a context of individual behavior must be conceptualized in terms of stimulus situations that have individual rather than group or organizational reference. While the effects of particular variables at both levels may coincide this is not necessarily to be assumed.

Identification of environmental variables that have predictable behavioral effects frequently depends on empirical study, not only of the patterning of specific events (as in the case of covarying weather phenomena) but also in order to verify the effects. Effects are usually facilitating or inhibitory of various behaviors. Some are obvious, such as the effect of weight of objects (gravity) on their maneuverability, which is directly observable and independent of cultural conditioning, while others may only be understood after extensive research. Even the obvious ones, however, have other effects that may require empirical analysis. For example, weight as a property of objects may also have effects comparable to the mood-inducing qualities of colors, to mention only one.

One important class of environmental variables depends on experience. Such variables resemble and overlap the types of norms referred to as customs and folkways, and involve standardized rules or conventions for behavior in specific types of situations. These are too pervasive for brief characterization, but may be illustrated by such diverse examples as "Hello" in answering the telephone, greeting by the words "How are you?", walking and talking softly in a library, shifting frames of reference concerning dress at home, in the office, at the beach, and so on, role attributes in dealing with older persons, younger persons, authority persons, customers, and others. These are learned by each individual in the context of the environmental situations of his individual life along with language, belief systems, values, and rules of conduct. Both shared (common) and idiosyncratic effects must be recognized.

Another important type of environmental variable, generated by various situational circumstances, resembles a *field force*. An example, based on the work of Barker and Gump (1964), is the effect on participation in an activity of the number of persons available to participate in relation to the optimal number required. As demonstrated by their studies of a wide range of school situations, when the number of persons available to participate exceeds the number required, forces of exclusion are generated; conversely, when the number of available participants falls below the optimal number, forces of inclusion are generated. Other examples include the effects of various organizational arrangements, such as competitive roles, conflicting role assignments, or obstructive communication channels; of various social circumstances, such as conditions of success or failure, growth or retrenchment, threat or security; and of various kinds of social interaction, such as the effects of group norms, status, factors conducive to coalition formation, cognitive dissonance; and others too numerous to enumerate, whose effects have been shown, in many cases, to follow lawful principles.

Behavior Settings are composed of physical and social aspects of the environment as suggested in the foregoing discussion, but they also have properties that reflect patterning or organization which is believed to be complex. Adequate specification of the organization of Behavior Settings is undoubtedly an interdisciplinary problem which should involve the participation of sociologists and anthropologists with respect to the ordering of distal aspects of Settings, social–cultural surrounds, as well as the more proximal and focal aspects and the Action setting. The environmental divisions of language, technology, customs, locales, human organizations, and Persons, respectively, represent bodies of scientific theory, knowledge, and investigative skill that must be thoroughly exploited toward understanding the organization of Behavior Settings which function as a major component of the effective environment in individual and group behavior.

Action Settings

If we may think of the Behavior Setting as the stage or the arena, the Action Setting is the play or the game taking place, which lends, further contextual structure to Behaviors. Action Settings also have distal as well as proximal aspects from the viewpoints of participants, as well as nested and sequential organization. They may occur over periods of time (for example, in school attendance or employment) and over wide geographic areas (such as in families that are separated or decentralized organizations).

Examples of Action Settings are endless and they require taxonomic ordering. To illustrate, we may mention a banquet, a meeting of a class, a birthday party, a church service, a football game, and a funeral, as Actions involving multiple participants, with ranging degrees of social standardization of a role-prescriptive and mood-prescriptive nature.

Actions such as sleeping, studying, shaving, driving to work, mowing the lawn, lighting a pipe, and dressing are commonly performed individually and actually constitute Behaviors. In these, the characteristic role and mood features of multi-person Actions are absent; many reflect ritualization of often-repeated behaviors. Whether or not individual acts should be considered as Actions in their context is an important question. In many cases, one Behavior could properly be considered an Action Setting for other Behaviors.

Event Structure

The linkages between Behavior Settings and Actions can be expressed as an $n \times n$ matrix in which the major intersections are defined as Events which have probabilistic prescriptive significance with respect to roles, moods, cognitive states, and overt behaviors. Events, in this context, imply the total specification of the physical and social environment in terms having predictable behavioral implications. Person variance is conceived as accounting for individual differences in Behaviors that are principally determined by Events.

The analysis of Event structure is a formidable task that goes beyond the expertise of most psychologists. Each of the major factors of language, technology, customs, organizations, locales, other Persons, and Actions, represents a wide range of circumstances such as may be encountered in cross-cultural studies, but less commonly in personality studies within samples drawn from available (campus or organizational) personnel.

Definition of Personality

Behaviors are probabilistic functions of the interactions of Persons and Events. Events control individual schedules, roles, resources, alternatives, rewards, and payoffs to such an extent that Person variance appears quite properly to be reduced to the magnitude of the residual in Helson's (1964) formulation of Adaptation Level Theory. It is important for the definition of Personality to understand the nature of the influence exerted by Events and by Person variance on Behaviors.

Influence of Events and Persons

Not too many years ago, "a mile in a minute" was considered a fantastic speed. This is illustrative of the influence of the Event structure on beliefs, which reflect the state of technology at a point in time, as well as other aspects of the total structure. Considering the implications of language, technology, customs, organization, and the rest, all together, it appears that every individual is fairly well committed to a "life orbit" that allows little deviation from a path that regulates thought, mood, and movement. Such determination is not complete, however, and variation is possible among Persons in essentially the same situation in a number of ways, which reflect Person variance. These sources of individual differences depend on (a) alternatives permitted within Events and (b) variations in individual capacities to perceive, interpret, integrate, and react to information presented. These are discussed below.

Alternatives Within Events

Psychologists have used such terms as ambiguity and structure to deal with the fact that Events vary in the number of alternatives or latitude of response permitted. An excellent discussion of this problem appears in the original edition of the social psychology text by Sherif and Sherif (1956). The degree of structure of a stimulus situation is defined as a negative function of the number of alternative responses permitted, and the determining influence of Events on behavior as a positive function of degree of structure. A high degree of structure exists, for example, when only one door is open or in a question concerning the sum of two digits, and in both cases the only available* response will generally occur regardless of approval, concern, or ideology of the respondent. On the other hand, when a choice of two or more doors is presented or when the question concerning number is less precise, as when specifying "a large sum of money," the respondent is almost forced to choose among alternatives, and in this case individual judgment scales, based on past experience and other selective factors, have an opportunity to function.

The determinism of Events thus depends on structure. While the comprehensive analysis of behavior includes situations that are relatively highly structured, it is important in studies focused on Person variance to make observations in situations that are relatively unstructured.

Individual Differences

Currently popular types of personality scales, with few exceptions,

* In the arithmetic question, incorrect responses are available, but in a situation calling for a correct response, no alternatives are possible. The alternative not to respond is also available in many highly structured situations; these permit one alternative.

focus on habitual orientations toward life situations that might be grouped under the broad heading of behavior style. Terms such as general activity, restraint, objectivity, friendliness, thoughtfulness, masculinity (Guilford), and reserved, outgoing, assertive, happy-go-lucky, conscientious, tough-minded, venturesome, suspicious, practical, apprehensive, conservative, group-dependent (Cattell), reflect what may be called stable tendencies rooted in physiological and anatomic endowments, modified by accumulated experience in life situations. By far the greatest amount of variance in factor analytic studies has been accounted for by three traits that can probably be recognized by the titles emotional stability, social extraversion, and the characterological term conscientiousness, which has a moral or dutiful flavor.

It is well known that factor patterns based on analyses of items or parcels of items are not invariant from sample to sample, to a large extent as a result of variations in backgrounds among subjects and in the Events pertinent to the conditions of testing. It is also well known that such stylistic traits have generally proven quite limited as predictors of behavior in such situations and with such behaviors as they have been analysed. The explanation of these meagre results warrants more extensive consideration than can be given here. However, it appears relevant to comment on some of the global assumptions implicit in the construction of most personality questionnaires, which result in problems such as the following:

1. Questions are written in relation to "usual" behavior and hence invite selective interpretation by each respondent with respect to his typical circumstances, as he perceives the inquiry. It is usually assumed that individual behaviors are consistent across circumstances, but such is frequently not the case. An individual may be very much at ease in family and social situations, but emotionally constricted and even withdrawn at work, or vice versa. Demand, challenge, and stress factors in different life situations may affect self-perceptions reflected in questionnaire responses variously and these may differ from appraisals by others in the same situations. Stylistic traits, reflecting as they do habitual modes of responding learned through experience in life situations, portray the personality as conditioned by roles and circumstances, but not the capacities that interacted with these roles and circumstances. In this regard, personality style reflects dispositions specific to circumstances, and interpretations should not be carelessly generalized beyond these circumstances.

2. Behavior samples incorporated in questions vary widely in appropriateness to sex, socioeconomic, and ethnic background, locale, and

other factors, resulting in variable representation of their respective domains.

3. Stylistic traits, even when sharply defined and assessed appropriately in relation to particular Event structures, may be only marginally related to highly structured behavior situations in which patterns of ability and motivation may frequently compensate for stylistic preferences.

Personality

In the functional equation in which Behaviors are expressed as interactions of Persons and Events, variance associated with Persons is independent of that associated with Events. As the preceding discussion has suggested, such independence has not been observed in the self-report questionnaire approach and as a result there are indeterminable confoundings of Person and Event variance in the typical questionnaire data.

In view of the hierarchical nature of biological development it is probably impossible to divorce the two major sources of variance completely. Nevertheless, another approach, intimated earlier in the discussion under Persons, offers advantages in relation to the requirements of independence. This involves the conception of the Person as a functioning system with a Behavior Trait Repertoire of abilities and affective responses which represent components of the functioning system. It is possible, as suggested by Saunders, to examine the implications of various configurations of components and as a result to describe systems with quite different behavior capacities. The definition of personality would then be formulated in terms of a typology of Person systems.

Saunders' model consists of a computer which simulates seven characteristics (abilities) of a functioning personality system. Information input is processed by an Input Buffer responsible for receiving information, recognizing, and coding it in forms usable by the system; the Input Buffer also processes some information retrieved from long term memory. Coded information proceeds from the Input Buffer to the Main Processing Unit, which also receives information stored in immediate access memory, as well as from the output buffer (and effector systems). Processed information passes to the Memory Bank, which is partitioned into Immediate Access and Long Term Memory compartments, which sort, classify, and store information. The Information Retriever organizes, orders, and sequences information stored in long term memory and extracts information from both immediate access and long term memory which is then passed to the Output Buffer where it is either translated from the coded form used by the data processing components to coding appropriate for various effector mechanisms or returned to the main processing unit for further processing. Two overall characteristics of the system, derived from the five components mentioned, are the overall Speed of Operation, which also depends on component stability, and the capacity for Self-Modification, which involves such abilities as short-cutting repetitive routines, perhaps by recoding with abstract symbols, transposing, and reprogramming, using new information. The last characteristic implies self-regulation and self-control and endows the system with a degree of autonomy.

The personality implications of these components are indicated partly by their respective critical features, but mainly by the effects of their interdependent linkages. The critical features are briefly as follows:

Memory, size or storage capacity;
Speed, basic speed in performing elementary operations, which affects capability of the system to perform "real time" applications;
Input Buffer, sensitivity versus certainty in (perceptual) operations; excessive sensitivity would imply tendencies to err in the direction of accepting erroneous information (misperception), while excessive leaning toward certainty could lead to rejection of correct information (which fails to meet criteria of acceptance);
Main Processing Unit, channel capacity which limits the number of operations that can be performed simultaneously;
Information Retriever, effectiveness in retrieving information from remote storage in organized, usable form and in appropriate temporal sequential relationships;
Output Buffer, logical capacity, corresponding to judgment, in evaluating processed information which it may refer back to the main processor or translate into output format;
Self-Modification, capacity to modify its own programs and procedures on the basis of experience.

It is rewarding to speculate, as Saunders did, about the implications of these features. For example, a system with limited storage capacity would be unable to retain much information and its overall functioning would be impaired. Low speed of operation would have a similar effect. A hypersensitive input buffer would introduce excessive erroneous information into the system and be unduly "field dependent" on environmental events. A one-channel computer would be greatly limited, in comparison with a multi-channel system, in the work that it could get done in any period of time and this limitation would require selection of transactions processed as well as of information used. An orderly and efficient information retriever would result in good time perspective, better use of stored information, and superior judgment, when compared with one that allows information to be disordered, fragmented, and confused in temporal sequence. Depending on its structure, the output buffer might require either too little or too much information for the conclusions that it reaches and "decides" to translate into overt behavior. In one case it might go off "half-cocked", while in the other it might be overcautious or ultraconservative. Finally, the implications of variations in *self-modification* capacity are obvious.

Saunders presented a number of "case" illustrations of different profiles, using a standard memory and values for the remaining six characteristics, expressed in relation to that for the memory bank. One of these was as follows: slow speed, average input buffer sensitivity, average channel capacity, highly organized and efficient information retrieval, low quality output buffer and low capacity for self-modification. Paraphrasing Saunders' description of this particular model of Zodiac, we have the following simulated clinical report:

Zodiac is fairly slow in proportion to his memory capacity; with respect to input buffer and his data processing unit he is about average in ability to retrieve long-term memory but in view of his ratings on output buffer and the dimension of self-control, he is unable to achieve in proportion to his memory capacity. The fact that he is below average in both speed and judgment (output buffer) means that he is relatively stimulus-bound in his perceptions and relatively environment-bound in his responses. That is, he is tied very closely to the real world in terms of both his inputs and his outputs. He has a lot of experience. At the same time he shows a relative lack of ability to change his behavior on the basis of this experience. As a result, such experience as he engages in tends to persist at a primitive level. This approach to experience is confirmed and intensified by his relatively high capacity to retrieve information. He is able to recall effectively the temporal relationships of experiences that have occurred in the past and to use them as a basis for behavior in the present without further modification. He is relatively very adept at recognizing and anticipating the sequence of behavior in which another person is engaged and is prepared on the basis of his good access to long-term memory to play a role that is expected of him and thereby to obtain the kinds of rewards in which he is most interested.

According to Saunders, this account is equivalent to the operational definition of the psychopathic personality. If this particular model of Zodiac could be incorporated in an operational simulation, following the lead of Loehlin's Aldous, and exposed over time to a programmed Event structure, one might speculate on how he would answer the 16 P.F. or the G–Z. This approach, with systematic variation of both the simulated system characteristics and the simulated environmental Events, might indeed be a profitable enterprise toward clarification of many of the questions raised earlier in this presentation.

The creativity of Saunders' Zodiac model lies mainly in his conviction that the major themes of personality "can only be worked out within the limits of a set of boundary conditions that are defined and empirically recognized as human abilities". Although he has not, so far as could be determined, pursued the idea further, Saunders recognized that Zodiac is a very much abbreviated model. At the conclusion of his paper he added that using the same principles, in conjunction with a set of about nineteen dimensions, it would be possible to lay bare a considerable fraction of personality.

The identity of the twelve remaining dimensions has not been revealed. However, those included in the Zodiac model are generally compatible with the conceptualization of the Behavior Repertoire presented here. Whether the implied definitions and the distinctions between the properties of several of the components would hold up empirically when applied to the structure of man is a question to be approached seriously in systematic formulation of the components of the Behavior Repertoire in the course of research on the implementation of the model.

In this connection it is likely that Saunders may have been too narrow in limiting his components to a specified set of abilities, which may be consistent with the structure of contemporary commercial digital computers, but not with either the potentialities of computer technology or the complexities of the subject *homo sapiens*. The literature of the neurosciences suggests that in addition to his extensive channel capacity in the central nervous system, man is endowed with supplementary data processing units, analogous to analog as well as digital computers, that may be sufficiently autonomous to warrant recognition as separate components. Then the division of memory into immediate access and long-term sections must realistically be regarded as only symbolic of a complex storage and retrieval subsystem which is not yet even adequately understood. Finally, components may need to be provided for affective, architectural, and other vital structures and functions of the intact organism that may moderate behavior as part of the central system rather than only as sources of information input to the central system.

Unquestionably present knowledge cannot support any claims to specification of the Behavior Trait Repertoire that faithfully represent the true structure of the human organism. It is likely, however, that a discriminable advance beyond Saunders' model is presently feasible and this should be encouraged. Research even with the crude model developed by Loehlin produced provocative answers to questions concerning differential effects of environmental dimensions on varying personality types as well as differential responses of the same personality to varying environmental circumstances.

Toward Development of the Model

The foregoing discussion has grouped sources of variance accounting for Behaviors into two broad categories, identified as Persons and Events. Personality was defined as a function of Person variance that is relatively independent of Events. The Person was viewed as a functioning system of interdependent components which together constitute a Behavior Trait Repertoire that sets boundary limits and implied probabilities for patterns of Behaviors. These components were referred to as Traits, but the discussion did not clearly distinguish between the constitutional (hardware) aspects and the effects of cumulative growth and experience, which affect biological structures and also the development and cumulative modification of "plans" or habit patterns for responding (software, programs). The intention is to define Traits as some integrated combination of both, but this requires further careful study. There are obvious temptations to be unduly enticed by the convenience of computer structures, but the "facts of life" are that the order of complexity of the biological organism is vastly greater than that of man-made electronic machinery. It is also tempting to "biologize"; yet the knowledge base to accomplish this is insufficient not only in relation to identification of the structures, but also in relation to the entire agenda of research on the structure of Events, which involves process and taxonomic studies of Behavior Settings and Actions.

The main thrust of the Personality model proposed is toward the construction of a functioning system of components that account for the sensory, perceptual, memory, logical, affective, motor, and vegetative operations of the organism. This system is housed in machinery (the body) capable of moving in space and performing repertoires of Behaviors under the control of a complex information-processing subsystem whose characteristics, by themselves and in combination, define its operational capacities. It is believed that various patterns of these operational capacities can be viewed as the basis for a Personality typology.

The utility of a Personality model must be judged on the basis of its capacities for prediction or explanation of behavior. The Personality system implied here represents only part of the information required for these purposes. It is necessary to specify both the Person and the Event setting in which he is located. Assessment of present knowledge in relation to the effort required to accomplish these specifications is a measure of the challenge to Personality research.

COMMENT ON SELLS' PAPER

DONALD W. FISKE

We need much more work of the kind represented by Dr. Sells' paper. We have a lot of theorizing about personality mechanisms and clinical symptoms but all too little thinking about personality as a topic concerned with that part of behavior which is not explained, or not fully explained, by general psychology. The phenomena in which personologists are interested are behavior, and as such, must be conceptualized in terms congruent with interpretations of behavior in general. As Sells points out, there is common behavior which can be understood in terms of the events (not just stimuli as that term is often narrowly construed), and there is variation around that common behavior which is the concern of personology.

Sells' paper makes many important statements: e.g. "Conceptualization and measurement are interdependent in the context of the scientific method" and "The focal concepts that appear essential to an ideal model for Personality are indistinguishable from those that one might require to model the integrated behavior of the organism." Even more significant and fruitful is the model he expounds. His exposition, however, is often so concise, almost cryptic, that the reader cannot be certain that he is following Sells' argument.

I am very much in agreement with Sells' general approach, with his view of the person as a functioning system, and of events and settings as playing a major role in determining behavior, a role all too often slighted by theorists. It is a view rather close to that developed by Guilford in his paper for this conference. Where the two views differ may be in terms of the presumed degree of regularity in behavior. A person is not like a vending machine that emits a specific product whenever an appropriate coin is inserted and a particular button is pushed. As Sells notes, organisms are continually functioning and their functioning is continually changing to a greater or lesser degree as consequences of each prior experience and of the person's state and mood. At best, we can hope to understand most behavior only on a basis of probability.

One intriguing question suggested by Sells' analysis is: What proportion of behavior variance is person variance? No one has really tackled that question. Analyses of self-reports by Endler and Hunt are interesting but much too indirect. Of course the question cannot be answered until we define what we mean by the totality of behavior variance. I suspect that, even in personology, we perceive more common variance than actually exists, simply because we cannot readily describe or explain all the individual variations on the common themes in behavioral responses.

Sells' discussion of trait is not fully clear to me. Perhaps he (like myself) is wondering whether our classical definition of a trait as a behavioral disposition is much too primitive. At one point, Sells says "Traits are defined as dispositions to manifest particular behaviors in particular settings," and here he seems clearly to be on the right track. If we are to retain the term trait, we have to link the disposition to specified settings. I particularly like Sells' emphasis on the delineation of behavioral settings "in terms of variables related to language, technology, customs . . ., locales . . ., human organizations, and Persons involved." He has contributed much to the growing recognition of the necessity for comprehensive descriptions and classifications of settings and environments.

To digress a moment, the question of what Sells means by trait is illustrative of a fundamental difficulty in the way of progress in personology. The same labels for components (such as trait, drive, or attitude) and the same labels for substantive forms (such as dominance, anxiety, or extraversion) are used by various theorists and investigators with slightly different meanings. The lack of consensus among personologists on the definition of any term is indicative of the immaturity of the field.

Returning to the matter of settings, Sells' emphasis on them evokes a question that troubles many of us who want to measure personality: if the setting plays such a critical role in behavior, that is, if behavior is to a substantial degree specific to the setting, how can we generalize from the response behavior we obtain in the specific setting used for measurement to other behaviors of the subject? Sells notes that settings may be viewed objectively or phenomenally, that is objectively and scientifically or "in relation to the participant's perspective". This distinction is reminiscent of Murray's alpha and beta press. While Sells makes the distinction, his further exposition suggests that he thinks there is no serious problem here. It is crucial, however, that we be able to describe settings solely in terms of the person's world. (As Vernon reminds us, Lewin and G. Kelly have stressed this approach.) For instance, this room and its occupants can readily be described in objective language to which we would all agree. For the personologist, however, the important matter is that, to understand Dr. A's behavior, we must discover that he sees this setting as appropriate for furthering his understanding, while Dr. B sees its possibilities for gratifying his need for achievement and Dr. C experiences it as a place for dozing as he recovers from the overwhelming beauty of the larger setting.

Why have personologists done so little to learn how the perceptions of a setting differ over people? The answer may be that personologists have felt that stimuli and settings provide a firm and constant base that they could hold on to, a base from which to try to understand the complexities and individualities in people's behavior. But if we view the person as a functioning system, the critical input is the setting as he perceives it; the setting as we objective scientists describe it may literally not be information put into the system.

Offhand, it would seem quite possible to develop a technique for having people describe situations in some common framework such as that provided by Osgood's Semantic Differential. The resulting data should enable us to determine the variance common to each of several settings, the variance common to each person's perceptions of the settings, and the proportion of variance specific to person-setting perceptions. (I must confess that a student and I once made a sketchy attempt to do just this. We found the results so highly perplexing that we quickly shifted our attention to some more manageable problems.) Moreover, we might find that a person's reported perceptions of settings provide a fruitful indirect way of estimating his strength on certain traits, just as subjects' reports of other perceptions and judgements have been shown by Jackson to offer promise as an assessment strategy.

Saul Sells has done us an important service in reminding us that the behavior of interest to personology is a function of the person and the stimuli or setting, and their interactions. We obviously must give up the simplistic attempt to attribute dispositions in various strengths to people without regard for the total picture. While a multivariate model of personality is clearly the only viable kind, the several variables must not be limited to those of just one type, such as traits.

COMMENT ON SELLS' PAPER

J. R. ROYCE

Without wishing to underestimate the difficulty of the task, I must record one objection to Sells' paper which I regard as a serious one—namely, that the overall tenor of what is presented is simply too programmatic. While there is little stated here that is objectionable, I come away with a "so what" reaction. Why? Because Sells does not really get down to concepts at a substantive level. While we can all applaud his plea that we need to bring in situational variance, what does he actually tell us concerning the relevant ecological dimensions such as temperature, relative humidity, barometric pressure, or other meteorological possibilities? And do we get an inventory of hypotheses or generalizations as to relationships between such ecological dimensions and various facts of behavior?

If one replies by saying that our knowledge in this domain is too primitive for substantive theory and that relevant metatheory and/or programmatic concepts need to be stated in any event, that would at least have the virtue of making it clear that we are not looking at theory *per se*. However, in that case we would be reacting to a paper whose intent is primarily metatheoretical, and presumably the conceptual-linguistic analytic skills of the philosopher (and/or philosopher-psychologist) should be manifest therein. This would involve, for example, an inventory of the several possible meanings of key concepts. And it might also include an analysis of the relevance and logical implications of alternative concepts. In short, I have no objection whatsoever to what Sells wants to do, whether it be substantive–theoretic, programmatic–metatheoretic, or both—but I would be more convinced about such an enterprise if he would first clarify his objective, and then put before us at least a partial achievement of said objective.

REFERENCES

Barker, R. G. (ed.) (1963). "The Stream of Behavior." Appleton-Century-Crofts, New York.

Barker, R. G. (1965). Explorations in ecological psychology. *Am. Psychol.* **20,** 1–14.

Barker, R. G. (1968). "Ecological Psychology." Stanford University Press, Stanford, California.

Barker, R. G. and Gump, P. V. (1964). "Big School, Small School." Stanford University Press, Stanford, California.

Barker, R. G. and Wright, H. F. (1955). "Midwest and its Children." Harper and Row, New York.

Helson, H. (1964). "Adaptation Level Theory." Harper and Row, New York.

Loehlin, J. (1963). A computer program that simulates personality. *In* "Computer Simulation of Personality." (Tomkins, S. S. and Messick, S. eds) pp. 189–212. John Wiley and Sons, New York.

Murdock, G. P. (1958). "Outline of World Cultures." Human Relations Area Files Press, New Haven, Connecticut.

Saunders, D. R. (1961). How to tell computers from people. *Educ. psychol. Measur.* **21,** 159–183.

Sells, S. B. (1963a). An interactionist looks at the environment. *Am. Psychol.* **18,** 696–702.

Sells, S. B. (ed.) (1963b). "Stimulus Determinants of Behavior." Ronald Press, New York.

Sells, S. B. (1966a). Ecology and the science of psychology. *Multivar. behavior. Res.* **1,** 131–144.

Sells, S. B. (1966b). A model for the social system for the multiman extended duration space ship. *Aerospace Med.* **37,** 1130–1135.

Sells, S. B. (1968). General theoretical problems related to organization taxonomy: A model solution. *In* "People, Groups, and Organizations." (Indik, B. P. and Berrien, F. K. eds), pp. 27–46. Teachers College (Columbia University) Press, New York.

Sells, S. B. and Will, D. P. Jr. (1971). Accidents, police incidents, and weather. Technical Report No. 15, Contract No. Nour 3436 (00), Institute of Behavioral Research, Texas Christian University.

Sherif, M. and Sherif, C. W. (1956). "An Outline of Social Psychology." Harper and Row, New York.

Will, D. P. Jr. and Sells, S. B. Prediction of police incidents and accidents by meteorological variables. Institute of Behavioral Research, Texas Christian University, Technical Report No. 14, Contract No. Nour 3436 (00).

Multivariate Approaches to the Study of Cognitive Styles

PHILIP E. VERNON

University of Calgary

Introduction

The term cognitive style seems to be a comparative newcomer to psychology. In the standard psychological dictionaries the only meaning given for style is Adler's style of life, that is the kind of technique which the child builds up in his early years and uses throughout life for coping with inferiority feelings. Though I have not been able to trace the inventor, I suspect that it arose largely as a result of Blake and Ramsey's "Perception: An Approach to Personality" in 1951, and particularly from Klein's chapter entitled: "The Personal World through Perception". Here he is discussing what he calls "perceptual attitudes" or *Anschauungen*, though he adds that: "A style of reality testing is expressed through it", i.e. through such an attitude, and elsewhere, an attitude is "a style of organization". R. W. Gardner wrote on categorizing as a cognitive style in 1953. Since then the term has been taken up by a number of other writers and been used and defined quite variously. My object is to survey these usages, and to see whether the notion of style really does embody anything which cannot be dealt with by the ordinary multivariate techniques of factor analysis, analysis of variance, and multiple regression.

Now although the term is fairly recent, it has many precursors, and I hope to show in particular that it is, in effect, a resuscitation of the idea of type, which flourished in German psychology in the 1900s to 1930s. During the early 1930s, under Gordon Allport's influence, I spent a considerable amount of time and trouble looking into the complexities of type theory (Allport and Vernon, 1930; Vernon, 1933a, b); and I think my best plan will be to trace this historically through to the current conception of styles.

Constitutional Types

Type, of course, has a very long history, going all the way back to the Romans and the Greeks, Galen and Hippocrates. One of the earliest, and most persistent, classifications was that of the four temperaments, sanguine, choleric, melancholic and phlegmatic, which were associated with characteristic physiques and expressions, and were believed to depend on the amounts of humours or fluids in the body, blood, bile, etc. The doctrine was familiar in Shakespeare's day ("Let me have men about me that are fat . . ."), and went through extraordinary variegations among eighteenth and nineteenth century French, German and Italian writers (cf. Roback, 1927), until it crystallized into Kretschmer's and Sheldon's well-known typologies. Kretschmer was by no means original, then, in describing types of personality associated with types of physique, but he did introduce new features, notably in taking psychopathological groups—schizophrenics and manic depressives—as the extreme exemplars of his classification of personality or temperament, in extending the typology to men of genius, for example pyknic empirical physicists and asthenic idealist philosophers, and incorporating differences in cognition, the schizothyme being characterized by dissociative or analytic attention, the cyclothyme by integrative processes (Kretschmer 1925, 1931).

Already we see then that the notion of type represents a classification which spreads over two or more domains, in this case physique or constitution, psychopathology, normal temperamental variations, genius and cognitive processes. Kretschmer was not worried by the objections that at once spring to the mind of the American or British psychologist trained in psychometrics: first that such attributes tend to be distributed normally rather than dichotomously, and secondly that one should demonstrate high correlations among all the attributes before claiming that they go together in the typical person. Kretschmer did indeed find more pyknics among manic depressives, more leptosomes among schizophrenic patients, though the correlation was far from perfect. And he or some of his followers such as Enke (1927), Munz (1924), and Kibler (1925), did do a number of experiments which claimed to show generality, or spread to other domains, even though the statistical treatment, if any, was quite crude. Enke, for example, studied perceptual and psychomotor behaviour; the latter included filling a glass of water and carrying it across a room. He stated that pyknics did this in a slapdash way, asthenics more cautiously and anxiously. Munz showed pyknics to be more extratensive in the Rorschach, giving more colour responses, leptosomes were more introversive with more movement responses. However Payne (cf. Eysenck, 1960) found a mean correlation of zero between 17 tests of dissociation.

To continue with Sheldon (1942), his scaling of the three somatotypes is much more systematic and objective than that of Kretschmer, and his theory of their embryological origins quite different. But the three corresponding temperaments, whose alleged correlations with the somatotypes are almost universally disbelieved, are obviously very similar to Kretschmer's.

Extraversion-introversion and Perseveration

Jung's (1923) typology seems superficially to be based on the classical division of the temperaments, though it arose from his classification of psychoanalysed patients into those who were oriented towards the outer, or towards the inner, world—the objective or the subjective. Also it postulated that the unconscious was directed to the opposite pole from that of the conscious Ego. Unlike many other typologists, Jung did not try to build a vast empire, by claiming associations with physique or other characteristics. But it has been enormously extended by subsequent investigators such as Eysenck (1947) to include tough versus tender-minded attitudes and philosophies, Pavlov's excitatory versus inhibitory and other differences in learning, together with some highly speculative neurological and biochemical correlates. The four functions which Jung superimposed—Intuition, Sensation, Feeling and Thinking, have never achieved the same recognition as extraversion-introversion, nor been subjected to any empirical study until they were taken up in the Myers-Briggs Type Indicator (Stricker and Ross, 1962) and shown to yield significant differentiation between different groups of professionals, and between more and less creative persons (cf. MacKinnon, 1962).

Yet another thread in this tangled skein is that initiated by Gross (1902), who distinguished primary and secondary functions; that is, the broad-shallow-mobile type of thinking from the deep-narrow-perseverative type. Jung himself identified these with extraversion and introversion respectively; and this perhaps explains why Spearman (1927) seized on perseveration as a supremely important factor in temperament. Its subsequent history is instructive. It demonstrated that calling something by the name "perseveration" does not mean that it is a unitary phenomenon. Tests of different kinds of perseveration, inertia or rigidity, often showed little or no correlation with one another, and no one ever proved that it had anything to do with introversion, though Cattell and Warburton (1967) did manage to salvage a more limited aspect of this construct with the tests of disposition rigidity in his O–A battery. Surely we are justified in suspecting that some of the cognitive styles that are nowadays receiving attention may turn out to be equally delusive.

Cognitive Types and Personality

Meumann (1907) talked of diffusive versus fixative attention, and Messmer (1903) distinguished synthetic and analytic types of perception in reading, that is taking in wholes versus detailed discrimination of parts. Külpe's (1904) colour versus form types covered somewhat the same ground, though based on the tendency to respond to very brief presentations of coloured figures either in terms of colour or of shape. Much more elaborate was the work of the brothers Jaensch (1930, 1938), who started off from the relatively innocuous B and T types, based on eidetic imagery and calcium metabolism. Later E. Jaensch described the integrated, or flexible, intuitive type of subjects, with various sub-types including the Outerintegrated and Innerintegrated. These he contrasted with the disintegrate types, whose perceptions and images are more dissociated and inflexible. What was even more curious was that, when Hitler came to power, the disintegrate developed all sorts of degenerate characteristics, such as liberalism and objective detachment, and turned out to be strongly present in Jews; whereas the integrate was Aryan. The sad ending to this story is mainly guesswork on my part; but as I see it Else Frenkel-Brunswik escaped from Hitler and Jaensch to California and there, with Adorno (1950) and Sanford, discovered the authoritarian syndrome, with its intolerance, ethnocentric prejudice, father domination, and aggressive tough-mindedness, which bore an obvious resemblance to the Aryan-integrate, while the opposite, tolerant, liberal, democratic type is, of course, much more likely to occur among Jews.

Though this is jumping ahead, it is interesting that Kirscht and Dillehay (1967) conclude their book on authoritarianism by suggesting that the most fruitful conceptualization for the future is as a cognitive style, encompassing closed-mindedness, inability to deal with the novel, and dependence on external authority for support. They play down the psychoanalytic overtones which characterized Adorno's book, and which play an important part in Klein and Gardner's styles.

The Validity of Rorschach Typologies

Perhaps the most comprehensive picture is that offered by Rorschach

(1921) who describes not 1 but 3 type classifications. There is the *Erfassungstypus* or apperception type, based on relative proportions of whole, detail and small detail responses. This is said to show the synthetic-philosophical or imaginative mentality, the practical-concrete, the small-minded pedantic, and so on, i.e. not the amount but the kind of intelligence. The *Erlebnistypus* or experience type is, as it were, two-dimensional. An excess of colour responses shows extratension or labile emotionality, an excess of movement responses shows introversiveness or inner creativity. Then, thirdly, a lot of colour *and* movement is ambiequal—a rich and productive personality, while very few or none is coarctative or constricted, impoverished personality. Note however that no particular category of response is supposed to carry an invariant significance; its interpretation depends on the context of other categories. For example, the meaning of colour responses differs according to the good or poor form rating. Finally, the Rorschach expert claims to throw light on the content as well as the style of the subject's conscious and unconscious psyche, through psychodynamic interpretation of the content of particular responses. I called the Rorschach comprehensive since there have, in fact, been several demonstrations of different patterns of response among subjects classified according to other type systems, for example Form versus Colour reactors (Oeser, 1932), Jaenschian integrates–disintegrates (Schenck, 1929), and pyknics-asthenics, as already mentioned. Again the Rorschach has frequently been used as a guide, or a source of supplementary evidence, in the interpretation of styles such as Klein and Gardner's, or Witkin's field-independence. It does not, however, correlate at all with extraversion-introversion as measured by the ordinary self-report test. Unfortunately, while it is still widely favoured by clinical psychologists, and can, I suppose, be of some use as a lead in psychotherapy, there seems to me no doubt that the weight of evidence as to its validity for personality assessment is negative. I do not base this condemnation on inappropriate validational studies such as correlations with objective tests or ratings, but on a large amount of research which has tried to use the Rorschach method as Rorschach intended, and to compare its findings with clinical criteria (cf. Vernon, 1964). The main defects seem to be, first, that so much of the interpretation of patterns of response is highly subjective; secondly, that the importance of situational factors has been neglected, since the numbers and kinds of responses depend greatly on the reactions of the subject to the tester and his interpretations of the object of the test; and thirdly, that the material it produces is spread far too thinly, as it were, to cover all the cognitive and emotional aspects of personality that it alleges to do. I have discussed the Rorschach at some length since its failure enjoins us to be very cautious (at the least) in accepting the claims that present-day tests of cognitive styles can give us valid information about broad intellectual or personality trends.

Ideal Types, and the Status of Type

Before concluding this discussion of type theory, there is one other type of typologies to mention—what Allport calls ideal types. These are associated with the work of Dilthey, Jaspers and Spranger. Spranger's (1928) book, entitled "Types of Men" is in fact concerned with types of basic values, and tries to show how a person's interests, attitudes, ideals, motives depend on whether he is predominantly theoretical, aesthetic, economic, social, political or religious. Clearly Spranger allows for mixtures or combinations; for example, the religious plus political gives us the prince of the church or cardinal. Though he certainly never thought of scaling the values quantitatively, I do not think he would be surprised at our findings with the Study of Values of approximately normal distributions for each value in the population as a whole. In other words, neither he nor other German typologists assume that all or most people manifest all the characteristics of a type. Indeed maybe no one is a pure specimen of a type. Further, a type is not considered as an empirically established grouping of attributes, although, as I have mentioned, many typologists do provide some experimental evidence that the majority of people classified according to one attribute also display some other attribute. Rather, one should think of a type as a generalization made by the typologist regarding the way in which the various phenomena interact dynamically; the type concept helps him to understand the diversities of human nature and intellect. Take for example a more recent type theory, Schactel's (1959) allocentric versus autocentric. The autocentric seeks security and safety, first in the mother's womb, and later in the peer group; he wants everything to conform to convention; he reacts to environment in terms of his personal needs—how does it affect him. The allocentric has outgrown this dependence; he is open to new stimuli, keen to explore them, and he accepts objects and other people in their own right. Schactel's classification, then, is supposed to help us understand contrasting modes of reacting to the world, and it also synthesizes a wide range of phenomena such as Freud's reality versus pleasure principle, and emphasis on the distance senses which give us objective knowledge as against the more primitive senses which mainly give us feeling. It overlaps, too, with Form versus Colour dominance, presumably with Rotter's (1966) internal versus external locus of control, with open versus closed-mindedness (Rokeach, 1960), as well as with field independence versus dependence. Yet no one is wholly allo- or autocentric; for example, we all shift towards autocentricity when we relax or go to sleep, or towards allocentricity when we wake up.

It helps, I would suggest, to realize that the type is really very similar to the stereotype. We expect the typical athlete or aesthete, the mother-in-law, the Jew, the hippie, and so on, to show certain combinations of characteristics, certain traits and attitudes, and very often certain physical differentia. They help us to pigeon-hole people we meet, to anticipate their reactions and understand them. Yet at the same time we are quite aware that any one mother-in-law or Jew whom we get to know well may show few of the attributes of the stereotype. The social psychologist usually condemns stereotypes as sources of prejudice. I would say rather that they typify the way we normally think, by helping us to classify and respond to the infinite diversities of people we meet, and that the typologist is merely doing the same thing in a rather more sophisticated manner.

Precursors of Styles

We can see then that there are a number of precursors to cognitive styles. The Rorschach test is one, and I have suggested that the authoritarian syndrome is another. Lewin had a very considerable influence both in emphasizing that personality must be considered in relation to the field in which it is operating, and in pointing out that our behaviour is determined not so much by the objective environment as by the environment that is perceived. His teachings were followed up by Carl Rogers' theories of psychotherapy as reorganizing the client's perceptions, and still more directly by Kelly's (1955) stress on the ways people construe their world.

Goldstein and Scheerer were contrasting abstract with concrete types of reaction to sorting and other tasks in 1941 instead of just measuring amounts of intelligence; and Hanfman at the same date described the conceptual as against the perceptual approach to the Vigotsky Blocks. It is but a short step from these to Bruner, Goodnow and Austin's strategies of thinking. A rather different thread, which certainly links up, is that of response sets (Cronbach, 1950), which might be defined as stylistic consistencies of response to the form rather than to the content of tests. The most frequently met are acquiescence or yea versus nay-saying, extremeness versus evasiveness of response, and inclusiveness which seems to merge into the well-known style of category width or equivalence range. Another influence, which at first sight sounds rather remote, is that of information theory. However it can be applied fruitfully in describing various ways in which information from the environment is taken in and processed, stored or transmitted. For example the contrast between a broad-band but shallow communication system, and a narrow-band but intensive system obviously corresponds to Gross's primary and secondary functions.

Klein and Gardner's Work

Let us now look at the work of some of those who explicitly use the term style, and try to see what they mean by it. The work of Klein, Gardner and their associates at the Menninger Clinic is outstanding, though in fact they talk of cognitive controls rather than styles, reserving the term style for a kind of overall pattern of controls, characteristic of the individual (Gardner, 1953; Gardner *et al.*, 1959, 1960, 1962; Gardner and Moriarty, 1968; Klein, 1969; Smith and Klein, 1953). The term control was substituted for the original perceptual attitude since it is conceived essentially as a regulatory mechanism built up by the Ego for mediating between the demands of inner needs on the one hand and outer reality on the other. It owes a good deal to Hartmann's and Rapaport's psychoanalytic theories of the Ego, and is indeed quite comparable to a defence mechanism. Being relatively permanent it tends to produce consistency and stability of behaviour. It is also a generalized tendency which shows itself in many aspects of perception and thinking; and since, basically, it is an attribute of personality organization, the assessment of a person's controls at the cognitive level should give us the clue to his type of Ego structure.

Some half-dozen controls have been investigated, both separately in order to show their generality in different tests or situation that are thought to sample the same control, and in relation to each other. I will define them quite briefly, since it would take too long to describe the particular manifestations and the tests commonly employed:

1. Levelling versus sharpening, that is coping with dissonant elements of experience either by levelling down and obscuring them, or assimilating them to the familiar, versus highlighting and differentiating them from the familiar.
2. Field independence or articulation, which I will discuss separately.
3. Tolerance for, or resistance to, unstable, ambiguous or unrealistic experiences.

4. Equivalence range or conceptual differentiation—using narrow or wide categories in grouping experiences.

5. Focusing versus scanning—concentrating the attention on dominant parts of a field versus letting it rove widely.

6. Constricted versus flexible control, which relates to the classical notion of perseveration versus susceptibility to distractions, and resembles convergent versus divergent.

Most of these, it may be seen, include features quite similar to those which interested German typologists. It is a moot point whether they can be regarded as factors similar to the cognitive factors of Thurstone, Guilford and others. Klein, indeed, strongly criticizes correlational studies, and clearly regards his attitudes, controls or styles as a better form of categorization than factors. True, a good deal of the basic research seems to have been carried out by comparing the performance on some task or tasks of those who scored high or low on some other task. Thus the initial approach to styles may have had a more experimental than psychometric flavour. Again, most controls (field articulation is an exception) are unlike ability factors since they are not tapped by tests calling for maximal performance (or only indirectly so). They rely more on perceptual or conceptual tasks that call for what Cronbach (1970) has called typical performance. However, observations of group differences on various tasks are, of course, merely an alternative expression of correlations, though sometimes more revealing than ordinary correlations if it turns out that regressions are non-linear. Also, when it comes to the crunch, almost all the published Menninger researches in fact relied very largely on correlations and factor analyses. Gardner's aim certainly appeared to be to show that the various manifestations of a control loaded on the same factor. Further, in the 1959 study, when the investigators went on to classify subjects by their overall styles, the styles were identified by patterns of factor scores.

Perhaps Klein sees the difference in that controls are believed to have personality correlates. They might be compared to Cattell's source traits, whereas ordinary ability factors are relatively surface clusters. Thus, most of the Menninger studies included, as well as quite large batteries of cognitive measures to cover the various controls, additional clinical assessments or tests such as Rorschach to help in interpretation or to link the control scores with hypothesized ego structures. But, as Pawlik and Cattell (1966) point out, several of the well established ability factors, such as fluency, flexibility of closure, even crystallized intelligence, also have quite well established personality correlates, or they span both domains. Alternatively, one might hope to discover separate sets of factors in the cognitive and the motivational domains, and to intercorrelate them, or match them as Cattell does with his *L–R*, *Q* and *T* factors.

Turning briefly to the results—I am afraid that they strike me as sadly unconvincing. Other psychologists may consider that they go a long way to confirm the authors' hypotheses, but as far as I can make out, scarcely any factors except field independence emerge consistently in different researches. Some of the other factors are apt to be spurious, since they derive largely from different methods of scoring the same test. But in many instances different scores hypothesized to test the same control do not load on the same factor, and the correlations with clinical or other criteria are seldom significant. One obvious reason for these inconsistencies is that the Menninger psychologists usually worked with quite small groups of about 30, ranging up to 60 at most, because of the elaborateness of the test batteries. Also they prefer mature adult volunteers to college students, in the hope of getting more representative samples, covering the whole range of ability. While this is praiseworthy, it may also mean that the subjects vary more widely in motivations, attitudes to the "typical performance" tests and interpretation of instructions than would more homogeneous college student groups.

The authors are entirely frank in admitting that some of the results do not confirm their expectations; but they tend to explain these away by producing all sorts of post hoc theories, or by ascribing them to the complexities of personality organization. I apologize if these judgments seem unduly critical, but the findings seem only too similar to those we had learned to expect from the shortcomings of German psychological types. Where the work on controls differs from that of the Germans is that the Menninger group try not only to operationalize their controls by defining them in terms of performance on specified tasks, but also to provide empirical evidence that different manifestations of a control do hang together.

The next group to consider is Kagan and his colleagues at the Fels Institute (Kagan *et al.*, 1963; Kagan *et al.*, 1964). They point out that over and above the general growth of thinking abilities in children there are qualitative differences in type or style of conceptualization. These differences are best displayed in object or picture sorting tests, where subjects tend to group things which are alike in one of three ways: first, in terms of analytic-descriptive resemblances, secondly, by functional associations, and third, by inferential-categorical generalizations. The first two are the most frequent and they are said to correspond to reflective, cautious versus impulsive, distractible personality qualities. For example, functional children showed more gross motor behaviour in the playground and less concentration of attention in the classroom. A large number of perceptual and conceptual tasks were tried out with children from Grades 1 to 6, and found to have substantial relations to analytic scores. Thus there is a good deal of published evidence for the generality of Kagan's two styles, though so far little or no confirmation by independent investigators. They are not, like Gardner's controls, interpreted psychodynamically; rather there is a suggestion of a constitutional basis, or they are attributed to differences in task involvement or anxiety over competence. Kagan doubts whether a reflective versus impulsive factor could be established, though he does not discuss the differences between factors and styles. So far, fairly small numbers in different age groups have been studied with rather different tests, which naturally precludes factorization. But one would certainly like to know the loadings of these tests on a factor defined chiefly by the conceptual style scores, also how far such a factor is distinct from general intelligence, field independence, or other recognized abilities.

Broverman (1960a, b, 1964) explicitly talks of cognitive styles, which he defines as "relationships between abilities within individuals". Two main dimensions are postulated: Conceptual versus Perceptuomotor, and Strong versus Weak Automatization, and he claims to be able to diagnose these from score patterns on the Stroop Color-Word Interference Test. Several studies are reported where small groups of students or adults were classified into 4 groups on these dimensions, and given additional PMA and other tests which, it is claimed, tended to confirm the nature of the dimensions. With other groups of adolescents and adults, factor analysis was used, with rather unstable results. The most prominent factors appear to contrast spatial, verbal-educational and psychomotor tests rather than the initial dichotomies. Broverman in fact criticizes the factorial approach, since he wishes to study differences within individuals; he therefore applied ipsative scoring so as to eliminate the effects of any general factor. However it would surely have been simpler to factorize raw scores, hold the general factor constant, and then interpret the bipolar factors with or without rotation. The results might have been less puzzling.

Bieri (1966) and his colleagues emphasize cognitive complexity versus simplicity, particularly in person perception. Some people employ many fine dimensions in viewing persons or objects, others use few coarse ones. This difference obviously relates to Harvey, Hunt and Schroder's (1961) abstract-complex versus concrete-simple stages, also to category-width, and to Kelly's personal construct theory; and a version of the REP test is Bieri's chief instrument. While some relations have been found, e.g. with Rorschach scores, a factorial study of some

20 tests by Vannoy (1965) showed that complexity is not a unitary trait. A number of different factors were found in different kinds of instrument. The Barron-Welsh (1952) test of preference for complex versus simple designs probably represents yet another variant.

The most persistent user of the term style is Witkin, and for him it seems to mean a factor or dimension which overlaps several domains—perceptual, conceptual, psychomotor, personality and pathology. It is likely that more empirical work has been carried out on field-dependence-independence by Witkin and his colleagues (1954, 1962), and other psychologists, than on all the other cognitive styles put together. The dimension was originally based on reactions to distortion of the vertical and was interpreted mainly as active coping versus passive dependence. It has now blossomed into the contrast between analytical-differentiated cognitive processes and primitive global processes. Though independence is still defined by spatial-perceptual tests, it has been shown to enter into conceptual clarity and objective analytic thinking, as well as into certain types of memorizing; and a lot of evidence has accumulated indicating that it goes with independence versus conformity of personality. It is claimed that the mother's own independence and the way she encourages or inhibits growth of independence in the child have a strong influence; but Witkin admits that it may also have some genetic basis. Although we know so much about it, there are several points that are still obscure. Witkin claims that the high correlations found with tests of *S* or *Vz* factor, Flexibility of Closure, and Adaptive Flexibility, reinforce his construct. But does this mean that perceptual independence is identical with *S* or British "*k*" factors? If not, what are the unique aspects of independence? At the moment different investigators are using all sorts of versions of Embedded Figures and Rod and Frame tests, which do not correlate very highly, and yet assuming that scores on any one of these is representative of the whole perceptual independence factor. Witkin further believes that independence is distinct from general intelligence, since correlations of independence or *S*-factor tests with verbal tests are usually fairly low. In fact, as so often happens with factorial controversies, the answer depends mainly on the heterogeneity of the population investigated. In a large Grade 8 group which was fairly heterogeneous, I found the mean *g*-variance to be 20%, the *S*-factor variance 17% in a battery of 8 independence or spatial tests. Thus a great many of the correlations claimed with other variables, conceptual maturity for example, disappear when *g* is held constant. It was not possible to discriminate an independence factor separate from the *S*-factor. However the personality and interest test correlates of the Rod and Frame test turned out to be quite different from those of Embedded Figures, Kohs and other spatial tests. Unfortunately I was unable to give the Body Adjustment test, but it does seem possible that proprioceptive and visuospatial factors are distinguishable, though oblique. A different kind of breakdown was suggested by Messick and Fritzky's (1963) very thorough study, where articulation of forms against a patterned background was shown not to load on the field independence factor, nor to possess the same personality correlates as articulation of discrete elements.

Another problem is whether field independence is similarly organized in the two sexes, though the mean scores for females always tend to be lower. The answer is no. In my study independence measures were quite differently related to other abilities, interests and personality in boys and girls, though I will not give any further details because of the conference focus on theory.

Divergent versus Convergent Thinking

Numerous other suggested styles might be discussed, risk-taking for example. But for my final example I will take divergence-convergence, often miscalled creativity-intelligence. Though this contrast is not commonly referred to as a style, it certainly seems to fall under the same heading; and Wallach and Kogan (1965) talk of "modes of thinking". Liam Hudson's provocative book, "Contrary Imaginations" (1966) points out that intelligence tests give little or no discrimination among highly intelligent students. So far as academic brilliance or vocational success are concerned there is nothing to choose between the 150 and the 130 IQ. On the other hand, what he calls "bias", namely relatively higher scores on convergent than divergent tests, does distinguish rather clearly between those inclined to the natural sciences and to the arts, respectively. He also provides a lot of evidence that this difference is bound up with a wide range of cognitive and personality characteristics. He denies the identification of divergence with creativity, indicating that these "biases" represent, rather, different defence mechanisms. The resemblance to Klein and Gardner's concept of control is quite a close one. Many other writers have pointed out that divergence-convergence becomes more meaningful at high IQ levels—the so-called threshold hypothesis. Guilford (1967), who was the first to draw attention to the distinction, holds that creativity is multifactorial, but the majority of subsequent workers seem to have reduced it to a single factor, a kind of combination of ideational fluency and originality; and this has proved to be partially, though not wholly, distinguishable from verbal intelligence. It is more or less oblique, depending on the homogeneity of the population studied. I will not comment on the findings obtained with this factor, or its correlates with other cognitive and personality variables, except to mention that my own research shows its significance to differ markedly in the two sexes. At Grade 8 level at least it tends to link with scientific interests and achievements in boys, but with artistic variables in girls.*

Now two of the best known studies in this area, those of Getzels and Jackson (1962), and of Wallach and Kogan (1965) employed a rather unusual approach for contrasting the so-called high creative with the high intelligence students. Wallach and Kogan went a step further by considering 4 groups which one may designate as $C+I+$, $C+I-$, $C-I+$, $C-I-$. Actually of course this is merely an alternative device to those of Broverman and of Hudson for obtaining ipsative scoring. All three are rather crude ways of studying what common variance exists when general ability is held constant. By separating off their 2 or their 4 groups, respectively, Getzels and Wallach have come up with quite a number of interesting differences in cognitive and personality attributes, which do show that students high in divergent thinking are rather different people from those high in convergent intelligence. This is, however, an inefficient technique for the analysis of data, and it is apt to be rather misleading in giving the impression that the divergent style of thinking is an entirely different type from the convergent. Cronbach (1968) stated that a more powerful and more appropriate technique is that of stepwise multiple regression. He himself took each of Wallach and Kogan's dependent variables in turn, i.e. those hypothesized as relating to creativity or intelligence,† and calculated first the variance accounted for by intelligence alone, then by adding in the divergent thinking battery, then any interaction terms, and fourthly sex differences. At each stage the increase in multiple R^2 was tested, and in fact many more significant F-ratios were obtained than Wallach and Kogan found by their dichotomizing technique. Interactions, of course, tell us when the effects of divergence differ at different levels of intelligence; for example, they cover Wallach and Kogan's finding that $C+I+$ children are more sociable and self-assured than $C-I+$, but also $C+I-$ are less sociable and self-assured than $C-I-$. Though we

* An interesting example of the kind of contradictions that often arose between different German typologies is provided by divergence, field independence and Kagan's analytic style. Some writers would regard divergence or creativity as a sign of independence or nonconformity; but for Kagan divergence is impulsive and it should therefore be related negatively to tests of analytic style.

† Cronbach in fact referred to these batteries as Achievement and Fluency-Flexibility rather than Intelligence and Creativity.

are not concerned with the results, the striking finding was how much of the variance of most of the dependent criteria was attributable to convergent intelligence, how little extra was contributed by divergence, interaction and sex differences. I have dealt with this at some length because Cronbach's analysis uses a highly sophisticated multivariate technique which could very well be applied in studies of other styles. Doubtless it could be extended to cover the problem of interpretation of multiple criteria, though I would doubt myself whether we yet have a clear enough conception of styles to justify such elaborate statistical treatment.

General Discussion and Conclusions

Our survey suggests that this area of research is particularly susceptible to the naming fallacy, i.e. assuming that various functions or tasks which appear to involve "analysis", "integration", "creativity", "levelling", etc. actually do intercorrelate without obtaining sufficient, well replicated, empirical evidence. Styles, like German types, come dangerously close to psychological stereotypes. At the same time, although correlational evidence and factor analysis have proved to be extremely useful in studying, say, field independence, divergent thinking, and perhaps other styles, I would doubt if they really supply the whole answer. Indeed, discussion of, and work with, styles seems to have grown largely through dissatisfaction with the straitjacket of factors. Eysenck (1960) may be quite happy to equate the uniqueness of an individual personality with a point in multifactorial space, but there are alternative ways of approaching taxonomic problems besides reducing them to linear correlations.

Some of the current definitions do not recognize any distinction. Thus Wallach (1962), in an excellent critical comparison of Kagan and Witkin, states that a style signifies that those who react in one manner in one situation will react characteristically in another situation. This would be equally true of a factor. Wiggins (1968) goes a bit further in saying that styles refer to consistent differences of expression in a wide range of content. I prefer the following formulation by my colleague Conklin: "It appears that most researchers conceive cognitive styles as a superordinate construct which is involved in many cognitive operations and which accounts for individual differences in a variety of cognitive, perceptual and personality variables." Possibly this definition might be met by a second or third order factor, and indeed Eysenck does refer to such broad factors as "types". Messick (1969) regards styles as typical modes of perceiving, remembering, thinking and problem solving, which are "inferred from consistencies in the manner or form of cognition, as distinct from the content of cognition or the level of skill displayed". He also recognizes that the generality of a style "appears at a higher order level in the factor-analytic sense". But a style seems to differ from any factor in implying the notion of a syndrome or complex of interacting characteristics—a dynamic Gestalt which contrasts strongly with the Gestalt at the opposite pole of the distribution. I do not see any difficulty in reconciling this notion with the known tendency of most attributes to be normally distributed, nor with the fairly low correlations that may exist between some of the attributes, provided we have evidence that these correlations are "hardy", to use Cattell's term. A style normally seems to differ from a factor in breadth of content; after all factors are usually sought in order to delineate the basic dimension underlying a fairly limited area. Moreover, it is in the very nature of Varimax or other commonly used techniques of rotation to minimise overlapping between different domains. For example, if abilities, interests and self-report variables are included in the same analysis, the three sets of measures usually tend to fall on different factors. Loadings of less than 0·3 are commonly ignored even when the population is large enough to make them significant. With a style, however, one is particularly interested in this overlap between domains, even if it is small, so long as it is adequately replicated. If there is anything in the notion of dynamic Gestalts, the psychologist must be allowed to employ experimental rather than psychometric approaches, provided they are multivariate, rather than classical univariate, in design. Wallach suggests that a style may be found in only a section of a population, and this implies the notion of moderator variables. Sex, for instance, is an extremely important moderator, though many experimental psychologists, test constructors, and others tend to gloss over the structural differences between the sexes that certainly become prominent in adolescence.

To conclude: few cognitive styles have so far been firmly established as stable and consistent syndromes, and as existing over and above such generally accepted factors as *g*, *V* or *S*. It is, however, entirely possible that they could be demonstrated and that their make-up might be rather different from that of conventional factors. Discriminant function has proved useful in studying nosological classifications (cf. Eysenck, 1960b); but it seems likely that Bottenberg and Ward's multiple regression analysis could better cope with problems of patterning, interactions and moderator variables, and nonlinear relations, as well as covarying intelligence or other independent variables.

Summary

The paper examines the concept of cognitive style, which has become increasingly popular in the past 20 years. While many rather different definitions have been given, the following appears to represent a consensus: "a superordinate construct which is involved in many cognitive operations, and which accounts for individual differences in a variety of cognitive, perceptual and personality variables". It is argued that there are several precursors to this construct, including the type theories which were elaborated especially by German writers such as Kretschmer, Jung, Gross, Jaensch, Rorschach and Spranger. Usually these theories could cope with the psychometric objection that human attributes tend to be normally, rather than dichotomously, distributed in the population. Most however fail to meet the criticism that the different attributes encompassed within a type must be consistently intercorrelated. The type (like the stereotype) was employed more as a subjective generalization about people than as an empirical clustering of attributes, and the same weakness is apparent in many of the modern styles.

The work of the Menninger group relied initially more on experimental studies of perceptual differences than on correlational approaches. However the more extensive studies which later attempted to establish several styles simultaneously as distinct factors have given disappointingly inconsistent results (partly because they were carried out on small populations). Kagan's, Broverman's, Bieri's and other styles are outlined; these also tend to illustrate the lack of consistency when measures of the various style components are intercorrelated. Witkin's field-dependence-independence is the most successful and replicable style so far investigated, though there are difficulties in establishing the nature of its unique content (e.g. how far does it coincide with Thurstone's *S* factor); and not all of Witkin's claims have been independently confirmed. A good case could be made for regarding divergent versus convergent thinking as a similar style which has wide cognitive and personality implications. Here also there is often overlapping with other factors e.g. verbal intelligence; and attention is drawn to Cronbach's stepwise multiple regression analysis of the Wallach-Kogan data, as a technique which could usefully be applied to the study of other styles. In conclusion, some styles can be subsumed under the notion of second or higher-order factors. But we should not rule out the possibility of syndromes or dynamic Gestalts, which could be better studied by multivariate experimental designs, or by discriminant function, than by factor analysis.

COMMENT ON VERNON'S PAPER

T. E. WECKOWICZ

Vernon's very interesting and scholarly paper should have had a sobering effect on students of the contemporary personality research literature. It definitely injects a dose of healthy scepticism regarding the claims of the so-called "cognitive styles" research. The historical introduction in which Professor Vernon reviews the development of the early conceptualizations concerning personality typologies and traits is particularly instructive. The problem of personality types and traits reflects the perennial philosophical problems of categories, classifications, and taxonomies—the problems which are full of semantic pitfalls and implicit metaphysical presuppositions. One can think of the following theoretical possibilities regarding classifications:

1. Discrete, mutually exclusive classes.
2. Partially overlapping classes.
3. Classes obtained by averaging the traits and characteristics of individual subjects. (Galton's "composite photograph" theory of universal concepts.)
4. Ideal types existing objectively in some kind of Platonic universe. (Chomsky's competence model of language presents a contemporary example of this approach.)
5. Ideal types existing as subjective categories in the mind of the observer, which enable him to grasp the essences of the perceived phenomena.

It appears from Professor Vernon's historical review that some of the early German typologies, such as for instance that of Spranger, were of the character described under the fifth category. They were ideal types existing subjectively *a priori*, enabling one to grasp the complex phenomena of human and social behavior. This approach is characteristic of the epistemology which was an offshoot of the Neo-Kantian philosophy, popular in Germany and Austria at the turn of the century. This approach to typology was closely related to the *Verstehen* methodology of the *Kulturwissenschaften* (humanities and social sciences) originated by Dilthey. Spranger's typology was proposed as a methodological tool to help a *Verstehen* psychologist, a clinician, a literary critic, and a historian to understand the behavior of persons in all its complexity and on the molar level. The personalities of the actors of the great drama called Human History were to be understood and not to be causally explained. Any analytic and measuring attempts were contrary to this approach.

The early typologies of German psychology were taken over by English speaking investigators, who did not subscribe to the theory of different epistemologies for *Geisteswissenschaften* and for *Naturwissenschaften*. They proceeded to objectify, to operationalize, and to measure the traits characterizing different types. Under the impact of these procedures the typologies disappeared and were replaced by dimensions along which subject populations were more or less normally distributed. One example of what happened is the fate of Jung's extroverted and introverted types, which at the hands of Eysenck were replaced by a continuous dimension of Extroversion–Introversion. The Allport-Vernon study of values constitutes another example. These investigators found that preferences for various values implied by Spranger's types were normally distributed, with the majority of subjects falling in between the type categories. Thus, it became quite obvious that an *n*-dimensional space, with the dimensions along which people varied, offered a better model for the description of individual differences than a typology with its assumption of discrete categories. Thurstone's newly developed mathematical model of multiple factor analysis provided a useful methodological tool for discovery of the important dimensions along which men differed. The dimensional approach is not incompatible with some kind of typology or taxonomy established on empirical grounds. The density of the population in a factorial space does not need to be uniform. Clustering of subjects in certain regions of the space indicates the existence of some objective categories and, therefore, types, although the boundaries of the categories may often be blurred and exist only in a statistical sense. Various techniques for finding these categories quantitatively have been proposed. Professor Vernon mentions discriminant function. This technique is applicable when external criteria of categorization exist. "Taxonome", invented by Cattell and Coulter, is another technique. This technique enables one to discover clusters of high density in the total distribution without any external criteria for categorization. Some investigators factor analysed factor scores with a view to establishing factor groupings which reflect the existence of types. And the Q-technique or inverted factor analysis, according to some authorities, can be used for the same purpose, although this claim is rather doubtful.

Canonical correlation, another multivariate technique, is useful in discovering the existence of an association between patterns of factor scores in two different domains, e.g. cognitive and personality-motivational domains. It offers the best prediction from a pattern of factor scores in one factorial space to a pattern of scores in another factorial space. The problem of cognitive styles constitutes that kind of problem.

The dimensionality of the space of cognitive abilities has been quite satisfactorialy mapped out and is relatively quite well established. Also the domain of personality, although not mapped out as well as the cognitive domain, has yielded replicable factors. Cognitive styles, as it were, span the two domains. As happens very frequently when using tests from different domains (e.g. personality and cognitive) we frequently get unsatisfactory factorial solutions and unstable factors. Thus, it seems reasonable to suggest that canonical correlations be tried as a tool in the investigation of so-called cognitive styles.

Canonical correlations may be obtained in relatively homogeneous populations between subjects' factor scores derived from the Structure of Intellect cognitive factors of Guilford and factor scores on personality factors such as, for example, the 16 P.F. of Cattell. Different orthogonal latent roots of the canonical correlations representing different patterns of relationships between the cognitive and personality factor scores could represent different cognitive styles or cognitive controls. It is an open question whether these latent roots of canonical correlations would correspond to the various cognitive styles previously described. Some tests used originally for establishing various cognitive styles could serve as the external criteria to which the latent roots of the canonical correlations could be related.

COMMENT ON VERNON'S PAPER

W. CLAEYS

If the assumption is true that Witkin's field-independence is nothing but "$g+k$" (see Vernon's assessment of Witkin's "style"), how can we explain (1) the strong environmental and cultural determinance of field-independence, clearly demonstrated by Witkin, Dyk, Berry *et al.* in their studies on the influence of child rearing practices and ecological factors on the development of ego-differentiation? This is in contrast with the high genetic determination of "g" and "k". (2) How can we explain the existence of various personality correlates of field-independence measures? Such correlates were never found for measures of "g" and "k".

I fully agree with Vernon's suggestion that styles could be higher-order factors. The second-order factors "gv" and "gf" found by Horn and Cattell (on the basis of a large battery of ability and personality tests) can be identified respectively as "field-independence" and "divergent thinking". It is not excluded that still other second-order factors (such as Cattell and Horn's "carefulness" and even "fluid intelligence") are to be interpreted in terms of styles rather than in terms of abilities or personality traits.

I do not see any essential difference between "types" in the German or Dutch sense (very similar to the stereotype, see Vernon, this volume, pp. 130–131), and the psychopathological syndromes "hysterics" and "dysthymics", conceived of by Eysenck as the fruit of the interaction between his two orthogonal dimensions of Neuroticism and Extraversion.

REJOINDER TO DISCUSSANTS' COMMENTS

P. E. VERNON

I am grateful to Weckowicz for his instructive historical resumé of the transformation of early type doctrines into factorial dimensions; also for his suggestions regarding alternative multivariate approaches to the statistical exploration of cognitive styles. I would agree too that a variety of categorizing or classificatory systems are possible, and that psychologists have not yet thought out sufficiently clearly which system is most apt to the study of styles.

Claeys raises a number of queries. Regarding genetic and environmental factors in field independence, it is true that Witkin and others have emphasized the effects of child rearing practices and ecology; but Witkin also quite explicitly recognized the possibility that independence is in part hereditarily determined. As to personality correlates, I would disagree that "*g*" is unrelated to personality. Many investigators have consistently found considerable associations with personality and character traits, and there is some evidence linking "*k*", perhaps to introversion. Cattell's new book, "Abilities, Their Structure, Growth and Action" (1971), discusses the overlap of cognitive, dynamic and personality factors in detail. I am not sure of the implications of Claeys' statement about German "types" and psychopathological syndromes. The nosological categories "hysteric", "anxiety neurosis", etc. are indeed closely similar to types, or to modern cognitive styles, whereas Eysenck's factorial categories are, of course, defined strictly in terms of certain combinations of objective test scores.

REFERENCES

Adorno, T. W., Frenkel-Brunswik, E., Levinson, D. J. and Sanford, R. N. (1950). "The Authoritarian Personality." Harper, New York.

Allport, G. W. and Vernon, P. E. (1930). The field of personality. *Psychol. Bull.* **27,** 677–730.

Barron, F. and Welsh, G. S. (1952). Artistic perception as a possible factor in personality style: Its measurement by a figure preference test. *J. Psychol.* **33,** 199–203.

Bieri, J. and Atkins, A. L. *et al.* (1966). "Clinical and Social Judgment: The Discrimination of Behavioral Information." Wiley, New York.

Blake, R. R. and Ramsey, G. V. (eds) (1951). "Perception: An Approach to Personality." Ronald Press, New York.

Bottenberg, R. A. and Ward, J. H. (1963). "Applied multiple linear regression." United States Department of Commerce, National Bureau of Standards, Washington, D.C.

Broverman, D. M. (1960a). Dimensions of cognitive style. *J. Personality* **28,** 167–185.

Broverman, D. M. (1960b). Cognitive style and intra-individual variation in abilities. *J. Personality* **28,** 240–256.

Broverman, D. M. (1964). Generalized and behavioral correlates of cognitive styles. *J. consult. Psychol.* **28,** 487–500.

Cattell, R. B. and Warburton, F. W. (1967). "Objective Personality and Motivation Tests." University of Illinois Press, Urbana, Illinois.

Conklin, R. C. and Zingle, H. W. (1969). Counsellor sensitivity and cognitive style. *West. Psychol.* **1,** 19–28.

Cronbach, L. J. (1950). Further evidence on response sets and test design. *Educ. psychol. Measur.* **10,** 3–31.

Cronbach, L. J. (1968). Intelligence? Creativity? A parsimonious reinterpretation of the Wallach–Kogan data. *Am. educ. Res. J.* **5,** 491–511.

Cronbach, L. J. (1970). "Essentials of Psychological Testing" (3rd Edn). Harper, New York.

Enke, W. (1928). Experimentalpsychologische Studien zur Konstitutionsforschung. *Z. ges. Neurol. Psychiat.* **114,** 770–794.

Eysenck, H. J. (1947). "Dimensions of Personality." Kegan Paul, London.

Eysenck, H. J. (1960a). "The Structure of Human Personality." Methuen, London.

Eysenck, H. J. (1960b). "Experiments in Personality." Routledge and Kegan Paul, London.

Gardner, R. W. (1953). Cognitive styles in categorizing behavior. *J. Personality* **22,** 214–233.

Gardner, R. W. and Holzman, P. S. *et al.* (1959). Cognitive control: A study of individual consistencies in cognitive behavior. *Psychol. Issues* **1,** No. 4.

Gardner, R. W., Jackson, D. N. and Messick, S. (1960). Personality organization in cognitive controls and intellectual abilities. *Psychol. Issues* **2,** No. 8.

Gardner, R. W. and Long, R. I. (1962). Control, defence and centration effect: A study of scanning behavior. *Br. J. Psychol.* **53,** 129–140.

Gardner, R. W. and Moriarty, A. (1968). "Personality Development at Pre-adolescence." University of Washington Press, Seattle.

Getzels, J. W. and Jackson, P. W. (1962). "Creativity and Intelligence: Explorations with gifted Students." Wiley, New York.

Goldstein, K. and Scheerer, M. (1941). Abstract and concrete behavior. *Psychol. Monogr.* **53,** No. 239.

Gross, O. (1932). "Die Cerebrale Sekundär funktion." Leipzig.

Guilford, J. P. (1967). "The Nature of Human Intelligence." McGraw-Hill, New York.

Hanfman, E. (1941). A study of personal patterns in an intellectual problem. *Character and Personality* **9,** 315–325.
Harvey, O. J., Hunt, D. E. and Schroder, H. M. (1961). "Conceptual Systems and Personality." Wiley, New York.
Hudson, L. (1966). "Contrary Imaginations." Methuen, London.
Jaensch, E. R. (1930). "Eidetic Imagery and Typological Methods of Investigation." Kegan Paul, London.
Jaensch, E. R. (1938). "Der Gegentypus." Bart, Leipzig.
Jung, C. G. (1923). "Psychological Types." Kegan Paul, London.
Kagan, J., Moss, H. A. and Sigel, I. E. (1963). Psychological significance of styles of conceptualization. *Monogr. Soc. Res. Child Dev.* **28,** No. 86.
Kagan, J. and Rosman, B. L. *et al.* (1964). Information processing in the child: Significance of analytic and reflective attitudes. *Psychol. Monogr.* **78,** No. 578.
Kelly, G. A. (1955). "The Psychology of Personal Constructs." Norton, New York.
Kibler, M. (1925). "Experimentalpsychologischer Beitrag zur Typenforschung." *Z. ges. Neurol. Psychiat.* **98,** 525–544.
Kirtscht, J. P. and Dillehay, R. C. (1967). "Dimensions of Authoritarianism: A Review of Research and Theory." University of Kentucky Press, Lexington, Kentucky.
Klein, G. S. (1969). "Perception, Motives and Personality." Knopf, New York.
Kretschmer, E. (1925). "Physique and Character." Kegan Paul, London.
Kretschmer, E. (1931). "The Psychology of Men of Genius." Kegan Paul, London.
Külpe, O. (1904). Versuche uber Abstraktion. *Ber. I Kongress exp. Psychol.*
MacKinnon, D. W. (1962). The personality correlates of creativity: A study of American architects. *Proc. XIV Congress on Applied Psychology* Vol. 2, 11–39.
Messick, S. (1969). Measures of Cognitive Styles and Personality and their Potential for Educational Practice. *In* "Developments in Educational Testing," Ingekamp, K. (ed.), 329–341.
Messick, S. and Fritzky, F. J. (1963). Dimensions of analytic attitude in cognition and personality. *J. Personality* **31,** 346–370.
Messmer, O. (1903). Zur Psychologie des Lesens bei Kindern und Erwachsenen. *Arch. ges. Psychol.* **2,** 190–298.
Meumann, E. (1907). *Vortrag z. Einf. in der experimentalischer Pädagogik.*
Munz, E. (1924). Die Reaktion des Pyknickes im Rorschachschen psychodiagnostischen Versuch. *Z. ges. Neurol. Psychiat.* **91,** 26–92.
Oeser, O. A. (1932). Some experiments on the abstraction of form and colour. Part 2. Rorschach tests. *Br. J. Psychol.* **22,** 287–323.
Pawlik K. and Cattell, R. B. (1966). Concepts in human cognition and aptitudes. *In* "Handbook of multivariate experimental psychology." (Cattell, R. B. ed.), 535–562. Rand McNally, Chicago.
Roback, A. A. (1927). "The Psychology of Character." Harcourt, Brace, New York.
Rokeach, M. (1960). "The Open and Closed Mind." Basic Books, New York.
Rorschach, H. (1921). "Psychodiagnostik: Methodik und Ergebnisse eines warhnehmungsdiagnostischen Experiments." Bircher, Bern.
Rotter, J. B. (1966). Generalized expectancies for internal versus external control of reinforcement. *Psychol. Monogr.* No. 609.
Schactel, E. G. (1959). "Metamorphosis." Basic Books, New York.
Schenck, H. (1929). Experimentell-strukturpsychologische Untersuchungen über den "dynamischen Typus." *Z. Psychol.* **113,** 91–208.
Sheldon, W. H. (1942). "The Varieties of Temperament." Harper, New York.

Smith, G. J. W. and Klein, G. S. (1953). Cognitive controls in serial behavior patterns. *J. Personality* **22**, 188–213.

Spearman, C. (1927). "The Abilities of Man." Macmillan, London.

Spranger, E. (1928). "Types of Men." Niemeyer, Halle.

Stricker, L. J. and Ross, J. (1962). An assessment of some structural properties of the Jungian personality types. *Educational Testing Service Bulletin* RB–62–33.

Vannoy, J. S. (1965). Generality of cognitive complexity–simplicity as a personality construct. *J. Personal. Soc. Psychol.* **2,** 385–396.

Vernon, P. E. (1933a). The American versus the German methods of approach to the study of temperament and personality. *Br. J. Psychol.* **24,** 156–177.

Vernon, P. E. (1933b). The Rorschach inkblot test. *Br. J. med. Psychol.* **13,** 89–118, 179–200, 271–291.

Vernon, P. E. (1964). "Personality Assessment: A Critical Survey." Methuen, London.

Vernon, P. E. (1967). "Intelligence and Cultural Environment." Methuen, London.

Wallach, M. A. (1962). Commentary. Active-analytic versus passive-global cognitive functions. *In* "Measurement in Personality and Cognition." (Messick, S. J. and Ross, J. eds), 199–215. Wiley, New York.

Wallach, M. A. and Kogan, N. (1965). "Modes of thinking in Young Children: A Study of the Creativity–Intelligence Distinction." Holt, Rinehart and Winston, New York.

Wiggins, J. S. (1968). Personality structure. *A. Rev. Psychol.* **19,** 293–350.

Witkin, H. A. and Lewis, H. B. *et al.* (1954). "Personality through Perception." Harper, New York.

Witkin, H. A. and Dyk, R. B. *et al.* (1962). "Psychological Differentiation: Studies of Development." Wiley, New York.

Zigler, E. (1963). Review of Witkin's "Psychological Differentiation." *Contemp. Psychol.* **8,** 133–135.

Comparative Studies of Multiple Factor Ability Measures

STEVEN G. VANDENBERG

University of Colorado

The dead hand of tradition, in the shape of the concept of a general, unitary, almost biologically predetermined intelligence, still lies heavily on psychology. Once Binet had turned away from (potentially independent) "faculties" to the more pragmatic idea of compiling a list of tasks that showed an age progression, the harm was done. Although Binet dignified the hodgepodge of items he selected by saying that they measured higher mental processes, his only criteria for inclusion were that the percentage of children able to perform the task should increase with age and that the task plus the instructions be clear, short, and uniform. The illusion of a unitary function was further strengthened by the practice of comparing the performance of a child to that of a normative group. Furthermore, the unitary illusion was underlined by Stern's introduction of the concept of "I.Q." The point is that we tend to forget that "intelligence quotient" is, in fact, a ratio between mental age and physical age. Even when the evidence began to mount that the performance of many individuals was not an even one, Spearman tried to salvage the concept of a unitary trait by searching for a general factor common to the various tasks. Tasks that correlated poorly were either dismissed as irrelevant or relegated to the position of unimportant specifics. Only grudgingly were these specifics gradually readmitted in Great Britain as worthy of consideration. Because most tests included were verbal in nature, this general factor tended to be a verbal reasoning one.

In the United States there has always been somewhat more acceptance of the possibility that there might be several aspects to intelligence, especially due to Thorndike Senior, Truman Kelly, L. L. Thurstone, and J. P. Guilford, yet even in the United States this "multifactorial" view of intelligence has not influenced clinical and education practice to any great extent. For example, Lubin *et al.* (1971) surveyed the use of psychological tests in U.S. clinical psychology during 1969. The WAIS and WISC ranked first and seventh, the Progressive Matrices 22nd and the DAT 27th, the Stanford Binet ranked 8th.

In 1961 Sundberg had reported that the Stanford Binet ranked first, as it had in 1935 and 1946. Furthermore, no truly multifactorial test battery is mentioned by Lubin.

That the Binet test was and is used so often is, of course, partly because it was the first useful intelligence test available. It is, however, wrong to regard it as a good measure of "general" intelligence and to point to the commercial success and wide acceptance of the Binet test as sufficient evidence for the existence of general intelligence as a unitary trait. Perhaps the most clear evidence against this position was produced by Jones (1949) when he showed that the content of the Stanford-Binet test items was different for children aged 7, 9, 11 and 13.

Table I. Percentage of variance at four ages contributed by 8 factors in the Stanford-Binet

Content:	Ages			
	7	9	11	13
Verbal	21·1	15·0	25·2	19·4
Reasoning I	18·3	13·7	—	11·8
Reasoning II	—	—	—	6·4
Memory	9·4	9·6	11·5	8·3
Visualization	—	—	—	7·8
Spatial	—	8·9	12·2	7·0
Residual	—	3·1	2·8	—
Number	8·8	—	—	—

Table II. Number of items at four ages measuring 8 kinds of factors

Content:	Ages			
	7	9	11	13
Verbal	11	15	14	13
Reasoning I	9	14	—	7
Reasoning II	—	—	—	4
Memory	7	7	9	6
Visualization	—	—	—	3
Spatial	—	10	11	4
Number	6	—	—	—

Table I summarizes the percentage of variance contributed by items belonging to 8 different factors for each of the four age groups, while Table II shows how many items dealt with content contributing to these 8 factors. It is clear that no general factor of a similar nature runs through the items of all ages.

Earlier McNemar had concluded that nearly all the significant variance in the Stanford Binet appeared to be lodged in the first centroid factor. This was due to the care with which Terman and Merrill selected items on the basis of internal consistency and age progression. McNemar (1942) himself stated that the results should not be taken to "lend support to a two* factor theory of intelligence! . . ." (p. 500). Jones' study makes it clear that the first centroid factor has a rather chameleon-like character and can hardly be considered a firm theoretical foundation on which to build. Jones (1949) also cited two earlier studies of the composition of the Binet based on analyses of item correlations. Wright (1939) found factors representing reasoning, number, spatial, verbal, induction and one unnamed one, while Burt and Jones (1942) found a general factor plus factors labelled verbal, numerical, spatial, memory, vocabulary, and comprehension, although Burt and Jones retained a general factor (of the same chameleon-like nature).

The various batteries proposed to measure what has been variously called "practical", "performance", "concrete", or "non-verbal" intelligence, such as the Pintner, Grace-Arthur, Cornell, Cox tests and many others, only aggravated the theoretical confusion because they were partly inspired by the ideal of measuring the same unitary intelligence by non-verbal measures, even though the names suggested that these tests measure something else. That tradition culminated in the Wechsler scales. Although the tests mentioned earlier (which derived from the formboard tradition of Seguin) started to break away from the CA–MA ratio by interposing a system of points which received different credits at different ages, it was Wechsler who combined successfully the tradition of group norms developed for the Army Alpha with the IQ tradition by assuming a normal distribution with a mean of 100 and a standard deviation of 16 at each age level. This was a very big step forward, but at the same time it helped perpetuate the notion of general intelligence. This occurred because the subtests were simply judged *a priori* by Wechsler as optimally suited for the measurement of intelligence in a wide variety of clinical situations. As a result the factorial composition of the Wechsler test(s) is not well defined in spite

* Spearman's theory is often called the two factor theory because he included specifics besides the general factor. Each test measures general ability plus its own specific factor.

of the studies by Cohen (1957a, b), Davis (1956) and Saunders (1959, 1960a, b).

The study by Davis goes farthest towards clarifying the nature of the Wechsler subtests. He used the Wechsler-Bellevue form I, an older version which is very similar in its items to the WAIS, and administered a number of group tests to 202 eighth graders for whom Wechsler records were also available. The results of his centroid factor analysis followed by rotation via the graphical method are shown in Table III.

Table III. Loadings of Wechsler and reference tests on the rotated factors (Davis, 1956)

Reference-Tests	A	B	C	D	E	F	G	H	J	K
Otis Beta	54		30						47	
Perceptual speed			30					52		
Numerical operations			74					31		
Arithmetic reasoning				32		44				
Mechanical principles		64		39						
Mechanical information				44						
Science information	57			32						
Recognition vocab. (synonyms)	75							31		
Recall vocab. (definitions)	80								37	
Information (group adaptation)	61									44
Comprehension (id.)	38						63			
Similarities (id.)					65	32		38		44
Wechsler subtests										
Information	42									56
Comprehension						33				
Digit span				34			37			
Arithmetic			36	34		57				32
Similarities	31				47					
Vocabulary	60									
Picture arrangement									49	
Picture completion		38								
Block design		44		41				39		31
Object assembly		34						42		
Digit symbol			52				30	37		

For every factor except *F*, *J* and *K*, some reference test had a higher loading than any Wechsler subtest, and no Wechsler subtest had a loading higher than 0·60. Table IV shows the proportion of variance in each Wechsler subtest accounted for by the 10 rotated factors.

Table IV. Proportion of variance in Wechsler subtest scores accounted for by 10 rotated factors (Davis, 1956)

Rotated factors	*WECHSLER SUBTESTS* Infor-mation	Compre-hension	Digit span	Arith-metic	Simi-larities	Vocab-ulary	pict. avg.	pict. comp.	block design	obj. asses.	digit symbol
A. Verbal comprehension	18	08			10	36					
B. Visualization		07			08	09	08	15	19	11	
C. Numerical Facility	06	05	08	13							27
D. Mechanical Knowledge	05		11	12					17		
E. Similarities doublet					22						
F. General reasoning		11		33		07					
G. Fluency		08	14			06		08			09
H. Perceptual speed									15	17	13
I. Education of conceptual relations							24	07	05		
K. Information	31			10	08			07	09		
Unaccounted variance (unique and error)	40	69	67	32	52	42	68	63	35	72	51

Davis concluded that all Wechsler subtests are of a complex nature. It is possible that a different selection of reference tests would have resulted in a somewhat different picture. In view of the current interest by behavior geneticists in spatial visualization, one could wish that more spatial tests had been included. Group adaptations of the Information, Comprehension and Similarities subtests of the WB form II obtained higher loadings than did the corresponding individually administered subtest. It would be interesting to know how much this is due to the psychological effect of test administration *per se*.

Cohen's studies have made it clear that the verbal subtests really measure quite different things than do the performance tests, while Saunders' studies have demonstrated the complex nature of the subtests in another way, namely by showing that the intercorrelations of the items within subtests are only moderately high.

One may ask why Wechsler did not limit his test to a few of the most reliable subtests or why, if he was interested in allowing for intra-individual variation, he did not select measures of uncorrelated abilities. Apparently all the work in the factor analysis tradition has had little influence on the clinical assessment of intelligence. This is understandable when we start looking for evidence regarding the pragmatic value of the multifactorial approach. Unfortunately, for many years most researchers in the factor analytic tradition were not looking for outside criteria such as differential diagnosis or prediction of success in job or school by the special abilities isolated.

A very legitimate question can be formulated somewhat as follows: Taking the Davis study as an example, what guarantee is there that the rotated factors reported there—as well as in other studies—represent any more real psychological processes than the subtest scores of the Wechsler or even general intelligence measures?

When one starts looking for evidence for or against the usefulness of multifactorial tests, it quickly becomes clear that there is no abundance of data. It is fair to say that until recently the question was rarely raised. Part of the available evidence comes from studies not especially designed to touch on this question. Admittedly it is no simple task to collect critically relevant data.

In 1968 I summarized some of the evidence, which I judged to be moderately in favor of the multifactorial theory of intelligence. In this paper new information concerning that view will be summarized. The same organization used in the 1968 paper will be followed here. We will look at further evidence relating to the following 7 criteria, leaving for a later date a final integrating of these two papers.

1. differential prediction of success in various curricula or jobs;
2. stability or comparability of factors over different age ranges;
3. cross-cultural generality of ability patterns;
4. existence of similar ability factors in retarded subjects;
5. differentiated effects of disease, brain damage or sensory deficits;
6. different rates of development.

   One more category or criterion will be added in this paper:

7. genetic factors.

In addition we will briefly look at the effects of experimental conditions on factor structure. There will also be a brief discussion of the relation between ability test scores and performance on learning tasks as well as between Piagetian experiments and ability tests.

I can, in a way, preface this part of the paper by recalling my amazement some years ago upon perusing old copies of the *Journal of Experimental Psychology* to find that frequently several pages were used to explain and justify the use of the correlation coefficient to demonstrate the existence of covariation between two variables. The period in which such a discussion was considered necessary (or at least not superfluous) did not last too long—perhaps five years. The usefulness of factor analysis or its modern equivalent has had to be defended for a much longer period. I put it to you that the relationship of a single correlation to a factor analysis is similar to the relationship between a single factor analytic study and a study of the congruence (comparability) of two or more factor analytic structures obtained in connection with one or another of the 7 kinds of critical tests of the empirical value and theoretical soundness of the multifactorial approach.

One further note is in order. Some otherwise useful studies will not be quoted because their results are less clear-cut for the above purpose because of inclusion of non-cognitive variables often dealing with environmental conditions which would tend to exaggerate any tendency favoring the emergence of a general factor: such variables as age, sex, race, socioeconomic status, parental practices, etc. While such a critical statement is easy to make, it is also easy to see why such variables tend to be included. The statistical method known as "Dwyer's extension", which allows one to relate variables excluded from the search for the major dimensions as part of the total test battery, has not been included in the more popular sets of "canned" factor analytic computer programs. For most investigators it is, therefore, a choice between throwing away data or including such variables in their multivariate analysis. The alternate approach of using multiple regression techniques to determine the relationship of a number of predictive (ability) measures to such "census" and environmental variables somehow has never been popular in psychology, in spite of efforts by Rulon and others. It is now necessary to elaborate on the 7 criteria.

1. Differential Prediction of Success in Various Curricula or Jobs

The optimal kind of evidence needed is simply not available. Schools or companies just do not administer a sizable battery of tests to students

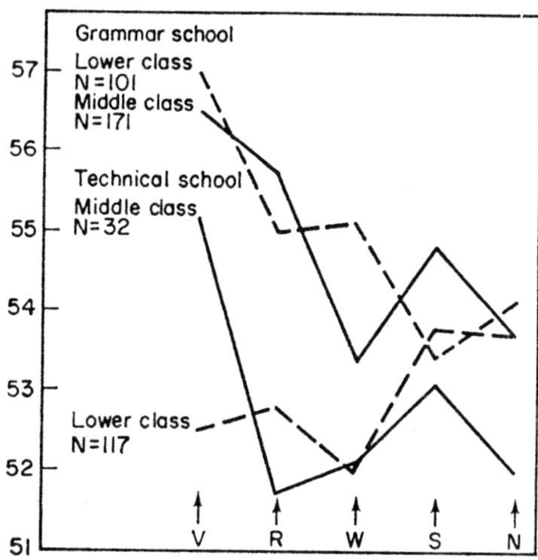

Fig. 1. Patterning of 5 Abilities in Lower and Middle class children in two types of English schools (Dockrell 1966).

in different types of classes or different types of jobs.* The U.S. Employment Service uses a battery of tests and they have some evidence for differential patterns associated with different jobs, but the battery is not as large as one would wish nor are the particular tests ideal for the purpose of validating factored abilities. Ghiselli (1966) has summarized thousands of studies on the use of tests in industry. Although he gives only broad conclusions, they do give some support to the multifactor position.

Dockrell (1966) administered Thurstone's PMA battery, plus 5 other tests to 12-year and 14-year olds, of middle and lower class attending grammar schools and technical schools. He assumed that the 12- and

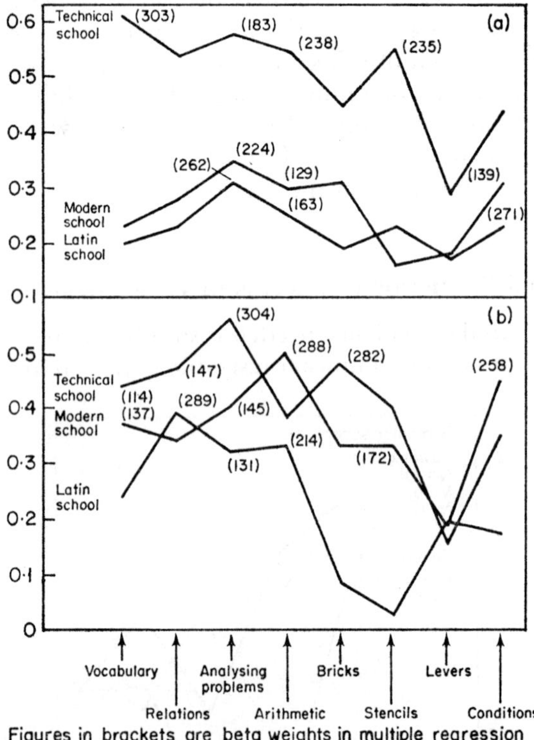

Fig. 2 a. Biserial correlations of completing school on 8 tests for boys attending 3 kinds of schools in Belgium (Coetsier 1966); b. Biserial correlations of completing school with scores on 8 tests for girls attending 3 kinds of school in Belgium (Coetsier 1966).

* The one exception is the large scale test development project of the Army Air Force's Psychology Program during the Second World War (Guilford, 1948), which successfully constructed test batteries predictive of performance on highly specialized jobs.

14-year-olds were comparable samples, representative of the students from the two social classes who attend the two types of schools. When this assumption is made, the conclusion seems warranted that the type of secondary school attended influences intellectual developments for children of lower class homes, but not for those of middle class homes. The mean scaled scores shown in Fig. 1 suggest that this conclusion holds particularly for the Verbal, Reasoning and Word fluency scores and not for the Spatial and Number scores.

Filella's study, published in 1960, does not allow strong conclusions because he only studied students attending different types of schools, so it cannot be said whether cause and effect is due to different ability patterns or different curricula. Nevertheless, it showed greater differences and different orderings for some abilities (such as verbal)

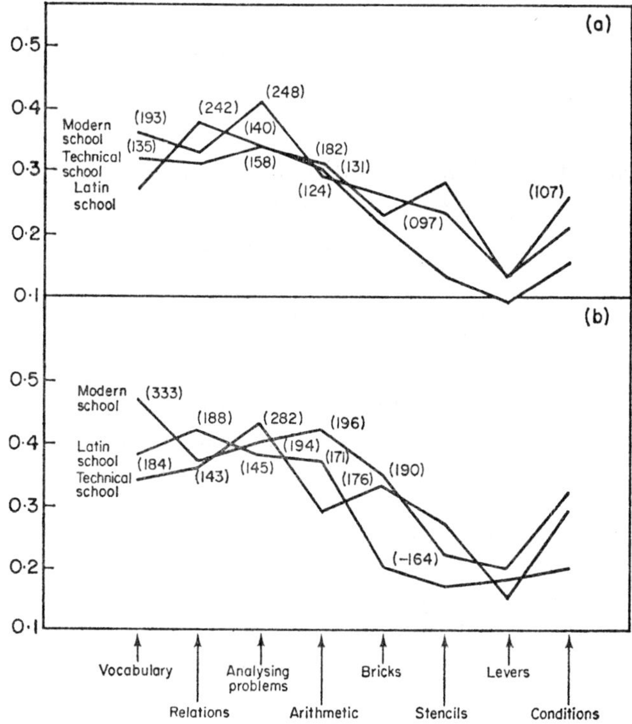

Figures in brackets are beta weights in multiple regression

Fig. 3 a. Correlations of rank in 12th grade with scores on 8 tests for boys attending 3 kinds of schools in Belgium (Coetsier 1966); b. Correlations of rank in 12th grade with scores on 8 tests for girls attending schools in Belgium (Coetsier 1966).

than for others (such as number ability). Success in a Belgian high school was measured by the criteria of pass–fail and grades in a study by Coetsier (1966). These criteria were correlated with the scores on 8 tests, separately for girls and boys, and separately for those attending three types of secondary schools: the Latin School in which there is an emphasis on classical humanistic subject matter, the modern school, in which there is an emphasis on science, mathematics and living foreign languages, and the technical school, where there is still an emphasis on science and mathematics but in a somewhat more applied context and where there is less time devoted to foreign languages. There is no need here to discuss the results in detail. The results are shown in Figs. 2 and 3. The main point to make in connection with this study is that different tests are the best predictor for success in each of the three schools. It is also of interest that the patterns are somewhat different for boys than for girls.

It seems fair to say that the evidence presented here, added to that in an earlier paper, does support the superiority of the multifactorial over the unitary conception of intelligence.

2. Stability or Comparability of Factor Patterns Over Different Age Ranges

We have no data on the persistence of intra-individual differences ("stability") of abilities because longitudinal studies have not employed multifactor tests. (However, data of this kind may be available on some persons on the Wechsler if records in various clinics, schools and institutions could be matched.)

In the Louisville Twin Study correlations were obtained by Vandenberg *et al.* (1968), between 5 parts of the Pacific Multifactor Test of Meyers *et al.* (1964) plus a number ability tests administered at 3 years of age and the Bayley Scale of Mental Development administered at 3 months, 6 months, 9 months, 12 months, 18 months and 2 years. The results are shown in Table V. Although these data do not shed light on the individual consistency of patterns, they suggest it may be worthwhile to start looking for such consistency. And there are indications that baby tests may be somewhat more successful in the prediction of later ability test scores than has generally been believed, provided that homogeneous subtests rather than global scores are used.

On the comparability across age levels there are some encouraging data. For example, Meyers *et al.* (1964) reported the factor loadings on 3 tests for each of 4 abilities for retarded and normal children of mental age 2, 4 and 6 years. Table VIa presents congruence indices between

Table V. Correlations between 6 abilities measured at age 3 with the Pacific Multifactor Test (PMT) and the score on the Bayley Scale of Mental Development administered at 6 different ages (and the number of cases on which each correlation is based, in parentheses)

PMT ABILITY at age 3 years	BAYLEY SCALE OF MENTAL DEVELOPMENT administered at 3 months		6 months		9 months		12 months		18 months		24 months	
Motor	08	(86)	17	(103)	22	(105)	25*	(113)	17	(100)	19	(95)
Perception	09	(64)	08	(76)	21	(80)	21	(84)	30*	(75)	43*	(72)
Language	—18	(79)	03	(96)	28*	(101)	19	(104)	43*	(93)	45*	(89)
Reasoning	01	(82)	24*	(100)	25	(102)	17	(108)	36*	(98)	43*	(94)
Memory	−24	(68)	21	(85)	30*	(86)	20	(90)	58*	(80)	37*	(77)
Number	—33	(31)	−02	(36)	33	(39)	34	(39)	57*	(35)	36	(37)

* $p > 0{\cdot}01$ Decimals omitted.

the three age levels for the normal children, and Table VIb for the retarded children.

Table VIa. Congruence between 4 factors found in 12 test scores of two, four and six year old children of normal intelligence (Myers *et al.*, 1964)

		4 Year olds M	P	L	R	6 Year olds M	P	L	R
2 Year olds	M. Hand-eye psychomotor	0·536	0·255	0·127	0·465	0·730	0·220	0·115	0·369
	P. Perceptual speed	0·154	0·901	0·055	0·067	0·069	0·909	0·004	0·129
	L. Language ability	0·052	0·072	0·843	0·292	0·104	0·009	0·719	0·217
	R. Figural reasoning	0·535	−0·009	0·176	0·748	0·447	0·022	0·193	0·606
4 Year olds	M. Hand-eye psychomotor					0·758	0·062	−0·051	0·370
	P. Perceptual speed					0·067	0·935	0·034	0·124
	L. Language ability					−0·109	0·053	0·772	0·257
	R. Figural reasoning					0·311	0·107	0·217	0·548

The four ability factors show fairly high congruence over the 3 age levels for both normal and retardates. The perceptual speed factor shows especially high congruence for the normal children. For the retarded the language factor shows the highest congruence. Although he did not do a factor analysis Khan (1970) administered 3 tests for

Table VIb. Congruence between 4 factors in 12 test scores of retarded children of mental ages two, four and six (Meyers *et al.*, 1964)

		Mental age 4				Mental age 6			
		M	*P*	*L*	*R*	*M*	*P*	*L*	*R*
Mental age 2	*M*	0·896	0·017	−0·184	0·519	0·844	0·335	−0·227	0·282
	P	0·008	0·931	−0·024	0·219	0·140	0·723	0·172	0·235
	L	−0·177	−0·023	0·932	0·317	−0·194	0·140	0·893	0·122
	R	0·490	0·256	0·335	0·612	0·256	0·391	0·134	0·662
			Mental age 4		*M*	0·848	0·415	−0·230	0·184
					P	0·126	0·797	0·170	0·250
					L	−0·177	0·158	0·887	0·118
					R	0·322	0·268	0·177	0·779

each of 4 abilities to children in grades 7, 9 and 11, with results which lend themselves to another test of the comparability hypothesis, and Orpet and Meyers (1966) identified 10 factors based on hypotheses derived from Guilford's structure of intellect theory. Although they are interested in extensions to four and two year old children, these data were limited to six-year olds.

Dye and Very (1968) compared 6 factor structures. They administered a battery of 20 tests to males and females at the 9th and 11th grade and college level. There were 77 males and 85 females with a mean age of fourteen years in the 9th grade group, 94 males and 99 females in the 11th grade group (mean age 16·2), and 87 males and 111 females in the college group (mean age 19·8). The tests they used were:

1. Number comparisons
2. Addition
3. Multiplication
4. Subtraction
5. Division
6. Perceptual speed
7. Arithmetic computation
8. Arithmetic reasoning
9. Matrices
10. Vocabulary
11. Nonsense syllogisms
12. Mathematics achievement
13. Induction
14. Judgment
15. Mathematical aptitude
16. Deductive reasoning
17. Mathematical puzzles
18. Inductive reasoning
19. Reasoning
20. Logical relationships

The six correlation matrices for each age and sex group were subjected to a principal components analysis and the resulting factors rotated by Varimax. They found some increase in the number of factors with age, supporting the differentiation hypothesis and a somewhat reduced number of factors in the females compared to the males, particularly at the two high school levels as shown in Table VII. The percentage of common variance accounted for by the different factors

Table VII. Factors* found at 3 age levels in males and females (Dye and Very, 1968)

	Males			Females		
	9th grade	11th grade	college	9th grade	11th grade	college
N	Numerical facility I 0·29	Numerical facility II 0·24	Numerical facility II 0·22	Numerical facility I 0·38	Numerical facility II 0·26	Numerical facility I 0·27
A	Arithmetic reasoning VI 0·14	Arithmetic reasoning V 0·14	Arithmetic reasoning I 0·20	Arithmetic reasoning III 0·22	Arithmetic reasoning VII 0·12	Arithmetic reasoning II 0·14
R	Reasoning II 0·17	Reasoning VI 0·10	Reasoning X 0·07	Reasoning IV 0·16	Reasoning VI 0·10	Reasoning VII 0·09
V	Verbal reasoning IV 0·11	Verbal reasoning VIII 0·09	Verbal reasoning VIII 0·07	Verbal reasoning II 0·24	Verbal ability I 0·19	Verbal ability V 0·10
P		Perceptual speed III 0·12	Perceptual speed IV 0·09		Perceptual speed III 0·12	Perceptual speed III 0·14
I		Inductive reasoning I 0·14	Inductive reasoning III 0·09		Inductive reasoning V 0·13	Inductive reasoning VII 0·11
E	Estimative ability V 0·11	Estimative ability VII 0·07	Estimative ability V 0·07			Estimative ability IV 0·08
D	Deductive reasoning VII 0·08		Deductive reasoning IX 0·06		Deductive reasoning IV 0·08	Deductive reasoning VI 0·07
S	Symbolic inductive III reasoning 0·10	Symbolic inductive IV reasoning 0·10	Symbolic inductive VI reasoning 0·07			
M			Mathematics achievement VII 0·06			

* The percentage of common variance accounted for by each factor is shown underneath.

at age levels for the two sexes are shown in Fig. 4. I have calculated congruence indices between the factors obtained at the 3 age levels, separately for the two sexes.

The formula used by me to calculate these indices is the one proposed by Tucker (1951):

$$\phi_{XY} = \frac{\Sigma x_i y_i}{\sqrt{\Sigma x_i \Sigma y_i}}$$

where *X* and *Y* are factors in the two matrices being compared and *x* and *y* are corresponding factor loadings in the two columns of the same factor in the two age groups.

Table VIIIa shows the congruence for males between the factors at the three age levels. To see whether values for the congruence between

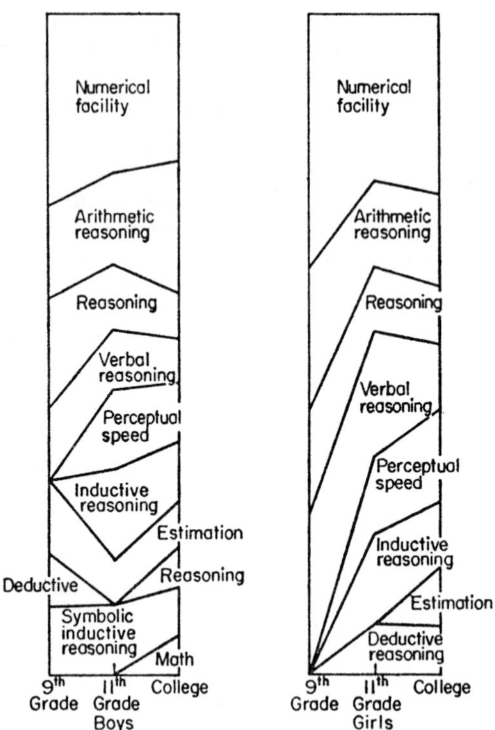

Fig. 4. Percentage of common variance accounted for by various factors at three ages for boys and girls (Dye and Very 1968).

the factors that are supposed to correspond to each other are indeed the highest, the columns and rows were rearranged so that the corresponding factors are in the same order for three age levels. Not too surprisingly, there is better agreement between the factors for the eleventh grade and college age subjects, than between ninth graders and eleventh graders or between ninth graders and the college students. In part this is due to the fact that different numbers of factors were rotated for each of these age groups. If an equal number of factors had been used, better agreement might have been found, but probably at the expense of ignoring statistically significant factors at the older ages or of including one or more factors without significance for the younger samples.

While the congruence indices between corresponding factors are not always high, in 16 out of 22 cases, they are the highest value in each column or row. The values for which this is the case have been set in bold type.

Table VIIIa. Congruence between ability factors at three age levels for males (Dye and Very, 1968)

			11th Grade boys							
			N	*A*	*R*	*V*	*E*	*SI*	*P*	*I*
			II	V	VI	VIII	VII	IV	III	I
9th Grade boys	*N*	I	**873**	453	125	245	179	303	636	424
	A	VI	512	**794**	329	367	120	546	131	562
	R	II	413	570	*491*	410	−608	678	381	627
	V	IV	244	411	323	**705**	242	103	302	652
	E	V	391	510	192	479	*557*	088	−015	332
	SI	III	340	507	303	410	−060	*610*	279	215
	D	VII	150	417	622	104	061	038	264	23

			College males									
			N	*A*	*R*	*V*	*E*	*SI*	*D*	*P*	*I*	*M*
			II	I	X	VIII	V	VI	IX	IV	III	VII
9th Grade boys	*N*	I	**896**	415	225	169	049	190	054	657	158	047
	A	VI	488	**775**	227	377	193	276	182	040	169	052
	R	II	346	718	*526*	287	022	369	237	369	547	−256
	V	IV	247	341	584	*636*	178	120	014	323	663	303
	E	V	185	538	205	395	**614**	064	159	−060	334	452
	SI	III	270	536	116	262	−037	**762**	121	292	161	400
	D	VII	140	359	048	−030	047	076	**782**	388	129	145

			College males									
			N	*A*	*R*	*V*	*E*	*SI*	*D*	*P*	*I*	*M*
			II	I	X	VIII	V	VI	IX	IV	III	VII
11th Grade boys	*N*	II	**958**	392	133	166	117	104	105	377	298	176
	A	V	366	**901**	366	337	207	230	277	227	301	301
	R	VI	149	373	*232*	148	042	225	768	095	483	007
	V	VIII	206	516	445	**925**	110	201	076	093	334	367
	E	VII	155	033	059	014	**793**	109	−007	065	225	050
	SI	IV	163	526	202	249	−049	**772**	103	047	152	−283
	P	III	484	262	090	−038	031	114	079	**940**	079	−011
	I	I	263	544	573	455	054	071	216	179	**647**	188

Table VIIIb shows the congruence indices for the females between the factors found at the same 3 age levels: ninth and eleventh grade and sophomore-junior college students. Similar comments could be made as for the male data. This time 11 out of 15 congruence indices for factors meant to correspond are the highest value in the row and column, indicating that the corresponding factors match each other better than they match any other factor.

Finally Table VIIIc shows the congruence indices between the factors found in the two sexes. Twelve of the nineteen indices for factors intended to match are the highest value for the column or row, suggesting that no other factor matched them better.

Table VIIIb. Congruence between ability factors at three age levels for females (Dye and Very, 1968)

			11th Grade girls						
			N	*A*	*R*	*V*	*P*	*I*	*D*
			II	VII	VI	I	III	V	IV
9th	*N*	I	**890**	188	237	309	552	324	114
Grade	*A*	III	434	*476*	616	604	−006	725	−137
girls	*R*	IV	274	632	*486*	276	242	562	373
	V	II	318	421	557	**836**	113	587	242

			College females							
			N	*A*	*R*	*V*	*P*	*I*	*D*	*E*
			I	II	VII	V	III	VIII	VI	IV
9th	*N*	I	**906**	178	134	125	526	104	210	119
Grade	*A*	III	401	**732**	374	408	196	529	−128	197
girls	*R*	IV	214	631	*282*	170	252	308	475	316
	V	II	162	521	185	*106*	224	247	130	355

			College females							
			N	*A*	*R*	*V*	*P*	*I*	*D*	*E*
			I	II	VII	V	III	VIII	VI	IV
	N	II	**959**	333	153	088	396	205	108	236
	A	VII	327	*695*	287	270	364	308	−015	700
11th	*R*	VI	220	520	**688**	269	116	381	051	265
Grade	*V*	I	259	567	561	*605*	274	636	107	379
girls	*P*	III	418	102	330	−031	**815**	004	199	161
	I	V	312	701	305	459	445	**677**	164	154
	D	IV	−054	−165	−030	−009	158	087	**642**	−033

It would be interesting to apply to these data one of the procedures for maximizing the agreement between factor structures such as that programmed by Cliff (1966) or Jensema (1972) to see whether the congruence between factors can be improved.

In a recent paper Very (1971) has outlined his continuing effort to develop a battery of tests which can be used over a wide age range. He has promised reports on factor analyses of data obtained on samples of fourth, fifth, sixth and seventh graders, with hints of support for the differentiation hypothesis. It will be interesting to study the congruence between these samples.

In a very elegant study of the comparability across ages (as well as across cultures), Flores and Evans (1972) administered the following battery of 18 tests to Canadian and Filipino students in grades 6 and 8: The tests used were: 1. Verbal meaning (PMA), 2. Vocabulary (ETS), 3. Word Endings (ETS), 4. Word Beginnings (ETS), 5. Spatial Relations (PMA), 6. Card Rotation (ETS), 7. Identical Pictures (ETS), 8. Maze Tracing (ETS), 9. Finding A's (ETS), 10. Number Facility

Table VIIIc. Congruence between males and females—ability factors at three age levels (Dye and Very, 1968)

			College females							
			N	*A*	*R*	*V*	*P*	*I*	*E*	*D*
			I	II	VII	V	III	VIII	IV	VI
	N	II	**973**	290	149	−003	473	113	198	−021
	A	I	288	**886**	603	490	281	471	286	033
	R	X	029	337	*192*	689	131	321	053	081
	V	VIII	108	252	411	*675*	003	472	517	−079
College	*P*	IV	494	115	248	024	**758**	005	026	296
males	;	III	134	277	438	173	305	*581*	241	−008
	E	V	085	221	257	−092	−072	046	**708**	088
	D	IX	−006	206	093	088	259	008	048	**789**
	S	VI	120	347	040	175	285	608	133	−042
	M	VII	125	321	322	087	−078	001	100	−010

			Eleventh grade females						
			N	*A*	*R*	*V*	*P*	*I*	*D*
			II	VII	VI	I	III	V	IV
	N	II	**951**	417	311	385	328	349	−045
	A	V	411	**654**	553	623	178	648	−182
11th	*R*	VI	215	303	**214**	549	135	450	474
Grade	*V*	VIII	216	438	388	**786**	149	389	−230
males	*P*	III	363	174	268	179	**910**	242	−035
	I	I	368	312	586	752	113	*475*	336
	E	VII	242	620	040	095	112	027	053
	SI	IV	221	302	463	365	077	807	229

			Ninth grade females			
			N	*A*	*R*	*V*
			I	III	IV	II
	N	I	**955**	452	319	330
	A	VI	409	**895**	508	435
9th	*R*	II	324	678	*369*	608
Grade	*V*	IV	306	293	160	**705**
males	*E*	V	059	293	425	545
	D	VII	259	080	601	245
	SI	III	304	518	452	490

(PMA), 11. Subtraction and multiplication (ETS), 12. Division (ETS), 13. Letter Series (PMA), 14. Word Grouping (PMA), 15. Number Series (PMA), 16. Progressive Matrices, 17. Picture Number Memory (ETS), 18. Object Number Memory (ETS).

Combining all 422 cases, they obtained iterative principal factors, followed by an oblique Promax rotation (Hendrickson and White, 1964). The resulting 6 correlated factors were further analysed to produce two uncorrelated second order factors. A higher-order Schmid-

Leiman transformation produced the final matrix with two general factors plus 6 columns representing the contributions of the original 6 factors after removal of the effect of the two general factors. The data for each of the four separate samples were then analysed by the principal component procedure using 8 factors rotated to maximal congruence (following Cliff, 1966) with the hierarchical solution based on all cases. The two higher order factors were named *R* (relational thinking), *A* (Associative learning). The variables loading on this factor are said to be subject to a high degree of automatization. *R* and *A* resemble Cattell and Horn's fluid and crystallized intelligence or Jensen's level II and level I abilities. The other, primary, 6 factors are *V* (verbal comprehension), *S* (spatial facility), *N* (numerical facility), *M* (memory), *O* (ordering), and finally a weak residual of the original perceptual speed factor. We will first look at their results with respect

Table IXa. Congruence indices Q between 8 factors for Canadian 6th graders and 8th graders (Flores and Evans, 1972)

		Canadian 8th graders							
		R	*A*	*V*	*S*	*N*	*M*	*O*	?
	R	*917*	635	396	569	053	284	344	204
	A	503	*841*	435	237	240	347	028	116
Canadian	*V*	479	328	*925*	071	131	275	−215	−038
6th	*S*	420	185	−181	*850*	009	−019	−075	103
Graders	*N*	−081	399	−064	−050	*506*	157	045	−325
	M	005	250	−081	−067	179	*581*	−042	012
	O	274	217	−283	−220	−106	−071	*855*	145
	?	340	159	195	407	−316	−204	−093	*371*

to the similarity between sixth and eighth graders in both cultures. Table IXa show congruence indices between the eight factors for the Canadian 6th graders and 8th graders and Table IXb show these results for the Filipino 6th and 8th graders. It can be seen that the indices are quite high for the two general or higher order factors *R* and *A* for both Canadians and Filipinos. They are still reasonably high for *V*, *S* and *O* in the Canadian data, and for *V* and *S* in the Filipino data. This also shows as expected that the first two factors show some congruence with part of the later factors. Looking only at the 6 later factors, the congruence indices are without exception the highest value in their column and row, in fact the off-diagonal elements tend to be quite small. There is clearly a good deal of comparability between the factor structures for the two age groups in both national groups.

Table IXb. Congruence between 8 factors for Filipino 6th graders and 8th graders (Flores and Evans, 1972)

		Filipino 8th graders							
		R	*A*	*V*	*S*	*N*	*M*	*O*	*?*
	R	*938*	634	471	467	419	055	200	105
	A	722	*910*	395	182	394	208	329	455
Filipino	*V*	368	365	*759*	=131	319	035	−204	−084
6th	*S*	541	388	−144	*669*	244	256	064	185
Graders	*N*	170	279	328	003	*496*	−247	−008	−138
	M	282	406	172	297	071	*540*	−226	191
	O	524	346	037	173	297	−209	*493*	124
	?	361	399	−191	198	−153	259	409	*512*

3. Cross-Cultural Generality of Ability Patterns

When individuals live in the same general culture and receive the same education, one might expect socioeconomic class and ethnic origin to produce only minor differences in ability patterns compared to studies of samples from different countries or even different continents. Nevertheless the data of Lesser *et al.* (1965) showed that such differences may in effect not be small at all, compared to differences between the groups in overall level.

In a study of Sitkei and Meyers (1969), the number of cases were too small to permit separate factor analyses which could be checked for comparability. However, they compared mean factor scores derived from a single factor analysis of middle and lower class Negroes and Whites and found only significant differences for cognitive semantics (usually called verbal comprehension). This study does show that ethnic and social status differences affect various abilities differently as shown in Fig. 5, a fact which gives further evidence in favor of multifactor tests in spite of the small number of tests.

The next study deals more directly with the generality of factors. McGraw and Joreskog (1971) administered 12 aptitude and achievement tests to 11743 subjects divided in four groups: high intelligence, high socioeconomic status (SES); high intelligence, low SES; low intelligence, high SES; and low intelligence, low SES. The same model of factor loadings was fitted to each of the four groups. Chi square tests indicated a satisfactory fit for the model. Mean factor scores for the four populations were obtained. The results are shown in Fig. 6. Again different abilities were found to be affected differently.

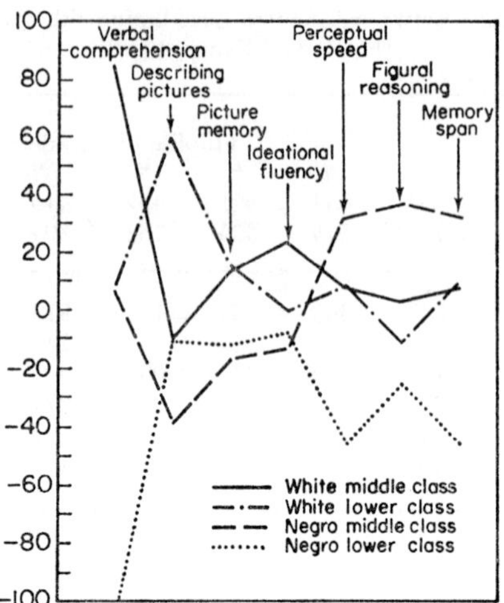

Fig. 5. Profiles of middle and lower class Negroes and Whites on seven abilities (Sitkei and Meyers 1969).

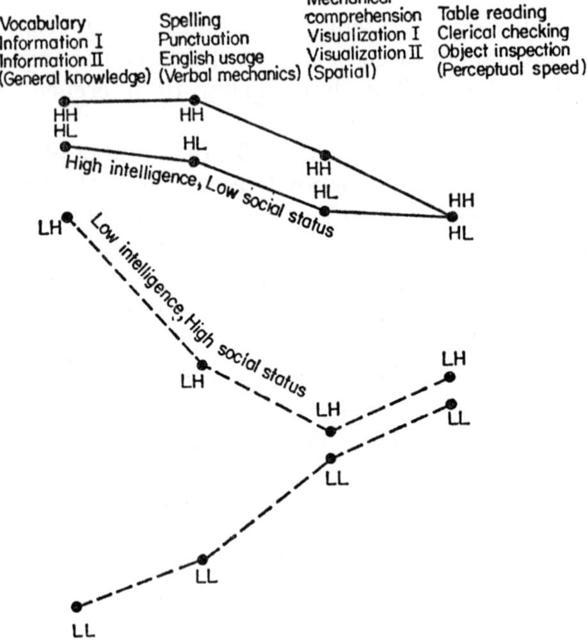

Fig. 6. Differential effect of social status on four ability factors (after McGraw and Joreskog 1971).

The study of Flores and Evans (1972), discussed earlier in connection with comparability across age groups, also provides evidence in favor of the comparability of factor patterns when the tests are administered in quite different cultures. Table Xa show the congruence indices I have computed between the Canadian and Filipino results for 6th graders and Table Xb for 8th graders. Without exceptions corresponding factors show the highest congruence index. A comparison between the congruence indices is shown in Table Xc. It is apparent that there is just about as much comparability between cultures as between ages within the cultures.

Table Xa. Congruence indices Ø between 8 factors for Canadian and Filipino sixth graders (Flores and Evans, 1972)

		Canadian 6th graders							
		R	*A*	*V*	*S*	*N*	*M*	*O*	*?*
	R	*951*	658	415	493	175	165	257	220
	A	664	*819*	261	166	360	250	370	163
Filipine 6th graders	*V*	453	316	*881*	−088	−002	−011	−291	030
	S	543	499	−068	*693*	119	019	070	413
	N	163	451	−046	127	*581*	134	141	−151
	M	364	221	042	196	232	*659*	027	−296
	O	404	336	−366	236	311	−045	*778*	068
	?	245	249	107	025	−262	−069	178	*418*

Table Xb. Congruence between 8 factors for Canadian and Filipino eighth graders (Flores and Evans, 1972)

		Canadian 8th graders							
		R	*A*	*V*	*S*	*N*	*M*	*O*	*?*
	R	*892*	652	378	532	033	181	364	261
	A	535	*933*	375	222	199	424	201	191
Filipine 6th graders	*V*	340	492	*690*	−103	323	187	024	−137
	S	424	137	−169	*838*	−052	046	−122	186
	N	159	474	299	118	*555*	075	−017	−387
	M	172	177	004	076	−186	*614*	−063	096
	O	297	192	−028	−152	−152	−075	*612*	255
	?	287	417	−068	173	−319	139	230	*595*

El-Abd (1970) reported the results of two factor analyses in Uganda. In both high school graduates and in university undergraduate students he found 7 hypothesized factors that are very similar to factors reported in European and American studies, while Nsereko-Gyagenda (1971)

Table Xc. Congruence indices for matching factors in the two age groups and the two cultures studied by Flores and Evans (1972)

	6th versus 8th graders		Canadian versus Filipino	
	Canadian	Filipino	6th grade	8th grade
R	917	938	951	892
A	841	910	819	933
V	925	759	881	690
S	850	669	693	838
N	506	496	581	555
M	581	540	659	614
O	855	493	778	612
?	371	512	418	595

found 11 factors based on Guilford's model in 33 tests administered to 11th and 12th grade boys and girls in Uganda.

Witkin (1967) has summarized the evidence for the view that there is a significant cross-cultural relationship between field dependence and child rearing practices. I see this as further support for the argument that measures of special abilities are more useful than global intelligence measures.

4. Existence of Similar Ability Factors in Retarded Subjects

When we discussed the comparability of factors over different age ranges, we mentioned the study of Meyers *et al.* (1964) on retarded and normal children of mental ages 2, 4 and 6 years. Let us now look at the comparability of the factors for the normal and the retarded children. Table XI shows the coefficients of congruence between the factors for the normal and the retarded at the three mental age levels. The factors which are supposed to match have indeed the highest congruence values, and most off-diagonal values are very small, except that *M*, the hand-eye psychomotor factor resembles *R*, the figural reasoning at the 2-year and somewhat less at the 4-year level. By the age of 6 there is no longer any resemblance.

One other study provides some direct support for the multifactorial position. Taylor (1964) administered the WAIS, the Bender-Gestalt, the Draw-a-Man, 3 achievement tests and a number of dexterity and mechanical assembly tests to 74 retarded adults working for Goodwill Industries. In addition, he obtained a number of ratings by supervisors. The intercorrelations among the 51 variables were subjected to prin-

Table XI. Congruence indices between ability factors for normal and retarded children of mental ages 2, 4 and 6 (Meyers *et al.*, 1964)

			Normal 2 year-old children			
			M	*P*	*L*	*R*
Retarded	*M.*	hand-eye psychomotor	0·701	0·075	0·000	0·582
children	*P.*	perceptual speed	0·076	0·929	0·034	0·061
mental	*L.*	language ability	0·072	−0·020	0·898	0·152
age 2	*R.*	figural reasoning	0·779	0·093	0·233	0·734
			Normal 4 year-old children			
			M	*P*	*L*	*R*
Retarded	*M.*	hand-eye psychomotor	0·720	0·151	−0·172	0·368
children	*P.*	perceptual speed	0·092	0·936	0·031	0·156
mental	*L.*	language ability	−0·184	0·042	0·961	0·228
age 4	*R.*	figural reasoning	0·577	0·110	0·296	0·729
			Normal 6 year-old children			
			M	*P*	*L*	*R*
Retarded	*M.*	hand-eye psychomotor	0·956	0·110	−0·047	−0·020
children	*P.*	perceptual speed	0·324	0·754	0·132	0·324
mental	*L.*	language ability	−0·075	0·182	0·882	0·039
age 6	*R.*	figural reasoning	0·010	0·187	0·061	0·824

cipal axis analysis followed by a Varimax rotation. Eleven factors were found, of which 8 were interpreted as: 1. General Dexterity, 2. Verbal-Numerical-Educational, 3. Social-Vocational Competence, 4. Gestalt Perception, 5. Distractability, 6. Mechanical Assembly, 7. Fine Discrimination, and 10. Filing. This study does not provide as much information about the structure of abilities as it might have because of the predominance of non-cognitive variables. The eleven WAIS scores were mainly split between Factors 1 (Digit Symbol, Picture Completion), Factor 2 (Information, Comprehension, Arithmetic, Similarities, Digit Span, Vocabulary, Digit Symbol) and Factor 4 (Picture Completion, Block Design, Picture Arrangement and Object Assembly). At least one can say that the usual three cognitive factors rather than one were found in WAIS, but a more crucial test of differentiated abilities in the adult retarded would have required administration of more cognitive tests of special abilities. A similar result was obtained in the study of Clausen (1966) who did not find separate cognitive abilities due to the fact that no measures of separate cognitive abilities were given.

The only additional evidence available on this topic since my 1968 paper is the following: while the Wechsler subtests may not have the "pure" character of tests developed in the factor analytic or psychometric tradition, they correlate low enough with one another to permit the demonstration of at least several factors. Witkin *et al.* (1966) have reported that mildly retarded boys performed poorer on the subtests loading on the verbal comprehension factor than on some of the performance tests. This is a well known finding that received new meaning in their hands because the authors also administered several perceptual tests of field dependence, such as the Rod and Frame and Embedded Figures Test. In earlier studies Goodenough and Karp (1961) and Karp (1963) had shown that some of the performance subtests of the WISC (Block Design, Picture Completion and Object Assembly) help define an analytical factor which resembles Cohen's "perceptual organization" factor, and is also closely related to the field dependence measures. This means the outcome of their study can be stated more provocatively. The mildly retarded boys did poorer on the verbal comprehension factor (Vocabulary, Information and Comprehension) than on the analytical factor. This distinction may be similar to the one made by Cattell (1963) and Horn and Cattell (1966) between crystalized and fluid intelligence. This seems a paradoxical finding: mildly retarded seem to do better on tasks that require less past learning. The authors attribute this partly to school policies related to routing children into different classes. This is especially interesting because the opposite pattern of Wechsler subtest scores is observed in Turner's syndrome, so this is clearly not just a special case of mild retardation. It may not be unreasonable to expect a special patterning of ability scores for each of a variety of genetic anomalies. While no strict comparability would be observed, such differential impairment would provide further support for the multifactor theory of intelligence.

5. Differentiated Effects of Disease, Brain Damage or Gross Sensory Defects on Ability Factors

We will first look at a study that could almost as well be discussed under the heading of effects of experimental conditions but, because the effect of drugs sometimes is called an artificial psychosis, we will consider it here. Lienert (1964) administered the 9 subtests of the Amthauer Intelligenz Struktur Test to 65 university students before and after LSD. The tests used were:

1. Sentence Completion SC
2. Which word does not belong WS
3. Association memory AM
4. Arithmetic reasoning AR
5. Number series NS

6. Analogies AN
7. Similarities SI
8. Figure completion FC
9. Cube comparisons CC

He also used Duker's modification of Pauli's concentration test which was not included in the factor analysis. He predicted and found fewer factors and larger correlations as most performances on the tests deteriorated. The average correlation rose from 0·30 to 0·42 under LSD. The verbal reasoning tests were influenced in the sense that persons changed their relative rank order. Some subjects reported using more imagery, i.e. the nature of the tests changed. Factors under normal conditions and under LSD are shown in Tables XIIa and b.

Table XIIa. Rotated factors under normal conditions (Lienert, 1964)

Test	A_0	B_0	C_0	D_0	E_0
SC	0·02	0·17	0·18	0·38	0·46
WS	0·14	0·03	0·22	0·02	0·48
AN	0·21	0·19	0·52	0·20	0·17
SI	0·07	0·03	0·51	0·05	0·17
AM	0·30	0·11	0·13	0·59	0·08
AR	0·76	0·33	0·31	0·29	0·05
NS	0·70	0·30	0·11	0·18	0·25
FC	0·19	0·69	0·16	0·31	0·17
CC	0·24	0·74	0·06	0·01	0·02
h^2	1·32 =28%	1·30 =27%	0·77 =16%	0·75 =16%	0·60 =13%

Table XIIb. Rotated factors under LSD (Lienert, 1964)

Test	A_1	B_1	C_1	D_1
SC	0·13	0·25	0·72	0·27
WS	0·27	0·09	0·63	−0·11
AN	0·34	0·21	0·75	0·31
SI	0·22	0·07	0·67	−0·11
AM	0·63	0·06	0·27	0·10
AR	0·64	0·40	0·42	0·16
NS	0·71	0·39	0·24	−0·16
FC	0·34	0·75	0·14	0·19
CC	0·09	0·76	0·14	−0·06
h^2	1·69 =29%	1·57 =27%	2·27 =39%	0·29 =5%

Lienert interpreted the factors as follows:

A_0 Reasoning
B_0 Spatial
C_0 Semantic relations
D_0 Associative memory
E_0 Semantic classification

A_1 Reasoning and attentiveness
B_1 Spatial
C_1 Verbal comprehension
D_1 Not interpretable

The limited number of tests does perhaps not permit clear resolution of the factor structure under either condition, but the results are highly suggestive of what can be done to study the influence on factored tests of drugs or other conditions that affect the brain. Because the raw data are all reported, alternate analyses such as canonical correlation or multiple regression could be attempted.

Juurmaa (1967) administered 23 tests to blind subjects and 22 tests to sighted individuals. Eighteen of these tests were the same for the two groups, so that congruence indices can be computed between the factors in the two studies. They are shown in Table XIII.

Table XIII

		Factors for the blind								
		I	II	III	IV	V	VI	VII	VIII	IX
	I	254	340	295	516	775	651	237	505	−297
	II	613	772	355	474	535	556	653	508	−141
Factors	III	054	119	618	138	484	393	032	212	081
for the	IV	619	502	387	764	207	371	463	298	376
Sighted	V	435	434	131	404	472	338	826	628	−077
	VI	666	552	569	465	153	400	374	286	−041
	VII	718	694	302	399	306	310	443	341	−048

There were 7 factors for the sighted which accounted for the following percentages of common factor variance:

I. Manual dexterity	15·05
II. Spatial ability	8·11
III. Spatial ability when blindfolded	15·73
IV. Memory	16·16
V. Seashore musical aptitudes	16·49
VI. Numerical ability	13·13
VII. Verbal comprehension	15·33

For the blind, there were 9 factors:

I.	Reasoning	9·68
II.	Verbal	11·67
III.	Spatial (plus some reasoning and dexterity)	15·60
IV.	Auditory memory	11·13
V.	Manual dexterity	13·67
VI.	Finger dexterity	8·72
VII.	Seashore musical aptitudes	18·84
VIII.	Tactual and loudness discrimination	8·27
IX.	Not interpreted	2·43

Probably the most interesting finding is that although the ability structure is quite different, it is as differentiated for the blind as for the sighted, and that the blind have spatial ability. In fact, the subjects who had been blind longer did better on these tests, probably because their haptic skills improved as the visual images faded. On the other hand, the blindfolded performance by the sighted group defined a factor independent of "visual" spatial ability. The congenitally blind were superior to the adventitiously blind, the partially blind, and the sighted group in mental arithmetic. Juurmaa emphasizes that scarcely any mental retardation is found in the blind.

In an earlier study published in 1963, Juurmaa compared the factor structure of deaf and normal ("hearing") subjects, based on a battery of 18 tests administered to both groups. The subjects were somewhat younger than in the study of the blind. Five factors were found for the deaf which accounted for the following percentage of common variance:

I.	Verbal ability	36·9
II.	Visual (spatial) and numerical ability	17·4
III.	A combined perceptual and memory factor	24·3
IV.	Perceptual speed	10·9
V.	Perceptual accuracy	10·5

For the hearing group 6 factors were found with the following percentages:

I.	Numerical ability	13·2
II.	Recognition of pictorial and verbal symbols	18·6
III.	Speed and accuracy of perception	17·3
IV.	Speed of ideation	14·9
V.	Carefulness in verbal tests	19·1
VI.	Visual (spatial) ability	16·8

The congruence indices between the two sets of factors are shown in

Table XIV. Clearly the factors are quite different for the deaf than for the hearing. In discussing the results Juurmaa stressed the fact that no

Table XIV. Congruence between factors found for deaf and hearing subjects

		Factors for the hearing subjects					
		V	II	VI	III	IV	I
	I	0·8335	0·4115	0·2475	0·3133	−0·0681	0·5264
Factors	II	0·3111	0·7054	0·5414	0·1382	−0·5890	0·3590
for the	III	0·3911	0·5743	0·7321	0·6644	−0·0744	0·1615
Deaf	IV	0·6113	0·2621	0·6776	0·7093	−0·0508	0·3161
	V	0·2665	0·0286	0·1398	0·1087	0·7740	0·1332

separate numerical ability factor was found for the deaf. Instead, numerical tests loaded on the verbal factor. In general the factors are less differentiated for the deaf than for the hearing.

Juurmaa made a comparison between the apparent handicaps of the deaf and the blind near the end of his 1967 monograph. He concluded that the deaf are more seriously affected than the blind due to a relative verbal retardation. In fact, he makes an interesting distinction between a "technical" handicap for the blind compared to a more basic, "semantic" handicap for the deaf. Thus, the poor reading ability of deaf children is a consequence of their retarded language development (Furth, 1966). See Bolton, (1971), for a review of factor analytic studies of the deaf.

Further support for the existence of separate factors comes from studies of brain damage. While it has been known since Broca that verbal ability is dependent on the left hemisphere, more recently it has been suggested that the hemisphere dominant for speech need not always be the left one (Goodlass and Quadfasel, 1954). The idea has also been advanced that the right hemisphere—and perhaps the left one in lefthanded persons—is predominant in spatial visualization as measured by copying drawings (Paterson and Zangwill, 1944), cube analysis, object assembly and drawing of a loop (McFie *et al.*, 1950), the Wechsler-Bellevue Scale (Reitan 1955), Gottschaldt figures, drawings and locating well known cities and states on a U.S. map (Battersby *et al.*, 1956), copying drawings and tachistoscopic presentation to the right or left half visual field (Gazzaniga *et al.*, 1965), matching of 3-dimensional objects with their unfolded shapes (Levy-Agresti and Sperry, 1968), Raven Progressive Matrices (Costa *et al.*, 1969), WAIS (Vega and Parsons, 1969). Scores on closure tests are also impaired by right temporal removals for the relief of epilepsy (Lansdell, 1968, 1970). Left temporal removals lead to poorer right ear perception of digits (Kimura, 1961; Oxbury and Oxbury, 1969). Left hemispheric dominance for speech has also been demonstrated by evoked potentials (Morrell and Salamy, 1971; Wood *et al.*, 1971). The development of such lateralization of function has been studied by Kimura (1964, 1967) and Knox and Kimura (1970). She found earlier lateralization (establishment of dominance) in girls than in boys. Buffery and Gray (1971) have reviewed the differences in structure and function between the two hemispheres in the context of possible sex differences. See also White (1969) for laterality differences in perception. The confounding effects of handedness due to the fact that perception of speech and visualization may have reversed lateral dominance in some lefthanded subjects has been studied by Ettlinger *et al.* (1956) and Gloning *et al.* (1969). Butler and Norrsell (1968) have suggested that vocalization may possibly be initiated by the minor (non-dominant) hemisphere. As more and more specialized tests are being introduced we can expect further clarification of the roles played by various parts of the human brain. Some of these functions may be found to resemble factors found in "factor analytic research".

6. Different Rates of Development for Different Abilities

Although the work on age changes in factor structure is somewhat relevant, the absence of a certain factor may not mean that this ability is completely absent but, rather, that it forms part of a less differentiated one. Furthermore, there are practically no longitudinal data on the development of separate abilities in individuals. What little we know is due to cross sectional studies. In addition to the information summarized in the 1968 paper I have found the following studies:

Glanzer *et al.* (1958) studied the decline with age in performance on 14 tests of 544 Air National Guard and commercial airline pilots aged 21–50 years (mean age 31·8). Of the 14 tests only two did not show a negative correlation with age but only 3 showed significance at the 0·001 level, another 2 at the 0·01 level and another 5 at a level of probability between 0·01 and 0·10. Although they reported the intercorrelations between the tests the varying number of cases precluded the possibility of carrying out a factor analysis. The tests that did not show a decline in this age range were: Mathematical Reasoning, Numerical Approximation, Reading Comprehension and Reoriented reading-words. The authors suggest that previously reported, more pronounced declines may have been due to the use of tests "not relevant to the life activities of the population tested".

Bilash and Zubek (1960) reported age differences (studied cross-sectionally) in 13 subtests of the King Factored Aptitude Test. They concluded that comprehension, verbal fluency, numerical and spatial

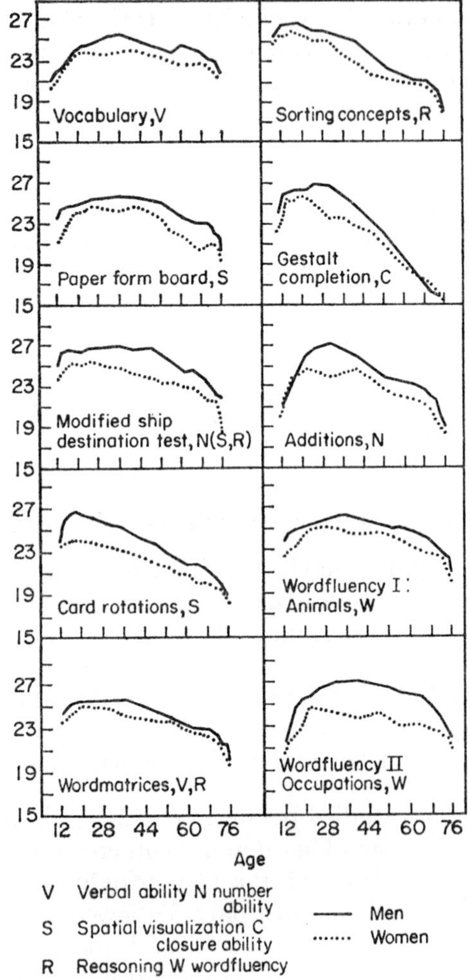

Fig. 7. Age changes for 10 test scores (Verhage, 1964).

abilities held up very well to the mid-forties while reasoning, memory perception and dexterity declined gradually from the teens to the seventies. These conclusions are based on a sample of 634 persons of a large variety of socioeconomic backgrounds. Only the group 50 to 60 and 60 years and older had a lower average education which would tend to make the decline in those age ranges seem worse.

Similar results were reported by Verhage (1964), who analysed the effects of age, sex, educational and occupational levels and urban versus rural residence on the ten subtests of a Dutch intelligence scale (GIT). His findings, based on the standardization material for this test, are shown in Fig. 7. It can readily be seen that different abilities reach their

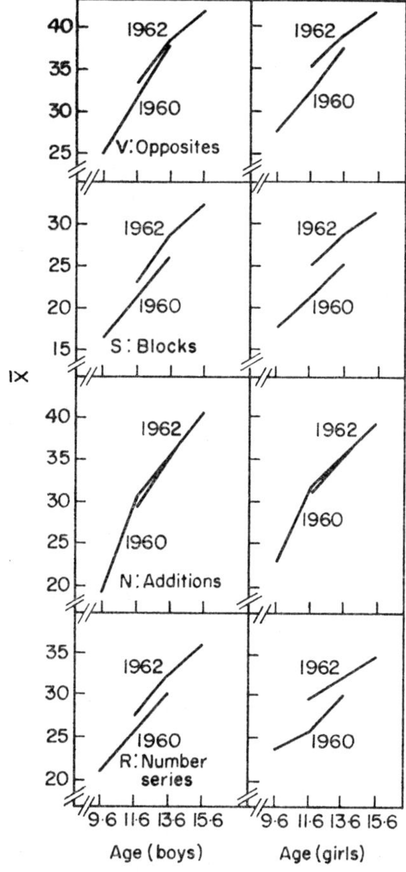

Fig. 8. Age changes in test ability (Berglund).

maximum at different times, and deteriorate at different rates. Table XV lists the tests in order of the age at which the maximum is reached by males. There are marked differences between the rates at which these abilities decline: Concept sorting and Gestalt completion immediately start dropping off markedly, after the maximum, while vocabulary and the two fluency tests show a relatively level pattern with only a gradual decline.

Table XV. The age of maximum performance by men and women on the 10 subtests of the Groningen Intelligence Test (after Verhage, 1964)

Test	Age, in years, at maximum score Men	Women
Concept sorting, *R*	20	16
Card rotations, *S*	20	20
Gestalt completion, *C*	26	18
Additions, *N*	32	42
Wordmatrices, *V.R*	36	21
Ship destinations *N*(*S*,*R*)	36	26
Wordfluency: animals *W*	36	28
Vocabulary, *V*	36	42
Paper formboard, *S*	38	26
Wordfluency—occupations, *W*	40	22

Berglund (1967) studied sex differences in mental growth in four abilities: Verbal, Spatial, Number and Reasoning. The subjects were $9\frac{1}{2}$, $11\frac{1}{2}$ and $13\frac{1}{2}$ years old at the time of the first examination. Two years later 871 of these children were retested. He obtained the results shown in Fig. 8.

7. Separate Hereditary Bases of Different Abilities?

The last criterion for the biological reality of separate abilities is provided by hereditary mechanisms. While most earlier studies on the role of heredity were concerned only with demonstrating that heredity played an important role in contributing to individual differences in general intelligence, newer studies have looked for, and found differential effects for different abilities.

The best known of these, described by Money (1968), involves Turner's syndrome. In this genetic anomaly one sex chromosome is missing so that the individual has only one X. Such XO individuals have lowered performance scores on the Wechsler, but normal verbal scores. Stafford (1961) and Hartlage (1970) have reported a pattern of correlations on spatial tests between father and son, father and daughter, mother and son, mother and daughter which suggest spatial visualization is X-linked. However Schaffer (1969) did not find such a pattern in a study of eleven year old boys and girls and their parents. The tests used by her were the Space Relations Subtest of the Primary Mental Abilities battery for grades 4 to 6 and Witkin's Embedded Figures Test. However the parents were not given a spatial test. The correlations obtained are shown in Table XVI.

Reports of multivariate analyses by Vandenberg (1965a, b), Bock and Vandenberg (1968), Loehlin and Vandenberg (1968), Roudabush (1968), Kolakowski *et al.* (1968), Bramble *et al.* (1970), show that the excess within pair variance of fraternal compared to identical twins, which is due to heredity differences within fraternal twin pairs, is not solely due to a general hereditary superiority of one twin over the other. Rather, one fraternal twin will excel on one test but the other twin on a different one. A Finnish study (Partanen *et al.*, 1966) of adult twins reported the same hereditary independence of several abilities.

Table XVI. Correlations between parents' EFT scores and children's EFT and Space Relations Scores (Schaffer, 1969)

	Mothers' EFT	Fathers' EFT
Boys EFT	0·22	0·39
N=40 Space Relations	−0·32	−0·46
Girls EFT	0·42	0·28
N=40 Space Relations	−0·19	−0·28

There has been much discussion about the nature or origin of ability factors. Some light is thrown on this subject by the effect of experimental conditions on a factor structure. Are factors rather firm configurations largely due to biological causes? The preceding evidence seems to suggest that this is the case. To be perfectly fair it is necessary to see to what extent factors can be modified by specific conditions.

Effect of Experimental Conditions on Factor Structure

Hürsch (1970) studied the effect of 3 noncognitive environmental variables on factor structure in a 12 variable test battery by administering these tests to 252 ninth graders with variations in the following conditions: 1. The experimenter was stern or friendly; 2. there was payment for each correct item or no payment; 3. he administered none, easy or difficult extra examples. Thus he had $2 \times 2 \times 3 = 12$ conditions. Subjects were assigned, by a latin square design, a different combination of conditions for the 12 tests. Each subject took each of the 12 tests under one of the 12 conditions, and there were different tests by condition combinations for each subject. In this way he studied simultaneously the factor structure over all conditions as well as the effect of each of the treatments. The effects that reached statistical significance are shown in Table XVII. There were also some interaction effects.

Table XVII. Statistical significance of three environmental conditions on 12 tests (Hürsch, 1970)

		Meili type factors	Thurstone factor	Attitude of: Exper.	Payment	Examples
LR	Syllogisms	Complexity	Reasoning			01
ZR	Number series	Compl., N	Reasoning			
AN	Analogies	Compl., N	Reasoning	005		
DO	Dominos	Plasticity I	Reasoning			
GO	Gottschaldt figures	Plast. I	Closure, Space		005	
LM	Anagrams	Plast. II	Wordfluency			
SG	Street Gestalt completion	Globalization	Closure			
VW	Mutilated words	Globalization	Closure	01		
CZ	Cattell drawings	Fluency	Wordfluency			
CW	Things round	Fluency	Wordfluency			
SR	Number operations	N	Number			05
ZB	Identical number or highest number	Plast. II	Number, Perc. Speed			005

Werdelin and Stjernberg (1971) were able to change the factor structure of some perceptual tests by varying the difficulty and complexity of the figures. They used 17 reference tests plus 10 "experimental" tests: Cubes I, II and III, Squares I, II and III plus two versions of "Same Figure" and "Gottschaldt Figures". They found that the more difficult these spatial visualization tests were, the higher its loadings on the spatial (S) and reasoning (R) factors, but the easier, the higher the loadings on the Number (N) and Perceptual Speed (P) factor, as can be seen from Table 18 in which the difficulty of the test is indicated by the mean number of items attempted per minute.

In this connection it is interesting to note the effort of Gerber and Meili (1971) to determine the importance of three factors thought to influence the difficulty of individual items in an Embedded Figures Test.

Shepherd and Metzler (1971) found a higher significant linear relation between the amount of rotation by which the orientation of two figures differed and the time it took subjects to decide whether they were the same or mirror images. This is one of the few mental ability type tasks in which difficulty of each item compared to every other one can

Table XVIII. Relation between difficulty (items per minute) and factor measured by the test. (Werdelin and Stjernberg, 1971)

		Factor			
Items/Min.	Test	*R*	*S*	*N*	*P*
3·01	Cubes I	40	05	−02	35
1·46	Cubes II	41	28	17	−03
1·97	Cubes III	30	26	−02	01
11·03	Squares I	−10	52	03	25
1·46	Squares II	06	62	−02	00
1·20	Squares III	08	56	01	04
12·76	Same Figure I	−09	19	−07	52
2·58	Same Figure II	−14	28	12	23
4·08	Gottschaldt I	09	40	13	17
1·27	Gottschaldt II	−03	58	21	03
—	Arrows	02	40	09	09

be defined in physical terms. Figure 9 shows two of the stimuli in different orientations.

When I was preparing this paper I planned to include a review of attempts to correlate performance on Piagetian tasks with more or less conventional ability tests. By the time all the reading, recalculating and thinking had been done, it became clear that Piagetian tasks would have to wait for another paper, and perhaps even another author. However, let me just mention a few studies. Tuddenham (1970) has

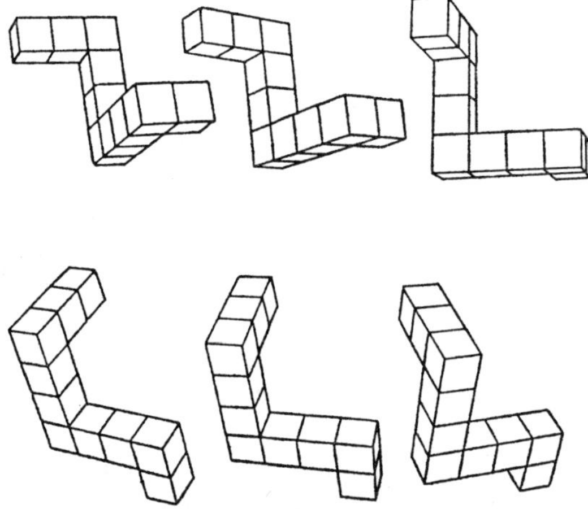

Fig. 9. Stimuli used in "mental rotation" study (Shepherd and Metzler, 1971).

Table XIX. Intercorrelations of Piaget-derived test items for 200 children in grades 1–3. (Tuddenham, 1970)

	1 Clay	2 Water Pouring	3 Sheep and Fields	4 Islands	5 Perspective	6 Tracks	7 Seriation	8 Transitivity	9 Geom. Forms	10 Water Level
1. Clay	—	65	36	23	30	01	35	22	13	19
2. Water pouring	65	—	41	27	24	09	37	31	12	20
3. Sheep and fields	36	41	—	15	17	08	25	07	17	20
4. Islands	23	27	15	—	15	13	22	13	12	21
5. Perspectives	30	24	17	15	—	07	30	26	11	29
6. Tracks	01	09	08	13	07	—	13	14	03	24
7. Seriation	35	37	25	22	30	13	—	28	12	27
8. Transitivity	22	31	07	13	26	14	28	—	06	24
9. Geometric forms	13	12	17	12	11	03	12	06	—	09
10. Water level	19	20	20	21	29	24	27	24	09	—

given the first report of his efforts to develop a psychometric assessment of a child's mental development based on Piaget's experiments. The intercorrelations between 10 tasks are shown in Table XIX. As the author remarks, these demonstrate that there is indeed considerable décalage, i.e. lack of uniform achievement across tasks but nevertheless there is a general tendency reflected in the fact that all correlations are positive and some are fairly high. The new British Intelligence Scale (Warburton 1970) attempts to incorporate at least some formal attributes of Piaget's scheme to its internal organization as can be seen from Table XX which shows the planned distribution of subtests.

Longeot (1969) administered 6 measures developed on the basis of Piaget's theories, plus 3 ability tests and 2 achievement tests, to 150 high school students aged 17. He obtained the intercorrelations, and next, using a method proposed by Nguygen-Xuan which is similar to Dwyer's extension, he determined the relationship of the Piagetian tasks to the three ability dimensions, Number, Verbal and Spatial. The correlations and three centroid factors they obtained are shown in Table XXI. This matrix was not rotated to simple structure, but the Piagetian "tests" were found to have substantial loadings on a combined spatial and numerical factor. In another sample of subjects some of the Piagetian tasks were not used and the factor structure shown in Table XXII was reported.

These findings of high loadings on a general factor and/or some overlap with the spatial and number factor are somewhat in contrast to the preliminary report of Meyers and Orpet (1971) who administered 7 Piagetian tasks as well as 26 ability tests to 70 middle class children of about $5\frac{1}{2}$ years of age. They found no tendency for the Piaget tasks to cluster on a general factor whether conceived as a Piagetian develop-

Table XX. Content of the British Intelligence Scale classified by ability and development level (Warburton, 1970)

	Stage	Reasoning	Number	Verbal	Fluency (Creativity)	Memory	Spatial
2. (i)	Preoperational (conceptual)	Simple classification Tactile testing Pattern completion	Counting Matching tasks	Picture vocabulary	Naming objects (fluency) Creative play with blocks	Recognition of toys Imitation (digit span) Object memory	Imitation Matching shapes
2. (ii)	Preoperational (intuitive)	Simple matrices Inclusion classes Inductive problems	Conservation Various	Verbal classification Differences Similarities General knowledge	Controlled word association Pattern meaning Unusual uses Consequences	Recognition of designs Recall designs Object memory Sentence memory Sense of passage	Block designs Matching involving reversals Copying tasks
3.	Concrete operational	Sorting (several attributes) Logical multiplication (matrices) Inference problems Induction (several variables)	Shapes	Definitions Social reasoning Similarities	Number of synonyms Meanings	As above	Block designs Visualization of cubes Reversal and rotation of shapes
4.	Formal operational	Matrices (sets and operators) Hypothesis testing (induction) Inference problems Propositional logic	Number bases Practical calculations	Abstract definitions Proverbs	As above	As above	Block designs (three dimensional) Cube development

Table XXI. Centroid factors and intercorrelations for 6 Piagetian tasks and 5 ability tests. (Longeot, 1969)

	I	II	III	Communality	*AN*	*P+P*	*B+B*	*LP*	Bal.	*N*	*V*	*S*	Arith.	French
1. Test of formal combinatory operations	0·61	0·39	−0·17	0·55	0·58	0·39	0·30	0·15	0·24	0·52	0·20	0·34	0·20	0·42
2. Anagrams	0·65	−0·45	−0·24	0·67		0·35	0·16	0·48	0·06	0·37	0·20	0·19	0·40	0·39
3. Test of formal operation of proportions and probabilities	0·68	0·23	0·16	0·54			0·32	0·28	0·21	0·21	0·43	0·37	0·35	0·50
4. Boxes and Gaskets	0·33	0·11	0·17	0·15				0·11	0·07	0·27	0·20	0·22	0·12	0·23
5. Test of formal operations of the logic of propositions	0·53	−0·07	0·13	0·30					0·24	0·24	0·30	0·21	0·33	0·30
6. Balances	0·33	0·12	0·23	0·18						0·25	0·24	0·09	0·36	0·14
7. Number test	0·51	−0·30	0·21	0·39							0·15	0·27	0·17	0·20
8. Verbal test	0·53	0·27	−0·27	0·43								0·17	0·44	0·54
9. Spatial test	0·45	0·08	0·36	0·34									0·20	0·19
10. Achievement in arithmetic	0·61	0·28	−0·22	0·50										0·58
11. Achievement in French	0·71	0·24	−0·37	0·70										

Table XXII. Hierarchical solution for 3 Piaget tasks and 5 ability tests (Longeot, 1969)

	G	Combinatory factor	INRC factor	Verbal and achievement
Combinatory operations	0·34	0·70	0	0·24
Logical propositions	0·54	−0·03	0·19	0·17
Proportions and Probab.	0·62	0·07	0·18	0·29
Number	0·38	0·53	0·08	0
Verbal	0·26	0·14	−0·01	0·58
Spatial	0·59	0·00	0·23	0
Arithmetic achievement	0·35	−0·06	0·04	0·63
French achievement	0·36	0·15	0	0·74

mental stage or as a "*g*" factor. Rather, each of the tasks had their highest loadings on a different factor as shown in Table XXIII. They named the 6 factors 1. Reasoning (*R*), 2. Auditory Span (*M*), 3. Mental manipulation or transformation (*T*), 4. Figural reasoning with 3-dimensional materials (*S*), 5. Unnamed, but Gestalt completion and ITPA analogies as well as several Piagetian tasks loaded on this (?), 6. Also unnamed; WISC Block Design and Digits forward as well as P_1 characterized this factor.

One can perhaps conclude from these two studies that Piagetian tasks can be meaningfully related to the results from the factor analytic literature and will thus provide a more theoretical and less dry as dust empirical basis for the multifactor theory of intelligence.

The other promised topic that will have to be merely touched on is the growing literature on the correlations between performance on learning tasks and ability scores. So long as intelligence was measured as a global trait by instruments of varying but predominantly verbal content, it was not surprising that the conclusion was made and taught in most textbooks that there is no correlation between intelligence and learning rate. It now looks as if what was thought to be a basic truth is wrong after all. Here are a few findings to support this statement:

1. Gagné and Paradise (1961) reported the correlations shown in Table XXIV. Except with the vocabulary test most correlations are above 0·50.
2. Merrifield *et al.* (1962) related some tasks traditionally used in learning studies to the structure of intellect model and obtained many significant correlations, so that these tasks appear to fit into Guilford's model.

Table XXIII. Varimax Factors, Five-Year Age Group (Meyers and Orpet, 1971)

Variable	Varimax Factors I	II	III	IV	V	VI
1. P1 Geometric Figures	47	09	20	50	26	33
2. P2 Discontinuous Quantities	−01	08	07	−02	66	03
3. P3 One for one Exchange	20	−17	61	02	−12	09
4. P4 One for one Correspondence	00	24	29	−01	33	23
5. P5 Intuition of Order	16	03	40	05	32	03
6. P6 Conservation of Length	22	39	03	09	−15	03
7. P7 Comparison of Length	10	17	07	−06	10	40
8. Gestalt Completion	58	−23	09	04	38	02
9. PMA Spatial	45	17	44	10	17	25
10. Jones Figure Completion	68	07	17	−05	27	09
11. Hooper Visual Organization	67	04	01	−08	−23	16
12. WPPSI Vocabulary	39	16	43	−29	04	20
13. WPPSI Arithmetic	13	19	48	−00	13	27
14. WISC Digits Forward	−08	62	20	−19	02	32
15. WISC Digits Backward	15	26	76	−04	10	02
16. WISC Picture Arrangement	61	09	15	17	06	16
17. WISC Block Design	25	22	14	21	−01	61
18. WPPSI Block Design	53	13	24	46	01	21
19. Hidden Figures	43	03	32	07	−01	−01
20. Hidden Pictures	63	25	31	12	07	−27
21. Nebraska Picture Analogies	34	13	42	−05	10	05
22. Nebraska Picture Association	46	04	29	09	31	31
23. Action Agent Divergent	10	07	03	−55	07	−08
24. ITPA Visual Closure	58	02	10	−02	−02	01
25. Knox Cubes, Visual Memory	26	−02	03	52	13	−29
26. Raven A	29	33	50	14	12	03
27. Raven Ab	41	29	22	10	08	11
28. Raven B	24	37	40	14	20	25
29. WPPSI Sentences	20	76	11	−18	26	18
30. ITPA Analogies	43	17	26	10	46	21
31. ITPA Auditory Seq. Memory	07	71	19	02	14	10
32. Aud. Seq. Memory, Backward	13	34	63	11	40	−05
33. ITPA Visual Association	48	22	05	03	01	09

3. Stevenson *et al.* (1968) obtained, on seventh graders, the correlations shown in Table XXV between learning tasks, Piagetian tasks and conventional "tests".
4. Jones (1968) related concept learning to structure-of-intellect abilities at different stages of learning and found many significant correlations.
5. Frederiksen (1969) not only obtained sizable correlations between ability measures and learning task parameters but was able to

demonstrate the effect of different learning strategies in an important study that cannot be summarized in a few sentences.

6. Traub (1970) found that performance on programmed learning tasks was relatively independent of 23 individual ability tests but did load on a factor called "following directions" which also relates to speed.

Table XXIV. Correlations between 6 ability tests and 3 measures of learning performance (Gagné and Paradise, 1961)

Measure	(N=118) 1	2	3	4	5	6	7	8	9
1. Addition, Subtraction-Multiplication		41	33	04	38	68	66	58	55
2. Picture-Number			39	14	34	62	58	56	54
3. Following Directions				12	34	58	54	53	52
4. Vocabulary V-1					05	22	14	12	18
5. Letter A						51	45	46	50
6. Performance test							84	82	78
7. Transfer test								78	75
8. Number of learning sets achieved									82
9. Time to complete program (sign reversed)									

In conclusion, it seems obvious that the vanishingly small use in most research of global intelligence measures should finally convince everyone but the most stubborn proponents of the unitary concept of intelligence that there are a number of separate abilities. Whether an hierarchical view, which allows for one or more "general" or higher order factors, or the view of many independent factors will prove most useful is still to be determined. Compromise may be the best strategy in politics, but in science one likes unambiguous solutions. In either case the number of (relatively) independent factors that really matter, in terms of their contribution to differential prediction, is also still to be established. I have hoped to show in this paper that substantial progress is being made towards answering this question.

Elsewhere, I have expressed some thought on the practical problems *of the availability and the obtaining of the kind of data needed for future research on human behavioral variables for use in differential psychology, behavior genetics, learning theory, and social psychology*. Some sciences, such as ornithology, have benefited considerably from the contributions made by amateur bird watchers. A number of "naturalist" journals all over the world make useful additions to traditional biology. Agriculture has perhaps been most successful in utilizing laymen (farmers) for scientific observations. Another device is exemplified by the section in the *American Scientist* through which large numbers of readers are invited to

Table XXV. Significant correlations among learning and problem solving tasks. (Stevenson, 1968)

Task	2	3	4	5	6	7	8	9	10	11	12
						Boys					
1. Paired associates (abstract words)	0·60*	+	0·30*	+	+	0·31*	0·55*	0·49*	0·54*	0·38*	0·53
2. Paired associates (abstract forms)		+	0·56*	0·38*		0·39*	0·47*	0·42*	0·47*	0·37*	0·46
3. Discrimination learning I			+	+			0·27*		+	0·21	
4. Discrimination learning II				0·25			0·37*	0·38*	0·36*	0·39*	0·40
5. Discrimination learning III					0·25			0·29*	+		+
6. Probability learning							0·51*	0·28*	0·22		0·37
7. Incidental learning								0·43*	0·47*	0·36*	0·56
8. Verbal memory											
9. Concept of probability-faces									0·50*	0·38*	0·45
10. Concept of probability-pegs										0·39*	0·43
11. Conservation											0·46
12. Anagrams											
						Girls					
1. Paired associates (abstract words)	0·64*	0·30*	0·56*			0·30*	0·57*	0·34*	0·20	0·56*	0·54
2. Paired associates (abstract forms)			0·51*		+	0·32*	0·69*	0·35*	0·25*	0·36*	0·64
3. Discrimination learning I			0·27*				0·23			0·26*	0·33
4. Discrimination learning II						0·33*	0·49*	+		0·57*	0·43
5. Discrimination learning III					0·25*		+			+	
6. Probability learning						+					
7. Incidental learning							0·46*		+	0·30*	0·31
8. Verbal memory								0·31*	0·35*	0·55*	0·62
9. Concept of probability-faces									0·33*	0·27*	0·30
10. Concept of probability-pegs										0·28*	0·30
11. Conservation											0·49
12. Anagrams											

build scientific instruments at home to observe scientific phenomena, and in another section they are invited to solve mathematical puzzles.

Can psychology use similar methods to obtain the larger bodies of data that may be needed to study its many unsolved problems? Such practices, though inviting, may raise a number of problems: the spectre of amateurism, ethical problems, huge organizational tasks for clerical and data processing work, etc. Nevertheless, no insurmountable obstacle appears to stand in the way of the use of the growing leisure time of Americans, which is now being frittered away on TV, do-it-yourself projects, collecting matchbooks, and so on. If even a small part of this energy could be channeled into auxiliary scientific work, a healthy correction could be achieved to the current dependence on college students, clinic and hospital cases, and other semi-captive populations. It may also be possible for some purposes to use firemen, policemen, and other personnel who are at times on rather inactive desk duty. It may also be possible to obtain subjects through various social clubs, senior citizens groups, and the Mensa organization.

Above all, the question should be asked: "Why do psychologists not use the rather large membership of their own organization more often for psychological studies?" Especially when data are to be collected on more than one generation of related individuals, such methods may have considerable merit, in spite of possible biasing factors, for which corrections can probably be devised. Finally a plea ought to be made again for the establishment of more archival arrangements for those bodies of data that may be useful to future investigators. It may prove necessary to charge users of such an organization a large fee, but perhaps these costs might be covered by subscriptions raised on a newsletter containing a descriptive summary of data stored. Many other arrangements of this kind may be envisioned. In any case, it seems time for behavioral scientists to start thinking about possibilities for enlisting more volunteers of different types. These alternatives to paid subjects merit serious consideration.

Summary and Conclusion

After a brief critique of the concept of a unitary ability, "general" intelligence, the following seven kinds of experimental evidence are reviewed which support the existence of independent abilities: 1. differential prediction of success in different curricula or jobs; 2. comparability of factors over different age ranges; 3. cross-cultural similarity of ability factors; 4. existence of similar ability factors in retarded subjects; 5. differentiated effects of disease, brain damage, or sensory deficits; 6. different rates of development; 7. multiple genetic factors.

There is less evidence of the first type than one might wish. The reason has been indicated. The comparability over different age ranges is quite good, especially when one allows for some increase in factors ("differentiation") during childhood and early adolescence. The cross-cultural similarity of ability factors is truly impressive. Perhaps it is time that emphasis is placed on the similarities rather than the differences between individuals from different cultures. Undoubtedly this high congruence is in part due to similarities in education, but at least it is clear that there are no serious obstacles in the way of an education preparing for careers in modern society. The evidence on the fourth topic suggests there are at least three or four more or less equally important abilities in the moderately retarded. In the more seriously retarded it becomes more difficult to distinguish different abilities, because there is a general inability to understand instructions. Evidence of the fifth type, differentiated effects of physical or mental disease, brain damage, or sensory deficits, is gradually becoming clearer and does suggest that different abilities have a life of their own and perhaps even a "local habitation" of their own, though surely not a small limited area or brain center, which would be the seat of only that ability or function. Rather, it may be that certain rather diffuse areas and tracts are generally essential for the development of a particular ability. There is a relative scarcity of information about the rates of development of different abilities, due to the difficulty of obtaining longitudinal data.

In recent years behavioral genetics studies have produced impressive evidence for the existence of a number of at least partly independent hereditary components in mental abilities. Next, in order to dispel any idea that I am advocating a return to the notion of predetermined faculties, the gradual individual emergence of which occurs with a minimal amount of stimulation, a few studies are reviewed on the effect of experimental conditions on factor structure.

The paper continues with some suggestions that performance on learning tasks can be fitted into the multifactorial view of intelligence and that substantial correlations are observed if the tasks studied are in the same domain as the ability tests. Finally, some studies are cited which suggest that performance on Piagetian tasks can also be fitted into a multifactorial theory of intelligence.

ACKNOWLEDGMENT

I am indebted to Dr. Gray for valuable suggestions and criticisms of the first draft of this paper. He pointed out to me that I tried to have things both ways, i.e. comparability of factor structures and interpretable differences between them. I have tried to clarify this point somewhat, but have probably not been entirely successful. I hope that I have not removed the ground from under Dr. Gray's discussion of my paper. At least I have resisted the temptation to steal his suggestion that biological sex differences may provide another strategy in the search for independent abilities.

COMMENT ON VANDENBERG'S PAPER

JEFFREY A. GRAY

Dr. Vandenberg has previously treated the same problem in 1968, and his presentation at this conference is a continuation of that treatment. Vandenberg's 1968 paper had as its Discussant Dr. David

Rosenthal, and I can do no better than take up the discussion at the point where Rosenthal left off. Rosenthal (1968, p. 70) summarized his discussion in six points corresponding to the six headings used by Vandenberg both in 1968 and in his present paper (cf. summary of evidence), though the latter has now added a seventh heading (genetic factors). I shall follow suit and deal with each heading in turn (Rosenthal's 1968 conclusion is given in each case between quotation marks).

1. "The abilities predict success in jobs and curricula about as well as I.Q., but not noticeably better." This conclusion still holds.

2. "Many studies support the belief that an increase in the number of independent abilities occurs up to adolescence, although many studies do not." This conclusion, too, can still stand. There is, however, something more interesting to notice about it than this. It will be evident from Rosenthal's conclusion that, in 1968, Vandenberg was more interested in the differentiation of abilities as a function of developmental maturity. In his paper at this conference, in contrast, he is more interested in the stability of factor patterns across ages; and his review shows that there is indeed some evidence for such stability. Is he not, then, trying to have his cake and eat it, too? If increasing differentiation of factor patterns was evidence for the usefulness and validity of the multifactorial approach in 1968 and stability of factor patterns is evidence for this very same thing now, what kind of evidence could refute Vandenberg's position? This is a point to which I shall return.

3. "The same factors are found in a variety of national groups, but the possibility that specific subject matters may be differentiated and segmented in the course of learning cannot be ruled out as an explanation of this finding." This time, the position is reversed, as will be evident from Rosenthal's conclusion; Vandenberg in 1968 emphasized the congruence between cross-cultural studies, whereas now he is emphasizing the differential effects of ethnic, cultural, and social status differences. One's suspicion that this is a "heads I win, tails you lose" game grows.

4. "Evidence suggests that the factors are comparable at different levels of ability, but are differently weighted." As Vandenberg (p. 171) states, very little further evidence has turned up relating to this point.

5. "We do not know if the separate abilities are affected differently by psychoses or neuroses, but the spatial and verbal factors may be associated with specific areas of the brain." Here, as Vandenberg noted in his 1968 paper (p. 17), lies one of the best hopes of obtaining objective evidence for the reality of the separate abilities, since evidence of an association between, say, lesions to specific areas of the brain and specific

abilities would show that the latter are "not only behaviourally distinct, but even physiologically separate". Here is a point at which, in my capacity as Discussant, I can pass from the role of critic to that of supporter, and I shall try to do this below.

6. "We do not know if the separate abilities develop simultaneously or at different times and rates." Vandenberg has now somewhat added to the evidence which would allow us to affirm that there are different rates of development and decline for different abilities.

7. Vandenberg's seventh heading—separate hereditary bases for different abilities—is his new one, so I cannot at this point rest on Rosenthal's broad shoulders. I shall also takc up this point below, again principally in a supportive rather than a critical role, with special reference to the genetic control of sex differences in cognitive skills.

First, however, we must examine more closely Dr. Vandenberg's strategy of finding support in evidence both of multi-factorial congruence and of multifactorial differentiation. He could simply be arguing (a) that congruence between factor structures, whether at different ages, or in the two sexes, or in different cultures, is evidence for the reality of the separate abilities, and (b) that differential changes as between these conditions in the level manifested by the particular abilities is equally evidence for the same conclusion; and this, I think, would be perfectly legitimate. I am however, left in some doubt as to whether he may not also be treating change in factor structure (e.g. Vandenberg this volume, p. 181) where he deals with the effects on factors of experimental conditions) as evidence for, again, the same conclusion. Really, it is difficult to see how congruence between factor structures and change in factor structures can both be evidence for the same theory.

Is it, in fact, a *theory* that Vandenberg is putting to us? He appears mainly to be concerned with the *usefulness* of the multi-factorial description of abilities. If that is so, we must ask "useful for what?" And there is nothing illogical about replying "useful for the description both of stability (congruence between factor structures) and of change (whether in level or in structure of factors)". This attitude implies nothing about the theoretical superiority of the multi-factorial description of abilities over the general factor approach (or the converse). For, if we confine ourselves to questions of usefulness, there is no incompatibility between the multifactorial and the general factorial approach. There would only be a conflict between these two approaches if it were not the case that all specific ability factors are positively intercorrelated; and it is agreed by nearly all investigators that they are. Theoretical arguments only become of importance when we consider (a) the causes of the separate abilities, and (b) assuming that we conclude that these do have separate causal backgrounds and are more than statistical conveniences—the causes of their positive intercorrelations.

In approaching these causal problems, the evidence from neuropsychology, and also the evidence from sex differences, has major importance.

Rosenthal noted in 1968 that "the spatial and verbal factors may be associated with specific areas of the brain". As Vandenberg points out, the evidence that this is so (visual–spatial ability normally being associated with the right hemisphere and verbal ability with the left) has continued to mount up since 1968 (Buffery and Gray, in press). It is now very convincing. There is also evidence for the differential lateralization of a number of other specific cognitive functions (Hécaen, 1969; Buffery and Gray, in press). Lansdell's factor-analytic work on patients with a variety of neurological disorders (Lansdell, 1971) makes it reasonable to suppose that the spatial factor (Vernon's 1950 *k*:*m* group factor) is related to right hemisphere functioning and the verbal factor (Vernon's 1950 *v*:*ed* group factor) to left hemisphere functioning. Thus, there would appear to be a solid neurological basis for the highest level division of the general intelligence factor into two major group factors. (Though it is to be noted that the level of the Primary Mental Abilities at which Vandenberg is operating is still less general than this.)

The biological reality of the group factors of spatial and verbal ability, respectively, is also strongly suggested by the known sex differences in them. Sex differences alone are insufficient to back up such a conclusion, since they may reflect nothing more fundamental than the patterns of schooling to which boys and girls are exposed (cf. Rosenthal's similar point concerning cross-cultural comparisons, point 3 above). However, coupled with evidence that they are under at least partial genetic control, sex differences can give rather solid backing to the hypothesis that the separate abilities reflect separate causal processes. Buffery and Gray (in press; see also Gray and Buffery, 1971) have summarized the evidence that females are superior to males in verbal ability and males to females in spatial ability. These authors have also reviewed the rather strong evidence (from studies of family correlations suggestive of sex-linked inheritance; studies of individuals with Turner's Syndrome, or the XO chromosomal constitution; studies of human infants; and studies of rats and chimpanzees) that the sex difference in spatial ability is partly under the control of genes carried on the X chromosome. Buffery and Gray (in press) have also suggested that this sex difference, and the sex difference in verbal ability, are due to a differential degree of lateralization of function in the two sexes.

If, however, there are biologically separate abilities, dependent on separate neurological structures and separately inherited (Vandenberg, 1968), we are left with the problem of why they intercorrelate positively to give rise to the general intelligence factor. Lansdell (1971) has shown that this is independent of any particular hemisphere, and suggests that it may reflect some overall parameter of cortical functioning. Given the high heritability of *g* (Jensen, 1969), the positive intercorrelations between the spatial and verbal factors are unlikely to be due to common environmental influences alone, though these may play some part. So, at the physiological level as at the statistical, it is unlikely to be a question of either multi-factorial or general intelligence, but rather both.

COMMENT ON VANDENBERG'S PAPER

J. P. GUILFORD

Vandenberg's paper gives the impression of attempting to ride several horses at the same time, some less successfully than others, in spite of the scholarly assemblage of evidence. For one thing, he bemoans the inertia of those who cling to the univariate view of intelligence and the lagging acceptance of the lead of multivariate psychologists who propose components of intelligence. His marshalling of numerous studies that have been made in various kinds of populations may contribute to new convictions of the need for multiple variables of intellectual functioning, but the clear lack of invariance of factorial variables reported by different investigators may well turn off those who would otherwise be convinced. The situation even appears to border on chaos, as only a few factor names, such as "verbal comprehension" and "perceptual speed" are often replicated. Vandenberg's paper highlights this unfortunate situation, while trying to establish other points.

Until there is much better agreement among factor analysts themselves as to what variables to believe in, one cannot expect the general investigator to place a high degree of credence in them. The trouble stems from the different choices of combinations of experimental variables to be analysed and from the many alternative computational routes taken by those who analyse. Factor analysis is a sensitive, searching tool, but it has serious weaknesses that are not sufficiently recognized by those who use it. The weaknesses are not to be overcome by inventing still other algorithms but by giving much more thought to psychological theory.

COMMENT ON VANDENBERG'S PAPER

K. PAWLIK

Professor Vandenberg has undertaken what I believe to be one of the most fruitful tasks in multivariate research at the present state of the game: to study the stability and transformations of factor structure across different variable sampling, subject sampling, and testing conditions. I am in full agreement with him on the weight he assigns to this study in the pursuit of an overall evaluation of a multi-factor model of intelligence. Thus, my comment here will be restricted to two rather specific points. One concerns Dr. Vandenberg's interpretation of the positive primary factor intercorrelations: Why could at least part of this covariance not be due to common environmental (rather than pure genetic) factors? My second point is more of a methodological nature: Comparing two contrasted groups in terms of separate factor analyses of the same set of tests is a legitimate (and valuable) *post hoc* technique. It suffers from the methodological shortcoming, however, that differences between the groups in factor means and variances are thrown out because of separate re-standardization of tests in each group. For this reason the factorization of one representative subject sample, with subsequent analyses of sub-group differences in the factor score matrix, might be preferable as a technique.

REFERENCES

Bilaski, I. and Zubek, J. P. (1960). The effects of age on factorially pure mental abilities. *J. Geront.* **15,** 175–182.

Bock, R. D. and Vandenberg, S. G. (1968). Components of heritable variation in test scores. *In* "Progress in Human Behavior Genetics." (Vandenberg, S. G. ed.) The Johns Hopkins Press, Baltimore, Maryland.

Bolton, B. (1971). A factor analytic study of communication skills and nonverbal abilities of deaf rehabilitation clients. *Multivar. Behavl. Res.* **6,** 485–502.

Bramble, W. J., Bock, R. D. and Vandenberg, S. G. (1970). Components of heritable variation in the Primary Mental Abilities Test (PMA). Research Report from the Institute for Behavioral Genetics, University of Colorado, Boulder, Colorado.

Brain, W. R. (1941). Visual object-agnosia with special reference to the Gestalt theory. *Brain* **64,** 43–62.

Brain, W. R. (1941). Visual disorientation, with special reference to lesions of the right cerebral hemisphere. *Brain* **64,** 244–272.

Brinkerman, E. H. (1966). Programmed instruction as a means of improving spatial visualization. *J. Appl. Psychol.* **50,** 179–184.

Buffery, A. W. H. and Gray, J. A. (1972). Sex differences in the development of spatial and linguistic skills. *In* "Gender Differences, their Ontogeny and Significance." (Ounsted, C. and Taylor, D. C. eds) Churchill, London.

Burt, C. and Jones, E. M. (1942). A factorial analysis of Terman–Binet tests. *Br. J. Educ. Psychol.* **12,** 117–127, 156–161.

Butler, S. and Norsell, U. (1968). Vocalisation possibly initiated by the minor hemisphere. *Nature,* (*Lond.*) **220,** 793–794.

Cattell, R. B. (1963). Theory of fluid and crystallized intelligence: A critical experiment. *J. Educ. Psychol.* **54,** 1–22.

Clausen, J. (1966). "Ability Structure and Subgroups in Mental Retardation." Spartan Books, Washington, D.C.

Cliff, N. (1966). Orthogonal rotation to congruence. *Psychometrika* **31,** 33–42.

Coetsier, L., Ossola, Y., Coetsier, P., Lagae, C., Symoens, M., Willequet, R. and Thurman, M. (1966). "Analyse van en Predictiemogelijkheden met een Differentiele Geschiktheids Batterij." (Analysis of and Prediction Possibilities with a Differential Ability Test Battery). Mededelingen van het laboratorium voor toegepaste Psychologie, Rijksuniversiteit te Gent, Belgium.

Cohen, J. (1957a). The factorial structure of the WAIS between early adulthood and old age. *J. consult. Psychol.* **21,** 283–390.

Cohen, J. (1957b). A factor-analytically based rationale for the Wechsler Bellevue Adult Intelligence Scale. *J. consult. Psychol.* **21,** 451–457.

Costa, L. D., Vaughan, H. G., Horwitz, M. and Ritter, W. (1969). Patterns of behavioral deficit associated with visual spatial neglect. *Cortex* **5,** 242–263.

Davis, P. C. (1956). A factor analysis of the Wechsler Bellevue Scale. *Educ. psychol. Measur.* **16,** 127–146.

Dockrell, W. B. (1966). Secondary education, social class and the development of abilities. *Br. J. educ. Psychol.* **36,** 7–14.

Dye, N. W. and Very, P. S. (1968). Growth changes in factorial structure by age and sex. *Genet. Psychol. Monogr.* **78,** 55–88.

El-Abd, H. A. (1970). The intellect of East African students. *Multivar. Behavl. Res.* **5,** 423–434.

Ettlinger, G., Jackson, C. V. and Zangwill, O. L. (1956). Cerebral dominance in sinistrals. *Brain* **79,** 569–588.

Filella, J. F. (1960). Educational and sex differences in the organization of abilities. *Genet. Psychol. Monogr.* **61,** 115–163.

Flores, Miguela B. and Evans, G. T. (1972). Some differences in cognitive abilities between Canadian and Filipino students. *Multivar. Behavl. Res.* **7.**

Frederiksen, C. H. (1969). Abilities, transfer and information retrieval in verbal learning. *Multivar. Behavl. Res. Monogr.* **69–2,** 82 pp.

Furth, H. G. (1966). A comparison of reading test norms of deaf and hearing children. *Am. Ann. Deaf.* **111,** 461–462.

Gagné, R. M. and Paradise, N. E. (1961). Abilities and learning sets in knowledge acquisition. *Psychol. Monogr.* **75** (14 – Serial No. 518).

Gazzaniga, M. S., Bogen, J. E. and Sperry, R. W. (1965). Observations on visual perception after disconnection of the cerebral hemispheres in man. *Brain* **88,** 221–236.

Gerber, A. and Meili, R. (1971). Figurale Merkmale, die Schwierigkeit des Herauslosens eingebetteter Figuren bestimmen (Figural attributes which determine the difficulty of analyzing embedded figures). *Schweiz. Z. Psychol.* **30,** 40–45.

Ghiselli, E. E. (1966). "The Validity of Occupational Aptitude Tests." Wiley, New York.

Glanzer, M., Glaser, R. and Richlin, M. (1958). Development of a test battery for study of age-related changes in intellectual and perceptual abilities. Research Report 56–138. School of Aviation Medicine. Randolph AFB.

Gloning, I., Gloning, K., Haub, G. and Quatember, R. (1969). Comparison of verbal behavior in righthanded and non-righthanded patients with anatomically verified lesion of one hemisphere. *Cortex* **5,** 43–52.

Goodenough, D. R. and Karp, S. A. (1961). Field dependence and intellectual functioning. *J. abnorm. soc. Psychol.* **63,** 241–246.

Goodglass, H. and Quadfasel, F. A. (1954). Language laterality in lefthanded asphasics. *Brain* **77,** 521–538.

Gray, J. A. and Buffery, A. W. H. (1971). Sex differences in emotional and cognitive behavior in mammals including man: Adaptive and neural bases. *Acta Psychol.* **35,** 89–111.

Guilford, J. P. (1958). Factor analysis in a test development program. *Psychol. Rev.* **55,** 79–94.

Hartlage, L. C. (1970). Sex linked inheritance of spatial ability. *Percept. Mot. Skills* **31,** 610.

Hécaen, H. (1969). Aphasic, apraxic and agnosic syndromes in right and left hemisphere lesions. *In* "Handbook of Clinical Neurology." (Vinken, P. J. and Bruyn, G. W. eds), Vol. 4: "Disorders of Speech, Perception and Symbolic Behaviour," pp. 291–311. North-Holland, Amsterdam.

Hendrickson, A. E. and White, P. O. (1964). Promax: A quick method for rotation to oblique simple structure. *Br. J. stat. Psychol.* **17,** 65–70.

Horn, J. L. and Cattell, R. B. (1956). Refinement and test of the theory of fluid and crystallized general intelligences. *J. ed. Psychol.* **57,** 253–270.

Hürsch, L. (1970). "Der Einflusz verschiedener Versuchssituationen auf die Faktorenstruktur von Intelligenz Leistungen." (The influence of different experimental situations on the factor structure of intelligence test performance.) Huber, Bern.

Jensema, C. (1972). A review of a rotation to obtain maximum similarity and simple structure among factor patterns. *Behavl. Sci.* **17,** 235–240.

Jensen, A. R. (1969). How much can we boost I.Q. and scholastic achievement? *Harv. educ. Rev.* **39,** 1–123.

Jones, Dorothy L. (1968). Relationships between concept learning and selected ability test variables for an adult population. Technical Report No. 51. Wisconsin Research and Development Center for Cognitive Learning, University of Wisconsin.

Jones, L. V. (1949). A factor analysis of the Stanford–Binet at four age levels. *Psychometrika* **14,** 299–330.

Juurmaa, J. (1963). On the ability structure of the deaf. Jväskylän studies in Education, Psychology and Social Research No. 4. Julkaisuvarasto, Jyvaskyla, Finland.

Juurmaa, J. (1967). "Ability Structure and Loss of Vision." Research Series No. 18. American Foundation for the Blind, 15 West 16th Street, New York, New York 10011.

Karp, S. A. (1963). Field dependence and overcoming embeddedness. *J. consult. Psychol.* **27,** 294–302.

Khan, S. B. (1970). Development of mental abilities: An investigation of the "differentiation hypothesis". *Can. J. Psychol.* **24,** 199–205.

Kimura, D. (1961). Some effects of temporal lobe damage on auditory perception. *Can. J. Psychol.* **15,** 156–165.

Kimura, D. (1964). Left–right differences in the perception of melodies. *Q. Jl. expl Psychol.* **16,** 355–358.

Kimura, D. (1967). Functional asymmetry of the brain in dichotic listening. *Cortex* **3,** 163–178.

Knox, C. and Kimura D. (1970). Cerebral processing of non-verbal sounds in boys and girls. *Neuropsychol.* **8,** 227–237.

Kolakowski, D., Bock R. D. and Vandenberg, S. G. (1968). A study of components of variations in some perceptual and cognitive tests. Research Report No. 29, Louisville Twin Study, University of Louisville School of Medicine, Louisville, Kentucky.

Lansdell, H. (1968). Effect of extent of temporal lobe ablations on two lateralized deficits. *Physiol. Behav.* **3,** 271–273.

Lansdell, H. (1970). Relation of extent of temporal removals to closure and visuomotor factors. *Percept. Mot. Skills* **31,** 491–498.

Lansdell, H. (1971). "Intellectual factors and asymmetry of cerebral function." Address presented at the meeting of the American Psychological Association, Washington, D.C.

Lesser, G. S., Fifer, G. and Clark, D. H. (1965). Mental abilities of children from different social class and cultural groups. *Monogr. Soc. Res. Child Dev.* **30,** 1–115.

Levy-Agresti, J. and Sperry, R. W. (1968). Differential perceptual capacities in major and minor hemispheres. *Proc. U.S. Natn. Acad. Sci.* **61,** 1151.

Lienert, G. A. (1964). "Belastung und Regression, Versuch einer Theorie der Systematischen Beeintrachtigung der intellektuellen Leistungsfähigkeit." (Stress and Regression, Sketch of a Theory of Systematic Influence on Intellectual Achievement). Anton Haih, Meisenheim.

Loehlin, J. C. and Vandenberg, S. G. (1968). Genetic and environmental components in the covariation of cognitive abilities: An additive model. *In* "Progress in Human Behavior Genetics." (Vandenberg, S. G. ed.) The Johns Hopkins Press, Baltimore, Maryland.

Longéot, F. (1969). "Psychologie differentielle et théorie opératoire de l'intelligence." (Differential Psychology and Piaget's Theory of Intelligence.) Dunod, Paris.

Lubin, B., Wallis, R. R. and Paine, C. (1971). Patterns of psychological test usage in the United States, 1935–1969. *Prof. Psychol.* **1,** 70–74.

McFie, J., Piercy, M. F. and Zangwill, O. L. (1950). Visual–spatial agnosia associated with lesions of the right cerebral hemisphere. *Brain* **73,** 167–190.

McGraw, B. and Joreskög, K. G. (1971). Factorial invariance of ability measures in groups differing in intelligence and socio-economic status. *Br. J. math. statist. Psychol.* **24,** 154–168.

McNemar, Q. (1942). "The Revision of the Stanford-Binet Scale; An Analysis of the Standardization Data". Houghton Mifflin Co., Boston.

Merrifield, P. R., Guilford, J. P., Christensen, P. R. and Frick, J. W. (1962). The role of intellectual factors in problem solving. *Psychol. Monogr.* **76** (16 Serial No. 529).

Meyers, C. E., Dingman, H. F., Orpet, R. E., Sitkei, E. G. and Watts C. A. (1964). Four ability factor hypotheses at three preliterate levels in normal and retarded children. *Monogr. Soc. Res. Child Dev.* **29** (5 Serial No. 96).

Meyers, C. E. and Orpet, R. E. (1971). Ability factor location of some Piagetian tasks at 5½ years. Proceedings of the 79th Annual Convention of the American Psychological Association.

Money, J. (1968). Cognitive deficits in Turner's syndrome. *In* "Progress in Human Behavior Genetics." (Vandenberg, S. G. ed.) Johns Hopkins Press, Baltimore, Maryland.

Morrell, L. K. and Salamy, J. G. (1971). Hemisphere asymmetry of electrocortical responses to speech stimuli. *Science, N.Y.* **174,** 164–166.

Nsereko-Gyagendo, Twaha. (1971). An investigation of eleven mental abilities in Uganda children. Unpublished doctoral dissertation. Makerere University, Kampala, Uganda.

Orpet, R. E. and Meyers, C. E. (1966). Six structure-of-intellect hypotheses in six year old children. *J. ed. Psychol.* **57,** 341–346.

Oxbury, J. M. and Oxbury, S. M. (1969). Effects of temporal lobectomy on the report of dichotically presented digits. *Cortex* **5,** 3–14.

Partanen, J., Bruun, K. and Markkanen, T. (1966). "Inheritance of Drinking Behavior." The Finnish Foundation for Alcohol Studies, Helsinki.

Patterson, A. and Zangwill, O. L. (1944). Disorders of visual space perception associated with lesions of the right cerebral hemisphere. Brain 67, 331–358.

Reitan, R. M. (1955). Certain differential effects of left and right cerebral lesions in human adults. *J. comp. physiol. Psychol.* **48,** 474–477.

Rosenthal, D. (1968). The genetics of intelligence and personality. *In* "Genetics," Glass, D. C. (ed.). Rockefeller University Press and Russell Sage Foundation, New York.

Roudabush, G. E. (1968). Analyzing dyadic relationships. *In* "Progress in Human Behavior Genetics," Vandenberg, S. G. (ed.). The Johns Hopkins Press, Baltimore, Maryland.

Saunders, D. R. (1959). On the dimensionality of the WAIS battery for two groups of normal males. *Psychol. Rep.* **5,** 529–541.

Saunders, D. R. (1960a). A factor analysis of the information and arithmetic items of the WAIS. *Psychol. Rep.* **6**, 367–373.

Saunders, D. R. (1960b). A factor analysis of the picture completion items of the WAIS. *J. Clin. Psychol.* **16,** 146–149.

Schaffer, Marilyn C. (1969). "Parent–child similarity in psychological differentiation." Unpublished doctoral dissertation. Purdue University, Indiana.

Schmid, J. and Leiman, J. M. (1959). The development of hierarchical factor solutions. *Psychometrika* **22,** 53–61.

Shepard, R. N. and Metzler, J. (1971). Mental rotation of three-dimensional objects. *Science, N.Y.* **171,** 701–703.

Sitkei, E. G. and Meyers, C. E. (1969). Comparative structure of intellect in middle and lower-class four year olds of two ethnic groups. *Dev. Psychol.* **1,** 529–604.

Stafford, R. E. (1961). Sex differences in spatial visualization as evidence of sex linked inheritance. *Percept. Mot. Skills* **13,** 428.

Stevenson, H. W., Hale, G. A., Klein, R. E. and Miller, L. K. (1968). Interrelations and correlates in children's learning and problem solving. *Monogr. Soc. Res. Child Dev.* **33** (7 Serial No. 123).

Sundberg, N. D. (1961). The practice of psychological testing in clinical services in the United States. *Am. Psychol.* **16,** 79–83.

Taylor, J. T. (1964). The structure of ability in the lower intellectual range. *Am. J. Ment. Defic.* **68,** 766–774.

Traub, R. E. (1970). A factor analysis of programmed learning and ability measures. *Can. J. behavl. Sci.* **2,** 44–59.

Tucker, L. R. (1951). A method for synthesis of factor analysis studies. PRS Report no. 984, Department of the Army: Adjutant General's Office, Personnel Research Section, Washington, D.C.

Tuddenham, R. D. (1970). A "Piagetian" test of cognitive development. *In* "On Intelligence." (Dockrell, W. B. ed.) Methuen, London.

Vandenberg, S. G. (1965a). Multivariate analysis of twin differences. *In* "Research

Methods and Goals in Human Behavior Genetics." (Vandenberg, S. G. ed.) Academic Press, New York and London.

Vandenberg, S. G. (1965b). Innate abilities, one or many? A new method and some results. *Acta Genet. med. Gemell.* **14,** 41–47.

Vandenberg, S. G. (1968). The nature and nurture of intelligence. *In* "Biology and Behavior: Genetics," Glass, D. C. (ed.), pp. 3–58. Rockefeller University Press and Russell Sage Foundation, New York.

Vega, A. and Parsons, O. A. (1969). Relationship between sensory motor deficits and WAIS verbal and performance scores in unilateral brain damage. *Cortex* **5,** 229–241.

Verhage, F. (1964). "Intelligentie en Leeftijd" (Intelligence and Age). Van Gorkum, Assen, Netherlands.

Vernon, P. E. (1950). "The Structure of Human Abilities." Methuen, London.

Very, P. S. (1971). "Development and Evaluation of a Factor Analytic Battery of Intellective Abilities". Unpublished Manuscript.

Warburton, F. W. (1970). The British Intelligence Scale. *In* "On Intelligence," Dockrell, W. B. (ed.). Methuen, London.

Werdelin, I. and Stjernberg, G. (1971). The relationship between difficulty and factor loadings of some visual–perceptual tests. *Scand. J. Psychol.* **12,** 21–28.

White, M. J. (1969). Laterality differences in perception: A review. *Psychol. Bull.* **72,** 387–405.

Witkin, H. A., Faterson, H. F., Goodenough, D. R. and Birnbaum, J. (1966). Cognitive patterning in mildly retarded boys. *Child Dev.* **37,** 301–316.

Witkin, H. A. (1967). A cognitive style approach to cross-cultural research. *Int. J. Psychol.* **2,** 233–250.

Wright, Ruth E. (1938). A factor analysis of the original Stanford–Binet scale. *Psychometrika* **4,** 209–220.

Wood, C. C., Goff, W. R. and Day, R. S. (1971). Auditory evoked potentials during speech perception. *Science, N.Y.* **173,** 1248–1251.

Theory of Functions Represented Among Auditory and Visual Test Performances

JOHN L. HORN*

University of Denver

Introduction

In this paper I want to focus attention on what I shall refer to as auditory abilities, a term which in my discourse will have a rather narrow meaning and one that may be somewhat different than the one to which you have become accustomed. I am not going to talk very much about the phenomena represented by psychological research on measuring elementary hearing capacities, as exemplified by the work of Stevens (1960). For most psychologists such elementary capacities represent the dominant referents for the term "auditory abilities". But while such capacities will be given some slight consideration here, the principal concern will be with attempts to measure the rather broad abilities which seem to characterize the production and perception of music and speech. This focus leads to a different collection of research than that represented by concern with psychophysical measurement of sensory capabilities.

I should also note, that strictly speaking what I shall refer to as auditory abilities are not abilities that depend upon auditory function alone but involve also some use of visual processes. That is, the tests which provide the operational definitions for what I will refer to as auditory abilities involve stimulus input exclusively through the ear, but require response by means of a pencil mark on a piece of paper and thus to this extent require use of the visual modality. In most cases it seems reasonable to suppose that the response modality will contribute a trivial proportion of variance to the obtained measurements, but this is not obviously true in all cases and is, as a matter of fact, an untested assumption. In any case it is probably wise to remain aware of the fact

* I am indebted to my co-worker, Lazar Stankov, for the considerable assistance I received from him in developing the ideas presented in this paper.

that what I refer to as auditory abilities are not abilities of a kind that would be measured in persons who are blind or have their eyes closed.

In speaking of auditory abilities in this manner my working assumption is that in some noteworthy respects these abilities are comparable to those functions which have become known as primary mental abilities through the pioneering work of Thurstone (1936) and the continuing research of such followers in the simple structure tradition as are referred to in the summaries of French (French, 1951; French *et al.*, 1963), Guilford (Guilford, 1967; Guilford and Hoepfner, 1971), Pawlik (1966) and Horn (1972a; 1973). This assumption may prove to be inappropriate or unproductive. To discover this is, in a sense, the concern of this paper. The purpose here is to examine this assumption both logically and empirically, and thereby attempt to gain some understanding of the ways in which the assumption is likely to be reasonable or unreasonable. The more global purpose is to begin to provide a basis upon which to build an integrative theory that will organize the regularities represented by replicated primary abilities of audition and vision.

It may seem to students of cognitive processes that little is known about how such processes are organized through the auditory modality. In fact it would be misleading to begin a discussion of auditory abilities with an assertion that little is known about such functions. Unfortunately, compared with the extent of possible, desirable and sufficient working knowledge of the expression of intellectual ability via the auditory modality, our present knowledge is relatively limited. But when considered relative to all that we do not know about other psychological functions, what we know about auditory abilities does not compare too badly. In a recent book, for example, Shuter (1968) has brought together an impressive collection of facts and informed conjecture about human capacities for musical expression and comprehension. Vernon, commenting on this information in the foreword of Shuter's book, was moved to remark "Indeed I would go so far myself as to claim that we can probably make better predictions from childhood to adult accomplishment in music than in any other specialist field." In a similar vein we can cite the books of Miller (1951), Carroll (1953), Brown (1958), Saporta (1961) and Staats (1968) as exemplifying the fact that we now have a quite respectable body of knowledge about speech perception and speech production, as this is mediated through the auditory modality. In these treatments, there is no dearth of theory about speech and musical abilities.

However while we do indeed have facts and theory about auditory functions, very little has been done to relate the factor analytic research in this area to that which has provided the base for what has come to be known as the structure of intellect. This is not to ignore the value of work by Wing (1955), Shuter (1968) and others in describing the extent to which musical abilities are independent of a general factor of intelligence. Nor is it to discount the work of Revesz, both in music perception (Revesz, 1953) and tactile-kinesthetic perception (Revesz and Berkeley, 1950), in indicating a basis for describing the ways in which abilities assessed through one sensory modality might be transposed in another modality. Similarly, this is not to deny that Guilford (1967) has made efforts in his theory to include some of the auditory factors indicated by the work of Carroll (1962), Fleishman *et al.* (1958) and Karlin (1941, 1942). In this connection, also, we must recognize that in his 1951 compendium of factors French included Karlin's (1941, 1942) results and thus made an effort to bring auditory abilities into a general theory of perceptual and thinking abilities. We should also recognize the very interesting efforts of White (1954) to show whether or not the primary factors known as flexibility of closure (*Cf*) and speed of closure (*Cs*) represent functions which transcend the visual modality and can be represented in auditory tests. While these efforts need to be recognized as contributing to our understanding of the relationships between auditory and visual primary abilities, they do not constitute a theory aimed at integrating these findings, nor are they presented as serving this purpose. They point to the fact that auditory input must be reckoned with in any full account of human intellectual functioning, but they provide little indication of the ways in which this reckoning should be made. In contrast, the major purpose of the present paper is to move along a path toward getting the two kinds of abilities together—that is, to begin to see in what ways the two are interrelated.

I will attempt to deal with these matters in a theoretical manner, as dictated by the requirements of this symposium. But I should confess at the outset that I am suspicious of much of what passes for theory in the behavioral sciences. It is so easy for what is highly regarded as theory in our field to float on a sea of fantasy—plausible and interesting conjecture perhaps, but fantasy nonetheless—and I am aware of a predilection for fantasy within my own make up. Yet such fantasy, I think, does not best serve the objectives of science. So although I shall speak in a speculative manner and refrain from presenting tables of findings, I will nevertheless try to keep close to such findings as seem to exist. I trust this myopic concern with the mundane will not offend my hosts.

A Metatheory Exemplifying a Basic Problem

In most thinking about human abilities one can recognize the often implicit acceptance of a metatheory which assumes that abilities are organized at different levels, represented by the organizations of sensation, perception, habit formation and thinking. This kind of metatheory also frequently involves a psychophysiological theory in which the processes at the various levels are believed to be localized to a considerable extent in the functioning of separate parts of the body. The abilities of sensation, for example, might be said to be most closely related to the functioning of receptor organs; thinking is presented as representing an executive organization localized somewhere in the cerebrum, perhaps principally in the frontal lobes, and perception and habit formation are assumed to indicate organizations somewhere along the neural route between a receptor organ and the neurons which carry out the executive function. It is in this way that Guilford (1967), for example, speaks of . . . "special abilities that have little or no claim to recognition as intellectual abilities . . . (namely), three factors represening sensitivity to colors: red sensitivity, green sensitivity and blue sensitivity . . . three dimensions representing sensitivity to sounds: long-wave sensitivity, moderate-wave sensitivity and short-wave sensitivity . . . a factor for pitch discrimination and one for loudness discrimination . . . a factor of kinesthetic sensitivity . . . and one or more factors of sensitivity connected with the static sense . . . these factors have to do with sensory functions and probably depend more upon sense-organ structures than upon brain structures".

Frequently, also, a metatheory of levels involves the notion that abilities are interrelated in an hierarchical manner. This kind of theory is offered most consistently and clearly by British factor analytic investigators such as Burt and Vernon. Burt (1949), for example, states the essential ideas of such a theory: "the mind, like the nervous system, is organized into an hierarchy of factors . . . the more general factors including the more specialized as countries includes counties . . . The processes of the lowest level are assumed to consist of simple sensations or simple movements, such as can be artificially isolated and measured by tests of sensory 'threshold' and by the timing of 'simple reactions'. The next level includes the more complex processes of perception and coordinated movement, as in experiments of the apprehension of form and pattern or on 'compound reactions'. The third is the association level—the level of memory and of habit formation. The fourth and highest of all involves the apprehension or application of relations."

Some theorists, perhaps most notably Guilford (1967), make a point of rejecting this kind of hierarchical theory. But even in these cases the ideas represented by at least limited hierarchies are accepted. Thus Guilford (1967) recognizes at several points in the development of his theory that some of the products and operations and contents of his model subsume other products or operations or contents and thus can be represented in hierarchies, although he argues that these ideas can be expressed as well by what is referred to as a morphological model.

A major difficulty with a metatheory of levels is adumbrated in a sentence which immediately followed the passage quoted above from Burt (1949). "Intelligence," Burt continued, "as an integrative capacity of mind, is manifested at every level . . ." in the hierarchy? The suggestion is that the intellect enters in some measure into performances which would seem to represent functions of a lower level and vice versa—sensation, perception, elementary conditioning and memory produce variance in performances that are assumed to represent the highest functions of intellect. Given a factoring of a variety of performances, how is one to sort out those factors which represent sensation, those which represent perception, and so on? This is a simple enough problem to state and thus may seem to be simple to solve, but I daresay that we are a long way from solving it with anything more exact than a rough distinction between the abilities of sensation and those of thinking, as exemplified in the remarks of Guilford which I quoted in the first paragraph of this section.

It might at first seem that the solution of this difficulty is through studies in which one samples widely from performances representing abilities of all levels and then performs higher order factor analyses, on the assumption that the higher order factors will represent broader organizing functions, such as those of intellect, while the lower order factors represent more elementary processes, the lowest being those of sensation. The problems with this seemingly reasonable solution are all too apparent to those who have worked with factor analytic methods. At no point is the truism "You get out of factor analysis only what you put into it" more obvious than when one designs a higher order factorial study. The samplings of variables and subjects determine how broad a factor will be, or whether it will appear at all. One can create a factor simply by including highly similar forms of what is essentially the same test and it is not too difficult a matter to create second-order and third-order factors in much the same way. A function such as that representing carefulness in avoiding wrong answers in ability tests (Fruchter, 1950, 1953; Horn and Bramble, 1967; Horn and Cattell, 1966) can be made to appear at the first-order or at the second-order depending upon how one chooses to sample variables. In general, a problem with trying to equate level of function with order of factors revealed by factor analyses is that unless there is representative sampling of variables at all levels of function, the order of factors may just as well represent emphasis in sampling variables as it can represent order of generality of functions. Cattell's (1950) notion of a personality sphere and Brunswik's (1956) ideas about representative design notwithstanding, we still have no compelling way of circumscribing the domain of ability variables and of sampling representatively from this domain. Moreover, the problems of sampling subjects in a representative manner present similar difficulties and there are no convincing reasons to suppose that either kind of sampling—of subjects or of variables, is usually, or can be, random with respect to influences, other than levels of functions, which can produce factors at different orders of analysis.

These, however, are not the only problems in trying to reveal levels of functions by doing higher-order factor analyses. As Cattell (1965) has pointed out in some detail, there are a variety of models for organizing the facts about human abilities. Only one of these is a neat hierarchy of the kind specified in Burt's theory and each implies something different about the relationship between function and order of factor analysis.

What a well designed factor analytic study indicates, basically, is that the investigator knows enough about the phenomena he is investigating to be able to sample variables and subjects in a way that will reveal regularities which he wishes to call to attention. If analyses are objective (as specified by Horn, 1967a), this is no mean accomplishment, but it is not a method of proof which, in the absence of compelling evidence from other sources, can reveal the level of function specified in the metatheories to which I referred above. The problem of distinguishing levels of abilities cannot be solved by the methods of factor analysis alone.

I have taken space to discuss metatheories of levels and to point to some of the problems with such theories because these problems have plagued me throughout in my studies of auditory and visual abilities. I have not, regrettably, found satisfying solutions for these problems. I think that the necessary solutions must be found, if indeed they can be found, by evidence additional to that provided by factor analytic study alone. Perhaps evidence such as that which might be revealed by studies relating factors to injuries or defects of physiological structures provides the needed bridge. But such evidence is in short supply. My cursory review of studies focused on physiological processes, usually involving the most elementary behavioral tasks, provided no insights of any consequence. As I see it, therefore, the unfortunate fact of the matter is that we must continue to live with arbitrary and crude designations of the levels of function represented by factors.

Notice also, that acknowledgement of this difficulty indicates the equally troublesome fact that we may misrepresent a factor as indicating a cognitive capacity when, in fact (i.e. with the wisdom of further study), it better represents an attribute of conation or affect or some other general class of functions.

Primary Abilities Revealed Through Auditory Tests

Factors of Sensory Discrimination and their Relation to Primary Abilities

It is not always easy to be clear about what we mean by a factor and what we mean by a test. For example, we know that the factor of verbal comprehension, is indicated by tests as diverse as those measuring knowledge of grammar and those requiring Gestalt closure in identifying mutilated words, but, after extensive review of studies in which this factor has been identified, French *et al.* (1963) recommended that forms of the simple multiple-choice vocabulary test be used to measure the factor. This suggests that one could have defined this primary mental ability, before the advent of factor analysis, by simply constructing a vocabulary test and saying "this is it". By similar logic one might believe that C. E. Seashore (1919) defined some of the primary abilities measurable through auditory stimulation when he constructed the tests which he referred to as measures of musical talent. In their most recent forms (Seashore, 1938) these tests are said to measure—

Pitch: the ability to identify the difference between two pure tones differing in frequency by between 2 and 17 Hz.

Loudness: the ability to tell the difference between two pure tones having equal frequencies but differing in loudness by between 0·5 and 4 decibels.

Rhythm: given two rhythmic beats, the ability to tell whether they are essentially the same or different.

Time: the ability to tell whether the second of two pure tones of equal frequency and intensity is longer or shorter than the first when differences in duration range between 0·05 and 0·3 sec.

Tonal Memory: given a pair of two, three or four-tone sequences in which one tone in the second sequence differs in pitch from the comparable tone in the first sequence, the ability to identify the tone which differs.

Timbre: given a pair of tones made up of a fundamental and the first five harmonics in which the intensities of the third and fourth harmonics is varied in some pairs, the ability to judge whether the two tones are the same or different.*

As noted in the previous section, Guilford (1967) has suggested that the first two of these tests do indeed indicate factors, but factors which represent abilities that are too narrow and too much of a sensory nature to be of use in understanding intellectual functioning. Granting this point for the moment, we still might wonder about the remaining tests. Does Tonal Memory, for example, represent a primary ability and if so, is it different from the three memory abilities that were clearly distinguished in Kelley's (1964) definitive study, and is it different from a fourth poorly defined factor which Kelley referred to as possibly indicating auditory memory—an ability . . . "to remember material by the formation of an auditory image"? Similarly, does the Timbre test represent a primary ability to comprehend relationships among fundaments that are sounds and, if so, is this the same ability that is required to comprehend relationships among fundaments which are geometric figures, the primary ability described in Guilford's (1967) system as cognition of figural relations (CFR)?

One drawback to identifying tests of the kind found in Seashore's battery with primary abilities of intellect is that they appear to be too simple. As Guilford (1967) observed: they seem to measure only sensory acuity, not the processes of abstracting, reasoning and relation-perceiving which are accepted as indicating aspects of intelligence. As argued in the previous section, however, this is a difficult judgment to make *a priori*. Also, as a matter of empirical fact, the simple Seashore tests have been found to have substantial loadings in the company of rather complex tests on factors that have been interpreted as indicating higher mental processes. In a study reported by Solomon, Webster and Curtis (1960) Seashore's Pitch correlated 0·60 with a broad factor defined also

* In contrast to what are referred to here as auditory tests are visual tests, in which the stimulus (item) input is through the eye. But it should be noted in this respect that when looked at from an ontological point of view and even, from some angles, from a physiological functioning point of view, almost any distinction between auditory and visual tests of intellectual abilities is rather grotesquely artificial. In the development of abilities, for example, it is clear that the verbal facility that is developed through hearing spoken words is at many points similar to, and complemented by, the development of verbal facility through seeing printed or written words. Moreover, the similarity between measurements of verbal facility obtained by use of visually presented and auditorily presented verbal materials would be expected to be larger than the similarity between verbal facility and, say, figural reasoning when both were measured by items presented visually. This does not discount the possibility that auditory and visual verbal comprehension may be rather independent abilities, however, and that each may be more closely related to other abilities than to each other. The empirical questions implied here are yet to be answered.

by a spoken vocabulary test (which correlated 0·56 with the factor), a distorted spoken vocabulary test (which loaded 0·52), and a test measuring comprehension of stuttering (which correlated 0·45). In the only other factor in which Pitch had a substantial loading in this study, the salient variables indicated comprehension of clipped sentences, comprehension of noise-masked words and several other somewhat similar measures of comprehension of sounds. In several studies the correlations of the Seashore tests with tests that are accepted as indicating aspects of intellect have been found to be significantly larger than zero. Moreover, there are findings indicating that the Seashore tests do not always correlate highly or significantly with measures of sensory acuity. Factors of hearing acuity were also defined in the Solomon *et al.* (1960) study. For example, the so called absolute threshold measurements of audiometer assessments being the salient markers, but the Loudness test of the Seashore battery was in the hyperplane of these factors. In general, then, the suggestion is that the Seashore tests do not always relate as one might suppose to measures of sensory functioning, but they appear to have noteworthy relationships with tests and factors which can be accepted as indicating intellectual functioning. Perhaps they do measure sensory functioning, but the evidence suggests that they also measure higher intellectual processes. The question in this case is at the crux of the unresolved problem to which I referred in the previous section.

Information relating to the question of whether or not to regard tests of the Seashore type as indicants of separate primary abilities of intellect can be found in results showing that the intercorrelations among the Seashore tests are in some cases rather high and average somewhere around 0·35. Shuter (1968) noted, for example, that in some 14 separate studies the average of the correlations between Pitch and Memory was 0·52 and the average of the intercorrelations among all six Seashore tests was 0·34. Since the tests have reliabilities in the neighborhood of 0·7 to 0·8, these intercorrelations are not too large to discount an hypothesis that the tests represent distinct factors. Nevertheless, these intercorreliatons, considered relative to test reliabilities, are not appreciably lower than the typical intercorrelations found among tests that have consistently defined primary mental abilities in the research reviewed by French (1951); French *et al.* (1963), Guilford (1967), Pawlik (1966) and Horn (1972a; 1973). Related to this observation is the fact that in at least two studies (Hanley, 1956; Soloman *et al.*, 1960) involving a variety of auditory measures, several or all of the Seashore tests appeared together with substantial loadings on one factor. In Hanley's eight-factor simple structure study, for example, in which there were 22 auditory measures besides the Seashore battery, all of the Seashore tests came together in one factor and had essentially no variance in any other factor. In the Solomon *et al.* (1960) study, all but the Loudness test had loadings above 0·35 on the first factor mentioned in the previous paragraph and all but Rhythm had loadings above 0·25 on the second-mentioned factor, and the variance of the tests in other auditory factors was trivial.

The findings of the last-mentioned studies suggest that either all or most of the Seashore tests measure a single factor. Yet there is the notion that Loudness and Pitch at least, and perhaps the other Seashore tests, represent distinct factors. Moreover, this notion is supported, in part, by the findings of Karlin (1942). In a study involving 29 variables, most of which were based upon auditory input, Karlin found a clear distinction between factors indicating pitch discrimination, loudness discrimination, and estimation of sound duration (time). Thus, these results indicate that Seashore's Pitch, Loudness and Time can be thought of as representing primary factors among auditory tests. How are these findings to be reconciled with the results—Hanley's and Solomon's—suggesting that the Seashore tests, when in the company of other auditory tests, measure primarily only one factor or perhaps two factors?

The apparent inconsistency in these findings reflects, I believe, different implicit assumptions about the variables to be sampled to determine a factor. Consideration of these assumptions helps to indicate just how narrow the abilities to discriminate Pitch, Loudness and Sound Duration may be. For what Karlin's results demonstrate is that in order to define a primary factor represented by one of Seashore's tests, one must include several* variations on the same test. For example, the factor of Loudness in Karlin's study was defined by the Seashore test of the ability to discriminate between intensities of pure tones, loudness discrimination of complex (i.e. piano) tones, loudness discrimination of very short pure tones and loudness discrimination among tones in which frequencies were varied to make apparent differences in loudness. It is theoretically possible for these tests to define quite different factors, but this does not seem likely, at least not after the fact of Karlin's study. In any case it seems a good deal more likely that these tests will define a simple factor of loudness than that the speech perception and sound perception tests employed by Hanley and Solomon will define such a

* In my experience at least three good markers are needed to properly over-determine a factor in an objectively rotated solution. Examining this matter systematically from the base of various chance models Humphreys, Ilgen, McGrath and Montanelli (1969) found that "Four markers are almost minimal within the limits of N available to most investigators."

factor (although there were tests in these batteries, such as reverberation masking and threshold for hearing sentences which *a priori* would seem to involve variance in loudness perception).

Taken all together the results from the rather different studies reviewed above, as well as findings from early studies by Karlin (1941) and Fieldhouse (1937), seem to indicate that in the company of diversified tests of auditory performances, the Seashore tests have much in common with each other and may, as a group, measure an intellectual function. But if one wants to recognize the separate Seashore tests as distinct sensory capacities, he can provide factor analytic support for this idea by performing analyses on tests which are very similar to corresponding Seashore tests, but which involve such variations as using piano, voice, or very short tones rather than pure tones.

Nonsymbolic Recognition Memory (*Mr*)

Analyses conducted by Lazar Stankov and myself have confirmed the previous findings of Hanley (1956) and Solomon *et al.* (1960) showing that when the Seashore tests are factored in the company of a variety of other auditory tests they tend to stand alone, as it were, to define a factor that represents an intellectual function, rather than merely an elementary aspect of sensory functioning. In our analyses 38 auditory tests were factored. Thirteen of these were modeled on visual tests that have been accepted as measures of replicated primary mental abilities—tests such as Analogies, Series, Classifications, Gottschaldt Figures and Form Boards. Another 13 of the tests were derived from speech perception studies—tests such as Cloze, Noise Masking, Low Pass Filter, Memory for Emphasis and Sound Blending. The remaining tests were taken from well known measures of musical abilities—tests such as the Analysis of Chords, Pitch Change and Memory from Wing's (1962) battery, Rhythm from Drake's (1956) tests and, of course, the Seashore tests (excluding loudness). The sample of subjects for this study contained 241 men between 16 and 54 years of age, inmates at either the Colorado State Penitentiary or the Colorado State Reformatory. Seven factors were indicated. These were rotated by application of the Varimax procedure followed by Promax, with power set at 5. The factor defined largely by the Seashore tests was third in order of common variance contribution.

These results, confirming those from previous analyses, thus leave us with a need to understand a fairly broad factor that is defined, in part, by the several rather simple tests which comprise the Seashore battery.

One possibility in this regard is that the factor represents what is sometimes referred to as an instrument influence (Horn and Cattell, 1965). Such an influence is indicated if all of the measures defining a factor are obtained through a particular instrument, as when the variables are obtained from electroencephalograph recordings or, more appropriate to the present discussion, if the measurements are obtained from tape-recorder administration of stimuli or if all stimuli are pure tones. In such cases it is possible that the factor does not represent individual differences at all, but instead indicates only variation in the recording instrument, as, for example, if the tape recording instrument were to run rapidly when one group of subjects was tested, run at an intermediate rate when another group was tested and run slowly when a third group was tested. This possibility was anticipated in our study: the Seashore tests were scattered throughout the battery and all tests were administered by the same tape recorder. Thus differences in tape recorder administration are not likely to account for the fact that just some tests, the Seashore tests and a few others, come together on a single factor. Since three of the five Seashore tests analysed in this study involved pure tone discrimination (Pitch, Time, Memory), it is reasonable to suppose that an instrument influence could be associated with the production or perception of pure tones. Against this interpretation, however, is the fact that two of the five Seashore tests which define the factor are not pure tone tests and several other tests enter with prominent loadings in the factor and are not pure tone tests. Similarly, although the Seashore tests in each case require the subject to choose the "correct" answer from only two choices, and thus the factor might seem to be a response set of the kind identified in Cronbach's (1941) review of such influences, the fact that several tests which correlate substantially with the factor do not have the "choice of two" format suggests that the factor is not simply a manifestation of individual differences in a tendency to select, say, the most "correct" response choice. Such possibilities have not been entirely ruled out by our analyses, however, so one should probably keep the notion of response set as a possible, if remote, interpretation of the factor.

Turning to a consideration of the content of the factor, it should be noted first that there are some inconsistencies in the information obtained from different replications of the factor. In our study the Loudness test was found to give a very low correlation with all of our auditory tests and for this reason was dropped from our factor analyses. Somewhat similarly, Loudness was in the hyperplane of the factor involving Seashore tests in the Solomon *et al.* (1960) study. But in Hanley's (1956) study, on the other hand, Loudness correlated 0·33 with the factor. In the studies reviewed by Shuter the average (over 14 studies) correlation of Loudness with Pitch and Time was 0·33, with Rhythm it was 0·22, and the averages of the correlations between Loudness and the other Seashore tests were not given. It is not clear, therefore, whether or not Loudness should be regarded as a part of the factor.

In all three studies in which the Seashore tests have been found to define a single factor, however, Tonal Memory was clearly the salient marker. In our results the factor also involved a variety of other tests in which a crucial part of the task was to recognize whether or not a sound—a pure tone, a chord, a rhythm pattern, a tonal pattern, was the same as a sound which had been presented a few seconds before. It appears, therefore, that the factor has something to do with recognition memory over a short period of time, where that which has to be remembered is a stimulus (a sound) that affected one only momentarily and then passed away. Moreover, for most persons (those with absolute pitch and good training in musical notation being possible exceptions) the stimulation that must be remembered is not of a kind that one readily codes into a symbol such as "G-flat", a letter or a word. I have called the factor simply "Nonsymbolic Recognition Memory", abbreviated *Mr*, to distinguish it from Rote Memory (*Ma*), Meaningful Memory (*Mm*) and Span Memory (*Ms*) factors established by Kelley's research. The factor may represent the same influence as was identified as Phonetic Coding by Carroll (1962) in the context of a rather different set of variables than have been considered here.

It is fairly clear from our results, and it is suggested by the findings of Hanley (1956) and Kelley (1964), that the Nonsymbolic Recognition Memory factor is distinct from Rote Memory, Meaningful Memory and Span Memory. In our results estimates of *Ma* and *Ms* correlated with *Mr* only about 0·25. Moreover, there is little reason to suppose that *Mr* should be equated with *Mm*, since the tasks which define it are not associational and the stimuli are not semantic and thus would not be regarded as particularly meaningful. In the Hanley study a memory for voices factor was defined separately from the factor determined by the Seashore tests and now referred to as *Mr*. If it could be accepted that remembering voices involves using meaningful associations, then these results could be interpreted as establishing the distinction between *Mm* and *Mr*. If this assumption is unacceptable, then at least the Hanley results indicate that *Mr* is distinguishable from another memory factor which, considered relative to established findings, is most likely either *Ma*, *Ms* or *Mm*. It should be recalled, too, that Kelley (1964) found a factor that was distinct from *Ma*, *Ms* and *Mm* and which was defined by auditory tests or tests composed of material which . . . "would lend itself well to auditory retention . . . by the formation of an auditory image."*

Taking these results overall, there is fairly compelling support for the idea that we can recognize a primary ability of nonsymbolic recognition memory that is largely independent of the established span, meaningful and rote memory abilities. In recognizing this ability and noting that it was isolated primarily among auditory tests, it should not be assumed (without further research) that it necessarily appears only in performances based on auditory input, just as it should not be assumed that the other established memory factors are revealed only in performances based on visual input. In fact, each of the three memory factors established by Kelley's work involved auditory input (the two salient markers for *Ma* were auditory variables). Also the factor in his study which seemed to adumbrate the *Mr* factor of our work was correlated to a noteworthy degree with a visual test (which, however, according to Kelley, seemed to "lend itself well to auditory retention").

It is not clear to me how this *Mr* factor should be considered in Guilford's model. In his 1967 book Guilford referred to Karlin's (1941) results, in which Seashore's Tonal Memory was found on a factor which French (1951) called "musical memory", and considered identifying it as MFS–A, memory for figural systems (auditory). He decided against this, however, and ended up classifying the factor as CFS–A, cognition of figural systems (auditory). I fail to see how Guilford's concepts of products and contents apply to the various kinds of stimulation represented in *Mr* and thus I can not really venture to classify the factor in Guilford's system. Indeed, I think that Procrustean procedures are needed to logically fit many auditory tests to the Guilford model and that for this reason the heuristic value of the model is somewhat reduced.†

The *Mr* factor was clearly distinguished from verbal comprehension in Hanley's study. The two factors were not separated in the Solomon *et al.* (1960) analyses, but this appears to be due to the fact that there was not a sufficient number of good markers to over-determine the verbal comprehension factor in this study. There were two vocabulary tests, one of the usual (synonyms) kind and one involving interrupted words. There were some other tests which one might think, *a priori*,

* Incidentally, in our results, as in Kelley's, there appears to be no need to distinguish between auditory and visual memory span: the two kinds of tests come together in a single factor.

† I have questioned the value of Guilford's model as a descriptive theory elsewhere (Horn, 1970a; 1972a; 1973). Knapp and I are preparing reports of several studies which provide further support for criticisms of this theory.

would help to determine *V*, but this may have been wrong thinking. On this assumption, there were only two markers for *V* and this would not be enough to separate it from *Mr*. In our results the correlation between *Mr* and the factor we defined as *V* was 0·49, certainly high enough to suggest that the two factors might be difficult to distinguish in some cases in objectively rotated solutions. In the Hanley study, however, the correlation between the two was only 0·16. But the subjects of his study were university students, whereas, in our study and in Solomon's the samples were more heterogeneous with respect to educational achievement. Solomon's subjects were air force enlisted men.

Laying aside the question of the independence of *V* and *Mr*, these results, indicating that the two factors are correlated and cooperative, reinforce the notion that *Mr* should be regarded as a primary ability of intellect.

Rhythm as a Primary Ability?

Considering the possibility that each of the separate Seashore tests represents a primary ability of audition, we examined the hypothesis that rhythm could be represented as a factor, much as loudness and pitch discrimination were found to be representable as factors in Karlin's study. In our first analysis pertaining to this issue we included the two Drake (1957) measures of rhythm, along with the Seashore Rhythm test, in a factoring which involved a wide variety of other auditory tests, some of which might call for some exercise of ability to deal with rhythms.

In one of the Drake rhythm tests the task is to continue a beat established by a metronome by keeping track of how many beats would have occurred in a period after the metronome stops, the periods of time being variable in length and ranging from roughly two seconds to about 20 sec. The subject is asked to keep the beat in his head so to speak, i.e., not tap his foot or move any part of his body in his efforts to maintain the beat.* In the second of the Drake rhythm tests the basic task is similar, but a notable element of distraction is introduced: the subject is to maintain a beat, but when the metronome that establishes the beat is stopped another metronome takes up either a faster or a

* We supervised the administration of this test carefully, and used practice trials, to effectively eliminate the use of obvious body movements to facilitate maintaining the beat. But we could not, of course, prevent the subjects from employing covert, small muscle movements, such as movements of the tongue and lips in counting. Thus, the Drake rhythm measurements probably should not be regarded as measuring only "thinking rhythm"; the measures probably include, also, at least some variance attributable to motor facilitation in maintaining a rhythm.

slower beat which continues throughout the period prior to the time that the response is called for.

It turns out that the two Drake rhythm tests are highly correlated ($r = 0{\cdot}69$), so in analyses that include them both a rather narrow rhythm factor emerges. That this factor is not simply a swollen specific, however, is indicated by the fact that it is also defined by Seashore's Rhythm and several other tests, and by the fact that when one of the Drake rhythm tests is dropped in the analyses, a rhythm factor, defined mainly by the remaining Drake test and Seashore's rhythm, still emerges. It is interesting in this regard, however, that in all analyses Seashore's Rhythm had a higher correlation with the factor that was determined largely by other Seashore tests than it had with the rhythm factor. The suggestion is that the ability to tell whether or not two rhythms are the same (the task of the Seashore test) is more a function of a nonsymbolic recognition memory process than it is a function of capacity to continue an established rhythm.

Performance on tasks requiring one to maintain a rhythm and to be sensitive to changes in rhythm requires close attention to the task under temptation to turn attention to other matters. Theoretically, the overt performance might well be regarded as primarily a function of a capacity to maintain attention, or primarily a function of willingness to exert the needed effort in this regard or, as seems most likely, a function of both these kinds of influences. But if a substantial proportion of the variance of the rhythm factor represents a capacity to maintain attention, there is good reason to suppose that the factor involves processes that are integral to intellectual functioning and thus can be regarded as a primary ability of intellect. Evidence bearing on this point has been reviewed elsewhere (Horn, 1970b; 1972b). In essence, the reviews suggest that ability to sustain attention in tasks involving only a low level of complexity of relationships, but in which distraction is likely, is indicative of an anlage function (Horn, 1968; 1970) which supports the expression of fluid intelligence. Thus, if this rhythm factor is indicative of a capacity to maintain attention, it is expected that it will relate to the primary mental abilities which, in previous work (see Horn, 1968; 1970b; 1972a; 1973 for reviews) have been found to define the rather broad dimension interpreted as indicating fluid intelligence. We will return to a consideration of this question at a later point in this paper, after other factors identified among auditory tasks have been discussed.

On Closure in Audition and Vision

One of the more interesting hypotheses in work on auditory abilities was provided by White's (1954) proposal that the two closure factors that were first clearly identified and separated by Thurstone (1944) might represent functions which regulate auditory perception as well as visual perception. The Flexibility of Closure (*Cf*) factor is defined by tests of the Embedded Figure variety in which one must identify a figure that is obscured because it blends into a surrounding field involving lines similar to those of the figure. This kind of test has been used to represent Witkin's (1959) concept of field independence. The Speed of Closure (*Cs*) factor is defined by Gestalt closure tasks in which one must see how an incomplete figure would look if it were completed. White selected two visual tests to measure each of these factors and then attempted to construct auditory tests that duplicated a corresponding visual test except for involving auditory stimulation instead of visual stimulation. For example, a test he called Hidden Tunes was designed to be like Embedded Figures except that the "figure" that was Embedded was a tune and the "ground" in which it was embedded was another tune. White found that this test correlated 0·66 with Embedded Figures, the reliabilities of the two tests being 0·83 and 0·90, respectively. This was the only clear success of cross modality measurement in White's study, however; the average of the correlations between the other three auditory tests and the four visual tests was 0·21 when the average intercorrelation among the auditory tests was 0·47 and the average intercorrelation among the visual tests was 0·60. A factoring of the data suggested two factors, one of visual closure (involving *Cf* and *Cs* plus Hidden Tunes), and a second of auditory closure.

The Hidden Tunes test was included with 5 markers for *Cs* and *Cf* and a variety of other visual and auditory tasks in the study reported by Fleishman *et al.* (1958). Here it correlated 0·28 with a factor defined most prominently by the two Flexibility of Closure markers, as would be predicted by White's hypothesis. A visual Speed of Closure factor was also defined in this study. Hidden Tunes had a correlation of 0·15 with this dimension. But the major loading (0·68) of Hidden Tunes was on a factor involving tests of ability to detect the dots and dashes of the Morse code.

The evidence of the White and Fleishman studies thus suggests that there might indeed be a small amount of correspondence between visual and auditory abilities in perception of a stimulus pattern embedded in a surround of similar stimulation, but that the major source of variance in tests designed to represent Flexibility of Closure or Speed of Closure is unique to the input modality, visual or auditory.

In our work with the cross-modality hypothesis we at first used the convergent-discriminant validation ideas suggested by Campbell and

Fiske (1959). To represent the visual concept of Speed of Closure we used forms of the well-established Street Gestalt (figural closure) and Mutilated Words tests. In addition we reasoned that a visual incomplete words test, in which the subject must supply missing letters to complete words (Word Cloze), and a Sentence Cloze test (Taylor, 1957), in which missing words had to be supplied to make sentences, might be regarded as measures of the Gestalt closure factor. These two tests correlated 0·55 and their average correlation with the two established markers for *Cs* was 0·35. These results, are comparable to those obtained by Ohnmacht, Weaver and Kohler (1970) in a study involving four forms of the Sentence Cloze test and two markers each for *Cs* and *Cf* (all tests being visual). In their studies the average of the correlations among the Cloze tests was 0·47 and the average correlation between the Cloze tests and the markers for *Cs* was 0·26 (exactly the same as the average correlation between the Cloze tests and markers for *Cf*, Flexibility of Closure). We also constructed two tests which were of the same form as the two visual Cloze tests except that the incomplete words and sentences were presented aurally (the words and sentences being different however from those used in the visual tests). We found that the average correlation of these tests with the established *Cs* markers was 0·28, but that the correlation between the two auditory tests was also only 0·26. Thus the auditory closure tests correlated at about the same level with the visual closure tests as they correlated with each other. Moreover, their average correlation with the two visual tests on which they were modeled was 0·42. A Rapid Spelling test was also considered as being a possible indicator of auditory closure. In this words were spelled once extremely rapidly, so rapidly that it seemed impossible to separately "hear" all the letters. The subject was required to identify the word (although not necessarily spell it correctly), and thus, again, Cloze the incomplete pattern. This test correlated 0·21 and 0·45 respectively with the Street Gestalt and Mutilated Words tests and it correlated 0·50 and 0·45 with the visual Word Cloze and Sentence Cloze tests. Its correlations with the auditory versions of these last mentioned tests were 0·27 and 0·55 respectively.

To consider the hypothesis that the ability to perceive patterns embedded within other patterns is common to both visual and auditory perception, we selected the Designs test (in which the subject identifies a Σ embedded among other lines) and the Copying test (draw a straight line design to be like another) to represent the visual *Cf* factor. An auditory test (Tonal Gottschaldt Figures) was constructed to represent this factor. This required the subject to choose one of four pairs of piano notes that had been embedded in a previously presented chord. This correlated 0·30 and 0·12 respectively with Designs and Copying, the correlation between these last two tests being 0·35. Wing's (1962) Chord Analysis and Pitch Change tests were also selected as possible measures of an auditory *Cf* function. In the first of these tests the subject must estimate the number of notes in a chord. In the Pitch Change test, the subject first hears a chord, then hears either the same chord or a similar chord in which one note has been moved up or down in the scale. The subject's task is to indicate whether or not the chords are the same and, if not, whether a note has been moved up or down. In both of these tests it seems that one must perceive notes embedded within a pattern of notes (i.e. a chord). The two tests correlated 0·20 and 0·27 respectively with Copying, 0·15 and 0·14 with Designs and 0·29 and 0·42 with Tonal Gottschaldt Figures. The correlation between the two was 0·34.

Results from these kinds of analyses thus provide neither convincing support for White's hypothesis nor a firm basis for rejecting the idea. On balance, considering the previous results and our own, it appears that there is a nonchance relationship between auditory and visual measures of an ability to perceive a complete pattern when parts of the pattern have been omitted, and an ability to perceive patterns embedded within other patterns, but there is more common variance within sets of auditory and visual tests designed to measure these functions than there is between comparable auditory and visual tests.

Since some of the tests we constructed for these analyses involve words and sentences, it is probable that familiarity with verbal forms is accounting, in part, for the relationships reported above. In the study of Ohnmacht *et al.* (1970), involving visual tests alone, variations of the Sentence Cloze test were correlated in the range of from 0·37 to 0·53 with vocabulary measures, although a Cloze factor was distinguished from verbal comprehension in an objectively rotated solution (the correlation between the factors being 0·58). To consider the influence of verbal comprehension on the intercorrelations among auditory and visual tests which could indicate closure of one form or the other, we partialled out (linearly) the effects associated with an auditory vocabulary test and a visual vocabulary test. The resulting partial correlations among closure tests were in all cases lower than the zero-order correlations mentioned above, this indicating that the vocabulary tests did, indeed, contain some variance that was also involved in the intercorrelations among the visual and auditory closure tests, but the patterns of intercorrelations did not shift in a way to indicate that *Cf* and *Cs* were cross-modality functions. To the contrary: the cross-modality correlations were reduced somewhat more by the partialing than were the intra-modality correlations. The simple average of the correlations among the putative closure variables that were all either visual or auditory went from 0·33 to 0·25 with the partialing of the two vocabulary measures, whereas the average of the cross-modality correlations for the same variables was reduced from 0·33 to 0·18 by the partialing procedure. The difference between these differences in zero-order and partial correlations very likely is not significant, but the fact that the difference was not in the opposite direction (within-modality correlations being reduced more by the partialing than the between-modality correlations) is damaging to the hypotheses stipulating that Speed of Closure and/or Flexibility of Closure are intellectual-perceptual functions that transcend the auditory and visual stimulus input modalities. Also damaging to these hypotheses were results from factoring the partial intercorrelations among putative closure tests: these results indicated two visual closure factors (*Cf* and *Cs*) defined separately from three auditory factors which had also appeared in our previously mentioned analyses of the zero-order intercorrelations among a broad sampling of 38 auditory tests. Moreover, although the intercorrelations among the auditory and visual closure factors were positive, suggesting that all were in the intellectual perceptual domain, the intra-modality correlations (average r=0·27) were somewhat higher than the inter-modality correlations (average r=0·13).

In general, then, although it is of some considerable interest to consider a theory stipulating that Speed of Closure and Flexibility of Closure are functions that transcend stimulus-input modalities, the evidence thus far adduced does not provide compelling support for crucial hypotheses derived from this theory. This is not to argue that necessarily the theory should be abandoned (the tests which have been run cannot be regarded as definitive), but it is to suggest that if support for the theory is to be found, then the measurements which will indicate the cross-modality processes probably need to be different from those that have been tried out thus far.

Turning now to a consideration of the factors which we found among auditory tests that were selected because they seemed to involve closure in some sense of this term, we may note first that one of these factors, when it was identified among the full complement of 38 auditory tests, did not seem to involve closure so much as it did reasoning. Discussion of this factor will be delayed until the next section. The other two factors seemed to represent abilities to recognize Speech that was camouflaged in some way, and thus might be said to involve closure in speech perception. Factors similar to these two were found in the earlier studies of Hanley (1956) and Solomon *et al.* (1960). In this earlier work one of these factors was characterized by accuracy in identifying sentences or words that had been distorted in different ways, as by putting speech recordings through filters that eliminated the higher (above 3500 Hz) or lower (below 850 Hz) frequencies, or recording speech in a way that made the sounds reverberate. This will be referred to as a Detection of Distorted Speech factor, abbreviated *DDS*. The second of the two speech perception factors identified in the Hanley and Solomon studies was defined primarily by tests in which the speech itself was left intact, but was masked by other sounds, such as superimposed talk, as if one were required to eavesdrop on a conversation at another table in a crowded restaurant. This factor will be referred to as Masked Speech Comprehension, abbreviated *MSC*.

In our study we found the *MSC* factor to be defined by detectability of words masked either by talk or by cafeteria noise and by tests of ability to understand speech when this was either recorded at 7·5 ips and played at 3·75 ips or recorded at the latter speed and played at the former speed. A measure of detectability of words masked by white noise did not have a prominent loading in the factor, however, but instead correlated with a factor similar to *DDS*. Principal defining variables in this latter factor were the filter and word distortion variables which had been prominent in the comparable factors of the Hanley and Solomon studies, but other defining variables included:

Incomplete Words, in which the subject must identify spoken words in which some sounds have been omitted.
Auditory Cloze, in which the task is to write down two words that are left out of an 8 word sentence, and
Rapid Spelling, in which one must write down familiar words that have been spelled so rapidly that it is unlikely that a subject would separately perceive and remember each letter that was spoken.

It can be seen that *DDS* has a faint formal resemblance to Speed of Closure, while, similarly, *MSC* bears some resemblance to the Flexibility of Closure factor identified among figural tests. As noted before, however, these formal alignments do not appear to represent functional alignments, at least, not insofar as these are indicated by linear correlations and factors.

It is possible that the *DDS* and *MSC* factors were distinguished in Karlin's (1942) study, but the results in this case are not clear. One factor in this study was defined by measures of accuracy in identifying words in singing and in speech in which either pauses or word groupings were haphazard and unusual. This factor looks much like *DDS*. A masking test—words masked by background speaking, correlated 0·30 with this factor, but this test also loaded on a separate factor with the only other masking test included in Karlin's battery. This latter might be interpreted as an under-determined form of the Masked Speech Comprehension factor.

Harris (1964) reported a study in which different kinds of background masking sounds and different kinds of signal sounds were systematically varied. Three separate masking factors were isolated in this investigation. The second of these was a clear example of the Masked Speech Comprehension factor. The first factor represented an ability to detect a variety of sound signals (shrimp noises, propeller noises) masked by a variety of sounds, provided only that the signal was not speech. The third factor was less clearly defined than the other two, but appeared to represent a sensitivity to different intensities of the signal under masking conditions. It was not possible in this study to tell whether or not this factor could be separated from a loudness factor of the kind identified in Karlin's (1942) work.

The conclusion we can write at this time about closure processes in the auditory domain is that at least two distinct closure-like factors can be identified among auditory tests, that one of these indicates an ability to complete incomplete auditory patterns and the other involves a process of correctly identifying an auditory pattern that is embedded in surrounding sounds that to some extent distort the signal, but that the two factors do not align with formally similar factors identified among visual (figural) variables.

Reasoning and Temporal Integration

One of the characteristics which distinguishes most auditory tests from most visual tests is the fact that the subject's work rate is paced by the task (i.e. indirectly by the test constructor), not by the subject. The items of an auditory test come at a rate established by the recording. The speed of item presentation might be too slow or too fast for some of the subjects most of the time and for most of the subjects some of the time, but in either case the subject does not control this rate. It is true that characteristically in some visual tests (viz. memory span) and for most tests in some studies (e.g. Morrison, 1960) visually presented items have been administered in a paced manner, but these are exceptions. Auditory tests, on the other hand, are almost always paced. This means that the subject has no opportunity to look back on problems to check his answers or make sure that he really understood a problem. This introduces a kind of uncertainty and pressing need to make decisions in accordance with an external pace. This requirement is not found to such a degree in most visual tests. This means, that the subject is forced to deal with information as it comes to him in a relentless stream and yet he must at times, when answers must be provided, integrate over sections of this stream and make the best possible estimate of the correct answer. A number of theorists, perhaps most notably Hearnshaw (1956) and Pollack (1969), have discussed this kind of behavior under the heading of temporal integration. It would seem that individual differences in a capacity (or capacities) for temporal integration should be particularly prominent in auditory tests.

In our analyses we found a factor defined by several variables which *a priori*, could be said to call for temporal integration. One of the tests most prominent in this factor, for example, required the subject to retain awareness of a sound while listening to determine when the same sound occurred again in a series of sounds. In a typical item the subject would hear 8 sounds (tones or voices), one after the other at a steady, fast rate. Only 4 of the sounds are distinct, however. The subject's task is to indicate when he hears each of the distinct sounds for the first time. For example, sounds might come to him in the order la, la, me, me, re, so, re, so, in which case the correct answer would be

r		r		r	r		
1	2	3	4	5	6	7	8

The task thus requires a subject to retain stimulus percepts in immediate awareness and compare them to see if they differ from new incoming perceptions that come to him persistently in a time-based stream of stimulation. Subjects become confused in trying to do this task and, partly for this reason, the task is difficult.

A second type of test defining this factor was what we called "Syllables Form Board", because it was modeled on the Visual Form Board test of Thurstone's studies. The fundaments of our test were nonsense syllable sounds. In each item three such sounds were presented one after the other. There was a slight pause, after which the subject heard the same three sounds again, one after the other, but in a different order. The task was to remember the order of the sounds on the first presentation, represent this by the numbers 1, 2, and 3 and when the sounds were heard the second time, write the numbers representing them in the order in which they occurred the second time. For example, if the sound heard third on the first presentation occurred first on the second presentation and the sound heard first on the first presentation was heard second on the second playing, the subject would need to write 3, 1, 2 on his answer sheet. Again, the task required the subject to hold percepts in immediate awareness while also attending to, and processing, incoming percepts of a similar kind. Other tests of the factor also call for this kind of ability. Seashore's Time had a correlation of 0·27 with this factor, a finding which suggests that the ability involves, in part, a capacity to maintain attention on a task.

We have labeled the factor Temporal Reordering (*Tr*) to suggest a link with temporal integration but to point to the fact that the variables that are salient in the factor not only require maintaining alertness to a stream-like series of stimulations and keeping distinct percepts in mind, but also a mental reordering of these for purposes of making a response. It is clear, too, that the factor could represent the memory span function which has been identified in many studies of visual tests. The correlation between *Tr* and an estimate of the Span factor obtained from digits forward and letters backward subtests correlated only 0·35, however, when the reliabilities for the two factor estimates were found to be no lower than 0·70. Thus *Tr* does not appear to be simply a manifestation in auditory variables of the established span of apprehension factor.

To some extent, at least, most of what are called reasoning tests involve temporal integration, particularly when the reasoning task is set within the stream of stimulation which auditory tests provide. In order to deal with an analogy or series problem, one must first perceive relationships among several fundaments, then hold this awareness in mind and consider several possibilities which might represent the relationships in regard to new stimuli. In other words one must integrate the past with the future in the present. In visually presented tests, of course, one can keep checking back on the relationship of the past and checking ahead to apply the relationship on the new fundaments, and thus the demand to retain the past, perceive the future and integrate the two in the present is not so great. But in an analogies or series item set within an auditory stream of stimulation, the checking back possibility is eliminated and one must truly keep the educed relationship in the present while considering new stimulus patterns. Thus, it might be expected that reasoning tasks defined by auditory stimulation would, perhaps to a considerable extent, indicate capacity for temporal integration.

To study the reasoning processes revealed through tasks involving auditory input, we undertook to construct auditory tests that would, as closely as possible, parallel corresponding visual reasoning tasks, such as Figural Series, Analogies and Classifications. In one such test, for example, an item consisted of a chord comprised of three notes followed by four sets of three notes played individually; the subject's task was to select the one of these four alternatives which involved the same three notes as were in the original chord. In the Tonal Analogies test the subject first heard two notes that were related in a particular way (e.g. one middle C and one high C), then he heard a third note (e.g. middle A), after which he was given three alternative notes. The task was to select the one of these alternatives which was in the same relation to the third note in the original presentation as the second note was to the first.

An interesting result of our analyses with such tests is that they came together in a factor that was also defined by variables which had been designed or selected to indicate closure. The auditory test designed to imitate the Gottschaldt Figures test, for example, loaded 0·49 on this factor and had no loading of appreciable size on any other factor. Similarly Wing's Chord analysis correlated 0·42 with this factor. Yet, as noted in the section on closure variables, the factor was not so much dominated by putative tests of closure as it was dominated by tests demanding relation-perception, and the application of this understanding in recognizing or inventing new exemplars of the observed relation. Perhaps the factors should be identified with the Inductive Reasoning (*I*) factor established in many previous factor analytic studies with visual tests (French *et al.*, 1963). In any case it seems that the factor represents some form of reasoning, if not *I*, then perhaps General Reasoning (*R*), Deductive Reasoning (*D*) or a kind of reasoning that is confined largely to auditory perception. We have called it simply Auditory Reasoning, symbolized *Ra* (to distinguish it from *R*).

Broad Patterns of Relationships Among Auditory and Visual Abilities

If the auditory functions discussed in previous sections are to be regarded as primary abilities either equivalent to or comparable to the primary mental abilities established by factor analytic work on visual tests, then it might be expected that the auditory primaries would interrelate among themselves and with visual primaries to indicate the broad influences in intellectual development which have been outlined in theories such as the theory of fluid and crystallized intelligence (Cattell, 1957, 1963, 1967, 1968, 1971; Horn, 1965, 1966, 1967b, 1968, 1970b, 1972a, 1972c). In general, what my view of this theory states is that by virtue of a broad pattern of acculturational influences which operate somewhat independently of a broad pattern of physiological and incidental learning influences, we should find at some level of analyses among intellectual abilities two broad factors, one representing the crystallization of intellectual potential through acculturation (*Gc*) and one representing the capacities of intellect which, for a variety of reasons, have remained relatively immune to these acculturational influences (*Gf*). In this form of the theory it is also proposed that capacities for visual experience are themselves organized somewhat independently of the capacities for forming concepts, abstracting, perceiving relations, drawing inferences, etc. which constitute the intellect and are represented in *Gf* and *Gc*. However, because most tests designed to measure important aspects of intellect involve spatial concepts and utilize information presented through the visual modality, part of the reliable variance of these tests will reflect individual differences in visual capacities rather than individual differences in the capacities of intelligence. It is further supposed that by inspection some tests can be seen to be relatively "easy" when judged in terms of the requirements they impose for exercise of the intellect, but still clearly require apt visualization. On this basis it is argued that factor analytic studies can be designed to demonstrate a distinction between fluid and crystallized intelligence and a broad dimension (*Gv*) characterized by a variety of tasks all of which, however, involve visualization of some kind.

In the present extension of this theory it is proposed that just as visual capacities are organized somewhat independently of the capacities of intellect, so too are the capacities of audition. In most existing tests of intelligence these auditory capacities have not been emphasized or have been assessed only very indirectly. If, however, the functions of intellect are measured through tests which are based upon auditory perception, it can be shown that fluid and crystallized intelligence and broad visualization are distinguishable from a broad factor representing the organization of auditory functions (*Ga*).

To investigate this idea we first brought together a wide variety of auditory tests and factored among them in an effort to more definitely establish a primary-level structure of intellect for auditory tasks. It is the results from these analyses which I have tried to integrate with previous findings in the preceding sections. Using these results as our guide we next selected several tests—a minimum of three—to measure each of the auditory primary abilities which seemed to be fairly well indicated by the results—namely, the primaries I have referred to as:

Mr, Nonsymbolic Recognition Memory
Ry, Maintaining and Judging Rhythm
DDS, Detection of Distorted Speech
MSC, Masked Speech Comprehension
Tr, Temporal Reordering
Ra, Auditory Reasoning

We also selected tests—two in most cases, but one in some instances and three in one case, to measure each of the following visual primaries:

EMS: Evaluation of Semantic Systems
CMR: Cognition of Semantic Relations
V or *CMU*: Verbal Comprehension or Cognition of Semantic Units
I or *CSS*: Induction or Cognition of Symbolic Systems
CSU: Cognition of Symbolic Units
CFR: Cognition of Figural Relations
CFC: Cognition of Figural Classes
S or *CFS*: Spatial Orientation or Cognition of Figural Transformations
Vz or *CFT*: Visualization or Cognition of Figural Transformations
Cs or *CFU*: Speed of Closure or Cognition of Figural Units
Cf or *NFT*: Flexibility of Closure or Convergence on Figural Transformations
Ma or *MST*: Associative Rote Memory or Memory for Symbolic Relations
Ms or *MSS*: Span Memory or Memory for Symbolic Units

These primaries were selected on the basis of previous results (Horn, 1966; Horn and Bramble, 1967; Horn and Cattell, 1966) as being markers for the factors of fluid intelligence, crystallized intelligence and broad visualization.

Although in most cases we had at least two tests to mark each factor, there was not a sufficiency of markers to over-determine several of the visual primaries in an objectively rotated solution. Accordingly, primary factor measurements were obtained by linear combination of the scores on tests selected to measure the factor. In the case of the auditory primaries, test scores were standardized and weighted in proportion to the correlation of the test with the factor in a Promax-rotated solution. Since for each visual primary ability the tests selected to measure it were scored in the same way (number "correct"), the scores for the different tests were summed, thus weighting the tests roughly in proportion to length and, therefore, reliability. In accordance with the findings of Wackwitz and Horn (1971), it can be supposed that higher order factors based upon these estimates of primary abilities would be more stable in cross-validation than would be results based upon factoring visual and auditory tests at the primary level.

The intercorrelations among the auditory and visual primary abilities measured in this way were in most cases positive and significantly larger than zero. With a sample of 241 subjects, a correlation of the order of 0·15 is significantly different from zero. By this criterion al[but 16 of the correlations were positive and significant, that is, roughly 90% of the correlations indicated positive, nonchance relationships among variables. This percentage is somewhat larger than that found by Guilford (1964) for a very large sample of correlations among putative tests of visual intellectual abilities.

Of 171 correlations, only 4 were negative, two being −0·03 and −0·07, not significantly different from zero, and two being −0·17 and −0·18, values which would appear to be significant. Both of the latter were for the Masked Speech Comprehension factor, the first being with *EMS* and the second being with *V*.

In factoring the intercorrelations among the auditory and visual primary abilities, application of the root-one criterion suggested four factors. In the Varimax and Promax solutions these factors were cooperative but a basis for interpretation in terms of previous results could be discerned.

Factor 1 was defined by the visual primaries *CFR*, *CMR*, *I*, *CSU* and *Ms*, but also by *Mr*, *Tr* and *Ra* in the auditory realm. This could therefore be interpreted as indicating fluid intelligence, manifested both in the visual and the auditory tasks. Contrary to one of our expectations, the Rhythm primary did not appear with a prominent loading on this factor. Factor 2 had its principal loadings on *V*, *CMR*, *EMS* and *CSU* among the visual primaries and the *DDS*, *Ra* and *Tr* of the auditory primaries. This indicates a crystallized form of intelligence also manifested in both visual and auditory primary abilities. The third factor was defined primarily by the factors involving figural content, but *Ry* had what appeared to be a nonhyperplane loading. However, the factor could be fairly readily interpreted as indicating the broad visualization function identified in previous analyses. The fourth factor was defined almost exclusively by auditory primaries, each of which had a noteworthy correlation with the factor. The only visual primary that looked as if it might have a nonhyperplane relation to the factor was *Cs*. This correlated 0·28 with the factor in the Varimax solution and 0·16 in the Promax results.

These results thus lend support for an hypothesis that intelligence is indicated by auditory tests of the kind described in previous sections of this chapter. The distinction between fluid and crystallized intelligence is manifested in the auditory realm as well as in the visual realm. Yet auditory tests contain systematic variance that is independent of that indicating *Gf* and *Gc*, as well as *Gv* (although there may be some slight overlap of the variance with that of visual Gestalt closure).

The primary which had the most prominent correlation (0·75) with the broad auditory factor (*Ga*) was *Mr*, the primary made up largely of the Seashore tests and interpreted as indicating Nonsymbolic Recognition Memory. *Mr* also correlated with *Gf*. Next in order of correlation with the *Ga* factor was *MSC*, the primary measuring comprehension of speech that has been distorted by procedures such as masking. The only prominent correlation this primary had was with *Ga*, and this was 0·74. The correlations of *Ra*, *DDS* and *Tr* with *Ga* were 0·59, 0·49 and 0·43 respectively, and each of these primaries also had prominent loadings on either *Gf* or *Gc*. Thus, whatever it is that the broad auditory factor represents about human functioning, these preliminary results suggest that it is characterized not so much by temporal reordering, as we might have supposed, but by the kind of perceptual keenness and retention represented by *MSC* and *Mr*.

Summary and Conclusions

This review of the results from a number of studies already in the literature and results obtained from studies underway at Denver indicate that intelligence is manifested through a number of abilities called forth in coping with problems presented through auditory stimulation. Capacities for temporal reordering and tonal reasoning indicate both fluid and crystallized intelligence, and the latter is indicated also by abilities for detecting distorted speech, while the former is manifested in nonsymbolic recognition memory. It appears, however, that the auditory tests thus far developed have somewhat more variance in a broad auditory function common to them all than they do in intellectual factors also defined, and defined most fully, by visual primary abilities.* This broad auditory function seems to be characterized by the ability to detect speech when sound is superimposed and an ability to retain a sound percept in awareness for a short period of time in order to compare it for similarity with another sound.

In the larger scheme of things our analyses here suggest that we should probably begin to consider relating work on auditory and visual abilities to results from studies of tactile and kinesthetic abilities. I understand that some research of this kind is currently being carried forth by Edwin Fleishman and his co-workers. Perhaps we may look forward to having some integrative theory from that source in the near

* In fact, however, this indication in our findings may be due as much to the somewhat heavier sampling of visual primaries (relative to auditory primaries) as to any replicable difference in the variance contributions of the individual primaries.

future. It is also possible that some amounts of variance in intellect are contributed through olfaction and taste. These considerations suggest a twist on the hoary complaint that IQ tests do not provide really adequate measurement of intelligence. For if intelligence is developed and manifested through the several sensory-perceptual modalities, yet existing IQ tests depend primarily upon input through only one of these modalities and part of the reliable variance of these tests indicates sensory-perceptual organization other than that of a central intellective function, namely *Gv*, then these tests would be poorly balanced or biased measures of intelligence. According to this view, psychometrically balanced (cf. Horn and Cattell, 1965) measures of intelligence would need to include subtests representing the primary abilities unique to each sensory-perceptual modality and items representing the different modality variations on primary abilities. At this point in history, however, we appear to be almost light years away from this kind of measurement.

COMMENT ON HORN'S PAPER

S. G. VANDENBERG

My first reaction to the title of Horn's paper was that now we were leaving the somewhat rarified upper atmosphere of some of the earlier papers that provided a very intoxicating overview but not much detail, and would return to the more safe and solid ground of data, to use a partially mixed metaphor.

In addition, I had two conflicting feelings: on the one hand I was unhappy to be reminded that there are even more abilities for the behavior geneticist to consider than Guilford has discovered, but on the other hand I was hopeful that some of these new abilities may be more closely related to biological mechanisms than are the abilities called visual by Horn. If that were indeed true these "auditory" abilities may be more promising variables for behavior genetics studies.

I was also grateful for the literature cited, but sorry that Horn decided to give relatively little detail about his own study, in the interest of the theoretical orientation of this Conference. I shall await another publication. I find, however, that Horn is so productive that I can barely keep up with him in reading while he is writing.

I was pleased to see Horn quote Cattell that there are different ways of organizing data and to see Horn state that ". . . the problem of distinguishing possible levels of abilities cannot be solved by the methods of factor analysis alone". I was happy about this, because this point of view was exactly what motivated my paper. I wish more of that spirit had been displayed in earlier papers. I believe that the points of view of Vernon and Guilford about intelligence are both correct within the restrictions they impose and that they can both be useful. I wish to second Pawlik's remarks that Royce's efforts at reconciling and integrating different systems was perhaps not fully appreciated for what it is.

After these general remarks I will now comment on a few specific points in Horn's paper. I am not sure that the term "visual" is a good choice of a name for the tests which do not use auditory stimuli, nor am I happy about the term "auditory". However, Horn has himself made it clear that he uses the latter term in a different way than is sometimes the case. Perhaps "tests presented through the auditory or visual modality" might be better labels.

I hope that Horn does not subscribe to the idea that different sensory functions are narrowly localized in what might be called "brain centers". Perhaps some areas are more important than others for certain functions, but precise localization is probably rare so that even if it occurs it is a very unstable, fleeting phenomenon. DeValois *et al.* (1966) have shown that the same cells are involved in the perception of all 3 primary colors and these also take part in form perception and perception of movement, but each time in different combinations and with different weights, so that the perception of a colored object and naming it probably involves many areas of the brain and not always the same cells.

Broadbent has studied some phenomena similar to those studied by Horn, but he presented stimuli to the two ears separately. While Broadbent has been more interested in the general experimental results, he has reported individual differences. For a general account of these studies see Broadbent (1971). Kimura's work (1964, 1967) may also provide relevant information.

Horn mentioned that the intercorrelations between the Seashore musical aptitude subtests average around 0·35. This seems rather high. I wonder if this could be an example of the kind of correlated errors which were mentioned yesterday. I would also like to know whether Dr. Horn has information about the size of test re-test correlations for these tests? Perhaps being capable of following instructions and sustained attention are the common elements in the performance on these tests which produce spurious correlations. It may make a difference whether the subject can somehow hold an auditory image of the stimuli as a counterpart of (visual) eidetic imagery.

Horn found a factor which he named "detection of distorted speech".

This sounded to me, as I was reading, rather like the mutilated words test of Thurstone which measures speed of closure, and the masked speech comprehension test sounded rather like the embedded figures test which measures flexibility of closure, and this is precisely what Horn found as I discovered when I continued to read. I was sorry that no final conclusion could be drawn about the question whether these two closure factors span the two modalities or whether tests within the same modality stay together. I wondered whether the two types of tests were administered in an intermingled order or whether the visual tests were given one after another and all the auditory tests together before or after the visual tests.

The term cooperative factors is used by Horn. Does this mean that some tests were loading on two or more factors?

How do the abilities described by Horn relate to tone deafness? Kalamus (1948) used tunes with one or more false notes in them to study what he called tune deafness in families, but he discontinued his work when he had satisfied himself that the data did not fit a single gene model. Nevertheless his technique may be useful for other studies. It is also possible that a polygenic model of inheritance might be fitted to his data.

In closing, I find Horn's work very promising and I hope he will be able to continue and extend it.

COMMENT ON HORN'S PAPER

J. P. GUILFORD

I was delighted to know that someone of Horn's energy and usual perspicacity has undertaken to extend our knowledge of abilities for processing auditory information, a badly neglected field. For some time I have predicted that we should find a complete set of 30 auditory-figural abilities, parallel to the visual-figural abilities, all but three of which have been demonstrated. There may be some auditory-symbolic abilities, also, but this seems less probable, since tests involving speech and tests involving musical tones have been known to go together on factors.

Although he may not wish to take credit for it, Horn has apparently discovered or confirmed a number of auditory-figural abilities that seem to be in the direction of structure of intellect (*SI*) abilities. My hypothetical identifications are: *Mr* with *MFU-A*, *DDS* with *CFU-A*, *Tr* with *MFS-A*, and *Rs* with *CFR-A*. There is also a probable *NFT-A* factor, parallel to the much replicated *NFT-V* factor, with hidden-melodies tests on the one hand clearly parallel with hidden-figures tests on the other. Factor *MSC* may be a perceptual or sensory ability rather than intellectual.

Like those of us who have analysed for *SI* abilities, Horn has found that it pays to develop auditory tests parallel in psychological nature to tests that have already marked visual-figural abilities. Some of the new auditory tests are quite ingenious. This strategy should be extended for other auditory abilities that may fit the *SI* model. The model would only need to be expanded to include a fifth content category. Applying the same research strategy, Feldman (1969), at the University of Southern California, differentiated (at the first-grade level) three pairs of visual and auditory abilities—two each for *CFU*, *MFU*, and *EFU*—and found them all related to achievement in first-grade reading. I should say, however, that in using parallels Horn's emphasis on closure tests was misplaced. In our research at USC we found that closure is not a necessary quality of tests for abilities *CFU* and *NFT*, the essential components of Thurstone's *C1* and *C2* factors.

An incidental error is Horn's misinterpretation of what is a visual test. For example, in planning his higher-order analysis, he included three first-order semantic abilities and two symbolic abilities among his "visual" factors. The fact that the sensory input to subjects is a printed page does not make the ability visual. This misconception has subtle ramifications in his thinking, and it applies to auditory tests as well.

I was pleased to see that Horn seems to agree with me on the uncertainty in finding higher-order factors by oblique rotations, when he says "The samplings of variables and subjects determines how broad a factor will be. . ." I believe that in his method of search for higher-order factors he is on the right track in principle, i.e., in finding tests to represent first-order factors, then to intercorrelate factor scores. Something more needs to be done in determining factor scores, however. A simple summation score is not likely to be colinear with its main factor, and its communality is short of unity.

For these and other reasons, I have been unable to accept the demonstrations proposed for "fluid" and "crystallized" intelligences. Logically, it would seem that if these broad variables exist as unities, the latter should be equivalent to the cognition abilities (perhaps only the semantic ones) of the *SI* model, since these abilities are so directly dependent upon memory storage, which is in turn dependent upon experience. "Fluid" intelligence superficially suggests divergent-production abilities (they are less directly dependent upon memory storage), but I suspect that it is meant to include more than that. The Horn–Cattell analyses have not confirmed the kind of differentiation that I have suggested. Their selection of first-order factors has not been sufficiently systematic, for one thing. The "broad visualization" factor that comes in addition to the expected higher-order dimensions might represent a broad visual-figural-cognition affair, although it is not certain how many of the abilities in that category are included. I am sure that not all of them have been systematically covered in their analyses.

COMMENT ON HORN'S PAPER

K. PAWLIK

I like Horn's paper and its emphasis on systematic exploration of auditory functions. The section I was particularly interested in is the one dealing with auditory-visual relationships. Several years ago, I became intrigued by the question as to whether or not sensory processes may show interindividual correlation across sense modalities such that interindividual differences in the exponent of the psychophysical power function would correlate between sensory continua. In a first (yet unpublished) study we got inconsistent results: The exponents for brightness and loudness correlated 0·46 in males, but 0·39 in females. It would be of interest to know whether Horn has found any related studies or similar findings.

REFERENCES

Broadbent, D. E. (1971). "Decision and Stress." Academic Press, New York and London.
Brown, R. (1958). "Words and Things." Free Press, Glencoe, Illinois.
Bruner, J. S., Goodnow, J. J. and Austin, G. A. (1956). "A Study of Thinking." Wiley, New York.
Brunswik, E. (1956). "Perception and the Representative Design of Psychological Experiments." University of California Press, Berkeley, California.
Burt, C. (1949). Subdivided factors. *Br. J. statist. Psychol.* **2,** 41–63.
Campbell, D. T. and Fiske, D. W. (1959). Convergent and discriminant validation by the multitrait-multimethod matrix. *Psychol. Bull.* **56,** 81–105.
Carroll, J. B. (1953). "The Study on Language." Harvard University Press, Cambridge, Massachusetts.
Carroll, J. B. (1962). The prediction of success in intensive foreign language training. *In* "Training and Education Research." (Glaser, R., ed.) University of Pittsburgh Press, Pittsburgh, Pennsylvania.
Cattell, R. B. (1950). "Personality." McGraw-Hill, New York.
Cattell, R. B. (1957). "Personality and Motivation Structure and Measurement." World Book, Yonkers-on-Hudson, New York.

Cattell, R. B. (1963). Theory of fluid and crystallized intelligence: A critical experiment. *J. educ. Psychol.* **54,** 1–22.

Cattell, R. B. (1965). Higher order factor structures: Reticular vs. hierarchical formulae for their interpretation. *In* "Studies in Psychology." (Banks, C. and Broadhurst, P. L., eds), Chapter 14. University of London Press, London.

Cattell, R. B. (1967). The theory of fluid and crystallized intelligence checked at the 5–6 year-old level. *Br. J. educ. Psychol.* **37,** 209–224.

Cattell, R. B. (1968). Fluid and crystallized intelligence. *Psychol. Today* **3,** 56–62.

Cattell, R. B. (1971). "Abilities: Their Structure, Growth, and Action." Houghton Mifflin, Boston.

Cronbach, L. G. (1950). Further evidence on response sets and test design. *Educ. psychol. Measur.* **10,** 3–31.

DeValois, R. L., Abramor, I. and Jacobs, G. H. (1966). Analysis of response patterns of LGN cells. *J. opt. Soc. Am.* **56,** 966–977.

Drake, R. M. (1957). "Manual for the Drake Musical Aptitude Tests." Science Research Associates, Chicago.

Feldman, B. (1969). Prediction of first-grade reading achievement from selected structure-of-intellect factors. Unpublished doctoral dissertation, University of Southern California.

Fieldhouse, A. E. (1937). A study of backwardness in singing among school children. Ph.D. dissertation. University of London.

Fleishman, E. A., Roberts, N. H. and Freidman, M. P. (1958). Factor analysis of aptitude and proficiency measures in radio-telegraphy. *J. appl. Psychol.* **42,** 127–137.

French, J. W., Ekstrom, R. B. and Price, L. A. (1963). Manual for Kit of Reference Tests for Cognitive Factors. Educational Testing Service, Princeton, New Jersey.

French, J. W. (1951). The description of aptitude and achievement tests in terms of rotated factors. "Psychometric Monograph No. 5." University of Chicago Press, Chicago.

Fruchter, B. (1951). Error scores as a measure of carefulness. *J. educ. Psychol.* **41,** 279–291.

Fruchter, B. (1953). Differences in factor content of rights and wrongs scores. *Psychometrika* **18,** 257–265.

Guilford, J. P. (1967). "The Nature of Human Intelligence." McGraw-Hill, New York.

Guilford, J. P. (1964). Zero intercorrelations among tests of intellectual abilities. *Psychol. Bull.* **61,** 401–404.

Guilford, J. P. and Hoepfner, R. (1971). "The Analyses of Intelligence." McGraw-Hill, New York.

Hanley, C. M. (1956). Factor analysis of speech perception. *J. Speech Hear. Disorders* **21,** 76–87.

Harris, J. D. (1964). A factor analytic study of three signal detection abilities. *J. Speech Hear. Res.* **7,** 71–78.

Hearnshaw, B. S. (1956). Temporal integration and behavior. *Bull. Br. Psychol.Soc.* **9,** 1–20.

Horn, J. L. (1965). Fluid and crystallized intelligence: A factor analytic and development study of the structure among primary mental abilities. Ph.D. dissertation, University of Illinois.

Horn, J. L. (1966). Short period fluctuations in intelligence. Final Report: NASA Grant in the Space-Related Sciences, Project No. DRI–614, Ns G–518. Denver Research Institute.

Horn, J. L. (1967a). On subjectivity in factor analysis. *Educ. psychol. Measur.* **27,** 811–820.

Horn, J. L. (1967b). Intelligence—why it grows, why it declines. *Trans-action* **5,** 23–31.

Horn, J. L. (1968). Organization of abilities and the development of intelligence. *Psychol. Rev.* **75,** 242–259.

Horn, J. L. (1969). On the reparation of a concept. *Contemp. Psychol.* **14,** 624–625.

Horn, J. L. (1970a). J. P. Guilford's "The Nature of Human Intelligence: A Review." *Psychometrika* **35,** 273–277.

Horn, J. L. (1970b). Organization of data on life-span development of human abilities. *In* "Life-span Developmental Psychology." (Goulet, L. R. and Baltes, P. B. eds), 423–466. Academic Press, New York and London.

Horn, J. L. (1972a). The structure of intellect: Primary abilities. *In* "Multivariate Personality Research: Contributions to the understanding of personality in honour of Raymond B. Cattell." (Dreger, R. M. ed.) in press.

Horn, J. L. (1972b). The Porteus Maze Test: A review. *In* "Seventh Mental Measurements Yearbook." (Buros, O. K. ed.) Rev. 429, 753–756.

Horn, J. L. (1972c). State, trait and change dimension of intelligence. *Br. J. educ. Psychol.* **42,** 159–185.

Horn, J. L. (1973). Personality and ability theory. *In* "The Handbook of Modern Personality Theory." (Cattell, R. B. ed.) in press.

Horn, J. L. and Bramble, W. J. (1967). Second order ability structure revealed in rights and wrongs scores. *J. educ. Psychol.* **58,** 115–122.

Horn, J. L. and Cattell, R. B. (1966). Refinement and test of the theory of fluid and crystallized intelligence. *J. educ. Psychol.* **57,** 253–270.

Kalmus, H. (1948). Tune deafness and its inheritance. *Proceedings of the 8th International Congress of Genetics.* Stockholm.

Karlin, J. E. (1941). Music ability. *Psychometrika* **6,** 61–65.

Karlin, J. E. (1942). A factorial study of auditory function. *Psychometrika* **7,** 251–279.

Kelley, H. P. (1964). "Memory Abilities: A Factor Analysis." Psychometric Monograph No. 11. William Byrd, Richmond, Virginia.

Kimura, D. (1964). Left–right differences in the perception of melodies. *Q. Jl. Expl. Psychol.* **16,** 355–358.

Kimura, D. (1967). Functional asymmetry of the brain in dichotic listening. *Cortex* **3,** 163–178.

Miller, G. A. (1951). "Language and Communication." McGraw-Hill, New York.

Morrison, J. R. (1960). "Effects of time limits on the efficiency and factorial composition of reasoning measures." Ph.D. dissertation. University of Illinois.

Ohnmacht, F. W., Weaver, W. W. and Kohler, E. T. (1970). Cloze and closure: A factorial study. *J. Psychol.* **74,** 205–217.

Pawlik, K. (1966). Concepts in human cognition and aptitudes. *In* "Handbook of Multivariate Experimental Psychology." (Cattell, R. B. ed.) Rand McNally, Chicago.

Pollack, R. H. (1969). Some implications of ontogenetic changes in perception. *In* "Studies in Cognitive Development." (Elkind, D. and Flavell, J. H. eds) Oxford University Press, London.

Revesz, G. (1953). "Introduction to the Psychology of Music." Longmans, Green, London.

Revesz, G. and Berkeley, G. (1950). "Psychology and the Art of the Blind." Longmans, New York.

Saporta, S. (1961). "Psycholinguistics." Holt, Rinehart and Winston, New York.
Seashore, C. E. (1919). "The psychology of Musical Talent." Silver Burdett, New York.
Seashore, C. E. (1938). "Psychology of Music." McGraw-Hill, New York.
Shuter, R. (1968). "The Psychology of Music Ability." Methuen, London.
Solomon, L. M., Webster, J. C. and Curtis, J. F. (1960). A factorial study of speech perception. *J. Speech Hear. Res.* 101–107.
Staats, A. W. (1968). "Learning, Language and Cognition." Holt, Rinehart and Winston, New York.
Stevens, S. S. (1960). The psychophysics of sensory function. *Am. Scient.* **48,** 226–253.
Taylor, W. L. (1957). "Cloze" readability scores as indices of individual differences in comprehension and aptitude. *J. appl. Psychol.* **41,** 19–26.
Thurstone, L. L. (1936). The factorial isolation of primary abilities. *Psychometrika* **1,** 175–182.
Thurstone, L. L. (1944). "A factorial study of perception." Psychometric Monogr. No. 4. University of Chicago Press, Chicago.
Wackwitz, J. H. and Horn, J. L. (1971). On obtaining the best estimates of factor scores within an ideal simple structure. *Multivar. behav. Res.* **6,** 389–408.
White, W. B. (1954). Visual and auditory closure. *J. Expl. Psychol.* **48,** 234–240.
Wing, H. D. (1955). Musical aptitude and intelligence. *Educ. Today* **5,** No. 1.
Wing, H. D. (1962). A revision of the Wing musical aptitude test. *J. Res. Musical Educ.* **10.**
Witkin, H. A. (1967). The perception of the upright, 1959. *In* "Problems of Human Assessment." (Jackson, D. N. and Messick, S. eds) McGraw-Hill, New York.

Theoretical Issues and Operational-Informational Psychology*

J. P. GUILFORD

University of Southern California

One of the significant fallouts from the construction of the structure of intellect model to represent intellectual abilities has been the proposal of a new point of view in psychology called "operational-informational" (Guilford, 1966, 1967). A complete system of operational-informational (OI) psychology has not been generated, but enough of the characteristics of such a system are sufficiently clear to enable us to relate the view to historical systems and to see how it deals with a number of the major systematic issues. It will be argued that an OI psychology has an excellent chance of becoming a frame of reference for a complete science of behavior.

Some Major Issues

Although the better-known historical issues are related in various ways, they can be differentiated sufficiently for purposes of discussion. The oldest issue with which modern psychologists were concerned pertained to whether the emphasis should be on mental powers or faculties or on mental operations. Herbart and the British associationists provided a lasting decision on that question a long time ago. With the emergence of factor analysis and its demonstrations of separate abilities, the issue has been raised again rather incidentally in this century.

In the beginnings of scientific psychology with the German philosophers, a major schism developed, stemming largely from Wundt on the one hand and Brentano on the other, as to whether psychology should be concerned with mental content or with mental acts. In the history of debates on this issue, apparently ending with Titchener

* The writer is indebted to Dr. Harry Helson, who kindly read and commented on a preliminary manuscript of this paper.

(1929), it seems not to have occurred to the protagonists that a complete psychology should give attention to both act and content. It is possible that Titchener was toying with that kind of solution before he died, as some who knew him well believed. Each summer he had given a course on Brentano, but if he had any such idea, he did not make it explicit. Subsidiary act-content problems had to do with what kinds of acts and what kinds of contents should be recognized or featured.

A host of problems arose under the general heading of "elementarism"; some said "atomism". In agreement with scientists of other breeds, psychologists accepted description as an essential goal, and they realized that description involves some kind of analysis. Any phenomenon has to be noted piecemeal, and communication (another scientific requirement) has to be accomplished item by item. Understanding also demands analysis. But in connection with analysis, a number of basic questions arose. How far should analysis go? What are the ultimate units that are needed? Should analysis be aimed at finding constituent elements or properties or variables, or all of these?

Analysis implies synthesis, and in psychology this led to the principle of association, first announced by Aristotle and developed into a cornerstone by the British associationists. The great success with this principle, from Wundt to Ebbinghaus to Watson, led to a considerable feeling of comfort with it and to overconfidence in accomplishments with its applications. The Gestalt psychologists were the first with the temerity to offer a real challenge to this conception.

What may be called an "objective-subjective" issue was raised with considerable impact by the behaviorists. Before Watson, psychologists had been little concerned with motor activity, except by incidental reference in connection with voluntary action and conation. Watson, fed up with the quibblings of the "mentalistic" psychologists and with their lack of objective, communicable observations, went all the way toward what he considered to be an entirely objective science, with restriction of observations to stimuli and responses, and to finding laws relating them. There was complete rejection of what older psychologists had called "content", and, in addition to rejection of introspective observations, there was little attempt even to infer mental events, called "implicit behavior", from observations of overt behavior.

In what follows, the various issues that have been mentioned will be considered in connection with various points of view or schools of psychology, and in connection with the operational-informational point of view that has been suggested by the structure of intellect (SI) conception of intelligence. It can be shown that these issues find much resolution from the latter direction. In the process, the issues will be elaborated in some respects.

The Structure of Intellect

It will be assumed that the reader has at least some acquaintance with the SI theory and model (Guilford, 1967; Guilford and Hoepfner, 1971). In briefest terms, all intellectual abilities, of which about a hundred have already been differentiated by factor analysis, are viewed from three different aspects. From the aspect of mental activity, each ability represents one of five kinds of operation: cognition (knowing, being aware of, or possessing, items of information); memory (committing items of information to storage); divergent production (searching for and generating items of information); convergent production (finding fully determined items in response to given items) and evaluation (comparing items and accepting or rejecting them).

From the aspect of content,* there are four substantive kinds of information or four major code systems: figural (having sensory characteristics); symbolic ("token" items, such as numbers and letters); semantic (items thought of, not sensed at the moment or imaged); and behavioral (psychological states, such as feelings and intentions). Within each of the four content categories, the same six formal kinds of information, or products, apply: units (relatively simple mental objects); classes (conceptions embracing the common features of sets of items); relations (meaningful connections between items); systems (organizations or relatively complex structures); transformations (changes, shifts, or reorganizations); and implications (expectations).

It may be noted that the term "item of information" applies to any kind of product in any kind of content. Each separate intellectual ability involves a particular kind of operation, kind of content, and kind of product, in a unique conjunction. For example, the ability might be for the cognition of symbolic transformations, for divergent production of figural systems, or for evaluation of semantic implications.

Faculties and Factors

By virtue of factor analysts' emphasis upon finding unique or unitary abilities, there is naturally a question of whether factor analysis has not given us a faculty psychology in new dress. The search for distin-

* In the SI view, "content" is the substantive aspect of information, where information is defined as "that which is discriminated". The act and content psychologists commonly equated "content" to consciousness. There is no similar implication in the SI view.

guishable abilities does offer a basic similarity in terms of goals, but beyond that the resemblances are superficial. Theorywise, when the faculty psychologist's thinking did not regard the powers as separate agents, thus flirting with animism, and if he regarded faculties as functions, his kind of conception is not to be condemned. His main trouble was that he had no empirical method for discovering unique powers or for testing his rational hypotheses regarding them.

The faculty psychologist was mostly, but not entirely, wrong about his taxonomy of unitary powers. He hypothesized a faculty of memory, but factor analysis has demonstrated 20 memory abilities, and very likely there are quite a few more than that. He conceived of a faculty of reasoning, but a large number of reasoning abilities have been found. The 24 known cognition abilities in the structure of intellect may be regarded as inductive-reasoning abilities, if we are willing to enlarge the conception of induction. The 15 known convergent-production abilities may qualify as deductive reasoning abilities, again, with enlargement of a conception. In place of a supposed faculty of judgment, we now know 18 evaluation abilities. In so far as there was a faculty of imagination, we can now cite the area of divergent production, in which 23 abilities have been demonstrated.* Thus, we might say that the faculty psychologists had anticipated the five operation categories of SI theory.

A very significant question regarding faculty psychology for us here is whether the psychologist's theorizing should emphasize powers or functions. As for modern aptitude factors, it is quite easy to take the logical step from factorial abilities to kinds of functioning. Intellectual abilities have had to be segregated by multivariate investigations of how individuals differ in goodness of performance in tasks that are systematically varied as to kind of information involved and as to kind of activity or processing that must be applied in connection with it. Once the differentiated functions have been pointed out in this manner, it is easy to see their relevance in the behavior of individuals and to initiate investigations for probing further into their properties, their development, and their roles in behavior.

The Act–Content Issue

Even at the time of his death, Titchener (1929) was saying, at least in print, "The student of psychology . . . must still make his choice for the one or the other. There is no middle ground between Brentano and Wundt" (pp. 3–4). Although Brentano and his followers insisted

* For details concerning all these distinctions, see Guilford and Hoepfner (1971).

that there is no act without a content, for in the definition of "act" it was said that an act "intends" a content, they paid little or no attention to content. On the other hand, Wundt and Titchener saw no place for acts, since their methods of observation permitted them to see only contents. In terms of SI categories of content, the Wundt-Titchener contents were restricted to figural and behavioral information, for sensations and images on the one hand and feelings on the other.

Although they were far removed from the mentalistic debates of the philosopher-psychologists, behaviorists developed a psychology that may be classified in the act category. At least it avoided content completely.

The American functionalists recognized both act and content, by analogy to organ and function in biology. They often spoke of consciousness as if it were an agent with biological utility, and paid relatively little attention to consciousness as content.

Thus, there were strong tendencies for schools of psychology to go one way or the other, as Titchener declared to be necessary, without sufficient realization that such psychologies could not be complete sciences. An operational-informational psychology based upon SI theory, however, gives full attention to both act and content (operations and kinds of information). Furthermore, the SI approach derives empirically a long list of kinds of acts, each intimately tied to different kinds of contents and products, all organized systematically.

It is possible to see in act psychologies a few distinctions suggestive of SI constructs. For example, Brentano's three main classes of acts included "ideating" and "judging". Ideating was described as if it embraced the SI categories of cognition, divergent production, and convergent production. His judging class appears similar to the SI category of evaluation.

Stumpf's (1906) functional psychology recognized two major classes of acts—intellectual and emotional. Within the former, he distinguished perceiving, which he conceived as including sensing and ideating, and which can be equated to figural cognition in SI terminology. His construct of comprehension or grouping seems like cognition also but the label "grouping" suggests the SI product of class, which is not an act. An act of grouping is best equated to convergent production of classes. He also spoke of an act of system forming, which can be equated to either divergent or convergent production of systems, with content unspecified. Other Stumpf constructs were "conception", which is described as if it were equivalent to semantic content, and "judgment", which can be equated with evaluation. Thus, of all the act psychologists, Stumpf went furthest in making distinctions resembling those among SI categories, but in places he seemed to fail to discriminate the three SI parameters. He evidently saw the need for informational constructs but tried to get along with operations only.

As already stated, Wundt and Titchener recognized figural information, but not as such, in their emphasis upon sensation. To the extent that they treated feelings and emotions as different from sensations, they also implicitly recognized behavioral information of the self-initiated variety. None of the act or content psychologists mentioned here recognized either symbolic or semantic information, at least as content, and none had much to say that would indicate awareness of SI products as kinds of items of information.

It is sometimes remarked by those who write about psychological theories that leaders, particularly those of act schools, tended to end up in the fields of epistemology and logic (Helson, 1925; Titchener, 1929). This trend may have been natural for the early philosopher-psychologists, who lived in an atmosphere of epistemology and logic. From the beginnings of modern psychology, the philosopher's question concerning how man can know was a strong instigating force. Even in contemporary times, we find that Piaget has also emerged with theory featuring epistemology and logic.

Some outcomes from the structure of intellect have given positive support to this kind of theory. The writer has proposed (Guilford, 1966, 1967) that the 24 kinds of information (four contents times six products) provide an empirically derived psychoepistemology, and that the 6 products provide a basis for a psycho-logic. The details of such a psycho-logic remain to be worked out, but however this may develop, the informational categories provide useful concepts for the fruitful descriptions of behavior, and the fears of involvement in logic and epistemology have proved to be unfounded.

Elementarism

Although the natural urge to analyse carried early modern psychologists a long way toward understanding many things in their subject matter, along the way there have appeared restraining voices regarding how much analysis should be applied, what kind it should be, and what kind of end results should be sought. In the process of searching for units, there was scepticism as to whether mental acts, as such, could be observed and described at all. There was also an urge for a science of psychology to stay close to observed data. Inferences from data were to be mistrusted. These circumstances were largely responsible for the content psychologies of Wundt and Titchener. The elements for the former were sensations, images, and feelings. For the latter, all were eventually reduced to sensations.

Following this choice to its logical conclusion, Titchener ruled meaning, as such, out of psychology. Meaning, he thought, belongs to epistemology. It can be reported but not observed, and scientific data must be observed. He sought to account for the phenomenon of meaning, however, by means of his context theory. Seen in terms of observable experience, meaning has a core composed of certain sensations and a context composed of other sensations, some of which are in the form of images. His rejection of meaning, as such, lost from his psychology the all important SI category of semantic information. He was thus left with the alternative of attempting to account for all mental events in terms of figural information. Although there are obvious parallels between figural and other kinds of information, and there are bridges in the form of translations between them, it is impossible to describe all mental processes adequately in terms of the figural language or coding only.

The objections just raised are not so much against elementarism, as such, as against restriction to one kind of information. Gestalt psychologists, on the other hand, attacked the usefulness of any kind of elements. They derided the goal of obtaining understanding of the complexities of mental functioning out of such building blocks; of obtaining something meaningful out of components that are in themselves meaningless. The analogy to chemistry, although faulty, was not missed. There may have been no intentional imitation of the successful science of chemistry, but a label of "mental chemistry" was sometimes justifiably applied by critics.

Some psychologists of the preceding century thought the cure for the deficiencies of Wundtian psychology was to be found in adding other kinds of elements, some of which became known as "imageless thoughts". This proposal suggests something meaningful, in other words, semantic information. In this way, meaning could be treated within the content observed by psychologists. The imageless-thought school believed that acts also could be observed, and they designed experiments to achieve this end. The observer was given a simple task, and after its completion he was to report what mental events took place in his thinking.

Examples of the tasks not only illustrate the range of mental exercises utilized but also clearly stand as prototypes of what later became known as mental tests. In his studies of judgement, Marbe gave tasks of lifting weights, reproducing tones vocally, adding numbers, and answering questions with "yes" or "no". Watt employed word-association and reaction-time tasks. Ach studied mental processes during voluntary actions, while Messer emphasized choices, decisions, and opinions. Bühler subjected his subjects to questioning, followed by retrospections on what thinking operations the questions instigated. Woodworth introduced the use of syllogisms and analogies. The list of tasks thus grew in resemblance to modern psychological tests. To make them into psychological tests, two steps were needed: to standardize the tasks and to obtain scores as objective data to replace self observations. Factor analysis has depended upon the execution of those steps.

Some of the new kinds of elements reported by the imageless-thought psychologists were known as *Bewusstseinslage* and *Bewusstheit*. The former is probably best translated as "mental attitudes", which observers could identify as having transpired in their carrying out of the tasks. Many of the attitudes mentioned are tinged with emotions, e.g. doubt, uneasiness, feeling of effort, hesitation, and vacillation, and some of their opposites, e.g. assent, conviction, and feeling of certainty. Less emotional attitudes included expectation, memory for instructions and rules, and familiarity with presented information.

Bewusstheit is often translated as simply awareness, but this category of elements included more than the kind of awareness represented by the SI category of cognition. Some elements of *Bewusstheit* were: meaning, relation, reproductive tendency, and *Aufgabe* (problem). The parallels in SI theory appear to be semantic content (for meaning), and the product of relation (for the element of the same name). Reproductive tendency could probably be most often observed in connection with divergent production and convergent production, because of the heavy involvement of recall in those operations. A problem is often a semantic system. Thus, the imageless-thought psychologists seem to have been taking steps toward recognition of SI contents and products. Although such items of information were said to have been observed, it can be suspected that many of them were only inferred. This conjecture is supported by occasional recognition that such things occur unconsciously as well as consciously.

The most violent critics of analysis into elements, of course, were the Gestalt psychologists, who came into prominence with their objections early in the 1920s. Again and again, they voiced objections to the theoretical manoeuvre of "*und-Verbingung*", insisting that "the whole is more than the sum of its parts". The institution of Gestalt psychology was undoubtedly stimulated in part by von Ehrenfels' *Gestaltqualität*, but the Gestaltists were quick to say that the latter was simply another element.

As is well known, Gestalt psychologists objected most to direct analysis of experience into constituent parts, for in doing so the most important thing is lost—the total configuration. In this view their objections included the elementarism in behaviorism, which sometimes sought to account for all behavior in terms of combinations of reflexes, usually conditioned. Gestaltists did recognize that there are parts to configurations, but always insisted upon the priority of wholes and upon the principle that parts derive their properties from membership in wholes. Although they often held up a prohibiting hand to analysis in general, according to Helson (1925), they favored a "functional" type of analysis, with primary interest in determining the necessary and sufficient conditions for the occurrence of configurations and the laws of perception, retention, and change of configurations.

It may be said that Gestalt psychology accepted both act and content as subject matter, but it did not attempt to develop a taxonomy of either kind. It was more concerned with discovering the laws of configurations at large, and it applied such laws quite broadly in behavior, at much risk of overgeneralization. By virtue of the general emphasis on phenomenology, they aimed always to stay close to observation. This may have accounted for their preference for experiments in the field of perception, with its consequent emphasis on figural information. There was a strong expectation that principles found applying to figural information would pertain also to other kinds of information. Although holding to the ideal of direct observation, on occasion they obviously resorted to inferences, as when Köhler reported what his primates perceived or thought, and when he insisted that a chicken that distinguishes a small difference between the lightness of two surfaces is perceiving a "step up" or a "step down".

There are so many points of contact between SI theory and Gestalt psychology that further thoughts on this subject are reserved for more detailed treatment later in this paper.

Associationism

Associationism went hand in hand with elementarism, being introduced to answer the question of how simple events get together to form more complex phenomena in psychological nature. The principle of association had behind it the prestige of Aristotle and the demonstrations of certain theoretical utilities in British philosophical psychology. It was apparently the answer to so many combinatorial problems in later psychologies that it was not often questioned. Ebbinghaus gave the principle priority in his investigations of memory, which set the pattern for many years, to the neglect of other kinds of memory events (see Guilford, 1971). Behaviorists found a different kind of associating to be the key to the forming of stimulus-response sequences, and the organizing of those elements into complex events in behavior.

As they challenged the traditional elementarism, Gestalt psychologists also took almost as vigorous exception to the principle of association. For example, they asked how meaning could arise out of hooking together meaningless elements. This begs the question, for the elements need not be meaningless, as Gestaltists themselves recognized when they insisted that so-called associations are not formed without regard to the properties of the things associated. In their conception, there are no fortuitous connections. They felt it necessary to withdraw from this extreme view later, however.

Thus, although recognizing the phenomenon known as association, they gave it their own interpretation. Koffka's definition is sometimes quoted (Helson, 1925, p. 354): "If A, B, and C have once or several times been present in experience as members of a configuration, and if one of them appears bearing its membership character, then the tendency is present for the whole structure to be completed, more or less fully and vividly." To be noted is the emphasis on "as members of a configuration". A totality of some kind must be in the picture, even presumably when such a totality is not observable, as in a word-association reaction. Köhler (1941) did go so far as to accept association by contiguity as a limiting case but he insisted that even in such an event there is a kind of unity about the outcome.

There has sometimes arisen a question as to whether there is a phenomenon that is justifiably called "association by similarity". It has been a troublesome problem for those who have insisted that no things can become associated without having occurred in juxtaposition. Koffka's answer was that similar things have the same structure (unfortunately he would have to accept the qualification "in part"), and structures, as such, are remembered.

As another indication of Gestaltist's views, it can be said that Wertheimer (1945) admitted that associations of classical kinds do occur in problem solving. Such instances were however considered to be exceedingly rare, and structural interpretations of problem-solving events were thought to be much more relevant. It will be shown later how the Gestaltists' conception of structure implies SI products. In other words, those products are kinds of configurations.

In the SI view, the traditional concept of association should be replaced by the informational product of implication (Guilford, 1966, 1967). If B occurs in close sequence with A, it is a matter of A coming to imply B. Later, if A comes, B is expected. In the parlance of modern logic, if A, then B. This interpretation is largely in agreement with the

Gestalt view. There is a kind of superior unity involved in an A–B pair. E. L. Thorndike referred to "belongingness" as a feature of such a unity. It should be added that although the traditional view is that the contiguity of events is the key to the formation of associative connections, in neither Gestalt nor SI views is contiguity regarded as a necessary or sufficient condition. There are other conditions for the formation of an implication.

It should also be remembered that in SI theory an implication is only one of six kinds of products. Following the lead of Ebbinghaus, traditional investigators have very much ignored problems of learning and memory for the other kinds of products (Guilford, 1971). Each product of information exists in its own unique way, having its own "structure". Factor-analytic research has shown that each product can not only be cognized but also stored in memory and retrieved for later use. A principle such as association is not needed to account for a product, nor would it be very useful in that role.

Koffka's account of the case of "association by similarity" properly implies the SI construct of class. It is easy to go from one member of a class to another member of the same class, for in retrieving information from storage, in general, the cue item is very frequently a class idea.

Psychology, Subjective or Objective?

Until John Watson came along, with few exceptions there was not much question of whether the eye of the observing psychologist should be turned searchingly inward toward his own mental events or outward toward the behavior of others and of animals of subhuman species, when basic problems were under investigation. This was true in spite of the purely objective studies initiated by Ebbinghaus and the pioneer studies of animal learning, brought into the laboratory by E. L. Thorndike. Watson went much further however in his readiness to discard the psychological developments of past centuries and to start all over again, with not only new methods but also new theoretical constructs. It is safe to say that today psychological investigators overwhelmingly seek objectively observed data, with minimal resort to self observations, in the study of basic problems. But there are issues with regard to what kinds of objective data should be sought, what concepts should be employed in their interpretation, and how far one should go by way of making inferences from the data.

The strict behaviorist has generally preferred to stay close to observations, especially avoiding inferences with respect to anything that he would regard as mentalistic. Intervening variables and theoretical constructs have been offered, sometimes in the form of little s-r sequences occurring between observed S's and R's. Because of the demand for use of the very simple S-R model, severe limitations are placed upon descriptions and interpretations. We have what might be called a "micropsychology", in contrast to "macropsychology", in which constructs of larger scope and greater complexity are common. Although contributing a few broad principles such as those of "reactive inhibition" and "reinforcement", micropsychology has made its most substantive contributions in connection with physiological problems. It clearly reflects its ancestry in the physiologist Pavlov. It has not been at all promising as an approach to the understanding of the "higher mental processes", which have never ceased to offer problems to the psychologists. A macropsychology with higher-order units of observation and higher-order constructs is needed to solve those problems.

Observations in terms of higher units can be made, as demonstrated by Gestalt psychologists and others, and the observations can be objective. The secret lies in the recognition of variables in stimuli that are in the form of tasks and in responses to those stimuli, and in applying systematic variations in the stimuli. Observations of resulting behavior are objective, although probably indirect, as when numerical scores are assigned to performances under specified conditions. Justification for this kind of research can be readily cited in nuclear physics and molecular biology, where observations are also indirect. Observations used in factor analysis are of the same general nature, without pushing the analogy too far. Inferences concerning mental events are made freely on the basis of the obtained results, with the expectation that if they are ill-advised, further observations will point to better inferences. It is recognized that science is essentially a history of hypotheses, whose half lives may not be very great. Hopefully, each new hypothesis is more useful and is a better approximation than the ones that it replaces.

It is of some interest here to note that one of behaviorism's innovations was to bring motor activity into much greater prominence. Gestalt psychologists also gave some attention to this segment of behavior, integrating it with the mentalistic body of psychology by applying Gestalt principles to bodily movements. Motor activity also finds a logical place in an operational-informational psychology. Factor analysis has demonstrated quite a number of basic variables that apply to somewhat isolated activities, and these psychomotor abilities have been organized in a matrix type of system (Guilford, 1958). It has been suggested (Guilford, 1967) that in the integrative control of motor actions, there is a family of variables that may be called "executive functions". They have to do with subgoals or intentions, and they can be differentiated by factor analysis. Two such functions in connection with voluntary emotional expressions have been suggested in one analysis (Hendricks *et al.*, 1969). It has been proposed that some of the same categories as appear in the SI model may be found to apply to the executive functions (Guilford, 1967), particularly the kinds of products, but also kinds of operations. Such parallels between intellectual and psychomotor items of information may be a key to the linking of thoughts to actions. In the ways just indicated, OI psychology can include motor activities.

How OI Psychology Deals with the Issues

In an attempt to place an OI psychology derived from SI concepts within the family of psychologies, a sketchy review of the issues that have beset the history of psychology has been presented. The ways of thinking in the various schools with respect to those issues have been noted, with some incidental references to similarities and differences with the OI psychology in question. Here we shall consider more directly how OI psychology stands with respect to the same issues.

It was noted how the applications of factor analysis, which have led to an OI psychology, have represented some of the same kind of thinking as that emphasized by faculty psychologists. It was also noted that by empirical methods OI psychology has arrived at considerable refinement in its taxonomy and has been much more successful in accounting for mental functioning in general. The system that is based upon SI theory is not merely a faculty psychology. It is much more appropriately classified as a functional psychology. But unlike American functionalism, it is without biological or Darwinian reference, thereby staying clear of any hint of teleology.

The only basis whatever for a possible charge of elementarism would be the large number of unique functions recognized. But those functions are not at all well described as constituent parts of larger wholes. Rather, they are different aspects of an information-processing affair. They are known to operate together in achieving results in complex tasks, such as learning concepts, solving mathematical problems, and reading to gain information. They can be induced to operate in relative isolation, as when well-controlled test tasks are given, but ordinarily they rarely do so. That is why it has been so difficult to recognize distinctions among them and it has required factor analysis to detect their separate ways. In the theoretical models of factor analysis, individual differences in each function or ability are represented by a vector, each vector with its unique direction from a common origin.

The mathematical model accounting for the contributions of two or more of the SI functions to performances in a task is a basic multivariate equation in theory and a multiple-regression equation in empirical predictions. There is internal consistency within the sphere of applications of the models. The upshot of this discussion is that we are here dealing with variables, not atoms.

The inapplicability of the traditional principle of association in OI psychology was treated earlier. It has been proposed (Guilford, 1966) that the six products of information be used to perform the required theoretical duties for many of which the construct of association was often drafted. None of the criticisms directed toward associationism apply to the OI psychology in question. This kind of psychology can take care of all the things to which association applied well, and much, much more.

SI-derived psychology is thoroughly objective without being behavioristic in the usual sense. Although the factor analyst may resort on occasion to introspective observation in developing hypotheses as to expected variables in mental functioning and also in the interpretations of factors psychologically, his hypothesis testing is based upon data of an objective kind. He is not concerned with consciousness, as such. So far as he knows, the information assumed to be cognized, produced, or evaluated, might be partially or wholly unconscious. Nor need he be concerned as to which it is, except as scientific curiosity about this question invites him to investigate. Theoretically, he could apply his methods to computers as well as to human beings.

Precursors in Gestalt Psychology

In its relatively greater success in dealing with the major issues enumerated earlier, Gestalt psychology offers more parallels with OI psychology than most schools of psychological thought. A few of the similarities were mentioned incidentally earlier. Some additional connections will be mentioned here, and a few differences will be pointed out.

Gestalt psychologists have very commonly mentioned the general continuity between perception and thought, insisting that the principles found in the investigations of perception (usually visual) apply also to thinking and problem solving. Phenomena such as closure, centering, and transposition are often mentioned in Gestalt literature, being applied quite broadly. This view might be taken as a forerunner of the parallels between abilities or functions in the SI model. For example, within two content categories there are pairs of abilities each having the same operation and same product in common. At one time, this writer was misled into accepting this Gestalt hypothesis, only to be forced later to conclude that difference in kind of information does make a difference in ability. Certainly parallels, but not identity.

Gestaltists apparently sensed the need for a construct such as that of "product" of information. They defined a configuration as a structure. Although "structure" suggests most clearly the SI product of system, it is easy to show that all other kinds of products have structures of different kinds, as will come out in future discussion. In Gestaltists' writings, frequent mention is made of the feature of transposability of configurations. It is easy to find examples of transposability of classes, relations, systems, and transformations. It is not so easy in the case of units or of implications, but this can be done.

Let us consider each kind of product in turn. What kind of structure is a unit of information? Familiar geometric figures obviously have unique structural properties. They are figural units. Nongeometric objects, figural or otherwise, have their unique collections of attributes. An object's attributes give it class memberships, but objects within the same class also have attributes that do not belong to the class and that therefore set them apart as individuals, distinguishable from other members. Thus, a unit stands by itself. In spite of its uniqueness, its transposability occurs as one encounters it on separate occasions. Recognition depends upon such transposability. It may undergo some changes from one occasion to another, but its identity is maintained.

A class conception ignores the irrelevant attributes in a collection of objects that are grouped by virtue of a combination of relevant attributes. The class idea is readily transposable from one set to another, as from the set: snow, rain, dew, to the set: drizzle, hail, sleet.

Of all the SI products, that of relation has probably been mentioned most often by Gestalt psychologists and has occupied a place of high importance in their scale of evaluation. For example, Köhler (1959) made a statement to the effect that relations are essential to all cognitive achievement. He was probably led to this view because so many of the insights that occurred during his observations of animal behavior involved seeing relations. He was not alone in placing relations so high in his list. It may be remembered that Spearman (1927) staked most of his theory of intellectual functioning on relations—eduction of relations and eduction of correlates (relata).

In its emphasis upon totalities, however, the psychology of Gestalt held that a relation is more than a connection between two things. The Gestaltists conceived of a relation and its relata as a total structure (Helson, 1926). To such a conception this writer has applied the term "relationship". The relation is a connection, but a meaningful one. It is a product in its own right. Then, of course, in the SI model there are quite a number of SI abilities, all concerned with relations, with differing content and operation.

Of all the SI products, that of system is most clearly configurational in its nature. In the field of perception an individual's spatial frame of reference has been proposed as a good example of a configuration (Helson, 1925). In the category of visual-figural cognition is found the SI ability CFS (cognition of figural systems), or spatial orientation. Gestaltists have recognized hierarchies also as configurations. Hierarchies are systems of classes and subclasses which can occur in any of the four content categories. In his account of problem solving, Wertheimer (1945) has observed another example of a system, in the problem solver's conception of the nature of the problem as a structure. For some time, those who have factor analyzed arithmetical-reasoning tests have interpreted the main factorial function as CMS (cognition of semantic systems). In mathematics beyond arithmetic, the problem might be conceived as a symbolic system, if algebraic, or a figural system, if geometric. SI systems occur in connection with all content categories and all operation categories, with at least 20 such abilities or functions distinguishable.

Gestalt psychology seems to have been the only one with a construct like transformation, and indeed Gestaltists have often used the term or a close synonym, such as redefinition. As an example of transformation, Wertheimer (1945) spoke of "realization of changes" in his treatment of problem solving. It was the concept of redefinition that led the writer (Guilford, 1950) to hypothesize a basic ability of that nature that should be relevant in connection with creative thinking. Tests designed for this hypothesis determined a common factor that was first known as "redefinition". Soon other factors were found that seemed to indicate flexibility in thinking. The flexible nature of redefinition was also noted, and all such abilities were classified under the more general label of "transformation". There was some toleration for a time of the hypothesis that transformation should be regarded as an activity or operation in the SI model rather than as a product of information. But that is not the way in which the abilities involving flexibility could be organized. It was also realized that transformations can not only be cognized but also remembered, produced, and evaluated.

As pointed out by the Gestaltists, transformations are basic to insights. Whether all insights depend upon transformations is very questionable, for some instances of insights can involve instead the sudden emergence of products where there were none before.

Since Gestaltists wished to avoid the traditional construct of association, they would undoubtedly look with some favor upon the product of implication as a replacement. Since they demanded something more than the indifferent hooking together of items of behavior, they should have welcomed the conception of an expectation as a substitute. Two things bound together with an expectation present properties of a total structure—a Gestalt.

With all the parallels cited between Gestalt psychology and the structure of intellect, it may be asked why Gestaltists did not arrive at something in the direction of that systematic construct. As a matter of record, they did not develop anything that could be called a system of psychology. They did not accept the challenge to produce a taxonomy, as other schools commonly did. One reason is that they possessed no adequate method for empirically untangling complex mental functioning. It has already been pointed out that they paid little or no attention to the kinds of SI content, assuming that Gestalt principles apply to all kinds alike. They would undoubtedly have unanimously rejected factor analysis as a method because of its additive equations. Finally, they may have avoided taxonomy construction because to them it smacked of elementarism.

Needed Extensions of OI Psychology

It cannot be claimed that, with confinement to intellectual functioning alone, a psychology based upon SI theory is a complete discipline. The important domains of motivation and emotion also need to be brought into the picture. Can they be dealt with in an OI psychology? Will categories of operations and information constitute a fruitful outcome? Gestalt psychology was also somewhat short in its coverage of these aspects of behavior, although Lewin (1936) took significant steps in those directions.

This writer has attempted to make a case for viewing motivation in terms of information processing (Guilford, 1965). The category of informational content involved is behavioral, of the self-initiated variety. This categorization is clearest in the case of organic needs that make themselves known to the nervous system. More generally, the individual becomes aware of other conditions that prompt "I-need" or "I-want" states of mind. Many of these contingencies arise from the environment as well, in what are known as "incentives". Thus, the content classification of motives seems plausible. It is not clear that all six product categories apply, but those of units and implications clearly do. There is a goal-oriented aspect to motivation, and this suggests anticipations or expectations, which are implications. This view avoids entanglements with teleology.

There have been a few efforts directed toward taxonomies of motives, e.g. McDougall's list of instincts. A much more extensive list of human needs, interests, and attitudes derived from factor analysis has been presented by the present writer in his book on personality (Guilford, 1959). Some groupings of these "hormetic" traits was possible, but no comprehensive system was proposed. There were some indications that such a system would be hierarchical in form.

Experienced feelings and emotions can also be regarded as items of information regarding the personal state of the individual. Efforts in the direction of a taxonomy of feelings have been somewhat successful. Brentano and other act psychologists emphasized a "loving-hating" class of acts, which refer to the very obvious bipolar pleasant-unpleasant dimension of feelings. Wundt added two hypothetical dimensions called "active-passive" and "tense-relaxed". These three dimensions have been verified empirically by Osgood and his associates (Osgood *et al.*, 1961) in their factor-analytic investigations of meanings of words. Multidimensional approaches have also been applied to emotions, but without definitive success as yet. It is possible that dimensional models are not the most fruitful type of model to apply to taxonomic studies of emotions.

As there appears to be a psycho-logic in the domain of intelligence, it may be that there is also a kind of logic yet to be discovered in the domains of motivation and emotion. The principle of opposition, as already demonstrated for feelings, may have general applicability in the nonintellectual realm. With the development of a comprehensive taxonomy in that realm, the framework for a complete operational-informational psychology should have been achieved.

Even within the scope of intellectual functioning, the morphological or matrix type of model provides much room for extension. From the fact that a few abilities concerned with auditory-figural input, in the operation categories of cognition and memory, have already been differentiated from parallel visual-figural abilities, a large set of abilities dealing with auditory-figural coding is predicted. There may also be kinesthetic and haptic abilities. And it may be that self-initiated behavioral content will turn out to be a code separate from other-initiated behavioral content.

The SI model is purely taxonomic in character. Although it lays out the frame of reference, other models of an operational nature are also needed. The writer (Guilford, 1966, 1967) has developed an operational model for problem solving that rests upon SI concepts, and other special models in the form of informational-flow charts can be generated. A comprehensive model for behavior in general is under development by the writer.

Summary

This paper first reviewed the major theoretical issues in the history of psychology, including that of faculties versus functions, acts versus contents, elementarism, associationism, and objective versus subjective observation and subject matter. Major points of view or schools of psychology were briefly examined with respect to their treatment of those issues. It was found that none of them dealt successfully with all the issues, and few provided adequate taxonomies or systems.

Although Gestalt psychology came closest to being a complete psychology, and in some respects anticipated some distinctions and constructs of an operational-informational psychology, it also fell short of the mark. It was shown how a psychology that looks upon the individual as an information-processing agent and that has been derived from the structure of intellect, embraces both act and content, avoids mental chemistry, and provides a systematic taxonomy. With extensions along similar lines, it could probably bring motivation and emotion into its system, thus offering a complete psychology.

COMMENT ON GUILFORD'S PAPER

K. PAWLIK

It is a privilege to have Guilford present notions inherent in or leading to his S-I model from a history of psychology point of view. Coming to this conference from overseas, I particularly like this paper's approach to reintegrate historical European and American lines of thought. I say this also in due recognition of Guilford's contributions to the field of multivariate aptitude research, particularly his influential work on divergent thinking, aptitudes, and social intelligence tests. On the other hand, I have some doubts as to the general validity of the model as a factor theory of intelligence and as to its heuristic appropriateness as a model guiding future factor analytic aptitude research. I shall put them into the form of four questions to Guilford:

1. In formal terms, the S-I model is an orthogonal facet model of the intellect. However, a number of primary factors are known to intercorrelate substantially and consistently (cf. Pawlik, 1965). How would you account for this covariance of primary factors of intelligence on the basis of the S-I model?

2. I doubt the empirical verifiability of as high a number of factors as implied by the S-I model. And, true enough, the implied factorial mosaic has been assembled successively by partly overlapping analyses. Has any attempt yet been made to explore this mosaic for the whole (or at least: the whole of one facet) of the S-I model?

3. "Ability" and "temperament" are classical undefinables in personality research. When would you define a factor as an "ability" factor, and would you consider it plausible (or at least possible) that some of the S-I factors are in fact temperament-aptitude hybrids?

4. To what extent is the S-I model indeed a psychological theory of intelligence factors or rather a logical scheme of intelligence *tests* and their facets of construction? What is the heuristic role of factor analysis in the construction of the S-I model since, obviously, the make-up of marker tests already fully determines the placement of a factor within a model, irrespective of its relationships to other factors? Can the S-I model be defended against the criticism that, due to the variable sampling being guided by the very model, the factors called for by the model will be obtained in due course?

COMMENT ON GUILFORD'S PAPER

J. R. ROYCE

Although most of Guilford's paper is focused on theoretical issues whose importance is primarily of historical value, it also contains a contemporary viability and general scope which should not be overlooked.

A good example of long history combined with contemporaneity occurs in the section on Gestalt Psychology. In this section Guilford reminds us of the powerful insights which the Gestaltists provided on the one hand, combined with their lack of adequate methodology and tight, systematic thought on the other hand. He then goes on to show how an O-I approach, armed with the more powerful analytic methodology of factor analysis, can lead to a more adequate and rational theoretical structure. Furthermore, the psychology zeitgeist (which we can briefly characterize as moving toward being more open and cognitive and/or less restrictive and S-R bound) is now much more amenable to Gestalt-like insights. In my opinion Guilford's O-I framework for Gestalt phenomena is conceptually powerful and should be pursued with vigor.

Similar hints of potential extensions of O-I thinking to the domain of motivation and emotion are also provided, ending with the last sentence of the paper "A comprehensive model for behavior in general is under development by the writer". I hope that Guilford can give us some clues concerning these potential extensions. Since space limitations will not allow for an adequate answer to such an open-ended question, perhaps he will confine himself to those extensions which will carry as much conceptual power as the OI-Gestalt linkage provides.

REJOINDER TO DISCUSSANTS' COMMENTS

J. P. GUILFORD

Pawlik should not have doubted the heuristic value of the structure of intellect model, which has been demonstrated many times over. More than 50 of the unknown abilities that it forecast were demonstrated in further analyses. On his numbered points:

1. The orthogonal nature of the SI model says nothing regarding intercorrelations among SI abilities. The appropriate model for this issue is the basic, dimensional factor-analytic model.
2. Naturally, not all of the 98 demonstrated SI factors have been brought out by any one analysis, owing to logistic limitations. A great many pairs have been separated in common analyses, however, some pairs many times over. Special attention was given to pairs expected to be difficult to separate.
3. I regard ability traits as being operationally defined, i.e. they are represented by tests in which examinees try to do their best, and the scores are intended to assess how well they perform. Tests of temperament traits must be of different kinds, or at least they must be scored differently, reflecting manner of performance. I regard all of the SI factors as abilities, for their tests satisfy the definition just given.
4. The SI model can be said to represent both abilities and kinds of tests. This follows from the fact that factor analysts commonly interpret obtained factors in the light of the tests that they share in common. It should be noted, of course, that the model would not necessarily classify tests in terms of their surface characteristics. The classification would be in terms of their psychological requirements. The hypothetico-deductive approach that we followed necessarily called for the use of test variables carefully selected for the purpose rather than a random sampling of tests. This approach helps the scientist get beyond random sampling at an early stage.

Royce's comments display considerable insight. He is right about Gestalt psychologists' insights as potentially fruitful starting points in further development of an O-I psychology.

The model of behavior referred to is a fusing of two earlier models, my own, for problem solving, and Crossman's model for psychomotor activity (Guilford, 1967), with some condensation of both. The psychomotor component includes what I call "executive functions", which are more general plans for muscular activity, and more specific components. Psychomotor abilities have been known for some time (Guilford, 1968). Some signs of factors for executive functions have just recently been reported (Guilford, 1972).

REFERENCES

Guilford, J. P. (1950). Creativity. *Am. Psychol.* **5,** 444–454.

Guilford, J. P. (1958). A system of psychomotor abilities. *Am. J. Psychol.* **71,** 164–174.

Guilford, J. P. (1959). "Personality." McGraw-Hill, New York.

Guilford, J. P. (1960). Basic conceptual problems in the psychology of thinking. *Ann. N.Y. Acad. Sci.* **91,** 6–21.

Guilford, J. P. (1965). Motivation in an informational psychology. *In* "The Nebraska Symposium on Motivation." (Levine, D. ed.), pp. 313–332.

Guilford, J. P. (1967). "The Nature of Human Intelligence." McGraw-Hill, New York.

Guilford, J. P. (1971). Varieties of memory and their implications. *J. gen. Psychol.* **85,** 207–228.

Guilford, J. P. (1972). Executive functions and a model of behavior. *J. gen. Psychol.* **86,** 279–287.

Guilford, J. P. and Hoepfner, R. (1971). "The Analysis of Intelligence." McGraw-Hill, New York.

Helson, H. (1925). The psychology of Gestalt. *Am. J. Psychol.* **36,** 342–370; 494–526.

Helson, H. (1926). The psychology of Gestalt. *Am. J. Psychol.* **37**, 25–62; 189–223.

Hendricks, M., Guilford, J. P. and Hoepfner, R. (1969). "Measuring creative social intelligence." *Reports from the Psychological Laboratory, University of Southern California,* No. **43.**

Köhler, W. (1941). On the nature of association. *Proc. Am. phil. Soc.* **84,** 489–502.

Köhler, W. (1959). Gestalt psychology today. *Am. Psychol.* **14,** 727–734.

Lewin, K. (1936). "Principles of Topological Psychology." (Trans. by Heider, F. and Heider, G. M.) McGraw-Hill, New York.

Osgood, C. E., Suci, G. J. and Tannenbaum, P. H. (1957). "The Measurement of Meaning." University of Illinois Press, Urbana, Illinois.

Pawlik, K. (1966). Concepts and calculations in human cognition and aptitudes. *In* "Handbook of Multivariate Experimental Psychology." (Cattell, R. B. ed.), 535–553. Rand McNally, Chicago.

Spearman, C. (1927). "The Nature of Intelligence and Principles of Cognition." Macmillan, New York.

Stumpf, C. (1906). Erscheinungen und psychische Funktionen. Abbl. preuss. Akad. Wiss, Berlin.

Titchener, E. B. (1927). "Systematic Psychology: Prolegomena." Macmillan, New York.

Wertheimer, M. (1945). "Productive Thinking." Harper and Bros., New York.

Part II

Toward a Comprehensive, Multivariate Psychological Theory

Multivariate Models of Cognition and Personality: The Need for Both Process and Structure in Psychological Theory and Measurement*

SAMUEL MESSICK

Educational Testing Service
Princeton, New Jersey

Over half a century of empirical research on intellectual functioning has uncovered a vast array of dimensions spanning the cognitive area from perception through memory, reasoning, and judgment to creative production. At the same time an additional profusion of factors has emerged in studies of other aspects of personality, such as temperament, personal-social motivation, controlling mechanisms, attitudes, and interests. This very proliferation of factors has forced serious scientific attention to a search for organizing principles to lend coherence to what otherwise would be an ever enlarging conglomeration of discrete psychological components.

Several multivariate models have been proposed for this task of factorial organization, and some of them will be reviewed in detail shortly. By and large these models are primarily structural in nature in that they represent classifications or taxonomies of dimensions based upon conceptual or empirical relations among factors. It will be argued here that such structural models of consistent individual differences are not sufficient, however, for dealing with complex psychological phenomena of prime concern to theory and application, such as perception, learning, problem solving, and creativity. In brief, the structural basis should be augmented to go beyond the specification of component

* Large sections of this paper originally appeared as part of Project Report 68–4, Disadvantaged Children and Their First School Experiences: Theoretical Considerations and Measurement Strategies, Educational Testing Service, Princeton, N.J., 1968. Some of the material was also presented in seminars when the author was a Visiting Scholar at The Center for Advanced Study in Theoretical Psychology, Edmonton, Alberta, Canada, in March, 1971. The author gratefully acknowledges an intellectual debt to J. P. Guilford, whose remarkable book on "The Nature of Human Intelligence" stimulated this effort.

variables and their intercorrelations to a consideration of functional relations among the components and of their sequential operation and interaction over time in complex mental functioning.

As has been indicated, several types of multivariate models have been proposed as a basis for organizing the morass of empirical dimensions in cognition and personality (see Guilford, 1967). One is simply a dimensional model that represents the dimensions as a set of vectors in multidimensional space. Another is a hierarchical model that recognizes classes of dimensions and classes within classes, thereby taking into account the fact that some of the observed dimensions are fairly general and others quite specific, and that some are highly intercorrelated and others relatively independent. This type of model organizes the categories of dimensions very much like a tree, with broad dimensions representing limbs stemming from the trunk of a general dimension, with minor dimensions representing branches on the limbs, and still more specific dimensions twigs on the branches. A third type of model, called morphological (Zwicky, 1957), is a cross-classification of factors, a grid with intersecting categories rather than categories within categories as in the hierarchical model. A fourth type of model, which might be called sequential, represents mental functioning as an interconnected series of operations, sometimes involving feedback loops and dynamic integration over time, as in cybernetic and computer simulation models (Miller *et al.* 1960; Tomkins and Messick, 1963; Reitman, 1965).

We shall begin our discussion of multivariate models of cognition and personality with a description and extension of the morphological model of intellect proposed by Guilford (1959; 1967). This model provides a cross-classification scheme for fairly specific cognitive dimensions that function at a relatively low level of generality. It primarily summarizes those dimensions derived over the years by Guilford and his co-workers in the Air Forces Aviation Psychology Research Program (Guilford and Lacey, 1947) and in the Aptitudes Research Project at the University of Southern California—although most of the dimensions derived by Thurstone and others can also be classified with varying degrees of confidence and arbitrariness.

Some cognitive dimensions, however, such as induction and perceptual speed, appear to be too general to fit unequivocally into one cell of the classification scheme, thereby suggesting the need for an extension of the system to handle broader, more complex higher-order factors that operate at higher levels of generality. Since such factors are subsumed naturally in a hierarchical model, attention will next be turned to some of the major hierarchical conceptualizations. Then, in an attempt at rapprochement between the two major approaches, Guilford's system will be generalized to a hierarchical formulation which, as Guttman (1958) has pointed out, is already implicit within it. In addition, many important cognitive functions, such as reading, speaking, conservation of quantity, or problem solving, are not only complex but are sequentially ordered and cannot be adequately represented merely by sorting their component processes into the appropriate combination of cells in Guilford's design. The model will therefore also be extended to include some provision for order of components, particularly order of complexity, so that we may discuss within the same overall framework response dimensions that depend upon particular sequences of events or upon dimensions or hierarchies of mastery; e.g. where a complex performance requires the previous mastery of prerequisite or component processes (Gagné, 1965, 1968; Kofsky, 1966).

The overall model thus consists of a set of dimensions arrayed in a cross-classification scheme capable of being organized into a hierarchy of levels reflecting differential breadth of functioning and having provision for different orders of complexity. More complex psychological phenomena are viewed in terms of sequences of these component factors. The resulting formulation thus combines features of dimensional, hierarchical, morphological, and sequential models. Implications of these views for psychological measurement are also discussed throughout.

Guilford's Structure-of-Intellect Model

Guilford's theory for the structure of intellect (SI) is an operational-informational model that postulates five intellectual operations (cognition, memory, convergent production, divergent production, and evaluation) and 24 categories of information.* The categories of information are further cross-classified in terms of four content categories or substantive areas of information (figural, symbolic, semantic, and behavioral) and six product categories or forms of differentiation (units, classes, relations, systems, transformations, and implications). The five operations, four contents, and six products provide a three-way cross-classification system yielding a box containing 120 cells.

As Carroll (1968) has pointed out, another way of presenting the SI model is to state that any cognitive dimension can be uniquely described by selecting one term from each of the following three columns:

* Guilford prefers to reserve the label "cognition" for the operation that deals with awareness and comprehension; he uses "intelligence" to refer to all the information-processing operations together.

<table>
<tr><td>Cognition (C)</td><td>Figural (F)</td><td>Units (U)</td></tr>
<tr><td>Memory (M)</td><td>Symbolic (S)</td><td>Classes (C)</td></tr>
<tr><td>Divergent production (D)</td><td>Semantic (M)</td><td>Relations (R)</td></tr>
<tr><td>Convergent production (N)</td><td>Behavioral (B)</td><td>Systems (S)</td></tr>
<tr><td>Evaluation (E)</td><td></td><td>Transformations (T)</td></tr>
<tr><td></td><td></td><td>Implications (I)</td></tr>
</table>

Thus, a vocabulary factor would be described as the cognition of semantic units (CMU). Although this form of presenting the model makes it seem like a Chinese dinner menu, it does provide a convenient means for adding facets to the basic design by merely adding columns to the menu, with the proviso that each cell be described conjointly by choosing one entry from each column. Definitions of the elements of the three facets of the SI model, as given in Guilford (1967) and Guilford and Heopfner (1966), appear in Table I (see p. 292).

Guilford's attempt to organize intellectual processes into a coherent system is in the mainstream of a long and honorable tradition in the history of thought. Plato recognized two kinds of abilities, sense and intellect; other writers later added memory and still others imagination or invention. Before the fall of the Roman Empire, speech and attention were often added for consideration, and finally movement was added (Spearman, 1927). Further increases in the list of faculties were generally obtained by subdividing these seven: sensory ability was split into visual, auditory, kinesthetic; intellect into conception, judgment, and reasoning; and so forth.

By the early twentieth century, modern lists contained a wide assortment of purported dimensions conceptualized at various levels of generality and with varying degrees of overlap. To provide some logical organization for these listings, Spearman (1927) proposed a system of three fundamental processes (the awareness of one's own experiences, the eduction of relations, and the eduction of correlates), each of which could be subdivided in terms of "(a) the different classes of relations that are cognizable, (b) the different kinds of fundaments that enter into these relations, and (c) the varying kinds and degrees of complexity in which such relations and fundaments can be conjoined". In addition to these qualitative distinctions, Spearman also proposed five quantitative "laws" to account for other sources of variability in test performance—span, retentivity, fatigue, conation, and primordial potencies (such as age, sex, heredity, and health). Some years later El-Koussey (1955; Guttman, 1958), working primarily in the area of spatial abilities, suggested that every test can be thought of as having three main aspects—content (e.g., numbers, words, figures, symbols, situations), form (e.g., classification, analogies, opposites), and function (e.g., deduction, induction, memory, visualization).

Guilford's conceptual analysis of some of the logical similarities and parallels among observed factors of intellect extends this venerable line of thinking to embrace a broader empirical array of dimensions, but a comparison of his model with earlier classification schemes suggests that still other elements might well be added, particularly in the sensory and response domains. A fourth facet could be added to the model, for instance, to represent sensory mode, with different levels on the facet referring to visual, auditory, kinesthetic, and other sensory processes. Indeed, the rudiments of this additional facet have already been included by Guilford (1967) in his attempt to classify visual, auditory, and kinesthetic candidates for the cell of the design corresponding to cognition of figural systems (CFS), as well as separate visual and auditory factors for the cognition of both figural and symbolic units (CFU and CSU).

Additional facets may also prove necessary to account for consistent individual differences due to response mode and test form: A response facet would reflect variations in mode of responding, such as oral, graphic, or motoric (pointing, marking, or performing), and a form facet would reflect variations in administration and format, such as timed versus untimed, individual versus group, or multiple-choice versus free response. Individual consistencies associated with such formal characteristics of a test are sometimes called method factors (Campbell and Fiske, 1959) or response sets (Messick, 1968). They appear to reflect the operation of stylistic and personality variables in test performance and may be particularly important in the responses of young children (Jackson and Messick, 1958; Damarin and Cattell, 1968).

Regardless of the adequacy of Guilford's scheme as a theory of the structure of intellect, his classification system does provide an extensive, integrated summary of known and potential factors of intellectual functioning and may thereby serve as a guide or check list for evaluating the adequacy of coverage of experimental test batteries designed to assess the cognitive domain. As a kind of periodic table of the mind, its unfilled cells also proffer prescriptions for test construction in as yet unexplored areas of intellectual performance.

Hierarchical Models of Intellect

Although many of the factors derived empirically in various laboratories can be classified into Guilford's scheme with varying degrees of certainty, some of them, such as induction, appear to be too broad to fit into any single cell. By appearing to span several cells, these broad factors seem to represent more general levels of functioning, which in turn subsume several of the SI cells as special cases. Such a relationship suggests a system of categories within categories, such as represented in the major competitor to Guilford's theory—the hierarchical model of intellectual functioning.

Guilford's SI scheme is a logical model, in that it derives from a conceptual analysis of perceived similarities among factors. The hierarchical formulation, on the other hand, is touted as a psychological model derived from the quantitative analysis of empirical correlations among factors. One might expect particular versions of the hierarchical model to differ somewhat as a function of the specific empirical relations summarized, but the general tree-like framework would remain the same. Both Cyril Burt (1949) and Philip Vernon (1950), for example, favor a hierarchical structure that places general intelligence (*g*) at the pinnacle with two major group factors immediately below. For Burt, these two broad group factors reflect logical thinking and aesthetic appreciation, both of which are thought to require the apprehension of abstract relations. For Vernon, the two major group factors derive from his attempts to integrate the results of several factor studies, wherein he observed that once the influence of *g* is removed, tests tend to fall into two main clusters—a verbal-numerical-educational type and a practical-mechanical-spatial-physical type. Below these broad group factors in both structures are found several minor group factors, and lower down still various specific factors.

In Burt's model, four levels of factors are represented below general intelligence: The lowest level (sensation) corresponds to simple sensory processes and simple movements, as measured by tests of sensory thresholds and reaction time. The next level (perception) consists of more complex processes of perception and co-ordinated movement, including a dimension of perceptual discrimination regardless of sensory content. The third level (association) embraces memory and habit formation; it contains formal factors of memory and constructive imagination, as well as content factors of imagery (reproductive imagination), verbal abilities (including both receptive and productive factors for both isolated words and connected language), arithmetical abilities, and practical abilities (including spatial and mechanical factors). The fourth level (relation), the highest below *g*, refers to thought processes of both a logical and an aesthetic type. Burt also mentions certain general processes, such as speed and attention, that appear to affect mental functioning at every level. Although some of the lower-level dimensions in Burt's system, such as the receptive word factor, can be readily classified in Guilford's scheme (in this case as CMU), other dimensions, such as memory or constructive imagination (divergent thinking), appear to span several content and product categories.

Hierarchy Implicit in the SI Model

Several of the higher-level dimensions in hierarchical formulations such as Burt's sound as if they may correspond to higher-level dimensions implicit in Guilford's scheme. These implicit higher-order SI dimensions, which provide the basis for extending Guilford's system to include a hierarchy of levels, are revealed by treating the SI model as an "analysis-of-variance" design (Guttman, 1958). Since the SI model may be viewed as a $5 \times 4 \times 6$ factorial (or facet) design, the dimensions corresponding to each cell may be considered to be a function of a general component plus three "main effects" (operations, contents, products), three second-order "interactions" ($O \times C$, $O \times P$, $C \times P$), and one third-order interaction ($O \times C \times P$) unique to the dimension. Any of these main effects of interactions may be negligible in a particular case, of course. Thus, in addition to factors corresponding to its 120 cells, the SI model generates 74 types of implicit second-order factors (30 for combinations of the 5 operations $\times 6$ products, 20 for combinations of 5 operations $\times 4$ contents, and 24 for combinations of 6 products $\times 4$ contents—e.g., factors reflecting skill in cognizing figural material regardless of type of product, or skill in the divergent production of transformations regardless of type of content); 15 types of third-order factors (5 for operations, 4 for contents, and 6 for products—e.g., general memory facility regardless of form of content or type of product); and 1 fourth-order factor (general intellectual facility).

Empirical factors may occasionally turn up, of course, that appear to represent intermediate levels in the SI hierarchy, such as a single factor for cognition of figural and symbolic units separate from cognition of semantic units or for a combination of cognition and convergent production of semantic relations. Although such complex factors may be mapped onto a combination of cells in the SI scheme, the mapping does not strictly follow the logic of the model or of this hierarchical extension. From the vantage point of the SI model, such factors are likely to have arisen because of inadequate coverage of the intellectual domain in the test battery in question, although they could be handled directly in a less logically constrained hierarchical system.

The logical nature of the higher-order dimensions in the SI model suggests that tests designed to assess them directly should be complex in nature—a measure of cognition of semantic materials, for example, should include six types of items to represent respectively semantic units, classes, relations, systems, transformations, and implications; while a general measure of divergent production should include 24 types of items, one for each of the product × content combinations. Thus, measures for a particular facet element (like *D* — — or —*F* —), or for an intersection of elements (like *CM* —), could be produced by adding together appropriate items that systematically cover the remaining facets, thereby achieving test homogeneity for the higher-order dimension in question through what Humphreys (1962) has called the "control of heterogeneity".

Illustrative Classifications of Major Factors in Terms of the Extended SI Scheme

One purpose in emphasizing the higher-order dimensions implicit in the SI model was to see if these additional higher-order categories would improve the prospect of accommodating factors derived in other laboratories within the extended SI framework. Let us first consider some of the well-known primary factors and then speculate about the two higher-order dimensions of fluid and crystallized intelligence proposed by Cattell (1943; 1963).

Primary Mental Abilities and Other Perceptual–Cognitive Factors

Thurstone (1938, 1944) and others have uncovered several dimensions of intellectual functioning over the years that can be classified more or less readily into the extended SI model (see French *et al.*, 1963; Guilford, 1972). In the area of verbal ability, for instance, Verbal Comprehension appears to correspond to CMU, Word Fluency to DSU, and Ideational Fluency to DMU; Guilford's laboratory has added to the list Associational Fluency (DMR), Expressional Fluency (DMS), and a naming or labeling factor (NMU).

In the area of spatial skills, Spatial Orientation corresponds to CFS, Spatial Scanning to CFI, and Visualization to CFT. Thurstone's (1944) Speed of Closure factor represents CFU and Flexibility of Closure, NFT.

In the area of memory, Associative Memory corresponds to MSR or MSI, and Memory Span to MSU or MSS.

In the area of reasoning, General Reasoning seems to correspond to CMS and Deduction to N—I (primarily measured as NSI and NMI).

Induction, as assessed by Thurstone, appears to fit in CSS, but as a general construct it seems to refer not so much to the cognition of systems (or classes or relations) as to their convergent production—for convergent production includes not only logical deduction but also the drawing of compelling inferences from input information sufficient to determine a unique answer (Guilford, 1967).*

Number Facility, as might be expected, is related to both NSI and MSI, but since computational skills are highly practiced and over-learned, numerical operations tests also contain a large specific dimension not shared with non-numerical measures of NSI. Such dimensions specific to particular subsets of operations within an SI cell would appear to represent a level of functioning still lower in the hierarchy (i.e. more specific) than the factors defined by the original SI model. Wide variations such as these in the specificity and generality of empirical factors are what led to hierarchical conceptions in the first place and are just about what would be expected by a "transfer theory of abilities" (Ferguson, 1954, 1956), which holds that factors represent behaviors that happen, for whatever cultural or environmental reasons, to be learned together, along with those similar behaviors that become associated through transfer of training.

Cattell's Dimensions of Fluid and Crystallized Intelligence

Another major hierarchical theory of intellectual functioning has been proposed by Cattell (1943, 1963), who claims that there is not a single *g* but rather two higher-order general abilities, which he calls "fluid" and "crystallized" intelligence. Fluid intelligence, which is said to have a substantial hereditary component, represents "processes of reasoning in the immediate situation in tasks requiring abstracting, concept formation and attainment, and the perception and eduction

* Induction is a mode of inference that goes from the particular to the general. Its operation implies abstraction, the process of selecting or isolating certain aspects of the specific information given to form a basis for more general classification or treatment. When applied to a particular product of information, induction results in more general products of information—e.g. when applied to units, induction might yield classes, relations, systems, transformations, or implications; when applied to classes, it might yield more general classes or relations on classes or systems; etc. The inverse mode of inference, deduction, goes from the general to the particular and primarily refers to the derivation of implications from the information given. Induction and deduction are two ways of generating information from given information and as such are intrinsically involved in both convergent production and divergent production. In convergent production, the problem is structured with sufficient restrictions that only one appropriate product (or a small set) can be induced or deduced correctly, while in divergent production restrictions are more lax and stress is upon the number and variety of appropriate products that may be generated acceptably.

of relations" (Horn and Cattell, 1966). Crystallized intelligence, which is said to owe more to the individual's learning history than to his heredity, is the "capacity to perceive limited sets of relationships and to educe limited sets of correlates as a consequence of prior learning" (Damarin and Cattell, 1968). Cattell's theory is one of the few structural models of intelligence that makes explicit provision not only for the operation of fluid intelligence but also for motivation, capacity for immediate recall, transfer of training, and relevant personality traits in the determination of crystallized achievement (Cattell, 1963; Damarin and Cattell, 1968).

Two second-order factors identified as fluid and crystallized intelligence were obtained by Horn and Cattell (1966), along with other second-order dimensions for fluency, general visualization ability, and general speediness (cf. Humphreys, 1967). The dimension of crystallized intelligence was marked primarily by Verbal Comprehension, Mechanical Knowledge, and other first-order cognitive factors, and as such it might possibly be interpreted as a higher-order cognitive dimension in the SI model (perhaps CM— or C— —). Fluid intelligence, on the other hand, was defined mainly by Induction and other reasoning primaries, thereby appearing to implicate in SI terms a higher-order convergent thinking factor. This level of interpretation, although admittedly highly speculative, is given modest support by the fact that the three other second-order intellectual dimensions obtained by Horn and Cattell (1966) also correspond fairly well to higher-order SI factors. The second-order fluency factor appears to represent DM— or possibly a truncated D— —; the general visualization factor may correspond to —F— (virtually every task involving figural content has a loading on the dimension); and the general speed factor, marked primarily by copying and matching tests, may involve general evaluation skills.

The Need to Consider Sequences of Operations

Many complex cognitive skills, such as reading and problem solving, involve sequences of operations performed upon various categories of information, sometimes with later performance being contingent upon the prior mastery of earlier components. If such complex skills are to be systematically included in multivariate models of cognitive functioning, some provision must be made for treating order of components, including order of complexity, within a general multivariate framework.

Orders of Complexity

When a complex performance requires the previous mastery of an ordered set of prerequisite or component processes, as in cumulative learning (Gagné, 1965, 1968) or developmental progressions (Peel, 1959; Wohlwill, 1960), a dimension or hierarchy of mastery emerges that may be represented in the SI model by adding a facet for order of complexity. Order of complexity in this case refers to the increasing subsumption of simpler components into more complex ones: If t_1 is the least complex element on the facet, for example, t_2 would require everything t_1 does and more, t_3 would require everything t_2 does and more, etc.

Guttman (1958) has developed some quantitative techniques for analysing relationships between variations in complexity and variations in test content. For tests of the same kind, variations in complexity lead to a structure that Guttman has called a simplex. For tests at a constant level of complexity, on the other hand, variations in kind of content lead to a structure called a circumplex. Variations in both complexity and kind lead to a structure known as a radex.

Orders of Sequence

Models of complex cognitive functioning should also provide some means of representing temporal sequences of processes, including feedback loops where applicable and dynamic integration over time, as in flow chart or computer simulation models (Tomkins and Messick, 1963). One prototype of such a sequential model is the cybernetic theory of behavior proposed by Miller, Galanter, and Pribram (1960), which adopts the feedback loop as its fundamental building block. This basic unit, which they have employed in the analysis of several psychological processes, is referred to in their terms as a TOTE sequence, which stands for Test-Operate-Test-Exit. This unit represents a sequence of operations in which a check is first made to ascertain whether or not a satisfactory state of affairs exists; if not, some operation is performed to rectify the situation, and a further check is made to determine the effectiveness of the operation. A satisfactory outcome would terminate the pattern (Exit), which otherwise would ordinarily continue until an acceptable test was obtained (TOTOT . . . TE).

The "Test" function of Miller, Galanter, and Pribram appears to be very similar to Guilford's operation of evaluation, and what they refer to as "Operate" could include in the intellectual realm the other four operations in the SI system. The TOTE framework could thus be used to build up combinations of operations in sequence to represent various complex cognitive processes (Guilford, 1967). A TOTOTOTOTE sequence alternating divergent production with evaluation, for example, would provide a summary representation of trial and error learning.

Complex Cognitive Processes as Sequences of Operations

Factor analysis attempts to derive from consistent individual differences in complex multiply-determined behaviors a limited set of underlying component variables which in weighted combination would account for the observed variation. The extended SI model and alternative hierarchical formulations provide organized summaries of most of the factors uncovered to date. Let us next explore the extent to which these factors, particularly those representing information-processing operations, may serve as components in sequential models of complex psychological processes.

Learning and Concept Attainment

Several studies have attempted to explore relationships between learning and various intellectual functions that may contribute to the learning process, perhaps differentially at different stages of practice (Allison, 1960, Duncanson, 1964, Fleischman, 1966; Stake, 1961). Bunderson (1965), for example, found that factors for three reasoning abilities as well as for visual speed related to scores on concept-attainment tasks differently at different stages of learning, suggesting that the learning process in this case might be composed of three component processes of problem analysis, search, and organization.

Dunham *et al.* (1968) recently studied three concept-learning tasks (one containing figural, one symbolic, and one semantic content) in relation to factors for the cognition, memory, divergent production, and convergent production of figural, symbolic, and semantic classes. They found that figural ability factors were implicated in the figural learning task, symbolic ability factors in the symbolic learning task, and semantic ability factors in the semantic learning task, and that cognition, memory, divergent production, and convergent production of classes were differentially involved at different stages of learning and produced somewhat different patterns of relationship for the three types of tasks. There was some indication that facility in the cognition of classes is a handicap early in concept learning but that it contributes more and more to success as learning progresses. The convergent production of classes tended to be more influential in the intermediate and later stages than in the beginning of learning, as did factors for the memory of classes. The divergent production of classes, on the other hand, was relatively important at the beginning of the semantic-concept task but not until the later stages of the symbolic-concept task, possibly because the greater difficulty of the symbolic task led to a greater reliance in that case upon trial and error strategies.

It would seem, then, that performance on a particular learning task can be represented as a sequence of complex processes, undoubtedly including motivational and personality processes, and that the relative contribution of component intellectual operations (such as cognition or divergent production) varies as a function of the stage of learning and of the difficulty or complexity of the task. The nature of the particular component factors involved also depends upon the content and form of the thing learned: Figural abilities seem likely to be implicated in learning tasks employing figural materials, for example, and the same kind of match would be expected for symbolic, semantic, and behavioral materials. Skill in dealing with classes appears to be relevant to concept attainment, as we have seen, but facility with other products ought to be emphasized in other forms of learning—e.g., relations and implications in paired-associate learning, systems in serial learning, and transformations in insight learning.

In reference to the SI component factors, then, learning tasks would be differentiated in terms of the content of the materials used and the product emphasized in the form of learning procedure employed, i.e. in terms of the category of information learned (the 24 $C \times P$ cells in the SI model). Thus, learning tasks may cover in a conglomerate fashion the same cells of the SI model already represented by specific ability measures, but scores from the learning task, particularly if derived separately for different stages of learning, would in addition reflect relative effectiveness in combining appropriate component skills for the achievement of a complex performance.

Similar conceptual analyses suggest that many other complex cognitive processes may also be represented in terms of sequences of SI operations and that consistent individual differences may appear as a function of the category of information processed in each case (Guilford, 1967).

Perception and Attention

Since distinctions between "perception" and "cognition" are difficult to draw in absolute terms, most psychologists usually just admit that a blurred area of overlap exists. Consider, for example, that in the tachistoscopic presentation of words at gradually increasing exposure times, information might be extracted from the stimulus materials in stages: during the earlier brief exposures, a subject might identify only single letters and not realize until later exposures that the combination of letters perceived forms some word, whose meaning would not be comprehended until still later exposures. In Guilford's terminology, these stages of information extraction proceed from the cognition of figural units through the cognition of symbolic units to the cognition of semantic units, all of which fall properly within the domain of cognition. Guilford is willing to follow traditional usage, however, and label the cognition of form as perception, but he feels that the awareness of semantic meaning and even the realization that a form is a sign for something else would technically fall beyond the perceptual area. For Guilford (1967), then, "perception may be said to overlap cognition where figural information is concerned" (p. 252).*

Perceptual abilities, such as figure-ground separation, discrimination, analysis, and synthesis, appear to be roughly ordered in levels of complexity, in the sense that analysis and synthesis seem to require the prior mastery of discrimination, which in turn presupposes figure-ground separation. Because of this, one might expect these skills to be developmentally ordered, with the more complex functions developing at later ages than the simpler ones (Birch and Lefford, 1963, 1967). As we shall see in a later section, such developmental orderings should also be expected for other intellectual abilities as well, primarily because certain products of information are intrinsically more complicated than others and thereby imply more complex processing skills; e.g., systems, as complexes of related or interacting parts, presuppose facility with relations; classes, as groupings of elements, presuppose facility with units.

In SI terms, tests of figure-ground separation assess the cognition of figural units (CFU). Tests of form discrimination assess primarily the evaluation of figural units (EFU), the criterion of evaluation being identity, but variance in CFU may also be reflected to a greater or lesser degree depending upon the level of prior mastery attained by the

* It should be emphasized in this context that it is not the content of the test materials that is classified in the SI model but the content of the information processed. One subject, for example, might respond to the presentation of a Chinese character as if it were a figure, another as if it were a symbol, and a third in terms of its meaning. Although we usually presume that test contents will be interpreted in the intended standard way and proceed to treat the test as a measure of X, these presumptions should be examined empirically in the light of obtained response consistencies across tests (factor patterns) and other means of inferring the respondent's subjective treatment of the materials. This point is very similar to the old caveat that tests do not have reliabilities or validities, only test responses do—and these vary as a function of subject characteristics.

subjects tested. If the form discrimination task involves identification after some kind of transformation such as rotation, then CFT would become a major component in performance. Form analysis, in the sense of locating in a whole figure certain isolated pieces of the figure, involves not only the cognition of figural transformations (CFT) but their convergent production (NFT) as well, with the latter function becoming more and more salient as the figures become more complicated. Form analysis of this type might therefore be a precursor of embedded-figures performance, since the dominant function in that task is also NFT (Guilford, 1967). Form analysis is said to involve a transformation, in this case a revised interpretation or use of lines, because the locating of a part within a whole requires that lines first seen as part of the larger figure must come to be reinterpreted as part of the piece. On the other hand, form synthesis (in the sense of choosing a set of parts that may be combined to construct a standard figure) would reflect the convergent production, and possibly the cognition, of figural systems (NFS and CFS).

One of the most critical problems in the area of perception is to account for why subjects do not perceive everything in the stimulus field all the time. This problem is usually handled by introducing the concept of attention, which implies some kind of filtering operation underlying the observed selectivity in perception (Broadbent, 1957, 1958). In addition to the notion of selectivity, however, the concept of attention usually also involves the notion of level or intensity of involvement, in terms of degree of vigilance or arousal. Since variations in level of attention occur as a function of stimulus presentation or change and so do systematic variations in muscular, electrocortical, and autonomic responses, individual differences in the strength and habituation of these bodily responses (which together are called the orientation reaction) have come to serve as indices of attentional variables (Lynn, 1966). Thus, components of the orientation reaction, including such straightforward measures as fixation time, provide reasonably objective indices of the intensity and amount of attention even for very young children (Kagan and Lewis, 1965).

In addition to questions of how much is perceived (selectivity), for how long (duration), and with what degree of vividness (intensity), there is also the question of what is perceived, i.e., the question of the direction of attention. When we consider this latter issue, it becomes clear that the direction of attention is a function not only of characteristics of the stimuli but of characteristics of the perceiver. It is influenced by individual styles of scanning the environment and is determined to a considerable degree by the intentions and desires of the subject. This is not just the point that the S-R paradigm must be modified to include organismic variables as mediators (S-O-R), but that the organism actively selects and structures its stimulus field as a function of its needs and motives (O-S-R) (Thurstone, 1923; Solley and Murphy, 1960).

Attentional variables thus appear to fall as much in the personality domain as in the cognitive and will be treated here as part of a separate category of variables, called controlling mechanisms, that cut across the relatively arbitrary distinctions between cognitive and personal–social functioning. Controlling mechanisms, which include stylistic and strategic determinants of behavior, thus offer a basis for articulating cognitive, personal–social, and affective domains as interrelated subsystems of the total personality organization (Gardner, Jackson and Messick, 1960; Messick, 1961). Some of these controlling mechanisms will be discussed further in a later section.

With respect to the SI model of the cognitive domain, then, attentional variables would be expected to play some role in all cells and at all levels. As previously noted by Burt (1949), attentional processes are general and influence mental functioning at every level of the hierarchy. Other authors have emphasized the role of attention in complex mental processes such as learning, and some have even claimed that attention is the major determinant of performance. Zeaman and House (1967), for example, have argued that individual differences in discrimination learning, even those between retardates and normals, are not due to individual differences in acquisition rate but to differences in attention.

Attentional processes, then, appear to involve variables that are not explicitly represented in the extended SI scheme but that very likely influence the operation of SI components in behavior. Such variables would need to be incorporated into sequential models of complex processes as moderators (i.e., as determinants of which SI components will operate under certain circumstances) or as amplifier-attenuators of SI factors.

Memory and Recall

The dimensions of memory categorized in cells of the SI model deal with the retention and retrieval of information in the same form in which it was learned and in response to the same cues in connection with which it was committed to storage. This type of retrieval has been called "replicative recall" by Guilford (1967). Within this paradigm, different dimensions of memory have been distinguished empirically in terms of the different kinds of products of information recalled. This suggests that memory storage may occur in a variety of forms, at least six according to the SI model, rather than in a single form, such as S-R connections. This possibility, which would emphasize classes and systems as well as relations and implications, offers a basis for encompassing notions of association along with notions of schema and structure within a common framework.

In addition to replicative recall, Guilford (1967) also distinguishes a type of retrieval he calls "transfer recall", in which information is retrieved from memory in response to cues not directly involved in the original learning. This type of memory retrieval is particularly relevant to divergent production, where the cues for recall are usually fairly general and cut across previous learnings and where sometimes, as in the divergent production of systems,* the particular elements retrieved have never even existed in combination before, let alone in connection with specific cues. In transfer recall, it is as if the subject scans his memory in search of patterns or products of information (or thinks of instances) that will match in a sufficient number of points a desired pattern defined by the given cues. It is as if the desired pattern serves as a template guiding the scanning activity, just like Duncker's (1945) "search model", with those products ultimately retrieved from memory being the ones found to match the model acceptably. The question of an acceptable match, of course, brings into play the operation of evaluation. Thus, the process of recall appears to involve a complex sequence of operations that includes divergent production and evaluation as well as the various "replicative" dimensions of memory *per se*, thereby taking on more the look of problem solving than of storage retrieval.

Problem Solving and Creativity

Several conceptual analyses of the problem-solving process and of the creative process have resulted in similar lists of operations occurring in sequence. Dewey (1910), for example, proposed five steps in the problem-solving process: (1) a difficulty is felt; (2) the difficulty is located and defined; (3) possible solutions are generated; (4) consequences are considered; and (5) a solution is accepted. Wallas (1926) proposed four steps for the creative process: (1) preparation, or the gathering of information; (2) incubation, or unconscious manipulation; (3) illumination, or the emergence of solutions; and (4) verification, or the testing of solutions. The final step in both series appears to corres-

* For example, write as many four word sentences as you can where the first word begins with W, the second with C, the third with E, and the fourth with N.

pond to the SI operation of evaluation, as does the initial step in Dewey's list, thereby suggesting that the general TOTE formulation of Miller *et al.*, (1960) may be applicable here. With the exception of incubation, the remaining steps in both lists appear to involve cognitive factors and a blending of divergent production and convergent production. Wallas's stage of incubation provides a puzzle, however, since there is little evidence about the nature of the unconscious operations that might be involved. Guilford (1967) has suggested the incubation involves transformations of information resulting from motivationally induced interactions among stored products of information in memory.

Guilford (1967) has also proposed a sequential model of problem solving but in the form of a flow chart, rather than a list, to permit multiple feedback options. The model emphasizes the role of cognition in structuring the problem and in obtaining information from the environment and from memory and the role of production, both divergent and convergent, in generating answers. The operation of evaluation occurs repeatedly throughout the sequence. An important feature of the model is that provision is incorporated for the transmission of information from memory to the central operations of cognition and production not only through the filter of evaluation but also directly, as would be the case in the suspended judgment technique in brainstorming.

These analyses of the problem solving and creative processes as sequences of component operations are descriptive of general features rather than being predictive of specific outcomes, and as such their major value is heuristic. These models emphasize both the distinctiveness of the component processes and the sequential nature of their combination in achieving the final solutions or creative products. This suggests, on the one hand, that the various component skills should be assessed separately in order to diagnose specific proficiencies and, on the other hand, that overall aspects of the total process (and possibly its major phases) should be assessed directly to gauge relative effectiveness in combining the appropriate components in task performance.

In considering component skills in creativity and problem solving, special attention should be given to the dimensions of divergent production, for they provide the basis for the essential function of generating possibilities. These dimensions include fluency of various types, such as figural (DFU), symbolic (DSU), ideational (DMU), associational (DMR), and expressional (DMS); flexibility, in the sense of producing varied classes of responses (e.g., DMC, "spontaneous flexibility") or producing transformations (e.g., DFT, "adaptive flexibility"); originality, in the sense of producing unusual, remote, or clever responses

(DMT); and elaboration, or the divergent production of implications (D–I, especially DMI, semantic elaboration). As has been noted, dimensions of evaluation also play a critical role in problem solving and creativity, and dimensions of cognition and convergent production are frequently required as well. Among the latter dimensions of particular relevance to problem solving are sensitivity to problems, or the cognition of semantic implications (CMI), and redefinition, or the convergent production of semantic transformations (NMT).

In the measurement of creativity, one common approach is to assess these various component dimensions directly as a means of tapping personal qualities that might be predisposing toward creative performance. Another approach, which could be used jointly with the first, is to evaluate actual products for the extent to which they exhibit properties usually considered to be creative. The products might be evaluated in terms of their relative novelty, for example, or their degree of appropriateness or fit, both internally among the parts and externally with the context. They might be judged for the extent to which they embody transformations that transcend immediate constraints or the extent to which they summarize the essence of the matter in sufficiently condensed form to warrant repeated examination (Jackson and Messick, 1965). The application of such criteria conjointly would make it possible to distinguish degrees of quality within the class of creative products—once the necessary requirements have been met for considering a product creative in the first place. In this connection, it is generally agreed that the minimal properties required for a product to be called "creative" are unusualness and appropriateness, with the latter being included primarily to rule out the bizarre and absurd (Barron, 1963; Jackson and Messick, 1965; Wallach and Kogan, 1965). This suggests that a good starting point for the assessment of creative tendencies would be measures of originality and evaluation, both of which could be derived from tasks requiring fluency in the production of uncommon (though appropriate) responses.*

Comparison of Sequential SI Operations with Other Summaries of Cognitive Processes

Some feeling for the provisional adequacy and appropriateness of considering SI factors as potential components in sequential models of

* It is sometimes possible to derive several scores from the same task to represent different dimensions of creativity, such as the number of common responses (ideational fluency), the number of uncommon responses (originality), the number of classes of responses (flexibility), and the number of inappropriate responses (evaluation). Complete reliance on this single task approach is not recommended, however, because of the potentially serious biasing effects of experimental dependencies.

cognition may be obtained by a brief comparison of this approach with other integrative summaries of cognitive processes. One of the most extensive of these summaries is the treatise on "Children's Thinking" by David Russell (1956), which distinguishes six major types of thinking: perceptual thinking, associative thinking, inductive-deductive thinking leading to concept formation or conclusions, problem solving, creative thinking, and critical thinking. As described by Russell, these six types of thinking are relatively complex processes, but in four of the six cases a particular component appears to be comparatively central. In perceptual thinking the major processes seem to be cognitive in Guilford's sense; in associative thinking the central feature is memory, particularly memory for implications and relations; in inductive-deductive thinking the dominant process is convergent production; and in critical thinking—which involves discrimination, comparison, and appraisal—it is evaluation. Both creative thinking and problem solving involve a combination of important components, but the role of divergent production is prominent in each. Thus, there is a notable match between the types of thinking described by Russell (1956) and the five operations of the SI model. The distinctions made by Guilford (1967) among the various contents and products of information processed are not similarly matched by Russell, however, who treats the materials of thinking more globally in terms of percepts, images, memories, and concepts—although Russell does consider subtypes of materials in terms of specific contents, such as percepts of space and concepts of the self, some of which could be translated into SI categories.

In another major integrative summary of cognition, Kagan and Kogan (1970) chose to structure their discussion of individual variation in cognitive processes under headings corresponding to components of the problem-solving process, which in their terms included encoding, memory, generation of hypotheses, evaluation, and deduction. Again there is a remarkable similarity between these constructs and the five operations of the SI model—memory and evaluation are represented in both schemes; encoding corresponds to cognition (with the additional operation of attentional variables); generation of hypotheses corresponds to divergent production; and deduction corresponds to convergent production. And again, consistencies in response related to different contents and products of information are not systematically treated in the Kagan and Kogan review.

It would appear, then, that the coverage of cognitive functions provided by the extended SI system is quite comparable to that of other summaries with respect to the types of psychological operations considered. It is generally more extensive and detailed than other treatments, however, with respect to the content and form of the information involved in those operations. These latter distinctions of content and form are far from trivial, for they derive not from subjective analyses of types of "knowledge", as in epistemology, but from empirical analyses of individual differences in performance, which could provide the basis for a kind of psychoepistemology (Guilford, 1967). Thus, the 24 categories of information in the content × product classification scheme not only provide a taxonomy of all the things that can be cognized, remembered, produced, and evaluated, but also a taxonomy of empirical dimensions of individual differences in information processing. Distinctions among various types of content and form were incorporated in the SI model because it was found to make a difference at the level of individual performance, whether one was dealing with classes or system, for example, or whether the content was figural or semantic. Relationships observed to hold for one kind of content did not necessarily hold for another, and the same was true for different types of products.*

In this connection, special attention should be given to the distinction between behavioral information and other types of content. Behavioral content includes information involved in social interactions, where the attitudes, needs, desires, moods, feelings, intentions, perceptions, thoughts, and actions of other persons and the self are important. This separating out of behavioral information as a distinct type provides a basis for accommodating within the SI framework the repeated finding that processes of perception, memory, learning, and reasoning tend to have different properties and correlates when social or affective materials are involved, presumably because of the implication of personality dimensions and controlling mechanisms (Fitzgibbons, Goldberger, and Eagle, 1965; Messick and Damarin, 1964; Rosenhan and Messick, 1966; Thistlethwaite, 1950).

The inclusion of behavioral content in the SI model incorporates what Thorndike (1920) called "social intelligence" into the system and furnishes an ability framework for dealing with the cognitive aspects of such problem areas as person perception, social sensitivity, and self-appraisal. The behavioral abilities hypothesized by the SI model in some cases seem to be counterparts of constructs already utilized in these areas, such as "forming impressions from fragmentary cues"

* Cronbach (1970) has questioned the empirical basis for distinguishing among factors in terms of the SI facets. Reasoning from clusters of average correlations, he concluded that the finegrained distinctions embodied in the SI system are not often supported by obtained correlational differences to the extent the model would predict. This point merits careful examination using factor analytic techniques to go beyond the inspection of correlational patterns—preferably based upon new data collected with refined instruments and test batteries experimentally structured to illuminate the issue.

(CBU) or "penetrating the defenses of another person" (NBT), but in other cases the SI distinctions appear to offer new perspectives. Thus, the notion of behavioral abilities as dimensions of social information processing affords a much needed additional basis for theoretical analysis and measurement in the particularly complicated area of social cognition (e.g. see Bieri *et al.*, 1966, Bronfenbrenner *et al.*, 1958; Diggory, 1966; Jackson and Messick, 1963; Sarbin *et al.*, 1960; Schroder *et al.*, 1967; Taft, 1956; Tagiuri, 1969; Warr and Knapper, 1968).

In short, the extended SI system provides a broad, integrated summary of known and potential dimensions of cognitive functioning. As such, it offers a guide or check list for evaluating adequacy of coverage in the measurement of cognitive phenomena and provides a system of component variables for sequential descriptions of cognitive processes. One important implication of this formulation for psychological measurement is that we should not just limit attention to the measurement of specific component dimensions, but should also attempt to assess the relative effectiveness of their combination in complex sequential processes such as learning or problem solving. The hierarchical features of the model serve to sensitize the investigator to questions of generalization and point to the major kinds of response consistency that would be required for the utilization of constructs having higher levels of generality, such as consistencies across different types of content or product or operation, or across various combinations of these facets (i.e., factors that span several SI cells).

The discussion up to this point has emphasized the potential fruitfulness of the extended SI system as a source of structural components for sequential models of psychological process. There are also several problems with the approach, of course, and two serious ones will be discussed in the closing sections of this paper. The first of these problems stems from the interdependence of the cognitive domain and other subsystems of the total personality. In brief, there are many dimensions of temperament, motivation, and attitudes that influence cognitive functioning and should, therefore, be incorporated into sequential models of cognitive processes, but which are not embodied in the SI system. Effective sequential models of cognition, then, must include component personality variables from outside the SI framework; some obviously relevant examples of such variables for cognitive functioning are cognitive styles, which will be discussed in more detail shortly. The other problem involves the phenomena of psychological development, particularly the occurrence of developmental stages. Since the concept of developmental stages implies a sequential order, usually invariant and universal, of qualitatively different organizational structures, the question arises as to whether component factors derived from response consistencies at one stage of development are appropriately descriptive of cognitive functioning at another stage of development. In short, the issue involves the extent to which SI dimensions are applicable across the entire age range.

Personality Organization in Cognition

The ability dimensions encompassed in the SI model essentially refer to the content of cognition or the question of what kind of information is being processed by what operation in what form. We must also be concerned, however, with the style of cognition or the question of "How?" (i.e., the manner in which the behavior occurs), for stylistic consistencies frequently interact with content factors to influence the achievement level of performance. For this reason it is important to assess the style of response to cognitive demands as well as the content of the response, for it is dangerous to make inferences about capacity from the achievement level of performance alone (Hertzig *et al.*, 1968). The concept of ability implies the measurement of capacities in terms of maximal performance, whereas the concept of style implies the measurement of preferred modes of operation in terms of typical performance, but both are necessary for a full understanding of cognitive functioning (Cronbach, 1970).

Stylistic aspects of cognition reflect personality dimensions that cut across affective, personal-social, and cognitive domains and thereby serve to interweave the cognitive system with other subsystems of personality organization (Gardner *et al.*, 1959; Gardner *et al.*, 1960; Gardner and Moriarty, 1968; Klein, 1970). The personality dimensions of primary interest in this connection are referred to here as controlling mechanisms, which are structural dimensions of personality determining the characteristic regulation and control of impulse, thought, and behavioral expression (Gardner *et al.*, 1959; Messick, 1961). These controlling mechanisms include such variables as cognitive styles, coping styles, attentional propensities, and defenses.

Cognitive System Variables

Some of the controlling mechanisms represent dimensions of individual differences in the structural characteristics of the cognitive system itself, or more broadly of the total personality system. These dimensions primarily reflect differences in the complexity of the system and derive in large part from the thinking of Lewin (1935, 1951) and Werner

(1948, 1957). Both of these theorists emphasized concepts of differentiation, articulation, and hierarchic integration in development, with Lewin in particular stressing the importance of developmental increases in the variety of units and in the independence of the parts. Several measures of individual differences in cognitive complexity have stemmed from these notions in recent years, thereby mirroring an increasing concern over system properties as controlling influences in behavior. These measures include such things as the number of different dimensions or constructs utilized by subjects in judging similarities and differences among people (Kelly, 1955; Bieri, 1961); the degree of gradation or articulation within each of these dimensions (Bieri *et al.*, 1966; Messick and Kogan, 1966; Signell, 1966); the diversity of content exhibited in the concepts generated (Signell, 1966); the number of different groups used in sorting common objects (Gardner and Schoen, 1962; Messick and Kogan, 1963); and the abstractness versus concreteness of conceptual systems (Harvey *et al.*, 1961; Schroder *et al.*, 1967). Related concepts of psychological differentiation are also stressed in the work of Witkin *et al.* (1962) and Rokeach (1960).

Cognitive Styles

Other controlling mechanisms appear in the form of crystallized preferences or attitudes, called cognitive styles, which determine a person's typical modes of perceiving, remembering, thinking, and problem solving. For the most part, cognitive styles are information-processing habits that develop in congenial ways around underlying personality trends (Messick, 1970). As such, it is not surprising that different dimensions of cognitive style have come to be associated with particular information-processing operations, e.g., scanning with perception, leveling-sharpening with memory, conceptual style and category breadth with divergent production, field independence with convergent production, and impulsivity-reflectivity with evaluation, but this association is far from perfect and many of the styles appear to influence information processing sequences at several points. Given the operation of such stylistic consistencies, it would be important to include these stylistic variables in detailed sequential models of cognitive functioning.

Developmental Changes in Cognition

We now turn to a consideration of the structure of the cognitive domain in childhood and the question of how far down the age scale the extended SI system might apply.

The Factorial Differentiation Hypothesis

In contrast to the notion that the major ability factors observed in adulthood may exist in rudimentary form fairly early in life is the hypothesis proposed by Garrett (1946) that a single general ability dimension is dominant in early childhood, which then differentiates in time into a few broad ability factors and later into more and more specific abilities. Guilford (1967) systematically reviewed the available evidence for and against the Garrett hypothesis and found the majority of the results to be nonsupporting. Some of the most critical evidence involved the repeated finding of differentiated abilities in very young children (ranging down to ages two and three), including the differentiation of such factors as *CMU* and *CMS* or *NMU* and *NMS* which differed in only one facet of the SI design (Hurst, 1960; Meyers *et al.*, 1962; Meyers *et al.*, 1964; McCartin and Meyers, 1966). Several cognitive dimensions were also uncovered in analyses of infants and pre-school children by Stott and Ball (1965), using items drawn from various standard infant and pre-school scales. These investigators attempted to identify the obtained factors with SI categories, and among the 31 intellectual dimensions isolated were represented all five of the operations, as well as all four contents and five of the six products.

Such evidence suggests that at least some dimensions reflecting the major distinctions of the SI model may emerge fairly early in life. Indeed, Guilford (1967) goes so far as to suggest that the five types of operations are inherited, that "the brain is apparently predesigned to perform in the five major ways, and it may also be predesigned to handle information in the form of the different kinds of products". He thinks it more probable, though, that uniformities in the child's environment, as processed by the innate operations, are primarily responsible for the different kinds of products formed as well as for the different types of content experienced. This would suggest that certain dimensions in the SI model would be expected to develop earlier than others, because of the differential salience of particular kinds of experience early in life. The child's first experiences, for example, are probably in the form of behavioral information having reference to his own internal states, followed closely by figural information as he responds to visual and auditory inputs, then by semantic information, and finally by symbolic information. Intuitively, it also seems likely that dimensions involving certain products of information ought to develop earlier than others, such as skill in processing units before skill with classes or facility with relations before facility with systems, mainly because some products appear to be intrinsically more complex than others.

These notions accord well with the accommodation aspects of Piaget's theory (Flavell, 1963), and some of the concepts of one formulation appear to be readily translatable into the terms of the other. The sensorimotor schema of Piaget, for example, seems to correspond to a behavioral system, which developed first from behavioral units that have come to form a class of action sequences.

By and large, then, the specific Garrett (1946) hypothesis of a single general ability that differentiates over time finds little empirical support, but the more general notion that cognitive structure tends to become increasingly more differentiated (and hierarchically integrated) during the course of development, as propounded by Werner and Lewin, appears to be viable in factor analytic terms.

Stages of Development

In the immediately preceding discussion, we were mainly concerned with the issue of developmental continuity versus discontinuity in cognitive structure as viewed in terms of differential psychology, where discontinuity would be indicated by changes in the number or size of dimensions over time or by changes in the meaning of dimensions, as revealed in new patterns of correlates or factor loadings (Emmerich, 1964, 1968). There is also the possibility, however, that individuals pass through a developmental sequence of qualitatively different structural organizations, usually held to be in an invariant order, which is the more classical developmental view of stage progression. Several theorists have postulated such a developmental sequence of stages, usually involving three major phases that encompass similar phenomena from theory to theory but are labeled in somewhat different terms—such as sensorimotor, perceptual, and conceptual (Werner, 1948); perceptual, imaginal, and conceptual (Thurstone, 1926); sensorimotor, preoperational, and operational (Piaget, 1950); or enactive, ikonic, and symbolic (Bruner *et al.*, 1966).*

Under these circumstances a different type of variable (and a different approach to measurement) must be added to our armory—one that focuses upon an individual's stage or level on the develop-

* Strictly speaking, the terms "enactive", "ikonic", and "symbolic" are used by Bruner to refer to characteristic modes of cognitive functioning rather than to developmental stages, although the three modes do emerge at different points in time developmentally.

mental scale. The emphasis here would be upon the assessment of qualitative features that are characteristic of particular stages of cognitive functioning and upon ordered sequences of tasks capable of gauging the transition from one stage to another. Individual differences within stage might also be assessed with these tasks. Although such measures could be classified in terms of SI categories, they are not primarily intended to assess specific dimensions of cognitive functioning. Such a classification—particularly as it reflects upon representativeness of coverage in terms of content, form, and operation—may prove to be of some relevance to stage measurement, however, because of the possibility that an individual may function at different developmental levels in different cognitive areas, as in Werner's concept of mobility of developmental level and Piaget's concept of horizontal décalage. The general point here is that particular component variables and their mode of combination in sequential models of cognitive process may differ as a function of developmental level.

Interactions With Environmental Variables

Many theorists, including Piaget and Guilford, emphasize the importance of interactions with the environment for intellectual development. Although the child may start with certain innate mechanisms, such as the predispositions underlying Guilford's five operations or Piaget's invariant functions of assimilation and accommodation, the rate of progression and the variety of content in cognitive functioning appear to depend upon the extent to which these mechanisms are exercised in interaction with a varied environment (Hunt, 1961). Thus, environmental factors may also have to be included in sequential cognitive models as interactive and moderator variables.

Indeed, Ferguson (1954, 1956) has suggested that cognitive factors themselves represent domains of behavior that happen to have been learned together, along with those similar behaviors that become associated through generalization of learning and transfer. Some of the determinants of these shared learnings are developmental, in the sense that certain things are experienced together because they are appropriate to particular ages, but most of the determinants appear to be more directly sociocultural (Lesser *et al.*, 1965). Direct evidence bearing on the transfer theory of ability development is sparse, however, because most of the training efforts studied have been limited and short term. What is clearly needed at this point to clarify these developmental and environmental determinants are "longitudinal studies in which the achievements of people with different experiences are compared"

Table I

Definitions of Categories in the SI Model

Operations	Contents	Products
C—*Cognition*. Immediate discovery, awareness, rediscovery, or recognition of information in various forms; comprehension or understanding.	F—*Figural*. Information in concrete form, as perceived or as recalled possibly in the form of images. The term 'figural' minimally implies figure-ground perceptual organization. Visual spatial information is figural. Different sense modalities may be involved, e.g. visual, kinesthetic.	U—*Units*. Relatively segregated or circumscribed items of information having 'thing' character. May be close to Gestalt psychology's "figure on a ground".
M—*Memory*. Retention or storage of information, with some degree of availability in the same form it was committed to storage and in response to the same cues in connection with which it was learned.	S—*Symbolic*. Information in the form of denotative signs, having no significance in and of themselves, such as letters, numbers, musical notations, codes, and words, when meaning and form are not considered.	C—*Classes*. Conceptions underlying sets of items of information grouped by virtue of their common properties.
D—*Divergent Production*. Generation of information from given information, where the emphasis is upon variety and quantity of output from the same source. Likely to involve what has been called transfer. This operation is most clearly involved in aptitudes of creative potential.	M—*Semantic*. Information in the form of meanings to which words commonly become attached, hence most notable in verbal thinking and in verbal communication but not identical with words. Meaningful pictures also often convey semantic information.	R—*Relations*. Connections between items of information based upon variables or points of contact that apply to them. Relational connections are more meaningful and definable than implications.
N—*Convergent Production*. Generation of information from given information, where the emphasis is upon achieving unique or conventionally accepted best outcomes. It is likely the given (cue) information fully determines the response.	B—*Behavioral*. Information, essentially non verbal, involved in human interactions where the attitudes, needs, desires, moods, intentions, perceptions, thoughts, etc., of other people and of ourselves are involved.	S—*Systems*. Organized or structured aggregates of items of information; complexes of interrelated or interacting parts.
E—*Evaluation*. Reaching decisions or making judgments concerning criterion satisfaction (correctness, suitability, adequacy, desirability etc.) of information. A process of comparing a product of information with known information according to logical criteria, such as identity, similarity, satisfaction of class membership and consistency.		T—*Transformations*. Changes of various kinds (redefinition, shifts, or modification) of existing information or in its function.
		I—*Implications*. Extrapolations of information, in the form of expectancies, predictions, known or suspected antecedents, concomitants, or consequences. The connection between the given information and that extrapolated is more general and less definable than a relational connection.

(Carroll, 1968) along with cumulative applications of a viable multivariate experimental methodology.

Conclusion

This paper has called for the development of sequential models of cognition and personality as a way of adding process to the primarily structural concerns of current multivariate models. At the same time, it has also pointed to the results of factor analysis, particularly as summarized in the extended SI system, as a source of component variables for such sequential formulations. The need to take into account personality, developmental, and environmental variables was also emphasized in the hope that the complexity of the task would be appreciated and confronted and that multivariate theorists would be challenged to engage in what Cronbach (1970) has called "deeper theoretical analysis".

COMMENT ON MESSICK'S PAPER

PHILIP E. VERNON

I am glad Guilford is a participant in the Panel to discuss Messick's paper, since I would have thought it more appropriate to have him as the main Discussant rather than an amateur factor analyst like myself. However, Messick raises so many interesting and original points that there is plenty for all of us to comment on. We are not concerned, in this discussion, with evaluating the SI model as such. Like Messick I am going to accept the SI system as providing "a broad integrated summary of known and potential dimensions of cognitive functioning". What we are concerned with are Messick's suggested extensions or elaborations of SI.

I am in general agreement with a great many of these, particularly with the notion of facets which might help to subclassify some of Guilford's cells, e.g., to distinguish sensory modalities and perhaps response modes. Then it is interesting, too, that SI categories often match closely the varieties of cognition distinguished by other writers such as Russell, or Kagan and Kogan; though I suppose this is to be expected insofar as both they and Guilford consciously set out to encompass the whole cognitive domain. Many other sections could be mentioned where I am grateful to Messick for his fresh approach and clarity of expression. Before looking at his main theme—concerning sequential processes—I would like to say a little about hierarchical models, in which, as he mentions, I have somewhat of a vested interest.

So far as my own work goes, I do not think it is correct to say that I regard, or have ever regarded, hierarchy as a psychological model. It is to me simply a convenient way, involving particularly simple calculations devised by Burt, for classifying test performances whereby one maximizes the variance of the most general factor first, then the major groupings, and so on to the minor factors as and when needed. This approach has the advantage of avoiding the proliferation mentioned by Messick, since it helps one to realize that some of the factors claimed in the literature add so little to the variance covered that it is unlikely that they would be of sufficient reliability or sufficient importance to aid in any decision-making. *Qua* psychological model, I think it is open to a lot of difficulty because the successive group factors do not have any very obvious psychological meaning. Thus, my verbal-educational and spatial-mechanical factors do not represent mental abilities; they are the residual common variance left when one has taken out, or is holding constant, the *g* factor. Similarly the minor group factors are residuals of residuals. The same sort of difficulty would arise if we followed the more usual procedure of arriving at a hierarchical model starting from oblique primary factors and calculating the second or higher-order factors from the correlations between the primaries, instead of, as in my own case, starting from the top and working downwards.

Burt's hierarchy is different in that, as Messick describes, it does owe a good deal to neurological and psychological theory, the higher-order factors being regarded as more complex, integrative abilities, built up from the simpler, more specific, abilities. But then his model is not a straight representation of the correlations of a battery of tests. In other words it is not empirical unless one carefully chooses tests to represent the successive levels. One research study by Moursy was designed in this way to represent sensation, perception, association and relational thinking. But, though it was confirmatory, it could not be regarded as representing the whole universe of testable abilities, as mine tries to do.

Turning to SI, I have often thought, apparently like Messick, that it implies hierarchy in the sense that many of the factors are likely to be oblique, and therefore it would make good sense to allow that some of them could be grouped or clustered, and second or higher-order factors calculated. But I understood that Guilford was averse to this, because the amount of obliquity among primary factors depended so much on the heterogeneity and other characteristics of the particular population tested. Thus, I would conclude this section of my discussion by agreeing with Messick that SI and hierarchy are not irreconcilable, though I would suggest that there are a number of practical difficulties in arriving at an agreed scheme, or interpreting it when one has got it.

Turning to the major theme, namely to provide "a system of component variables for sequential description of cognitive processes". Obviously this is the most controversial of Messick's contributions, and although he offers a cogent argument, I do not feel altogether convinced. It is not a question of whether or not factor analysis could be applied to the study of developmental or sequential processes; Cattell, for example, has provided some leads on this in his own work with P- and O-techniques. But such processes seem to me to belong to a different realm of discourse, as it were, from the R-technique as employed by Guilford and the great majority of factorists. I would have thought that their factors are invariably cross-sectional; that is, they represent the skills attained at a particular stage of learning, or degree of success in solving problems on the basis of previous learning, but never the processes of learning or of handling problems. It is true, of course, that investigations such as Fleishman's enable us to factorize simultaneously several stages of learning or development, and therefore throw useful light on sequential processes. But these are still a series of cross-sections; they do not yield process factors. And the same would seem to apply to Allison's, Bunderson's and other studies cited by Messick. Some of the various learning abilities isolated at ETS are, I think, already included in the Memory category of Guilford's model, or might be added to it; but again this is an extension of structure rather than incorporation of process into the model. Furthermore, as Messick points out, the *M* factors already discovered are all based on replicative recall, which to me is a rather artificial type of learning. No doubt it is of interest to psychologists and actors, and some school teachers, but far from typical of everyday learning processes. Guilford himself has described what Piaget calls assimilation and accommodation, that is schema-building processes, but so far as I know these have not yet provided any measures suitable for factorization.

Perhaps I am unduly suspicious of Messick's arguments because, about 20 years ago, I was stung by a criticism of factor analysis put forward by Professor Hearnshaw of Liverpool. He stated that factorists always work with end-products of cognition and ignore the temporal aspect—what went on over time in reaching these end-products. He suggested some ingenious techniques for a first approach to measuring temporal aspects of certain abilities. His tests required the Subject to integrate information provided over certain periods of time, not all given simultaneously. I tried out these and some other similarly designed tests, along with reference tests, and found that any factor present in the temporal integration tests was fully covered by non-temporal tests of *V*, *I*, *S*, and *N*. Maybe this reminiscence is not entirely relevant, but it was yet another attempt to study process by R-technique factors which apparently failed. Thus, for the present at least, it seems advisable to think of factorial and experimental studies of learning as complementary, and both needed, rather than hoping that either could absorb the other.

I would like to pose another rather general query about the paper, namely to suggest that perhaps Messick is being almost too ambitious in his attempt to make the SI model truly comprehensive. Besides bringing in the facets that I noted, and hierarchical levels and sequential processes, he draws our attention to personality and social influences, and to variables which cut across these, such as attention and cognitive styles or controls. Probably all of us would admit that the segregation of the cognitive from the motivational domains is artifactual; and the controlling mechanisms which have come to be known as styles are interesting constructs for trying to bridge the gap (even though I offer some criticisms in my own paper). I would like to suggest, however, that factor analysis works best when it does confine itself to a fairly restricted domain that requires mapping out. Thus, when intellectual tests, self report personality questionnaires, and interest measures are included in the same factorial study, and rotated by procedures such as Varimax, these domains always tend to separate out; and the loadings of bridging variables are often too small to receive much consideration. This, of course, is more a criticism of factor analysis as a method than of SI or other factorial models. In conclusion, then, I would certainly favor Messick's objectives, though I believe that progress toward them will, in practice, have to be piecemeal, a bit at a time. This indeed is the way Guilford himself worked toward his SI model.

COMMENT ON MESSICK'S PAPER

J. P. GUILFORD

In view of Messick's liberal and favorable attention to the structure of intellect model and its utility, I am naturally pleased with his paper. His grasp of the subject is unusual. In only a very few places would an updating of definitions and information have improved it.

If there are to be higher-order factors of intelligence, and I am quite willing to tolerate the idea, I think that Messick is correct in suggesting that they are in terms of groupings of similar first-order abilities in the SI model. It may be that not all of the 74 projected groupings will materialize when the search is systematically made. But it seems certain that a simple hierarchy is precluded, however, because one higher-order factor would cut across others.

Some experiences in the Aptitudes Research Project lend some indirect support for Messick's suggestions. For example, we found that abilities differing only with regard to kind of product of information were sometimes difficult to separate. We were not sure, however, how much this tendency was due to inadequate test construction. When we aimed certain tests in the direction of the ability memory-for-figural-relations, for example, some of them came out with significant loadings also on the factor for memory-for-figural-transformations. There might be a higher-order factor that these two abilities have in common, but an alternative interpretation is that examinees tended to process relations as transformations. Not all MFR and MFT tests were of complexity two. There were other examples, and the alternative interpretation in terms of failing experimental controls within tests was always tenable. Because of such possibilities, the problem of estimating intercorrelations of lower-order factors is by no means a simple one.

COMMENT ON MESSICK'S PAPER

K. PAWLIK

I am grateful to Messick for his lucid exposition of the need for process-oriented personality research and of the mutual interdependence of research on process and research on structure. I agree with him in most respects and I also share some of his comments on the S-I model and his evaluation of the differentiation theory of intelligence. I may have some doubts on the statement (cf. Messick's footnote on page 278) that the S-I model really considers psychological processes in the way a subject solves a test; at least, at the time when the S-I model was set up, there was no information available on these processes and presumably the model only considers item content and parameters of the logical make-up of a test. I may also be a bit hesitant regarding the possibilities of explaining learning processes in terms of the S-I model concepts rather than the other way round. My major comment, though, concerns the alleged explanatory psychological role of higher-order factors, which Messick stressed in the oral presentation of his paper. Higher-order factors, as a rule, explain less variance of the test measures than the respective lower-order factors from which they have been calculated. Only the special algorithm of the Schmid-Leiman solution, by means of the special model adopted in this solution, achieves a subsequent boosting-up of the variance of the higher-order factors at the cost of lower-order factors. Is it this special case that Messick has in mind when he talks about a hierarchy of factors?

COMMENT ON MESSICK'S PAPER

J. R. ROYCE

Messick's paper provides us with a rich overview of what must be done if we are to evolve a comprehensive, multivariate, psychological theory. In particular, he underlines the need for going beyond taxonomic structure to dynamic process, and he alludes to the necessity for establishing sequential linkages of the relevant components of such complex processes as problem solving and creativity. I found the paper particularly rewarding, for it not only pays attention to the full scope of the problem, but it goes considerably beyond the usual programmatic platitudes and gets down to cases at the important level of the most relevant overall model, basic concepts, and the data. In short, his contribution is directly on target in terms of the three criteria for these conference papers—namely, that they be multivariate, theoretical, and substantive.

However, I think Messick would agree that if we dig deeper into the details of a given complex process we are seldom satisfied with the presently available elaborations of sequential linkages. There are many reasons for this, which we can probably sum up by saying that we simply do not know enough yet. What I am groping toward are clues concerning the key roadblocks to further progress along these lines. For example, I am reasonably convinced that the major stumbling block is the relative paucity of insightful conceptualizing to date. (N.B. No criticism intended concerning the contributions made by a mere handful of substantively oriented multivariate theoreticians. In fact, the state of our advance is due solely to their efforts.) Furthermore, I am convinced we have not even done a proper job on Phase One—namely, the identification of a comprehensive and appropriate taxonomic structure (e.g. style structure). If this is true, it is clearly premature to venture too far in the direction of process at this time. My own guess on this point is that we will evolve a viable psychological structure within the next decade or two, and that we can simultaneously launch (i.e. with knowledge pay-off) tentative probes into selected complex processes.

May it be agreed that top priority must be given to shaping up the taxonomic structure? And on the assumption that the time is right for some process analysis, what direction should it take (i.e. which processes should be investigated), and why?

REFERENCES

Allison, R. B. (1960). Learning parameters and human abilities. ONR Technical Report and doctoral dissertation. Educational Testing Service, Princeton University, Princeton, New Jersey.

Bieri, J. (1961). Complexity–simplicity as a personality variable in cognitive and preferential behavior. *In* "Functions of Varied Experience." (Fiskel, D. W. and Maddi, S. R. eds) Dorsey Press, Homewood, Illinois.

Bieri, J., Atkins, A. L., Briar, S., Leaman, R. L., Miller, H. and Tripodi, T. (1966). "Clinical and Social Judgment: The Discrimination of Behavioral Information." Wiley, New York.

Birch, H. G. and Lefford, A. (1963). Intersensory development in children. *Monogr. Soc. Res. Child Dev.* **28** (5, Serial No. 89).

Birch, H. G. and Lefford, A. (1967). Visual differentiation, intersensory integration, and voluntary motor control. *Monogr. Soc. Res. Child Dev.* **32** (2, Serial No. 110).

Broadbent, D. E. (1957). A mechanical model for human attention and immediate memory. *Psychol. Rev.* **64,** 205–215.

Broadbent, D. E. (1958). "Perception and Communication." Pergamon Press, New York.

Bronfenbrenner, U., Harding, J. and Gallwey, M. (1958). The measurement of skill in social perception. *In* "Talent and Society." (McClelland, D. C., Baldwin, A. L., Bronfenbrenner, U. and Strodtbeck, F. L. eds) Van Nostrand, Princeton, New Jersey.

Bruner, J. S., Olver, R. R. and Greenfield, P. M. (1966). "Studies in Cognitive Growth." Wiley, New York.

Bunderson, V. (1967). A transfer of mental abilities at different stages of practice in the solution of concept problems. Research Bulletin 67–20. Educational Testing Service, Princeton, New Jersey.

Burt, C. V. (1949). The structure of the mind: A review of the results of factor analysis. *Br. J. Educ. Psychol.* **19,** 100–111; 176–199.

Campbell, D. T. and Fiske, D. W. (1959). Convergent and discriminant validation by the multitrait–multimethod matrix. *Psychol. Bull.* **56**, 81–105.

Carroll, J. B. (1968). Review of "The nature of human intelligence." *Am. educ. Res. J.* **5,** 249–256.

Cattell, R. B. (1943). The measurements of adult intelligence. *Psychol. Bull.* **40,** 153–193.

Cattell, R. B. (1953). Theory of fluid and crystallized intelligence: A critical experiment. *J. educ. Psychol.* **54,** 1–22.

Cronbach, L. J. (1970). "Essentials of Psychological Testing." Third Edn. Harper and Brothers, New York.

Damarin, F. L. Jr. and Cattell, R. B. (1968). Personality factors in early childhood and their relation to intelligence. *Monogr. Soc. Res. Child Dev.* **33** (6, Serial No. 122).

Dewey, J. (1910). "How We Think." Heath, Boston.

Diggory, J. C. (1966). "Self Evaluation: Concepts and Studies." Wiley, New York.

Duncanson, J. P. (1964). Intelligence and the ability to learn. ONR Technical Report and Research Bulletin 64–29. Educational Testing Service, Princeton, New Jersey.

Duncker, K. (1945). On problem solving. *Psychol. Monogr.; Gen. Appl.* **58** (5, Whole No. 270).

Dunham, J. L., Guilford, J. P. and Hoepfner, R. (1968). Multivariate approaches to discovering the intellectual components of concept learning. *Psychol. Rev.* **75,** 206–221.

El-Koussy, A. H. (1955). Trends of research in space abilities. *International colloquium on factor analysis*. Paris.

Emmerich, W. (1964). Continuity and stability in early social development. *Child Dev.* **35,** 311–332.

Emmerich, W. (1968). Personality development and concepts of structure. *Child Dev.* **39,** 671–690.

Ferguson, G. A. (1954). On learning and human ability. *Can. J. Psychol.* **8,** 95–112.

Ferguson, G. A. (1956). On transfer and the abilities of man. *Can. J. Psychol.* **10,** 121–131.

Fitzgibbons, D., Goldberger, L. and Eagle, M. (1965). Field dependence and memory for incidental material. *Percept. Mot. Skills* **21,** 743–749.

Flavell, J. H. (1963). "Development Psychology of Jean Piaget." Van Nostrand, Princeton, New Jersey.

Fleishman, E. A. (1966). Human abilities and the acquisition of skills. American Institutes for Research, Washington, D.C.

French, J., Ekstrom, R. and Price, L. (1963). *Manual for kit of reference tests for cognitive factors*. Educational Testing Service, Princeton, New Jersey.

Gagné, R. (1965). "The Conditions of Learning." Holt, Rinehart and Winston, New York.

Gagné, R. (1968). Contributions of learning to human development. *Psychol. Rev.* **75,** 177–191.

Gardner, R. W., Holzman, P. S., Klein, G. S., Linton, H. B. and Spence, D. P. (1959). Cognitive control: A study of individual consistencies in cognitive behavior. *Psychol. Issues* **1** (4, Monogr. No. 4).

Gardner, R. W., Jackson, D. N. and Messick, S. (1960). Personality organization in cognitive controls and intellectual abilities. *Psychol. Issues* **2** (4, Monogr. No. 8).

Gardner, R. W. and Moriarty, A. (1968). "Personality Development at Pre-adolescence: Explorations of Structure Formation." University of Washington Press, Seattle.

Gardner, R. W. and Schoen, R. A. (1962). Differentiation and abstraction in concept formation. *Psychol. Monogr. Gen. Appl.* **76** (41, Whole No. 560).

Garrett, H. E. (1946). A developmental theory of intelligence. *Am. Psychol.* **1,** 372–378.

Guilford, J. P. (1959). Three faces of intellect. *Am. Psychol.* **14,** 469–479.

Guilford, J. P. (1967). "The Nature of Human Intelligence." McGraw-Hill, New York.

Guilford, J. P. (1972). Thurstone's primary mental abilities and structure-of-intellect abilities. *Psychol. Bull.*, **77,** 129–143.

Guilford, J. P. and Hoepfner, R. (1966). Structure of intellect factors and their tests, Los Angeles: University of Southern California Psychology Laboratory. Report No. 36, 1966.

Guilford, J. P. and Lacey, J. I. (eds) (1947). *Printed classification tests: Army Air Force Aviation Psychology Research Program Reports*. Report No. 5. Government Printing Office, Washington, D.C.

Guttman, L. (1958). What lies ahead for factor analysis? *Educ. Psychol. Measur.* **18** (3), 497–515.

Harvey, O. J., Hunt, D. E. and Schroder, H. M. (1961). "Conceptual Systems and Personality Organizations." Wiley, New York.

Hertzig, M. E., Birch, H. G., Thomas A. and Mendez, O. A. (1968). Class and ethnic differences in the responsiveness of preschool children to cognitive demands. *Monogr. Soc. Res. Child Dev.* **33** (1, Serial No. 117).

Horn, J. L. and Cattell, R. B. (1966). Refinement and test of the theory of fluid and crystallized intelligence. *J. educ. Psychol.* **57,** 253–270.

Humphreys, L. G. (1962). The organization of human abilities. *Amer. Psychologist* **17,** 475–483.

Humphreys, L. G. (1967). Critique of Cattell's "Theory of fluid and crystallized intelligence: A critical experiment." *J. educ. Psychol.* **58,** 129–136.

Hunt, J. McV. (1961). "Intelligence and Experience.' Ronald Press, New York.

Hurst, J. G. (1960). A factor analysis of the Merrill–Palmer with reference to theory and test construction. *Educ. Psychol. Measur.* **20,** 519–532.

Jackson, D. N. and Messick, S. (1958). Content and style in personality assessment. *Psychol. Bull.* **55,** 243–252.

Jackson, D. N. and Messick, S. (1963). Individual differences in social perception. *Br. J. soc. clin. Psychol.* **2,** 1–10.

Jackson, P. W. and Messick, S. (1965). The person, the product, and the response: Conceptual problems in the assessment of creativity. *J. Personality* **33,** 309–329.

Kagan, J. and Kogan N. (1970). Individual variation in cognitive processes. To appear in "Carmichael's Manual of Child Psychology." (Mussen, P. H. ed.) (3rd edn) Wiley, New York.

Kagan, J. and Lewis, M. (1965). Studies of attention in the human infant. *Merrill–Palmer Quarterly* **11,** 95–127.

Kelly, G. A. (1955). "The Psychology of Personal Constructs." Vol. I. Norton, New York.

Klein, G. S. (1970). "Perception, Motives, and Personality." Knopf, New York.

Kofsky, E. (1966). A scalogram study of classificatory development. *Child Dev.* **37,** 191–204.

Lesser, G. S., Fifer, G. and Clark, D. H. (1965). Mental abilities of children from different social-class and cultural groups. *Monogr. Soc. Res. Child Dev.* **30** (4, Serial No. 102).

Lewin, K. (1935). "A Dynamic Theory of Personality." McGraw-Hill, New York.

Lewin, K. (1951). "Field Theory in Social Science." Harper and Row, New York.

Lynn, R. (1966). "Attention, Arousal, and the Orientation Reaction." Pergamon Press, London.

McCartin, Sister Rose Amata and Meyers, C. E. (1966). An exploration of six semantic factors at first grade. *Multivar. Behavl. Res.* **1,** 74–94.

Messick, S. (1961). Personality structure. *In* "Annual Review of Psychology." (Farnsworth, P., McNemar, O. and McNemar, Q. eds) **12,** 93–128.

Messick, S. (1970). The criterion problem in the evaluation of instruction: Assessing possible, not just intended outcomes. *In* "The Evaluation of Instruction: Issues and Problems." (Wittrock, M. C. and Wiley, D. E. eds) Holt, Rinehart and Winston, New York.

Messick, S. (1968). Response sets. *In* "International Encyclopedia of the Social Sciences." (Sills, D. L. ed.) Macmillan and Free Press, New York. **13,** 492–496.

Messick, S. and Damarin, F. (1964). Cognitive styles and memory for faces. *J. abnorm. soc. Psychol.* **69,** 313–318.

Messick, S. and Fritzky, F. J. (1963). Dimensions of analytic attitude in cognition and personality. *J. Personality* **31,** 346–370.

Messick, S. and Kogan, N. (1963). Differentiation and compartmentalization in object-sorting measures of categorizing style. *Percept. Mot. Skills* **16,** 47–51.

Messick, S. and Kogan, N. (1966). Personality consistencies in judgment: Dimensions of role constructs. *Multivar. Behaviorl. Res.* **1,** 165–175.

Myers, C. E., Dingman, H. F., Orpet, R. E., Sitkei, E. G. and Watts, C. A. (1964). Four ability-factor hypotheses at three preliterate levels in normal and retarded children. *Monogr. Soc. Res. Child Dev.* **29** (5).

Myers, C. E., Orpet, R. E., Atwell, A. A. and Dingman, H. F. (1962). Primary abilities at mental age six. *Monogr. Soc. Res. Child Dev.* **27** (Whole No. 82).

Miller, G. A., Galanter, E. and Pribram, K. (1960). "Plans and the Structure of Behaviour." Holt, Rinehart and Winston, New York.

Peel, E. A. (1959). Experimental examination of some of Piaget's schemata concerning children's perception and thinking, and a discussion of their educational significance. *Br. J. educ. Psychol.* **29,** 89–103.

Piaget, J. (1950). "The Psychology of Intelligence." Harcourt, Brace, New York.

Reitman, W. R. (1965). "Cognition and Thought." Wiley, New York.

Rokeach, M. (1960). "The Open and Closed Mind." Basic Books, New York.

Rosenhan, D. and Messick, S. (1966). Affect and expectation. *J. Personality Soc. Psychol.* **3,** 38–44.

Russell, D. (1956). "Children's Thinking." Ginn, Boston.

Sarbin, T. R., Taft, R. and Bailey, D. (1960). "Clinical Inference and Cognitive Theory." Holt, Rinehart and Winston, New York.

Schroder, H. M., Driver, M. J. and Streufert, S. (1967). "Human Information Processing." Holt, Rinehart and Winston, New York.

Scott, W. A. (1963). Conceptualizing and measuring structural properties of cognition. *In* "Motivation and Social Interaction." (Harvey, O. J. ed.) Ronald Press, New York.

Signell, K. A. (1966). Cognitive complexity in person perception and nation perception: A developmental approach. *J. Personality* **34,** 517–537.

Solley, C. M. and Murphy, G. (1960). "Development of the Perceptual World." Basic Books, New York.

Spearman, C. (1927). "The Abilities of Man." Macmillan, New York.

Stake, R. E. (1961). Learning parameters, aptitudes, and achievements. *Psychometric Monogr.* No. 9. William Byrd Press, Richmond, Virginia.

Stott, L. H. and Ball, R. S. (1965). Infant and preschool mental tests: Review and evaluation. *Monogr. Soc. Res. Child Dev.* **30** (Serial No. 101).

Taft, R. (1965). Some characteristics of good judges of others. *Br. J. Psychol.* **47,** 19–29.

Tagiuri, R. (1969). Person perception. *In* "Handbook of Social Psychology." (Lindzey, G. and Aaronson, E. eds) (2nd edn). Addison-Wesley, Cambridge, Massachusetts.

Thistlethwaite, D. (1950). Attitude and structure as factors in the distortion of reasoning. *J. Abnorm. Soc. Psychol.* **45,** 442–458.

Thorndike, E. L. (1920). Intelligence and its uses. *Harper's Magazine* **140,** 227–235.

Thurstone, L. L. (1923). The stimulus-response fallacy in psychology. *Psychol. Rev.* **30,** 354–369.

Thurstone, L. L. (1926). "The Nature of Intelligence." Harcourt, Brace Co., New York.

Thurstone, L. L. (1938). Primary Mental abilities. *Psychometric Monogr.* No. 1. University of Chicago Press, Chicago.

Thurstone, L. L. (1944). A factorial study of perception. *Psychometric Monogr.* No. 4. University of Chicago Press, Chicago.

Tomkins, S. S. and Messick, S. (1963). "Computer Simulation of Personality." Wiley, New York.

Vernon, P. E. (1950). "The Structure of Human Abilities." Wiley, New York.

Wallach, M. A. and Kogan, N. (1965). "Modes of Thinking in Young Children: A Study of the Creativity–Intelligence Distinction." Holt, Rinehart and Winston, New York.

Wallas, G. (1926). "The Art of Thought." Harcourt, Brace Co., New York.

Warr, P. B. and Knapper, C. (1968). "The Perception of People and Events." Wiley, New York.

Werner, H. (1948). "Comparative Psychology of Mental Development." (Rev. edn). Follett, Chicago.

Werner, H. (1957). The concept of development from a comparative and organismic point of view. *In* "The Concept of Development. An Issue in the Study of Human Behavior." (Harris, D. B. ed.) University of Minnesota Press, Minneapolis.

Witkin, H. A., Dyk, R. B., Faterson, H. F., Goodenough, D. R. and Karp, S. A. (1962). "Psychological differentiation." Wiley, New York.

Wohlwill, J. (1960). A study of the development of the number concept by scalogram analysis. *J. Genet. Psychol.* **97,** 345–377.

Zeaman, D. and House, B. J. (1967). The relation of IQ and learning. *In* "Learning and individual differences." (Gagné, R. M. ed.), pp. 192–212. Charles E. Merrill Books, Inc., Columbus, Ohio.

Zwicky, F. (1957). "Morphological Analysis." Springer, Berlin.

The Conceptual Framework for a Multi-Factor Theory of Individuality*†

JOSEPH R. ROYCE

The Center for Advanced Study in Theoretical Psychology

Introduction

Multiple factor analysis, essentially an application of matrix algebra, is a typical mathematical model in the sense that it is abstract or neutral. That is, factor analysis *per se* tells us nothing substantive; it

* Presented at the Third Banff Conference on Theoretical Psychology, "Contributions of Multivariate Analysis to Psychological Theory," September 25–October 2, 1971, at Banff, Alberta, Canada. Earlier versions were presented as a Distinguished Visiting Scholar Seminar at Educational Testing Service, September 1965; as an Invited Address, Annual Meeting of the Canadian Psychological Association, University of British Columbia, Vancouver, B.C., June 1965; as an Invited Address, Annual Meeting of the British Psychological Society, May 1966, Keele University, England; as an Invited Address, Symposium on Personality Theory, XIXth International Congress of Psychology, University of London, 1969; as a lecture at the Max Planck Institute of Psychiatry, Munich, Germany, 1969; and as one of four Seminars-in-the-Round given at San Fernando Valley State College in February 1971.

† The author hereby acknowledges the indirect feedback received from his Center colleagues, Fellows, and students, as well as direct assistance received from the Individuality Project Group, namely: Allan Buss, David Johnson, George Kawash, Wayne Poley, and Douglas Wardell. These project participants were partially supported by a Canada Council Grant (68–0137 and S70–0433) and an Alberta Human Resources Research Council Grant. I particularly wish to acknowledge the general assistance provided by Dr. George Kawash in his capacity as Research Associate on the project. For example, in addition to general coordinating, he is responsible for the hierarchy depicted in Figure 5, as well as the accompanying text. Special acknowledgment is also due Allan Buss, Graduate Research Assistant, who, in addition to serving as a general utility man, provided much of the material for the section on cognitive structure, and was of particular help in the sections where Eysenckian thought was brought to bear on our model (e.g. the section on the biology of affective traits). I also wish to acknowledge the contributions of Graduate Research Assistant Douglas Wardell to the section on styles. And finally, I wish to thank Dr. Lorne Yeudall for his critical review of the section on the Neurological Mechanisms of Individuality and the constructive suggestions from Dr. John Loehlin, University of Texas, regarding the concepts of heredity dominant and environment dominant factors.

merely provides a skeletal framework which can be filled in variously to account for a range of phenomena which have been observed in what is referred to as the real world. Thus, in principle, factor analysis is a general scientific methodology, applicable to any discipline of study where the problem is to identify several unknowns as determinants of multiple covariation. As a matter of fact, factorial methodology has already been applied in all the major scientific disciplines, ranging from a study of cosmic rays in physics to the decisions of supreme court judges in the field of political science (Royce, 1965a). It is, incidentally, one of the few scientific methodologies which has been widely imported by other disciplines from psychology.

While factor theory has been with us for several decades now,* it has remained an essentially uninterpreted (Rozeboom, 1970) or empty theory. There are good reasons for this, most of them having to do with a variety of technical and methodological problems which required solution before factor analysis could move into the empirical world with sufficient reliability and validity. Perhaps the most crucial of these problems is that of factorial invariance, the demand that we be able to identify the same factor despite shifts of sampling of measures, subjects, and investigators. Fortunately, a few mathematically oriented researchers (including a handful of professional mathematicians such as Albert, Lawley, and Bartlett) interested in the factor model have resolved many of the difficulties, at least to the point where the most recent model provides us with basic transportation, and even shows some signs of esthetic improvement over previous models. For example, in spite of a considerable proliferation and fragmentation of intellectual and personality factors, the concept of simple structure has provided visible leverage on the problem of invariance, having given us such intimate awareness of factors in some domains of study (e.g. pilot aptitudes and intelligence) that qualitative pre-judgments which specified measures that would serve as anchors for the identification of certain factors have been repeatedly confirmed. Furthermore, such qualitative invariances now show some promise of giving way to quantitative indices of invariance, a very stringent and convincing test of the scientific validity of a factor. We should also mention, in passing, that the recent advances in computer technology constitute a revolu-

* Although Galton and Pearson gave us the correlation statistic at the turn of the century, and mathematicians Hamilton, Cayley, and Grassman developed matrix algebra in mid-19th century, Charles Spearman's 1904 paper is considered to be the first contribution to factor theory *per se*. The matrix theory formulation of factor analysis did not emerge until around 1935 when Thurstone published his APA presidential address and later his *Vectors of Mind* (see Royce, 1958).

tion in efficiency, for the previously cumbersome procedures of desk calculated controid analyses and visual rotations have now given way to high speed factoring procedures and computerized rotation to approximate simple structure, followed by a relatively small number of mopping up graphic rotations (blind rotations constitute the most stringent requirement) to either oblique or orthogonal simple structure.*

All this is by way of saying that factor analysis has been tooling up for over sixty years now, and it is time we moved beyond the purely mathematical aspects of this approach to what it can contribute to a substantive theory of behavior. The most extensive utilization of the factor approach has been in the area of intelligence and aptitudes, and it has, in fact, already served us well as a theory of human abilities, with both scientific and practical implications. Its recent extensions to other domains of behavior, however, are not well known, nor are the implications of these extensions well understood. The fact is that factor methodology has now been applied to learning, perception, comparative and physiological psychology, motor skills, attitudes, social behavior, etc.—that is, to all the major domains of behavior. Although most of this work has merely been inventoried rather than interpreted, as in the case of the monographs by French (1951, 1953; French, Ekstrom, and Price, 1963), the personality book by Guilford (1959), and a variety of summarizing articles for a given subdomain of study (see Royce, 1958, and Cattell, 1966), there have been several interpretive theoretical efforts (e.g. Guilford, 1956, 1961, 1967; Eysenck, 1953, 1967, 1970; Cattell, 1957, 1971; Cattell and Scheier, 1961) during the past two decades which provide the beginnings of a multi-factor theory to account for all behavioral variability. In what follows I will offer a conceptual framework for a theory of individuality which is consistent with, but not limited by, the factor model, and which has, hopefully, profited by extensive exposure to the major efforts produced

* Unfortunately the number of investigators who take the last step is very small. There are many reasons for this, the most potent being a misplaced belief in the "objectivity" and "analytic power" of the computer (i.e. the claim that the computer can do the job better than a highly skilled graphic rotator). The point is that no *existing* solution has the characteristic of being able to accommodate all cases of simple structure (e.g. oblique as well as orthogonal, and "weak" as well as "clean" simple structure), which is not to say that an appropriate formulation is impossible, or that some other criterion, such as distinguishability (Butler, 1969), might not eventually replace simple structure as the best route to invariance. One consequence of the present cultist "faith" in the computer is that very few investigators actually know how to perform the necessary visual rotations (that is, they are ignorant, which is neither shocking nor criminal). It is sheer nonsense, however, to regard such ignorance as virtue by merely pronouncing that computerized solutions are "better" than graphic rotations.

to date.* Although the presentation will focus on *theory*, it should be understood that there is massive empirical data available as a platform from which the ensuing theoretico-inductive leaps were made. The tough theory construction task we have here, and it is very difficult, is to come up with both condensation and synthesis without doing violence to the data. Such a task is difficult enough, but when the data itself are both incomplete and contradictory (however, I find that state of affairs to be typical of psychology in general), it may be impossible at worst, and premature at best.†

The Basic Conceptual Model

Very few psychological phenomena are constant across species and across individuals within species. In general, the lower the species in the phylogenetic order, the more instinct-controlled, constant, and pre-

* In the pages that follow, the influence of several factor scholars will become apparent. While the list includes most of the Conference participants in one way or another, there are three contributors to the substantive–theoretical literature whose influence has been fundamental. These are R. B. Cattell, H. J. Eysenck, and J. P. Guilford. Without their contributions an effort such as this, and indeed, the Conference itself, would be improbable events. For their contributions have been pioneering efforts in jungle-like domains where there is little place for fainthearted men. I have profited from their work and counsel, both via the written word and via direct contacts over the last two decades. However, in spite of all the help I have received, and in spite of the amount of effort already put into this project, it merely represents a beginning. That is why the title reads the "conceptual framework" for a theory of individuality. Subsequent work on this project will include a section on epistemological styles as part of style structure, and a section on principles and mechanisms of personality integration. It will also involve paper-length elaborations of various sections, such as an extension of the gene-factor model (Royce and St. John, 1973), a theory of emotionality (Poley and Royce, 1973), the concept of psychological structure (Royce and Buss, 1973), the relationship between cognitive structure and learning (Buss, 1972), and a more adequate statement on the ontogeny of factors (Buss and Royce, 1973). Finally, the author plans on an expansion of the present conceptual framework to a book-length statement.

† As a result of several side trips I've taken into philosophy during recent years, I have come to the conclusion that psychology is not alone in this regard. In short, this may be "the way things are"—that is, relatively certain (in the logical sense) only in highly formal disciplines, but essentially interpretive whenever we deal with data or/and "life". Thus, because of the typical contradictoriness of data and the overwhelming complexity of our subject matter, theory construction must be put forward as both a tentative and risky formulation. But, we must make such efforts, even if they are premature and inadequate! Why? Because a "facts only" approach does not move us toward explanation and understanding. Just as a "facts only" approach is conceptually arid, so is an "ignore the facts" approach scientifically dangerous. We have, therefore, kept the empirical findings (in spite of their inadequacies) in our sights at every phase of our deliberations. Our approach has been to construct theory as insightfully as possible on the one hand, and to regard data as empirical constraints on our conceptualizing on the other hand. In this way it has been our hope to strike a reasonable balance between theoretical progress and keeping one's feet on the empirical ground.

dictable the behavior.* Human behavior is far more variable, and therefore less predictable than that of any other species. However, predictions concerning the variability of psychological phenomena can be made, particularly if stated in terms of probabilities. In fact, the normal probability curve provides the best available description of psychological variables.

However the theory which lies behind the normal probability function states that such distributions occur whenever there is complex, multiple causation, (i.e. many factors, components, or elements contributing to the behavioral variability in question). This means that the variability of observed complex behaviors, such as intelligence and emotionality, are determined (i.e. caused by or accountable on the basis of) by the combinations of a finite number of elements or components commonly referred to in psychology as factors. In simplified mathematical terms this has been expressed as follows:†

$$z_{ji} = a_{j1}F_{1i}+a_{j2}F_{2i}+a_{j3}F_{3i}+ \ldots\ldots +a_{jm}F_{mi} \quad (1)$$

This equation says that the score (standard scores in this case, where $z=\frac{x}{\sigma}$) on any behavioral measurement j is equal to the product of the loading (a_{jm}) of the measurement j on factor one (F_1) times the amount of this factor possessed by individual i, plus the product involving the loading of the variable on factor two ($a_{j2}F_2$), plus the product involving the loading on factor three, etc. until all the common factor variance is accounted for.

If we now restate equation (1) in the more compact matrix form, we get

$$z = AF \quad (2)$$

Since the focus of our attention is on the underlying components rather than the original observations, we solve for F and get

$$F = A^{-1}Z \quad (3)$$

* Such primarily gene-determined behaviors are particularly characteristic of sub-mammalian forms, and have received considerable study by the ethologists. The less variable the behavior the more complete the isomorphism between the underlying genotype and the subsequent behavioral phenotype.

† For the sake of simplicity we have confined ourselves to orthogonal (i.e. uncorrelated) common factors; the uniqueness and error components of each variable are omitted.

Although equation (3) is algebraically sound, it contains a matrix, A, which is neither square or non-singular. The point is that an inverse does not exist for such matrices (Harman, 1967, p. 346). Thus, equation (3) is not applicable. This has lead to the development of several factor estimation procedures, the most important of which involve variations of multiple regression, least square fits. The most widely used formulation, attributed to Thurstone and derived in Harman (1967, p. 382), is indicated below as equation (4):

$$F = A'R^{-1}Z \tag{4}$$

Since any factor can be estimated if all the correlations (i.e. between variables, and between variables and factors) are known, and since equation (4) does not require an inverse for matrix A, we now have a feasible procedure for estimating factor scores.

A major concern of this paper is to elaborate on the hereditary and environmental determinants of individuality; but the major implication of equation (1) is that by properly combining a relatively small set of identifiable components it is possible to account for the observable variability of individuality. Thus, we must find a way to link hereditary and environmental sources of variation to the underlying factors. The simplest way to do this is to assume that any factor score F_t can be partitioned into two parts, hereditary (F_h) and environmental (F_e), thereby giving us

$$F_t = F_h + F_e \tag{5}$$

If we now solve for variance, we get

$$\sigma^2_{F_t} = \sigma^2_{F_h} + \sigma^2_{F_e} + 2 \operatorname{cov} F_h F_e \tag{6}$$

which is the usual variance decomposition, but expressed in terms of factor scores. Thus, the extent to which either heredity or environment contributes to factor performance is reflected in the terms of equation (6). For example, if a particular factor is what I have labeled heredity dominant (see p. 348), $\sigma^2_{F_e}$ and the covariance term will approach zero. Conversely, if a particular factor is completely environment dominant (see p. 348), then $\sigma^2_{F_h}$ and the covariance term of equation (6) would equal zero and $\sigma^2_{F_t}$ would equal $\sigma^{2*}_{F_e}$

Part I. The Structure of Individuality

The theoretical exposition developed in this paper is meant to apply to the variability of all behavior, whether it be cognitive, affective, or social.† The factor model is general, it applies in principle to anything that varies. Details of organizational structure and dimensionality will undoubtedly differ from domain to domain. The underlying dimensionality can be expected to range enormously; for example, from the three or four underlying receptors of color perception to the 100 to 200 probable components of intelligence. Also, as theory evolves in different domains of study, general and bipolar factors may make sense in one area of investigation, but not in another. Similarly, orthogonal factors may best describe the data in an area such as sensory discrimination, whereas obliquity may be required to account for the positive manifold so ubiquitously reported in the domain of intelligence. Such structural

* For the sake of conceptual simplicity the correlational terms have been dropped in equation (6). Although they should be included for complete accuracy, it is not uncommon for these terms to be dropped, even in computional work. An alternative formulation would be

$$\sigma^2_{F_t} = \sigma^2_{F_h} + \sigma^2_{F_e} + \sigma^2_{\mathrm{I—c}} \qquad (7)$$

where $\sigma^2_{\mathrm{I—c}}$ contains the total of the interaction and correlational terms. Either formulation assumes that the correlations are of negligible magnitude, a reasonable assumption for our present purposes (see, for example, Falconer, 1960).

The present formulation involves the sequential juxtaposing of the factor analytic and analysis of variance models. That is, one obtains factors and then follows with an analysis of the variation of factor scores. We are interested in exploring alternatives. For example, if it makes conceptual and algebraic sense to decompose matrix A in equation (4) into H+E+I (where A is the usual n × m factor structure matrix, H is an n ×m factor structure matrix due to genetic sources of variance, E is an n × m factor structure matrix due to environmental sources of variance, and I is an n × m factor structure matrix reflecting genetic-environmental interactions), then one can substitute for A in equation (4), expand and come up with

$$F = H'R^{-1}Z + E'R^{-1}Z + I'R^{-1}Z \qquad (8)$$

which expresses any factor score as a sum of three sub-matrices.

We are aware of only one other formulation—the one by Meredith (1968). We are looking into its relevance to our problem.

†The focus of this paper is on organismic constructs as determinants of individual differences. I make no attempt to deal with situational determinants *per se*. That is, I do not offer a dimensional analysis of the ecology. Clearly, this must eventually be done if one is interested in a complete theory of behavior.

details will have to be worked out as we go rather than arbitrarily hung around our necks *a priori*. If we take this point seriously we will do best to introduce the concept of structure in the broadest possible terms—namely, as a nomological net (Feigl and Scriven, 1956). Elsewhere I have defined a factor as a theoretical construct (Royce, 1963). Putting all this together, we can now define a *nomological net as a set of theoretical constructs (e.g. factors) and their interrelationships*. Such a theoretical structure makes no *a priori* statements about the number of constructs required, their breadth or narrowness of range, or whether they form a hierarchy. Nor does it specify the exact nature of the relationships (linear, non-linear, exponential, logarithmic etc.) which obtain between them.* In terms of factor models, it allows for any of the solutions which have been put forward to be viewed as special cases of a particular segment of observables. Thus, some kind of hierarchy, strata, chain, simplex, or circumplex (see Cattell, 1965) constitutes a sub-set of the more general lattice or reticule.†

Cognitive Structure

We can now define three overarching concepts which provide the beginnings of psychological flesh for a hitherto substantively empty set

* While extant factor models are linear, it does *not* follow that the relationships between constructs of the underlying nomological net are linear and non-interactive. In fact, it is highly probable that they are non-linear and interactive. The point is that factor analysis *per se* merely identifies potentially useful theoretical constructs, it does *not* provide us with functional relationships between constructs.

† At the metatheory level I see the factor theory concept of simple structure as a "for instance" of the general philosophy of science notion of theoretical structure or nomological network. That is, the criteria of simple structure provide guidelines for arriving at a nomological net (see Royce, 1963), the exact structural details of which will vary widely and are to be empirically determined. The generality of the concept of simple structure may be the basis for both its strength and its weakness. Its major strength is that it guides us to underlying theoretical structures (and the scientific power of this should not be underestimated). Its major weakness becomes clearest when we demand a unique mathematical solution for rotation to simple structure. It seems intuitively reasonable to conclude that no one set of equations would be able to accommodate all possible varieties of underlying theoretical structure. My suggestion in this regard is to recognize the general nature of the simple structure criteria, and hence to retain it for what it is—a general scientific paradigm. This implies that the characteristics of *classes* of underlying theoretical structures (e.g. hierarchical, simplex, etc.) can probably be stated more precisely than they have been to date and hence are more amenable to exact mathematical formulation. Thus, it seems reasonable to anticipate the need for a variety of formulations, depending upon the class of structures under accommodation. The methodological implication of this state of affairs entails the availability of an armamentarium of computerized rotations, a best guess on the part of the researcher as to the most relevant transformation to use in the light of the most probable underlying theoretical structure, and finally, graphic rotations as to the adequacy of fit to the structure in question.

of remarks. I will define *psychological structure* as a multi-dimensional, organized system of processes*† *(subsumes mental structure) by means of which an organism manifests behavior and mental phenomena.* And I will define *mental structure as a multi-dimensional organized sub-system of processes (subsumes cognitive and affective structure) by means of which an organism manifests mental phenomena,* where mental phenomena‡ refer to internal (i.e. neurologically coded) representations. Parallel to the previous two definitions, I will define *cognitive structure as a multi-dimensional, organized sub-system of processes (subsumes perceiving, thinking, symbolizing) by means of which an organism produces cognitions,* where cognitions refer to those mental phenomena which are products of cognitive processes (i.e. perceiving, thinking, symbolizing). It should be apparent from these definitions that we are describing a general system and its sub-systems, and that a given structure is nested or embedded within a more inclusive structure (see Fig. 1a). This means, for example, that cognitions (e.g. percepts, ideas, insights; see Fig. 1b) evolve primarily from cognitive structure, but that such cognitions are also influenced by the underlying mental structure, which, in turn, is influenced by the organism's total psychological structure.

At this juncture structural modeling runs into a variety of conceptual difficulties primarily having to do with the essential arbitrariness of defining sub-domains of cognition. For example, the term cognitive has been used to include such sub-domains as sensory processes, perception, thinking, and memory, but designations such as intelligence and psychomotor skills have not been included. The factor analytic literature, on the other hand, tends to subsume memory and thinking

* The concept of psychological structure is undergoing more detailed analysis in another paper (see Royce and Buss, 1973). For present purposes it will be sufficient to point out that it is determined by performance level on each of the factors combined with the degree of correlation between the factors. In terms of the basic factor equation, i.e. equation (1), we are talking about the *F* values (factor structure), plus the implicit correlations between the factors (hierarchical structure). It should be noted, in passing, that psychological structure *per se* is *not* concerned with factor loadings (i.e. the a_{jk} coefficients of eqn. 1). Rather, factor loadings have to do with what we have referred to as the structure of the task. We have found this approach to the nature of structure of particular value in our analysis of structural change, particularly where developmental and learning effects are operative (e.g. see pages 362–366; Buss, 1972; and Buss and Royce, 1973).

† See p. 38 and the second half of this paper for my conception of process. At this juncture it is sufficient to indicate that, although factors are intimately connected with processes, I do not *equate* factors with processes. Rather, processes refer to how the factors or constructs of a system are combined, and how they change over time.

‡ Mental phenomena are meant to "represent" both "real" and "non-real" events. That is, they include the full range of internal events; such non-veridicalities as wishes, desires, beliefs, fantasies, dreams, illusions, delusions, hallucinations, etc. as well as ideas, insights and percepts.

processes under the intelligence label, with psychomotor factors receiving a variety of aptitude and ability designations. This dilemma

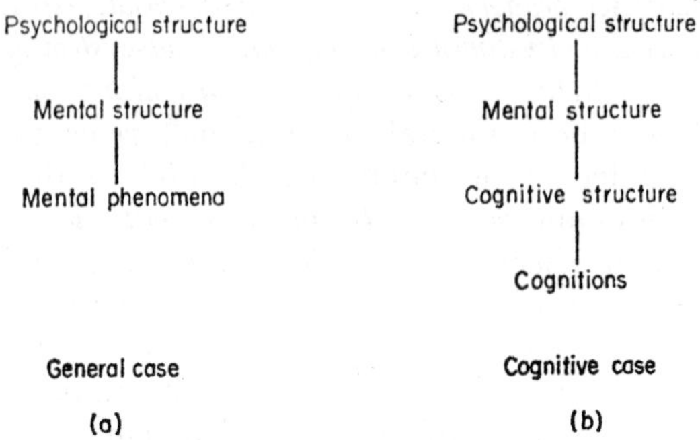

Fig. 1. The hierarchical embeddedness of cognitive structure.

should point up the essential arbitrariness involved in the designation of any sub-domain, and highlight one of the truly valuable characteristics of the factorial methodology, namely to identify underlying functional unities regardless of previous surface labeling. The implication is that the determination of the exact nature of these inductively generated concepts will be a long, slow process, and *a priori* factor and domain designations should be seen as relatively feeble efforts to speed up attempts to evolve a viable factor taxonomy. We will, therefore, tentatively use terms such as sensory, perceptual, and intelligence to identify sub-domains only because factor analytic findings have been summarized under these rubrics, not because they constitute conceptually powerful designations. And, since the bulk of the empirical work has been conducted in the sub-domain of intelligence, we will begin with that class of phenomena.

*The Structure of Intellect**

If we begin with first order factors (see Table I) and a "strong"† criterion for invariance, we come up with seven primaries as follows: space (*S*), perceptual speed (*P*), induction (*I*), number (*N*), verbal (*V*), word fluency (*Fw*), memory (*Ma*), speed of closure (*Cs*), and flexibility of closure (*Cf*). Relaxing the invariance criterion somewhat, we can add visualization (*Vi*) and ideational fluency (*Fi*). Relaxing the invariance

* The reader is referred to Appendix A for brief definitions of all cognitive factors.

† Our strong criterion means a given factor that is considered "established" by the following five major works: Ahmavaara (1957), French (1963), Guilford (1967), Pawlik (1966), and Thurstone (1941). As a given factor is cited by fewer than these five authors, we move from "strong" invariance to "weak" invariance.

criterion further allows us to include expressional fluency (*Fe*), associational fluency (*Fa*), and general reasoning (*R*). Continuing in this manner, the following primaries complete our taxonomy: figural adaptive flexibility (*Xa*), deduction (*D*), spatial scanning (*Ss*), semantic redefinition (*Re*), syllogistic reasoning (*Rs*), sensitivity to problems (*Sep*), spontaneous flexibility (*Xs*), originality (*O*), and memory span (*Ms*). Thus, we come up with a first order taxonomy ranging from 9 to 23. If we then introduce Guilford's SI model,* we can increase the upper limit to 98 identified to date, and 120 if his mental periodic table is eventually completed.

Although high intercorrelations and positive manifold have been repeatedly reported in this domain, there has been surprisingly little work done on higher order factors. There have, of course, been numerous claims for "*g*" at the second or higher order, but these claims have usually emerged from *a priori* solutions of one kind or another. In addition to "*g*", the most persistent and replicable higher order factors are fluid intelligence (G_f) and crystallized intelligence (G_c), with increasing evidence emerging for general visualization (G_v), cognitive speed (G_s), and general fluency (G_{f1}). (Horn, 1965; Horn and Cattell, 1966, 1967).

The most comprehensive and viable model to date is Guilford's orthogonal, facet model. However, with very little imagination it would be possible to regard his facet designations, namely "operations",

* I have refrained from incorporating all of Guilford's factors into the models that follow since there is little cross-laboratory evidence for their factor invariance. However, there may be value in indicating which of Guilford's factors are most firmly established within the context of his own laboratory and which may eventually receive closer attention. Evidence for invariance of Guilford's factors comes largely from tables in Guilford and Hoepfner (1971). In examining this evidence, our criterion for invariance was whether three of the marker tests loading on a given factor were replicated on three independent occasions. None of Guilford's factors was able to meet this stringent criterion. However, some factors approximated it much more closely than others. At this juncture it was decided to introduce two categories labelled "strong invariance" and "weak invariance." Where these terms now refer to within laboratory rather than across laboratories (see 2nd footnote on page 314) such procedure reflects the abandonment of a rigorous quantitative criterion and the adoption of a more subjective and qualitative approach. Thus, strong invariant factors include (letters stand for operations, contents, and products, respectively): DFU, DFS, DSU, DMU, DMC, and DMR. Weak invariant factors include: CSC, CSR, CSS, CSI, CMU, CMC, CMS, CMT, CMI; and MFS, MMI, MMT, MST; and NFT, NSS, NST, NSI, NMR, NMS; and DFI, DSC, and DSR.

In summary, it can be said that in terms of *operations* (first letter) the divergent production factors are most invariant, followed by cognition, convergent production, and memory. None of the evaluative factors met the lenient subjective criterion for weak invariance. In terms of *contents* (second letter), symbolic and semantic are equally represented, followed by figural. Behavioral contents are not represented. In terms of *products* (third letter) the order of representation from high to low is systems, transformations, units-relations-implications (these three tie for third place), and finally, classes.

Table I. Cognitive ability factors considered 'established' by various reviews. One moves from strong to weak invariance as one descends the column

Number of authors that consider factor established	Factor	Established by: 1963 French	1967 Guilford	1957 Ahmavaara	1966 Pawlik	1941 Thurstone
5	spatial relations	*S*	*CSF*	*S*	*S*	*S*
	perceptual speed	*P*	*ESU*	*P*	*P*	*P*
	induction	*I*	*NST*	*R*	*I*	*I*
	number	*N*	*NSI*	*N*	*N*	*N*
	verbal comprehension	*V*	*CMU*	*V*	*V*	*V*
	word fluency	*Fw*	*DSU*	*W*	*W*	*W*
	memory (associative)	*Ma*	*MSR*	*M*	*Ma*	*Ma*
	speed of closure	*Cs*	*CFU*	*Cl*	*Cs*	*C*1
	flexibility of closure	*Cf*	*NFT*	*C*2	*Cf*	*C*2
4	visualization	*Vi*	*CFT*	*Vi*	*Vi*	
	ideational fluency	*Fi*	*DMU*	*If*	*Fi*	
3	expressional fluency	*Fe*	*DSS*		*Fe*	
	associational fluency	*Fa*	*DMR*		*Fa*	
	general reasoning	*R*		*GR*	*R*	
2	figural adaptive flexibility	*Xa*	*DFT*			
	deduction			*D*	*D*	
	spatial scanning	*Ss*	*CFI*			
	semantic redefinition	*Re*	*NWT*			
	syllogistic reasoning	*Rs*	*EMR*			
	sensitivity to problems	*Sep*	*EMI*			
	spontaneous flexibility	*Xs*	*DMC*			
	originality	*O*	*DMT*			
	memory span	*Ms*	*MSU*			

"products", and "content", as more general, higher-order factors (e.g. see Messick, this book). Or one could generate a hierarchical model from the existing data, as we have done in Fig. 2 below.

In keeping with the general inductive nature of the factor analytic strategy, we begin with what is empirically given, namely the 23 primary factors indicated in Table I. Inspection of these first order factors reveals several interesting conceptual groupings. There are, for example, five reasoning factors summarized in Table I: induction, deduction, syllogistic reasoning, spontaneous flexibility, and general reasoning. There are also four fluency factors and two memory factors.* It seems reasonable to anticipate that such groupings will have functional significance as well as being conceptually meaningful. We have, therefore, postulated six such clusters. We have also postulated six second order factors to accommodate each of the clusters: memory, intellectual speed, reasoning, fluency, verbal, and visualization. (See Fig. 2.)

* My bias on the eventual number of invariant first order intelligence factors is in the direction of Guilford's model. If this turns out to be the case, we can anticipate over-determination of the higher order factors indicated in Fig. 2, as well as the identification of additional higher order factors. For example, see Guilford (1967) for evidence for around twenty first order memory factors.

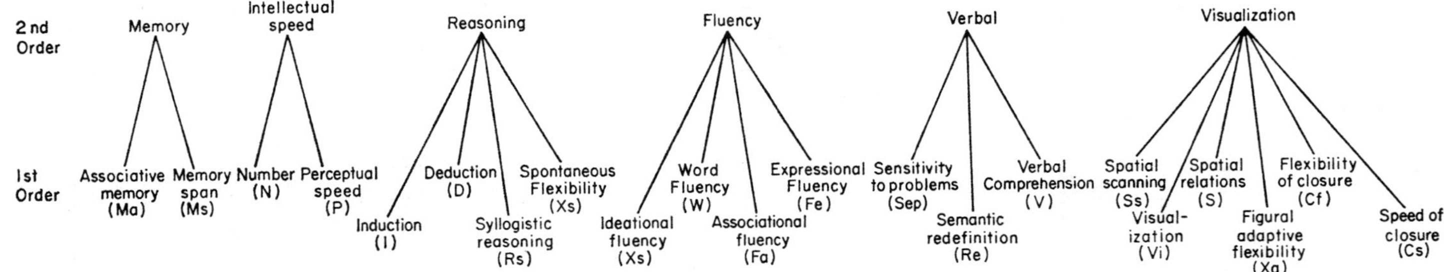

Fig. 2. Hierarchical structure of intelligence factors.

Although the groupings* depicted in Figure 2 are speculative, we were so struck by the "compelling" character of what emerged that we reviewed the literature for possible empirical confirmation of these postulated second order factors. We found, for example, that evidence for a higher order memory factor goes back to Spearman (1927). He concluded there is a cross-modality memory factor which synthesizes the specific memory factors of visual and auditory information and verbal and nonverbal memory. Consistent with this line of reasoning, Spearman claimed there were no separate factors for immediate versus delayed memory, nor for recognition versus recall memory, a statement which Guilford (1967) takes issue with. French (1951) has reviewed the evidence for an intellectual speed factor, and it has been consistently reported by Horn (1965, 1966; Horn and Bramble, 1967 and Horn and Cattell, 1966, 1967). Thurstone (1944) found that speed of judgment correlated with general intelligence, indicating a speed component of general intelligence. Bottenberg and Christal (1961) found evidence for a higher order reasoning factor in that induction and deduction correlated 0·50. Botzum (1951) found a higher order factor (labeled abstract thinking) on which both deduction and induction loaded significantly, and Rimoldi (1951a), using Spearman's methods, found a higher order factor using tests of induction, deduction, and reasoning. Indirect evidence for a higher order fluency factor comes from Johnson and Reynolds (1951). Using orthogonal rotation procedures, they found that word fluency, associational fluency, and expressional fluency all contributed to the factor of "verbal fluency". Denton and Taylor (1955), using oblique rotation of primaries followed by second-order analysis, found a broad verbal fluency factor. These results have been confirmed by Horn (1965, 1966), Horn and Bramble (1967), and Horn and Cattell (1966, 1967). A higher order verbal factor is also consistent with Vernon's (1961) verbal group factor. A higher order visualization factor receives support from Horn (1965, 1966), Horn and Bramble (1967), and Horn and Cattell (1966, 1967), as well as Pawlik's (1966) review of the intercorrelations for twelve primary mental ability factors.

The Structure of Sensory-Motor Abilities

Elsewhere (Royce, 1973, p. 17) I have used the term cognition as

* For several reasons (e.g. simplicity, communication), we have not shown all *overlapping* connections (e.g. sensitivity to problems probably has a loading on fluency as well as verbal) between higher and lower order factors, especially in the case of first order factors. However, when the empirical evidence was especially strong, we have indicated such connections (e.g. see Fig. 3). Furthermore, we have made a point of showing such connections at the higher order levels (e.g. see Fig. 4), where theoretical synthesis is more crucial.

"those internal (i.e. neurologically coded) representations or mental phenomena (e.g. ideas, insights, percepts) which are products of cognitive processes (i.e. perceiving, thinking and symbolizing)." Subsequently, under a discussion of what is being represented via cognitions, I suggested that cognitions "can represent anything, ranging from a wild, highly autistic superstition or fantasy to very prosaic, literal objects of the everyday world." And, both elsewhere (i.e. Royce, 1973) and in this paper (see section Cognitive Structure), I have defined cognitive structure as "a multi-dimensional, organized sub-system of processes (subsumes perceiving, thinking, symbolizing) by means of which an organism produces cognitions." The point is that my usage of the term cognitive is meant to include both central (e.g. perceptual and intellectual) and peripheral (e.g. sensory and motor) sub-systems. While it is probably true that the more peripheral sensory-motor factors are not as important to our understanding of cognitive structure as the more central perceptual-intellectual factors, I take the position that they, nevertheless, constitute an important segment of cognition.

With this in mind, we can now move on to a consideration of the organizational structure of sensory-motor factors. Although there is little to report on the sensory side, a significant body of empirical work is building up in vision and audition, and at least one investigator (Horn, 1971c) has launched a long-range attack on the factor structure of sensory processes. Part of Horn's research program includes the possibility of identifying higher order, cross-modality, integrating factors. But it remains to be seen whether a hierarchic structure makes sense in this domain. In fact, most of the research reported to date points to an orthogonal structure. This includes Jones' (1948) color vision factors (red, blue and green sensitivity), Henry's (1947) primary auditory factors for hearing tones at different pitch levels (low, intermediate and high frequency sensitivity), and Karlin's (1942) auditory factors (pitch discrimination, loudness discrimination and auditory integral).

In the area of psychomotor abilities there are seven factors meeting the criterion of strong invariance (Pawlik, 1966). These are: psychomotor coordination, aiming, wrist-finger speed, manual dexterity, finger dexterity, reaction time and steadiness. Six additional psychomotor factors are less invariant, these being: ambidexterity, articulation speed, speed of arm movements, tempo of large movements of limbs and trunk, tempo of fast movements, and tempo of hand movements. It is possible to organize these thirteen factors in a hierarchic structure as depicted in Fig. 3.

Since no higher order analyses have been reported in this domain, the

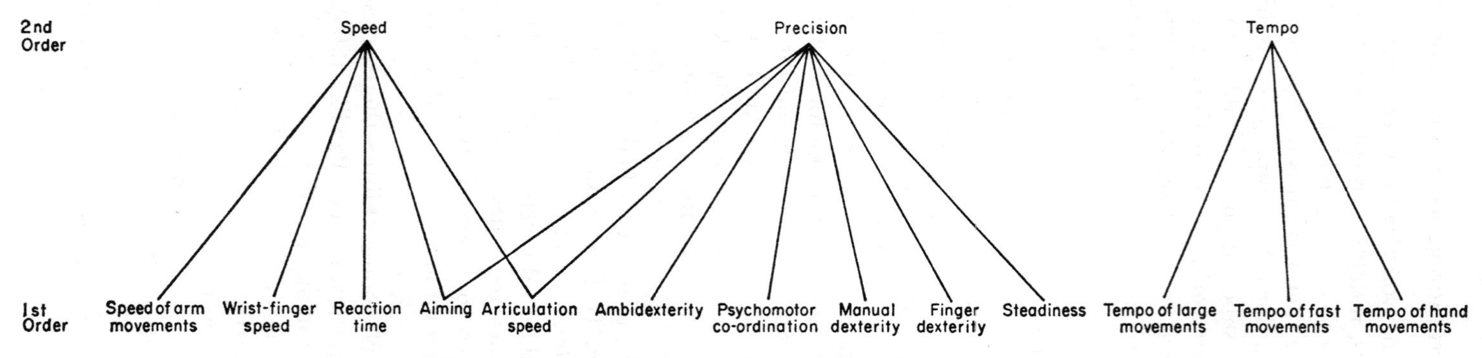

Fig. 3. Hierarchical organization of the psychomotor factors.

hierarchy shown in Fig. 3 must be regarded as speculative. However, indirect evidence for the postulated second order psychomotor factor of motor tempo comes from Rimoldi (1951b), who found that a broad, personal tempo* factor was indicated by the clustering of relevant primary factors. Similarly, Guilford (1959) provides for both a speed and precision category in his conception of the psychomotor factors. In our model we simply shift these to the second order.

A Tentative Hierarchy of Cognitive Factors

In previous sections we elaborated on the first and second order factors of sub-domains of cognition. In this section we are concerned with the entire cognitive domain. We handle it by focusing our attention on higher order factors as cognitive synthesizers. Thus, in Fig. 4 we have postulated a general intelligence factor at the fourth order, and five general third order factors labeled sensory integration, verbal, non-verbal, speed and psychomotor integration.

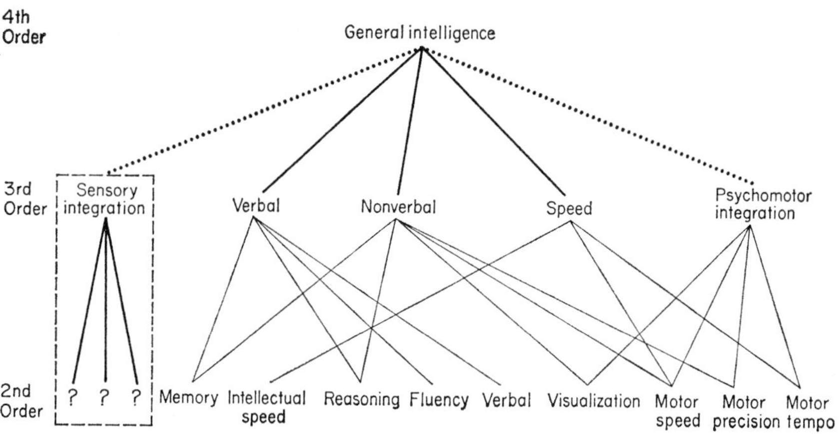

Fig. 4. Tentative synthesis of cognition.

We see the general intelligence factor as Spearman's (1927) "*g*", but we have tentatively placed it at the fourth order rather than at the first order as suggested by Spearman, or the second order as suggested by Thurstone. Whereas Burt (1940) and Vernon (1950) also place "*g*" at the fourth order, they pre-postulate it. In our case, it emerges more inductively, although its placement at the fourth order is, of course, a

* See the section on stylistic factors for higher order linkages between cognitive structure and affective structure.

tenuous one. In any event, in the present hierarchy (see Fig. 4) it is primarily defined (solid lines) in terms of the "central process" third order factors of verbal, nonverbal, and speed, with secondary loadings (dotted lines) from the more peripheral third order factors of sensory integration (information input) and psychomotor integration (response output).

The present gap in our knowledge of sensory factors is indicated by the dashed line rectangle on the left side of Fig. 4. The motor counterpart, however, is indicated on the right side of Fig. 4 in the form of a postulated third order factor of motor coordination. It is conceived as the ability to provide coordinated movement of various parts of the body. Such integrating functional unities are seen as providing linkages between the more central cognitive processes, such as memory and visualization, and the more peripheral sensory and motor processes. Thus, motor integration is viewed as involving "mental" components and some kind of cognitive-motor coupling in order to allow for action. What we have in mind here has been conceptualized by Miller *et al.* (1960) and Pribram (1971a, b) as achieving the "image" by executing a "plan". It is for these reasons that the second order visualization factor is included with motor speed, precision and tempo in defining general psychomotor integration.

Focusing on the more central aspects of cognitive structure, we have postulated a third order verbal factor which is defined in terms of the second order factors of memory, reasoning, fluency, and verbal. Such a grouping is clearly brought out by our definition of the general verbal factor as being the ability to acquire and utilize language elements, i.e. words, symbols, ideas, meaning, etc. If we ignore the numerical component, this factor bears some resemblance to Vernon's (1961) verbal-numerical-educational factor (*v: ed*). Our general nonverbal factor is defined in terms of the second order factors of memory, reasoning, visualization, motor speed, and motor precision. It is defined as the ability to effectively interact and structure nonverbal elements of the environment within the context of a defined problem or goal.

Postulating general verbal and nonverbal factors is consistent with extant nonfactorial conceptions of intelligence (e.g. Wechsler, 1958) where intelligence is divided into the two broad categories of verbal and performance. More importantly, factor analyses of the WAIS and WISC have consistently found these two broad factors (Balinsky, 1941; Birren, 1952; Burt, 1960; Cohen, 1957, 1959; Davis, 1956; Jackson, 1960; Maxwell, 1959; Saunders, 1959). Cropley (1964) and Horn (1971b) have both reviewed the factor analytic research and have concluded that such studies support the notion of two large groupings. Such empirical convergence lends plausibility to this interpretation, but leaves the issue of order level unresolved.

Our general speed factor is defined in terms of intellectual speed, motor speed and motor tempo. It can be thought of as the ability to respond quickly and efficiently to the demands of a given task. Such a factor has been alluded to in a wide variety of investigations but it receives direct support as a higher order cognitive factor in a study by Davidson and Carroll (1945). Pawlik (1966) brings out the additional point that this factor may be only part of a broad personality factor. This brings up the interesting and important issue of cognitive-affective linkages, which will receive elaboration later under the section on "styles".

Affective Structure

I will define *affective structure as a multi-dimensional, organized sub-system of processes (subsumes temperament and emotionality) by means of which an organism manifests affective phenomena.* This conception is comparable to that of cognitive structure. The implication is that affect emerges out of affective structure, which is directly influenced by mental structure, which, in turn, is influenced by the organism's total psychological structure.

Clarification of sub-domains is even more difficult in the domain of affect than it is in cognition. I have attempted to cut through all this by working with only two areas, namely temperament and emotionality.*

* The reader may have noticed omission of two key terms—personality and motivation. The word personality has received such a variety of uses that we have not used it in the section on affect at all, although so-called personality factors, such as Cattell's 16 PF, have been subsumed under the temperament classification. We have reserved usage of the word personality for the total Gestalt—the total structure and functioning of the person.

Omission of the term motivation is a more serious matter. It is serious for the reason that complete understanding of behaviour obviously demands an exposition of motivational constructs. What, then, is our defense for such a blatant omission? It is fourfold. First, there is serious doubt that motivation should be treated as a class of traits comparable to cognitive and affective traits. Does it make sense, for example, to think of hunger or thirst as a trait? We think not. It seems more reasonable to regard such phenomena as processes which provide direction for the components of individuality. Second, for whatever reason, there is a paucity of research under this rubric, so that there would be little of conceptual significance to be put forward at this time. There is one statement, however, which the interested reader should consult, namely that of Cattell (1957, 1958). Third, there are certain molar, motive-like constructs which have been included in the section of this analysis under the heading of evaluative structure. These are primarily interest and value constructs which we see as linkage factors between the cognitive and affective domains. Finally, we anticipate that the dynamic aspects of individuality will be dealt with at great length in the extended version of the theory (see 1st. footnote on p. 308), and to some extent in Part II of this manuscript. Thus, whether or not these "dynamisms" constitute an adequate treatment of motivation remains to be seen.

Because of methodological and terminological differences, I propose to summarize the situation in each of these sub-areas separately, followed by a conceptual synthesis.

*The Structure of Temperament**

Although there are confirmations and extensions from the animal and experimental literature, the bulk of the findings in this area comes from human questionnaire research. If we follow a strong invariance criterion, we can identify 15 factors, namely: affectothymia, anxiety, conscientiousness, consideration, cycloid disposition, dominance-submissiveness, excitability-calmness, general arousal, introversion-extroversion, impulsivity, masculinity-femininity, rhathymia, sociability, critical thinking, and trust versus suspiciousness.

The major studies employed in the determination of this taxonomy are those conducted over the years by Guilford, Cattell and Eysenck, and the recent comparative studies reported by Eysenck and Eysenck (1969), Howarth and Browne (1971) and Sells, Demaree and Will (1970). Comrey's work (Comrey and Jamison, 1966) was also considered. In order to be included a factor must have been identified in at least two different laboratories employing at least two different major procedures. This results in a minimal but hard core, inventory of temperamental dimensions. Thus, while some investigators will be tempted to suggest additions to the list, we see no real basis on which to argue for deletions.

This inventory is shorter than we should like to see, but there are some very positive and encouraging features. There is agreement among the investigators as to: (1) how to measure these factors, (2) how to define the factors, (3) the fact that they are reliable in their manifestations in spite of differences in methodology employed and (4) an acknowledgment that they represent fundamental dimensions of temperament and are well worth further theoretical and empirical investigation. There are many divergences of opinion beyond this, of course, but the convergences indicated above provide the basis for inclusion in this category.

The next step in the taxonomy was to establish a moderately invariant list of factors. This involved relaxing the requirement that a factor must appear across laboratories and methodologies. Solid replication within one laboratory satisfies one kind of invariance criterion—replication within one set of procedures. In this list we have included all Guilford and Cattell questionnaire factors as they appear in their most

* The reader is referred to Appendix B for brief descriptions of all affective factors.

recent statements (Guilford and Zimmerman, 1956; Cattell, *et al.*, 1970), Comrey's factors (1961, 1962), Cattell's first four second order questionnaire factors (Cattell, *et al.*, 1970) and Cattell's and Eysenck's factors which have been located in the objective domain. This list includes, of course, only those factors which do not already appear in the "strong" taxonomy above. The total number of factors in this category is about 40.

A minimal invariance level of this taxonomy includes, finally, a number of factors identified only once, but not replicated simply because replication has not been attempted or has not been given a good opportunity to occur. This includes the remaining Cattell second order questionnaire factors and the newly reported third order factors (Cattell, *et al.*, 1970), Eysenck's first order factors (Eysenck and Eysenck, 1969) and the Howarth and Browne (1971), and Sells, Demaree and Will (1970) factors not represented above. The total number of factors in this category is about 25, bringing the grand total for the entire taxonomy to approximately 80.

I would now like to turn to our hierarchy for organizing the temperament factors. The first problem we face is to decide on which factors to include. We decided to limit our analysis to factors in the "strong invariance" category. This decision reflects a cautious attitude, and a concern for dealing realistically with the current profusion of "personality factors". While this decision will result in some loss of comprehensiveness in the short run, it is our hope that, by limiting the present model to highly invariant factors, we will construct a solid foundation which will allow for expansion as additional invariant factors become available in the future. The model adopted is strongly influenced by the work of Cattell and Eysenck, if only because these investigators have been responsible for the majority of the higher order factorings available. In the construction of this hierarchy we have omitted two "strong" factors (i.e. general arousal and masculinity-femininity), we have placed two factors at the second order (i.e. introversion-extroversion and anxiety) and we have introduced another second order factor, superego. The resulting hierarchy appears in Fig. 5.

The three second order factors have been reliably located by Eysenck and Cattell. Most of the first order factors subsumed under these higher order factors have been placed there on the basis of empirical findings. The only exceptions are excitability-calmness and considerateness, both of which were given their positions on rational grounds.

What we have here is a hierarchy with three second order factors marked by a total of eleven first order factors. Two of the second order factors, extroversion-introversion and anxiety, are well known in the

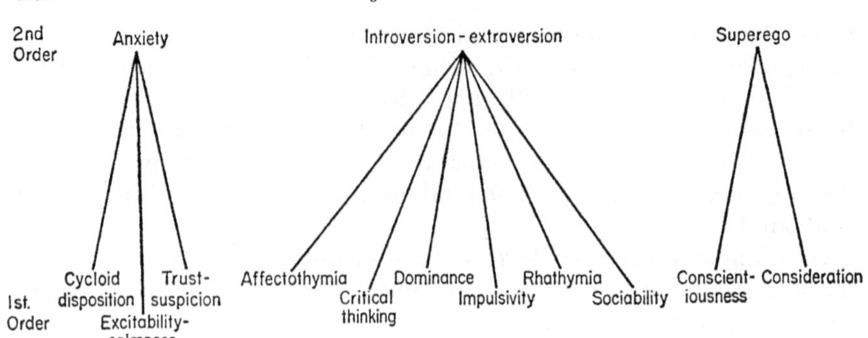

Fig. 5. Hierarchical structure of temperament factors.

clinical and personality literature. Extroversion is characterized by a desire for extensive contact with others, uninhibited behavior at parties and social gatherings, and a general desire for an active, outgoing life. All of the subordinate, first order factors reflect behavioral manifestations of this factor. For example, affectothymia is characterized by a warm, outgoing and participating manner, and is a clear marker of this dimension. The same is true for sociability, a desire for meeting people, going out frequently, and a preference for an active and lively social life. The remaining factors are consistent with our general conception of extroversion: the carefree, happy go lucky attitude of the rhathymia dimension, the quick responding, act-before-one-thinks manner of impulsivity, the socially assertive manner of the dominance factor, and the meditating, reflective aspect of the critical thinking factor, which is characteristic of the introversion pole of the introversion-extroversion dimension.

Anxiety has a number of possible conceptualizations, depending on the theoretical predilections of the person who is doing the defining. In the multivariate personality literature this factor is usually viewed as reflecting an emotional response combined with feelings of worry or concern about real or imagined stimuli. It can also be accompanied by tendencies to excitability and sudden shifts in mood, the latter probably often the result of ideational recall of distressing stimuli. The excitability and mood swing aspects (i.e. the cycloid factor) appear at the first order of our hierarchy, and Cattell and his co-workers see the trust versus suspiciousness factor as a first order marker factor for anxiety. Cattell has labeled the suspiciousness pole as "protension" (for "projection of inner tension"), a mechanism which he compares to projection in the classical sense. While the direction of cause and effect is not clear, it can be seen that this would be a sensible co-variate of anxiety.

Our third second order factor, superego, represents a behavioral pattern of concern for the feelings of others, adherence to the moral codes of the individual's milieu, responsibility to others, feelings of a sense of duty, and a self-disciplined demeanor. It must be considered the most speculative in the hierarchy for two reasons—the factor itself is not in our strong taxonomy, and the subordinate considerateness factor has not been empirically linked to it. However, there are good reasons for including it somewhere in the hierarchy, for it has been identified by Cattell at all three orders (Cattell, *et al.*, 1970). Its first order manifestation (see Fig. 5) has been labeled conscientiousness, a persistent, emotionally disciplined, moralistically conventional behavioral pattern. Thus, the location of the conscientiousness factor, along with Guilford's considerateness factor, as subordinate to the second order superego factor, was done on essentially intuitive-rational grounds.

The Structure of Emotionality

In a general review of factor analytic research in comparative-physiological psychology, Royce (1966) has identified seven factors of emotionality which appear to be invariant across species. These are as follows: autonomic balance, motor discharge, activity level, thyroid, reactivity to avoidance conditioning, responsiveness to handling, and aggressiveness. Also, in a recent report of a comprehensive experimental project on mouse emotionality, Royce and his associates (Royce, Poley and Yeudall, 1973a) provide evidence for nine factors which are invariant across a wide variety of genotypes. These factors (which include three of those listed above) are autonomic balance, motor discharge, and activity level, plus territorial marking, acrophobia, audiogenic reactivity, underwater swimming and tunneling 1 and 2.* And in a recent pilot analysis of unpublished data Royce and Poley identified several higher order factors, the most relevant of these being a third order emotional reactivity factor and second order factors described as motor reactivity and anxiety. Putting all this together, we come up with the partial hierarchy indicated as Fig. 6. This hierarchy shows a general emotional reactivity factor at the third order and two factors at the second order level. The second order motor reactivity factor provides for a variety of skeletal muscle expressions, such as the freezing behavior of acrophobia and the epileptic-like reaction to sound via the audiogenic reactivity factor. The second order anxiety factor represents a

* See pages 358–362 ff. for more details concerning these factors.

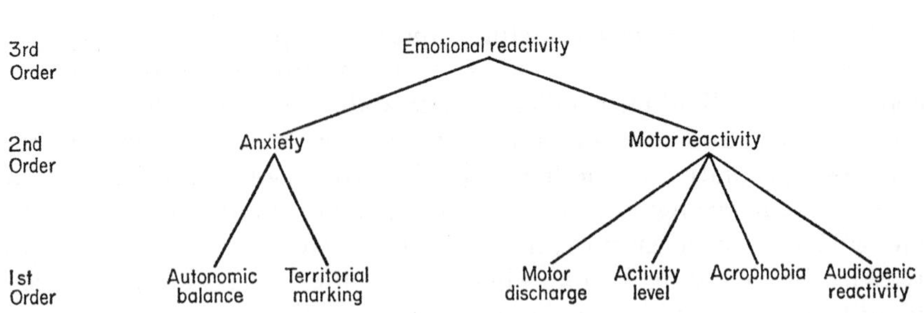

Fig. 6. Hierarchy of emotionality factors.

more visceral, internal mode of emotional expression, as exemplified by the first order factor of autonomic balance.*

A Tentative Synthesis of Affective Factors

Figure 7 represents a coalescence of the temperament hierarchy depicted in Fig. 5 and the emotionality hierarchy depicted in Fig. 6. Since there is considerable overlap in the two hierarchies, the following remarks will be brief, and confined to the higher order factors. At the third order we have two factors, emotional reactivity and cortical excitation-inhibition. Emotional reactivity refers to the overall tenor of a person's emotional expressivity. The present model† allows for two major second order modes of expression via motor reactivity or anxiety. The implication is that aroused energy (via the limbic system; see pp. 372 ff.) is either externally released via the skeletal musculature (i.e. via first order factors of acrophobia, activity level, audiogenic reactivity, and motor discharge), or it is internalized via a disposition to anxiety (i.e. via first order factors of autonomic balance, cycloid disposition, excitability-calmness, and trust-suspicion).

By cortical excitation-inhibition we are referring to the general level of neural activity in the cortex. Thus, this is a molar characteristic, reflected neurologically in such gross indices as EEG wave patterns, and psychologically in terms of mental activity. A cortical-neural imbalance in the direction of excitation reflects a highly aroused, active, or even agitated mental state, whereas a cortical-neural imbalance in the direc-

* Although the Territorial Marking factor is included as part of the emotionality hierarchy in Fig. 6, it was deleted in the conceptual synthesis shown in Fig. 7. The reason is that we see no adequate way to handle it within the present conceptualization. In short, it is alluded to as one of several conceptual loose ends which must eventually be accommodated.

† Subsequent extensions of the model may, of course, lead to additional first and second order factors.

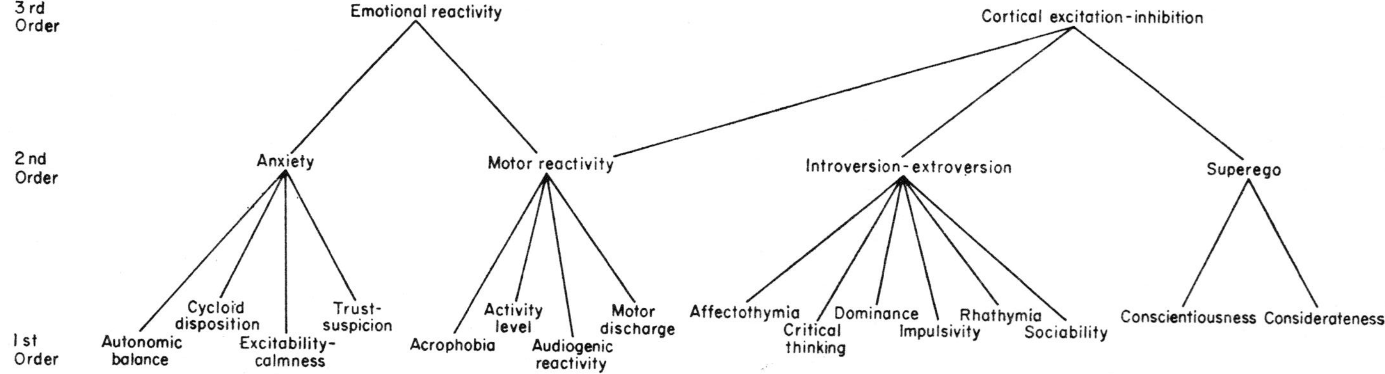

Fig. 7. A conceptual synthesis of temperament and emotionality structure.

tion of inhibition reflects a relatively inactive, sluggish, or even sleepy mental state. Figure 7 allows for three second order consequences of degree of cortical excitatory-inhibitory balance. The implication is that aroused energy (via the reticular activating system; see pp. 368 ff.) is either externally released via the skeletal musculature (i.e. via the same second order factor as emotional reactivity) or it "reverberates" internally (i.e. relative degree of introversion) on the introversion-extroversion dimension (and its six first order factors), or it is socially externalized and transformed via the superego factor (and its two first order alternatives).

An elaboration of the bio-behavioral implications of the proposed hierarchy is given in a later section on the neurology of affective traits. (See pp. 370 ff.)

The Structure of Cognitive–Affective Linkages

Having explicated both cognitive and affective structure, it now becomes possible to explore the possibility of cognitive-affective linkages which provide for integrating certain aspects of these two broad domains. I will make use of two classes of linkage constructs, i.e. style factors and evaluative factors.

*Style Structure**

A style is a characteristic mode or way of manifesting cognitive and/or affective phenomena. I will define *style structure as a multi-dimensional, organized sub-system of processes (subsumes cognitive, affective, cognitive-affective, and epistemic styles) by means of which an organism manifests cognitive or/and affective phenomena.* Thus, style structure is a sub-system of psychological and mental structure which serves a synthesizing role either within a sub-domain, such as cognition (e.g. cognitive style) or affect, or between cognitive and affective structures (see upper half of slashed line section of Fig. 8).

When the style construct is linked primarily to cognitive phenomena we will refer to it as *cognitive style.* When it is linked primarily to affective phenomena we will refer to it as *affective style.* When it cuts across both domains we will refer to it as *cognitive-affective style.* And when the style construct simultaneously invokes a valid truth criterion (i.e. leads to a justifiable knowledge claim in addition to being a

* The reader is referred to Appendix C for brief definitions of the fifteen styles mentioned in the text.

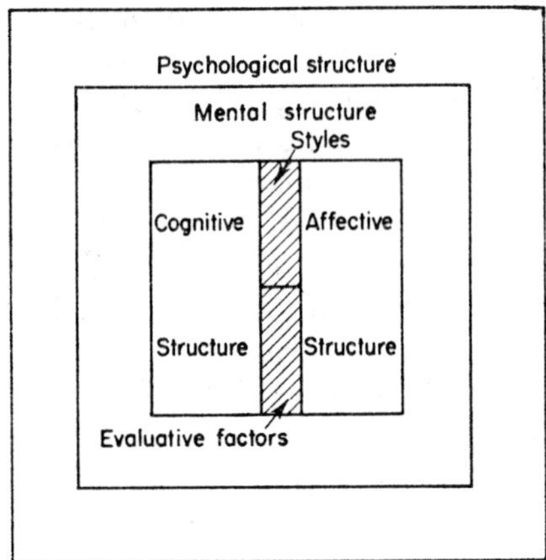

Fig. 8. Relationships between style and evaluative factors (shaded areas) and various structures.

characteristic mode or way of interacting with the environment) we will refer to it as *epistemic style*.*

At present, research on style is concentrated at three locations: The Menninger Foundation, Educational Testing Service, and the Fels Research Institute. Researchers from the Menninger Clinic (Rapaport, 1967; Klein, 1951, 1958, 1970; Gardner, 1953, 1959, 1970; Gardner, *et al.* 1959, 1960, 1968) have used the term "controls" rather than "styles", relegating the notion of style to a profile of controls. The work by Messick and others at ETS (Jackson and Messick, 1958; Messick and Fritzky, 1963; Messick, 1965, 1967; Messick and Kogan, 1963, 1965,

* Due to both theoretical and empirical inadequacies of the taxonomy of style constructs it is clearly premature to explore this class of style constructs at this time. However, the prospects for eventual theoretical synthesis via the epistemic styles of empiricism, rationalism, and metaphorism are exciting. Very briefly, these three ways of knowing can be described and contrasted as follows: Empiricism involves knowing via sensory inputs. It is an inductive process whose epistemological validity is primarily dependent on perceiving accurately. Rationalism involves knowing via the formation and elaboration of concepts. It is a deductive process whose epistemological validity is primarily dependent on logical consistency. And metaphorism involves knowing via the construction and elaboration of symbol systems. It is an analogical (or abductive) process whose epistemic validity is dependent on the extent to which the metaphorical patterns (e.g. art forms such as plays and paintings) achieve universal significance. For a more complete analysis of this position see "The Encapsulated Man" (Royce, 1964) and the author's presidential address to the Division of Philosophical Psychology of the American Psychological Association (Royce, 1973). Also see several papers for relevant empirical findings (Royce, 1970; Royce and Smith, 1964; Smith, *et al.*, 1967). For an extended critical review of the relevant literature on knowing see a forthcoming book (Royce, 1973). And for a summary of related reports see the recently issued report of the 2nd Banff Conference (Royce and Rozeboom, 1972).

1966) provides a more rigorous statistical precision for the constructs originated at the Menninger Clinic. The Fels work is carried on by Kagan and his colleagues (Kagan, 1965a, 1965b, 1966; Kagan, *et al.* 1963, 1964, 1966) who, with Messick, have elected to use the term "style" as I have here. There are many other pockets of investigation on styles, particularly the work of Bieri (Bieri and Blacker, 1956), Broverman (1964), Bruner (Bruner, *et al.* 1956), Kelly (1955), Pettigrew (1958), Scott (1969), and Witkin (Witkin, *et al.* 1962). These workers, and many more, have produced a vast non-factorial empirical literature which constitutes the bulk of the evidence for the construct validity of each of the following styles:

a. Field articulation or analytic versus global style,* known originally as field independence and later as psychological differentiation (Witkin, *et al.*, 1962; Gardner, *et al.* 1959; Messick and Fritzky, 1963; Karp, 1963; Gardner and Moriarty, 1968).

b. Extensiveness of scanning (Gardner, *et al.* 1959; Holzman, 1966; Gardner and Moriarty, 1968).

c. Conceptual (or "cognitive") differentiation, once linked to equivalence range.†

d. Leveling versus sharpening, once called assimilation (Klein, 1951; Holzman, 1954).

e. Tolerance for the unconventional or for "unrealistic experiences" (Klein, 1951; Klein, *et al.* 1962).

f. Constricted versus flexible control (Klein, 1954; Gardner, *et al.* 1959; Sloane, Gorlow and Jackson, 1963; and Messick and Kogan, 1963), probably referred to by strong versus weak automatization (Broverman 1964) and cognitive interference or interference proneness (Klein, *et al.*, 1967, p. 510).

g. Category width or broad versus narrow categorizing (Pettigrew, 1958), also called equivalance range (Sloane, Gorlow and Jackson, 1963; and Messick and Kogan, 1965).

h. Reflection versus impulsivity (Yando and Kagan, 1970).

i. Cognitive complexity (Kelly, 1955; Bieri and Blacker, 1956; Gardner and Schoen, 1962; Messick and Kogan, 1966; Vannoy, 1955; and Wyer, 1964; Zimring, 1971; and Langley, 1971).

j. Analytic versus relational categorizing (Kagan, *et al.* 1963).

* For a discussion of these terminologies, see papers in Messick, S. and Ross, J. (eds), "Measurement in Personality and Cognition" (1962).

† Conceptual differentiation is conceptually and empirically distinct from category width or equivalence range. (Gardner and Schoen, 1962.) Conceptual differentiation and integration are also distinct (Wyer, 1964) and considered to be aspects of cognitive complexity (Gardner and Schoen, 1962; Langley, 1971; Zimring, 1971).

k. Compartmentalization (Messick and Kogan, 1963; Langley, 1971).
l. Conceptual (or "cognitive") integration.
m. Physiognomic versus literal (Klein, 1951).
n. Abstract versus concrete: preferred level of and capacity for abstraction (Harvey, *et al.* 1961), probably referring to the ability to form concepts as distinct from conceptual differentiation (Gardner and Schoen, 1962); possibly not a style at all.
o. Contrast reactivity (Gardner, 1970), probably another name for constricted versus flexible control.

Other styles have been proposed (e.g., Paul, 1959; Scott, 1966, 1969; Shapiro, 1968) or factorially discovered (Sloane, Gorlow and Jackson, 1963; and Karp, 1963) but these have not received further substantiation or integration into the literature. In addition, there are many variables in the psychological literature which have not been considered as stylistic, but probably will be as the concept takes on more theoretically integrating power.

Let us now turn to the problem of style taxonomy. Since there have been relatively few factorial investigations* on style, it is not possible to invoke as stringent a factor invariance criterion in this domain as we have in the cognitive and affective domains. Thus, our strong taxonomy is defined as identification at least three times factorially and/or strong nonfactorial construct validity. Only field articulation and extensiveness of scanning qualify in this category.

Field articulation (Gardner, *et al.* 1959, 1960; Witkin, 1962; Karp, 1963; Messick and Fritzky, 1963; Gardner and Moriarty, 1968) refers to the extent an individual is able to articulate, specify, and delineate his experience; to be active and analytic as opposed to passive and global (the latter implies accepting experience in an uncritical, diffuse, hazy and ill-defined manner). Field articulation is typically measured by the subject's ability to quickly find selected figures among others (e.g. the embedded figures test), or his ability to assess how vertical he (or an object) is in a field of non-vertical cues. Field articulate individuals can overcome the influence of a tilted frame when judging the perpendicularity of a rod within it (the rod and frame test), and they are able to overcome the influence of a tilted room when judging their own perpendicularity (the body-adjustment and room-adjustment tests). In perceptual tests field articulate people are able to experience embedded figures or their own bodies as discrete entities, unfused with the rest of their experience.

* For each style described in the following taxonomy factor analytic research identifying that style is listed immediately following that style's name.

More generally, field articulate individuals appear to "keep things apart" in a wide variety of situations. For example, they are more likely to structure ambiguous stimuli (such as Rorschach ink blots), and less likely to change their stated views on a particular social issue in the direction of the attitudes of the majority. They are highly autonomous individuals with a stable self-view, socially they show little interest in and need for people, and they manifest a relatively intellectual and impersonal approach to problems. In general, they are influenced little by authority, tending to be guided by values, standards and needs of their own.

Finally, Witkin reports that field articulate individuals use relatively specialized and complex defenses, such as isolation and intellectualization rather than denial and repression. As psychiatric patients they are more often delusional, attempting to maintain an identity, however unrealistic, while field inarticulate patients are more hallucinatory, with little struggle to maintain an identity.

Extensiveness of scanning (Gardner, *et al.* 1959; Gardner and Moriarty, 1968) refers to the broad and intensive deployment of attention over stimulus fields. Extensive scanners are characterized not only by intense concentration on the central task, but they also possess a wide ranging peripheral sensitivity which renders many aspects of the field available to conscious recall. Modal extensive scanners sample a large amount of information before commitment to a response. They seem preoccupied with veridicality, exactness, and the adequacy of their response, and perhaps control over impulses. Extensiveness of scanning has been measured in a variety of size estimation tasks. For example (Schlesinger, 1954; Holzman and Klein, 1956), subjects have been asked to estimate the size of discs (which they held in their hands). Some discs had pictures on them, and they all varied in weight. Scanners were more responsive to the incidental aspects (they could recall them better), and could overcome distortions of size (they were more accurate estimators). In another size estimation task (Gardner and Long, 1962a, b) scanners were less likely to overestimate the size of objects in the center of the visual field. They deployed attention throughout the field, thereby counteracting the natural tendency to overestimate the size of objects in the middle of a field. Studies of eye movements during such tasks showed that scanners employ more extensive sweeps and more intensive fixations than poor scanners. In addition, extensive scanners take longer to adjust a comparison stimulus to the standard, look more at the standard, and spend more time "checking" their judgment after their final adjustment of the comparison (Gardner, 1959).

Another typical measure is the inverted T illusion, where the vertical bar looks longer than the horizontal bar. When the horizontal bar is the standard, extensive scanners are more susceptible to the illusion because this bar looks shorter to them. However, if the vertical bar is the standard, extensive scanners are less susceptible to the illusion because now the vertical bar looks shorter to them (Gardner and Long, 1960a, 1960b; Gardner, 1961).

Although scanners have stabilized conceptions of objects, they are less attuned to feelings. While they can provide more incidental recall on tasks such as the Stroop color-word test, when asked to sort pictures on the basis of affective connotations they place a large number of pictures in the "indifferent" pile. Finally, they are more likely to use such ego defenses as isolation of affect and projection, and as patients they are more likely to be paranoid schizophrenics. Their intensely "hard, close look" attitude is generally reflected by doubt, uncertainty, and mistrust.

The next six styles in the list satisfy minimal requirements for a moderate taxonomy, namely, factor identification at least once and/or moderate non-factorial empirical construct validity. Conceptual differentiation (Gardner, *et al.* 1959; Gardner and Moriarty, 1968; Gardner and Schoen, 1962) refers to the differentiation of concepts, (such as "size") into increasingly more viable concepts (such as "height" and "width"). Leveling versus sharpening (Gardner, *et al.* 1959, Gardener and Lohrenz, 1960; Klein, *et al.* 1962) refers to the loss or preservation of distinctions among a series of stimuli. Tolerance for the unconventional (Gardner, *et al.* 1959; Klein, *et al.* 1962) refers to the acceptance (as opposed to denial) of experiences which do not agree with what one knows to be true (such as apparent movement). Constricted versus flexible control (Gardner, *et al.* 1959, 1968; Broverman, 1964) refers to the proneness to interference by perceived contradictory or intrusive cues. Category width (Pettigrew, 1958; Sloane, Gorlow and Jackson, 1963), or equivalence range, refers to the fineness of the distinctions made within a given category. Reflection versus impulsivity refers to the consistent tendency to display slow or fast response times in problem situations with high response uncertainty.

The remaining eight styles are relegated to the weak taxonomy, though in some cases there is non-factorial support for them. As with the affective taxonomy, while some investigators may be tempted to make additions to the strong or moderate taxonomies (e.g. on the basis of unpublished research), it is our opinion that the styles in question are at least in the taxonomy we have designated.

However, since the available empirical evidence on the factorial definition of these constructs is limited, we feel it is premature to spell out a comprehensive style structure at this time. Rather, we propose to present the details for one style in each category as examples of the kind of empirical-conceptual linkages we envisage in this domain. These are indicated in Fig. 9a.*

Extensiveness of scanning, reflection versus impulsivity, and field articulation are our examples of cognitive style, affective style, and cognitive-affective style, respectively. While we cannot specify order

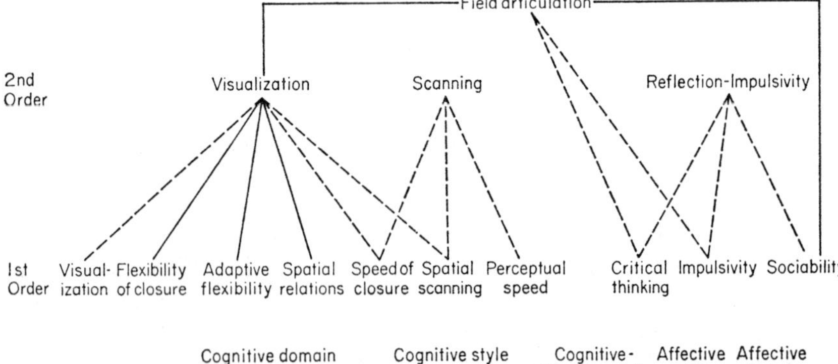

Fig. 9a. Postulated linkages of style factors to cognitive and affective structure (solid lines indicate empirically based linkages).

level of style constructs at this time, it appears that extensiveness of scanning and reflection versus impulsivity are related to first order factors in the cognitive and affective domains, respectively, while field articulation is simultaneously linked to a higher order factor in the cognitive domain and to first order factors in both the cognitive and affective domains.

Inspection of Fig. 9a indicates that the cognitive style factor, scanning,

* The relationships indicated in Fig. 9a are based on a mixture of empirical evidence and rational-intuitive guesses. As an example, linkages shown for field articulation and reflection-impulsivity reflect both empirical and rational considerations, whereas relationships involving the scanning construct are based entirely on rational grounds. The general lack of empirical factor analytic evidence further confounds the picture. For example, the empirical evidence in the case of reflection-impulsivity is entirely non-factorial. Overall, the evidence is the most convincing for the field articulation construct, as it includes all the criteria; that is, both conceptual and empirical, with both factorial and non-factorial empirical evidence. The relative strength of this construct is reflected by the greater number of connections, including four solid line connections (implying strong empirical evidence, most of which is factor analytic).

is linked to the three first order factors of speed of closure, perceptual speed, and spatial scanning. All three abilities involve scanning the perceptual field. The most important of these, spatial scanning, involves being able to quickly survey a complex spatial field to find a particular configuration representing a pathway through the field. Speed of closure requires that the field as a whole be "taken in" quickly so that likely material can be "filled into" unseen portions. And perceptual speed requires that the field be scanned quickly so that specified small elements of the pattern can be identified.

The affective style factor, reflection-impulsivity, is linked to critical thinking, impulsivity, and sociability. The essence of this construct is "the degree to which a subject considers alternative hypotheses in contrast to reporting hypotheses with minimal consideration of their probable validity" (see Appendix C). The affective factors of critical thinking (i.e. meditative, reflective) and impulsivity (i.e. minimal consideration of alternatives) are obvious temperament counterparts of reflection-impulsivity (Kagan, *et al.* 1963). Although the relevance of the sociability (i.e. meeting people, active social life) factor is not as obvious, it makes intuitive sense to suggest that it is the impulsivity end of the style continuum which correlates with high sociability. There is, in fact, some empirical evidence that this is the case (Kagan, 1965b).

Field articulation is our example of a cognitive-affective style. Cognitively it focuses on an analytic versus a global way of perceiving; affectively it is concerned with the extent to which an individual is autonomously guided and the degree to which he is affected by social and emotional stimuli. Field articulation is primarily a perceptual rather than a conceptual style, as evidenced by its linkages to the six first order factors of visualization, flexibility of closure, adaptive flexibility, spatial relations, speed of closure, and spatial scanning (Gardner, *et al.* 1960; Witkin, *et al.* 1962). These linkages occur via the second order factor of visualization, a general ability concerning the structuring and restructuring of spatial elements. The primary perceptual manifestations of the field articulation style occur via flexibility of closure, adaptive flexibility, and spatial relations (solid line connections in Fig. 9a). All three of these draw heavily on abilities required to imagine changes in spatial arrangements and to select out or identify parts embedded in "distracting" stimulus configurations. The affective manifestations occur via the temperamental factors of critical thinking, impulsivity, and especially sociability. The implication is that the field articulate person is autonomous, socially uninvolved, and relatively deliberate (Witkin, *et al.* 1962; Elliot, 1961; Evans, 1967).

Many other linkages between styles and affective or cognitive constructs have been found* (in varying degrees of adequacy), but much more research is necessary before a definitive style structure becomes apparent. However, it appears reasonable to say that styles are embedded throughout affective and cognitive structures, and probably provide higher order linkages between them.

In addition, we can anticipate a hierarchy of style factors. This might occur in two ways: (1) when style constructs link higher order cognitive or/and affective factors, and (2) when style constructs link other styles. Thus, while we do not know the order level of the three style constructs summarized in Fig. 9a, it is probable that scanning and reflection-

* First, on the cognitive side, Langley (1971) has suggested that the combination of low conceptual differentiation and integration defines the style of compartmentalization, a construct which Messick and Kogan (1963) found and related to low ideational fluency. In addition, Gormly (1971) has suggested that low conceptual integration (called "cognitive comprehensiveness") is related to high dogmatism. Less recently, Baggaley (1955) suggested that high scores on level of concept formation ("analytic" performance) correlated with inductive and deductive reasoning, and speed and "strength" of perceptual closure. The suggestion (Kagan, *et al.*, 1963) that field articulation is related to analytic versus relational categorizing in the conceptual area receives some support in a critical review (Wallach, in Messick and Ross, 1962) and an empirical investigation (Messick and Fritzky, 1963). Pettigrew (1958) and Messick and Kogan (1965) have found that the style of category width influences quantitative ability, although this influence has not been clarified. Relations between certain memory abilities and leveling versus sharpening have been suggested by Paul (1959), Gardner and Lohrenz (1960), and Gardner, *et al.*, (1960). One could suggest that the physiognomic versus literal style may be related to fluency factors, or that speed and tempo factors may reflect a style of "personal tempo" (Guilford, 1959). Similarly, the suggestion may be made that extensiveness of scanning is related to Bruner's (Bruner, *et al.*, 1956) strategies of concept attainment (see French, 1965, and Phillips and Torrance, 1971). Some evidence suggests that leveling-sharpening is related to associative memory (Gardner, *et al.*, 1960; Gardner and Lohrenz, 1960; Paul, 1959).

On the affective side, Evans (1967) has replicated the negative correlation of field articulation with the second order extroversion factor, and Oltman (1964) suggested that field articulate individuals are more cortically aroused. Gardner, *et al.* (e.g. 1959, pp. 127–136; 1968, pp. 155–203) have related defense mechanisms to styles. The correlations of extensive scanning and projection, constricted control and compulsion, and levelling and repression at least suggest that these styles influence factors such as trust versus suspiciousness, carefulness and anxiety, respectively.

Finally, Pemberton (1952a, b) has furnished some evidence for linkages across cognitive–affective structures. She found a connection between flexibility of closure (and thus, field articulation), and the flexibility required to solve analytical reasoning problems and problems utilizing highly practiced symbols where meaning is not important (deductive reasoning). In addition, she found a more tenuous connection between speed of closure and inductive reasoning. On the affective side, she suggested that flexibility of closure related to lack of sociability and schizothymia (or lack of affectothymia), carefulness, and a lack of critical thinking.

Horn (1971a) recently reviewed putative relationships between speed of closure, flexibility of closure, "school education" factors, and fluency factors to Cattell's U.I. 17 (Inhibition), U.I. 19 (Independence), Superego, and both U.I. 21 (Exuberance) and surgency (rhathymia), respectively. A multitude of other possibilities and findings are reported by Klein (1951), Messick (1965, 1966), Messick and Kogan (1966), Gardner, *et al.* (1959, 1960), and Witkin, *et al.* (1962).

impulsivity are second order constructs, and that field articulation is a third or fourth order construct. It is also tempting, but premature, to suggest that the field articulation factor subsumes the scanning and reflection-impulsivity factors as part of a more complex style hierarchy. Elaboration of style structure is an exciting prospect which shows promise of providing syntheses which are both pervasive and insightful.

Evaluative Structure

I will define *evaluative structure as a multidimensional, organized subsystem of processes (subsumes, interests and values) by means of which an organism manifests evaluative phenomena.* Evaluative factors are seen as functional unities which include both cognitive and affective facets (see the lower half of slashed line section of Fig. 8). For example, an individual who is high on political value implies an organized subsystem of both cognitive and affective dimensions relating to political issues. Such an individual may be able to construct a highly technical and rational argument (cognitive aspect) for his allegiance to socialism which is charged with an emotional commitment (affective aspect) that becomes apparent under external threat. Furthermore, he usually behaves in a manner which is consistent with the cognitive and affective aspects of this value. We have conceptualized this process as involving evaluative behavior; the organism evaluates relevant environmental events with respect to his evaluative structure (i.e. interest and value dimensions) and manifests behavior which is consistent with this structure.*

An inventory of empirically based interest and value factors is presented in Tables II and III, respectively. The tables speak for themselves, indicating the strength of invariance as one descends the columns. Figure 9b represents the proposed taxonomic relationships between values and interests. Values are seen as higher order constructs (probably second and third order), which modulate interest factors (probably first order). For example, social value implies an interest in social service and health service. Aesthetic value may manifest itself in any or all of the following interest factors: musical, literary, artistic

* Of course the organism does not always behave consistently with his particular organization of evaluative structure. Such cases can be accommodated by moderating variables (Ghiselli, 1963) such as the state of the organism (mood) and environmental conditions (threat). It should be noted that if the organism is forced to behave in a manner inconsistent with his evaluative structure, he may accommodate and change that structure such that it is consistent with his behavior. Forced racial integration is justified on this premise.

Table II. Confirmed vocational interest factors

Factor	Number of Studies That Consider Factor Established	1948 Kuder	1954 Guilford, *et al.*	1964 King, *et al.*	1941 Ferguson, *et al.*	1931 Thurstone	1940 Gernes	1971 Adcock
		Established by:						
Social Service	7	X	X	X	X	X	X	X
Scientific	6	X	X	X	X	X		X
Artistic Expression	5	X	X	X			X	X
Literary	4	X		X	X	X		
Outdoor	4	X	X	X				X
Business	4		X			X	X	X
Mechanical	2	X	X					
Computational	2	X	X					
Clerical	2	X	X					
Persuasive	1	X						
Health Science	1			X				
Musical	1	X						

Table III. Confirmed value factors

Factor	Number of Studies that Consider Factor Established	1951 Allport, *et al.*	1962 Super	1961 O'Connor, *et al.*	1959 Guilford	1940 Duffy, *et al.*	1937 Lurie	1941 Ferguson, *et al.*	1970 Sciortine	1954 Brogde
		Established by:								
Social	9	X	X	X	X	X	X	X	X	X
Aesthetic	6	X	X	X				X	X	X
Political	5	X	X	X	X			X		
Theoretical	5	X				X	X	X		X
Economic	4	X	X	X						X
Religious	4	X			X		X		X	
Pleasure vs. task orientation	2		X	X						
Other vs. inner direction	2		X	X						
Philistine (utility and power)	2					X	X			

expression, and outdoor. The structure indicated in Fig. 9b is completely speculative as there have been no empirical factor studies reported on the possible relationships between values and interests.

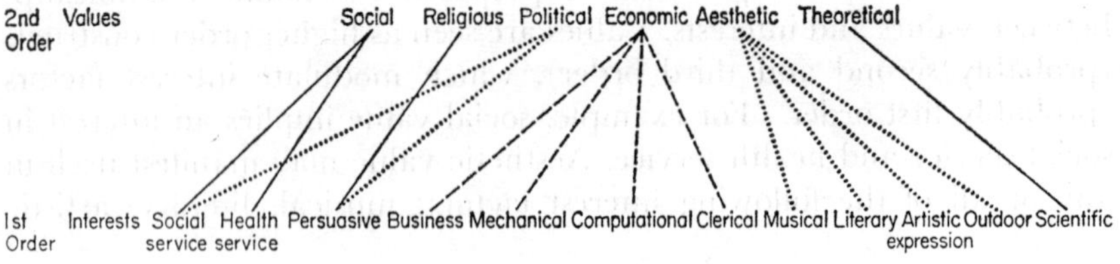

Fig. 9b. A postulated evaluative structure.

Part II. Functional Processes of Individuality

In this section we are concerned with process—such questions as how each component behaves over time, the interactions of components, and the manner in which "organized complexes" change. The point is that a factor or dimension of individuality is not the static entity it appears to be (possibly due primarily to the typical cross-sectional approach in factor analytic studies). Rather, each factor is conceived as a dynamic variable, a theoretical construct which is an active part of the total, changing, multidimensional system we call a person. Thus, the focus of our attention in Part II is on the functional significance of factors *per se*. Although we are not, at this stage, concerned with how these components might be sequentially organized to account for particular psychological processes such as problem solving and creativity, it is anticipated that more adequate knowledge of the structure and function of components *per se* will provide the building blocks for such analyses. Furthermore, a basic assumption, borrowed from biological thought, is that structure and function are intimately related, and that it is necessary to understand structure before it is possible to understand function. Thus, with the structural model now before us, what can we say about function? We'll open the inquiry by first looking at what happens to factors over time, followed by such questions as factor differentiation, biological and cultural determinants of individuality, and the relevance of higher order factors as personality "organizers".

The Ontogeny of Factors

Figure 10 can be taken as a typical mental growth curve. Four constants, K_1 to K_4, allow for a variety of rational interpretations. For example, the location of K_1, the *y* intercept, indicates the extent of prenatal mental development, and the value of K_2 indicates a theoretical upper limit of performance at maturity. The line segment connecting K_2 and K_3 indicates the decline (or improvement) of mental ability for

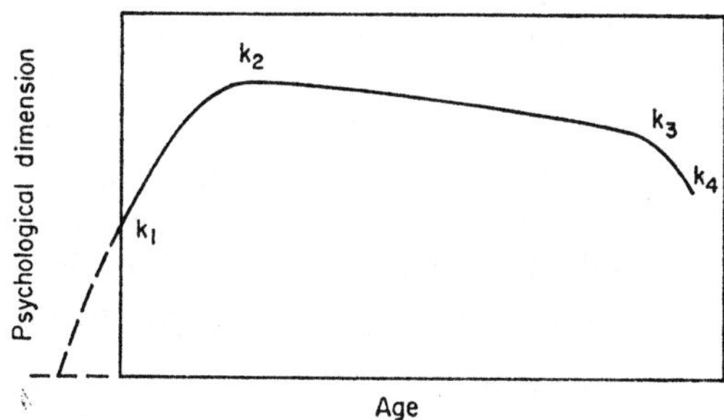

Fig. 10. Psychological dimension as a function of age.

the main portion of the life span. The typical lack of slope in the middle years reflects the relative constancy of the I.Q. The inflection point at K_3, usually at an advanced age such as 70, indicates the onset of senescence, while the slope provided by K_3–K_4 gives us the rate of senescent decline.

Let us now generate a family of curves similar to Fig. 10, but with one important modification—we shall fix K_1 at a specified value, thereby retaining a single trunk from which subsequent branches later emanate. Note that the other parameters K_2, K_3, and K_4 are free to vary.

In Fig. 11 we have depicted several factors, labeled *A*, *B*, *C*, *D*, and *E*, as differentiating out of a common source, increasing rapidly in

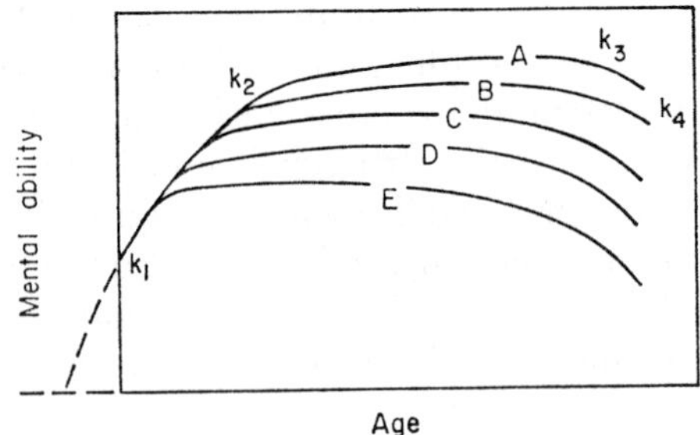

Fig. 11. Factors as a function of age.

early age, reaching a peak or upper limit at maturity, remaining relatively constant throughout the life span, usually* declining slightly over the life span, and finally declining rapidly at an advanced age. Such intellectual development, from relative homogeneity to heterogeneity (i.e. many factors), is seen as merely one example of the major growth principle which states that, in general, tissue growth and behavior become successively more differentiated, moving from undifferentiated and global capacities and activities to more finely fractionated and specialized ones; that is, from few-general to many-specific processes. We will henceforth refer to this growth process as factor differentiation, and we will postulate that factors appear at any point in the life span as a consequence of both hereditary and environmental causes. It should be noted in passing that the relative homogeneity from birth to K_1 (see Fig. 11) is not inconsistent with a

* Factors A and B are exceptions. Factor A shows an increase so that K_3 rather than K_2, represents maturity for this particular factor. And Factor B remains constant throughout most of the life span.

multi-gene, multi-factor theory of individuality. Rather, it reflects the fact that the organism is still developing (e.g. biological differentiation is in progress)—that time is needed for potential to become manifest.

However, we need a complementary growth principle to deal with the increase in complexity, for the mere proliferation of parts would only allow for cancerous rather than controlled growth. This problem has usually been handled by looking for coordinating systems and levels of organization. This is most obviously exemplified by the nervous system, with reflexes handled at the spinal level, various vegetative functions being coordinated in the mid-brain, and the more complex psychological functions being mediated via a variety of sub-cortical and cortical anatomical areas. Although growth mechanisms are not well understood, it has been postulated that they are hierarchically organized. It seems reasonable, therefore, to postulate a factor hierarchy (as exemplified by Figs. 4 and 7). In terms of structure this simply means there are higher order, in addition to first order, factors. In terms of function, it implies that higher order factors play an integrating role. In terms of the developmental process, the implication is that both higher order and first order factors "appear" and "decline" throughout the life span, and that there are changes in psychological structure (subsumes mental, cognitive, and affective structures; see definitions given above) both in terms of relative importance of individual factors and shifts in the overall hierarchical structure. We will elaborate on the problem of hierarchical structure and personality integration in the expanded version of this manuscript (see 1st footnote p. 308).

Hereditary and Environmental Sources of Variation

In Fig. 11 we showed several factors as a function of age. In Fig. 12 we show differential performance levels of the same factor, *A*, as a function of age. The implication is that the same factor can become

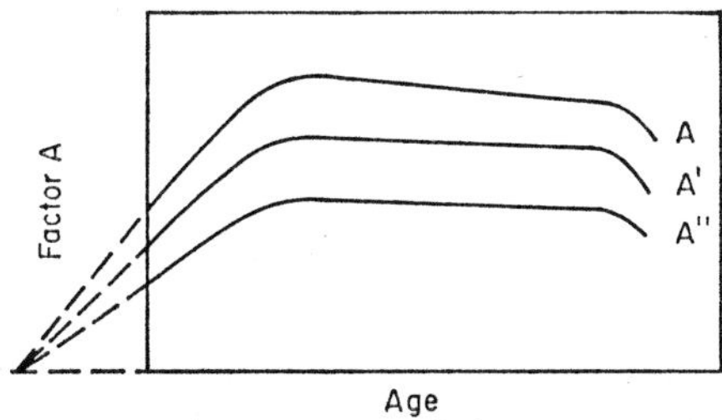

Fig. 12. Differential performance levels of the same factor as a function of age.

manifest at a high level as in A, a middle level as in A', or a low level as in A''.

The relationship between actual performance level and performance level limit is brought out in Fig. 13. Here we see a difference between actual and potential performance level for a given factor, where actual

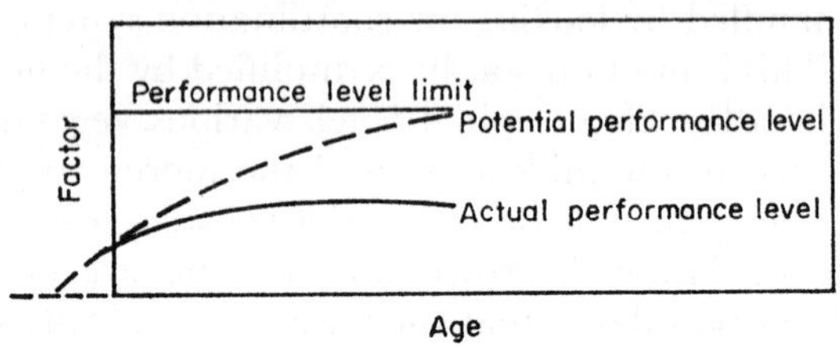

Fig. 13. The relationship between performance level and performance level limit.

performance level refers to the observed score on a given factor, and potential performance level refers to a heredity-environment determined theoretical upper limit.

A similar set of concepts is called for when we focus on age of maturity, the age at which maximum performance occurs. However, in this case (see Fig. 14) the difference between actual (M_a) and

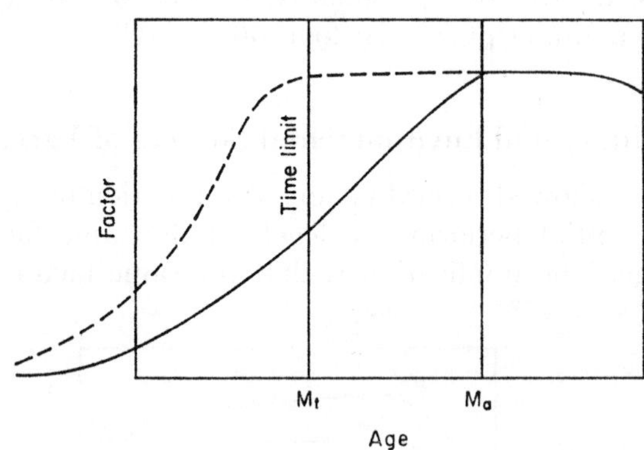

Fig. 14. The relationship between performance and age of maturity.

potential (M_t) performance is a matter of timing rather than level of performance *per se*. M_t denotes the heredity-environment determined earliest possible age of maturity.

Let us now take a closer look at these relationships. Note, for example, that the actual performances depicted so far are due to both heredity and environment. Hence, it will be necessary for us to tease out exactly how such effects are operating. Before proceeding further, however, let me offer several additional definitions. Henceforth I shall refer to the *age of maturity performance limit as the time limit.* This limit implies that the performance in question does not occur earlier for a given genotype and performance level regardless of amount of training or other environmental interventions. *The performance level limit refers to the highest possible level of performance for a given genotype in interaction with the most optimal environment, independent of time (i.e. given infinite time).** Further, by hereditary effect I shall mean any observed variance due to the genotype. And, by environmental effect I shall mean any observed variance due to differences in the environment. Let us now combine performance level and age of maturity curves with genetic and environmental effects. These are depicted in the next four figures. In Fig. 15 we have plotted several different performance levels at a constant age of maturity (i.e. time limit held constant). In Fig. 15a the variations in performance level are due to variations in the genotype, but in Fig. 15b they are due to variations in the environment.

Figure 16 depicts different ages of maturation at a constant performance level (i.e. performance level limit held constant). In Fig. 16a the observed differences in age of maturity are due to heredity since the environment is held constant, whereas the differential performances in

* The concept of limit is both interesting and debateable. And whether the reader sees value in it or not, it has received considerable attention in the scientific literature (e.g. the speed of light as an upper bound for rate of change and the mathematics of limits). In the present context I view the matter quite pragmatically. If the concept helps us in developing a viable theory of individual differences, let us keep it. If it serves no useful purpose it should be dropped. I found it to be of value in coming to grips with the hereditary and environmental sources of variation. I think it should be retained for the simple reason that all organisms, including man, are obviously finite. Thus, this concept is part of my set of underlying assumptions regarding the nature of man.

On the other hand, I trust it is clear that our present state of knowledge about these matters is so thin that whatever empirical and/or theoretical magnitudes we attach to a particular limit should be regarded as an hypothesis. This is the main reason I have defined both performance level limit and time limit in terms of observables. Thus, if we define *optimal environment* as a set of environmental conditions which results in the highest observable performance for a given genotype, it follows that such limits are not regarded as fixed for all of time. In short, limits are to be established on both theoretical and experimental grounds, and are taken as tentative, rough estimates which are subject to modification as new data and ideas force a change. At this writing I am not at all clear how feasible it is to actually assign quantitative values for a particular limit. For our purposes, namely to establish a plausible theoretical structure, it is not necessary to provide an answer to this problem. However, as the present theory takes on more and more plausibility, it will obviously be necessary to make some kind of contact between the theoretical construct of limit and the empirical assessment of it.

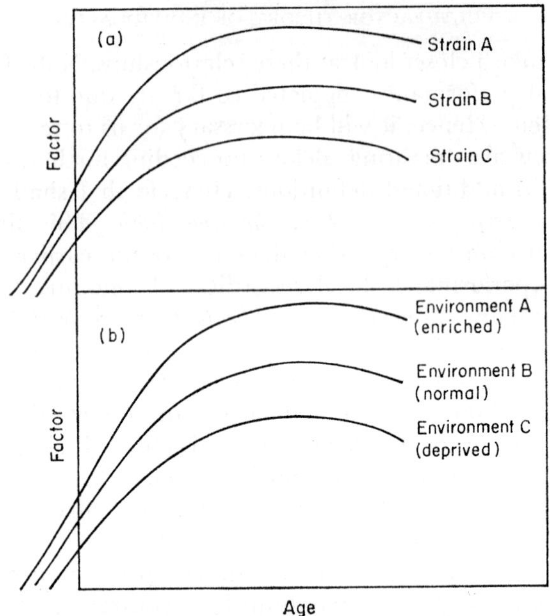

Fig. 15. Variations in performance level when age of maturity (i.e. time limit) is held constant.

a. Environment constant, heredity varied.
b. Heredity constant, environment varied.

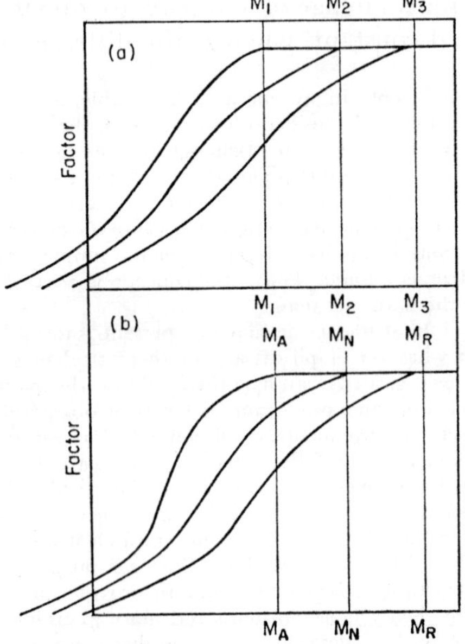

Fig. 16. Variation in age of maturation when performance level limit is held constant.

Fig. 16b are due to differences in environment. Thus M_N represents the normal or average time required to reach maturity, M_A represents an accelerated age of maturity, and M_R represents a retarded developmental curve. Since heredity is held constant, these curves imply that environmental variation (e.g. deprived environments) is controlling the timing in development and/or that learning is crucial in development.

If we now synthesize the analysis thus far, we can characterize two classes of factors under the rubrics of heredity dominant factors and environment dominant factors. Elaboration of what is meant by these concepts can be implemented by reference to Figs. 17 and 18.

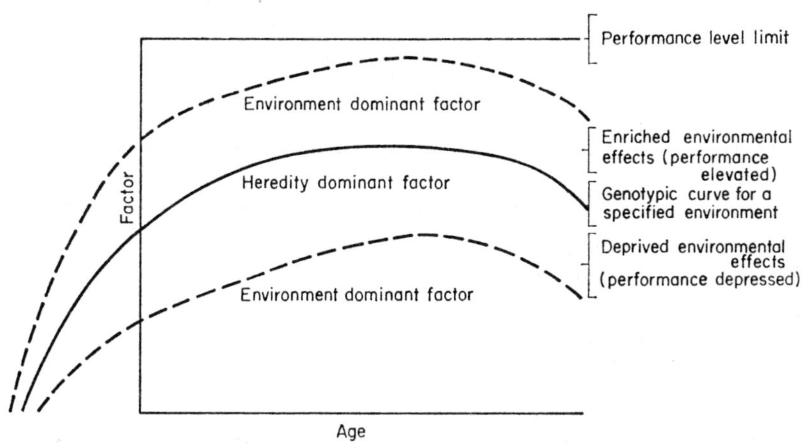

Fig. 17. Heredity and environment dominant factors in terms of performance

The solid line curve in Fig. 17 shows the performance level for a particular genotype in interaction with a specified environment. To the extent performance can be shifted in either direction from this genetic base line we get environmental effects. If the effect of environment is severe, performance level will be drastically changed, as in the case of the two dotted line curves labeled environmental dominant. If the effect is minimal, there will be no significant departure in observed performance, hence the solid line curve is labeled heredity dominant. Similar effects concerning age of maturity have been idealized in Fig. 18. Environmental effects can either speed up, retard, or have no effect on age of maturity. Those factors (dotted line curves) which are highly susceptible to such effects have been labeled environment dominant, whereas the solid line curve has been labeled heredity dominant.

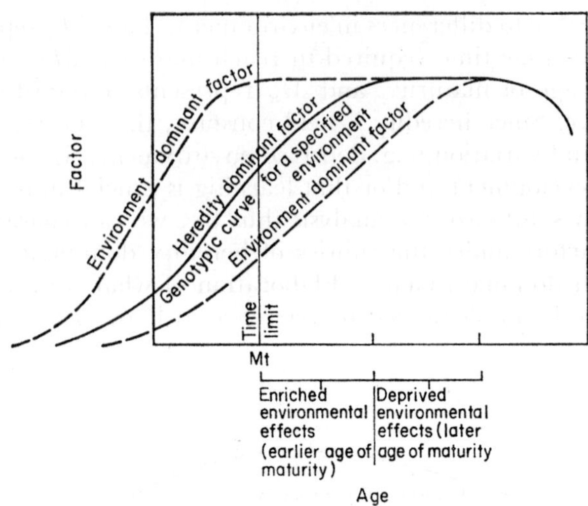

Fig. 18. Heredity and environment dominant factors in terms of age and maturity.

Thus, *a heredity dominant factor is a primarily genetically determined dimension with a development curve which is highly resistant to environmental effects*. It is statistically definable in terms of relatively small variations from the genotypic curve despite attempts to induce environmental effects. *An environment dominant factor is a dimension with a primarily environmentally determined developmental curve which is relatively uninfluenced by hereditary effects*. It is statistically definable in terms of relatively large variation from the genotypic curve as a result of attempts to induce environmental effects.

It should be obvious that these are idealized extremes, and that most cases, being subject to both environmental and genetic influences, will fall in between.* There may be some value in referring to such interaction cases as partial heredity dominance or partial environmental dominance, in accordance with the direction of the major effect. Furthermore, it should be apparent that complete or partial hereditary or environmental dominance may occur in connection with either or both genetic-environment limits. The point of immediate importance is that this analysis provides an interesting and plausible theoretical

* We should anticipate the fact that very few factors will behave in complete accordance with these idealized curves for the simple reason that it is not possible for either σ_H^2 or σ_E^2 to equal zero. That is, there will always be some variance due to environment in the case of heredity dominant factors and vice versa. This is the case for the simple reason that there is *always* an interaction going on between heredity and environment; that is, it is impossible for genes to function independently of environment, and it is impossible for environment to determine phenotype independently of gene effects.

foundation for empirically finding out the extent to which various factors are heredity dominant or environment dominant.

Although the extant empirical work is not adequate to the task, some of Horn's and Cattell's recent work is germane to this formulation. If we bracket their concern for a second order fluid intelligence factor (G_f) and focus instead on the first order factors which cluster under the G_f umbrella, we get the following plots:

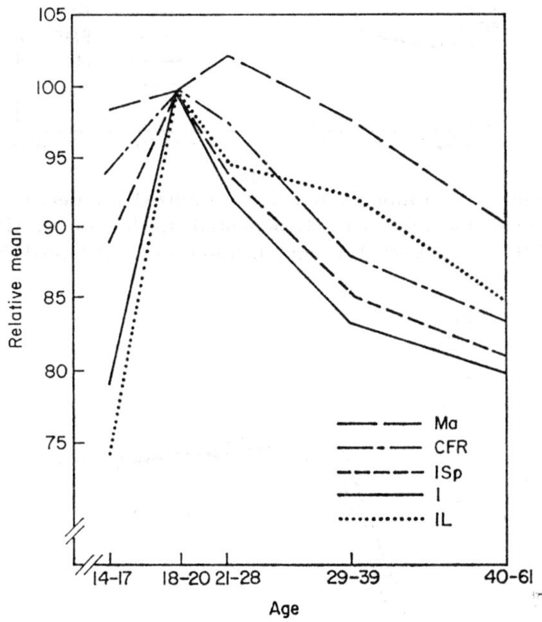

Fig. 19. Performance as function of age. Fluid abilities: Associative Memory (MA), Figural Relations (CFR), Intellectual Speed (ISp), Induction (I), and Intellectual Level (IL). (Adapted from Horn and Cattell, 1966.)

These factors can be characterized as gene dominant, and further, they are primarily biologically (in contrast to culturally) determined. The factors depicted in Fig. 20, on the other hand, have been classified as components of crystallized intelligence. The rationale is that variation along these dimensions is due primarily to differences in the culture and sub-cultures. Thus, principles of conditioning and learning are relevant here. We'll take a look at possible relationships between factors of individuality and learning in a later section.

In Fig. 21 we show several examples of the modal case, the case

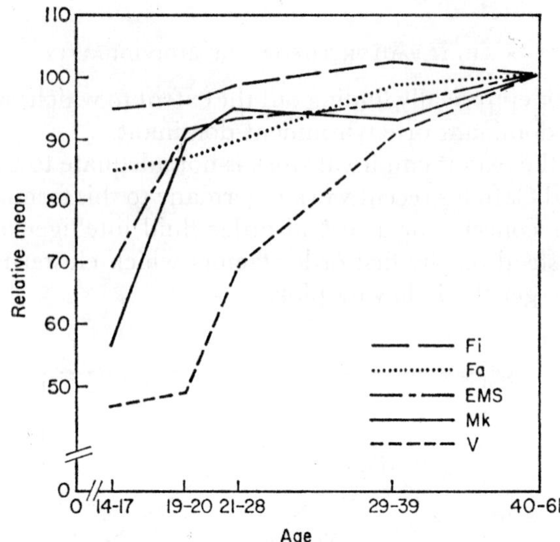

Fig. 20. Performance as a function of age. Crystallized abilities: Ideational Fluency (Fi), Associational Fluency (Fa), Experiential Evaluation (EMS), Mechanical Knowledge (Mk), and Verbal Comprehension (V). (Adapted from Horn and Cattell, 1966.)

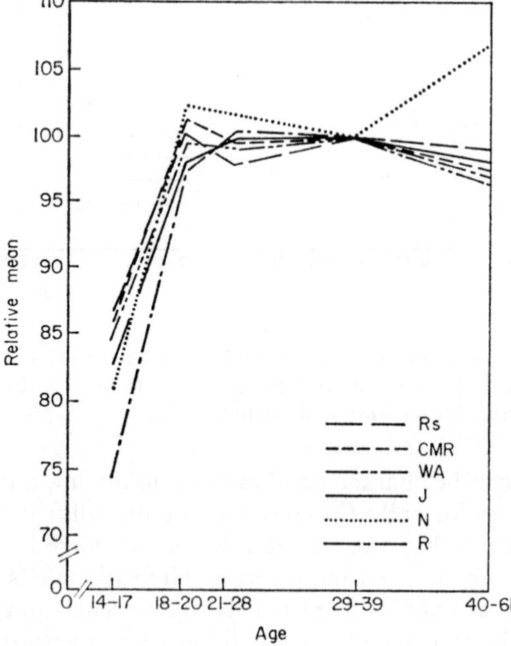

Fig. 21. Performance as a function of age. Mixed fluid-crystallized abilities: Logical Evaluation (Rs), Semantic Relations (CMR), Common Word Analogies (WA), Practical Judgment (J), Number Facility (N), and General Reasoning (R). (Adapted from Horn and Cattell, 1966.)

where both heredity and environment contribute about equally (or at least not dominantly) to the observed variability.

The Factor-Gene Model

In Fig. 22 we have depicted my guess as to the most probable

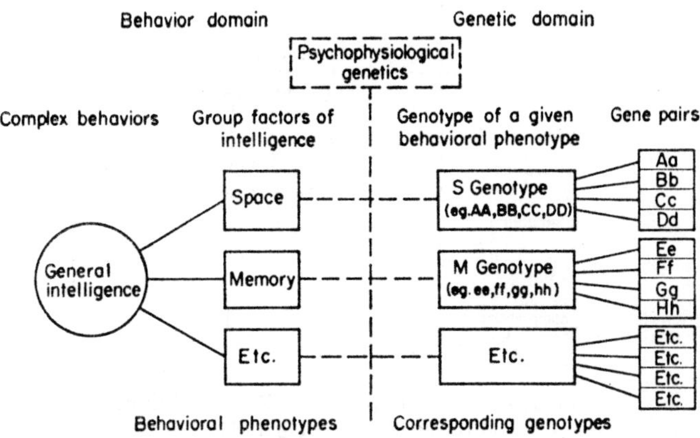

Fig. 22. Showing the most probable linkage between the multiple-factor theory of psychology and the multiple factor theory of genetics (Royce, 1958). The capital letter signifies the presence of the trait or phenotype; the small letter means the absence of the characteristic.

linkage between the multiple-factors of behavioral variation and the underlying multiplicity of genes, linked via a variety of unspecified, intervening biological mechanisms* (labeled psychophysiological genetics). Note that in both the behavioral and genetic domains many elemental factors account for a complex. On the behavioral side many different factors of behavioral phenotypes account for the complex we call general intelligence. On the genetic side, various combinations of many genes account for a particular behavior phenotype such as S or M. Thus, a person may inherit all of the capital letter forms of the gene pairs of the space factor (i.e. *AA*, *BB*, *CC*, *DD*). Since this means that the individual has the maximum number (four chosen arbitrarily) of capital letter genes for this particular genotype, and assuming optimal environmental conditions, we would expect him to perform at the highest level in tasks involving the perception of spatial relationships. If another person inherited genes e, f, g, and h from the available gene

* However, see the sections on Brain Function and Cognitive Abilities and the Neurology of Affective Traits for examples of such biological mechanisms.

pairs of the *M* factor, we would expect a minimal performance on pure memory tasks.

Such profile differences are brought out most dramatically when the element or component aspect of factor analysis is contrasted with the component obfuscating results of more traditional psychometric approaches. For example, if we average the two profiles depicted in Fig. 23, we get exactly the same value, 50, or an I.Q. of 100. If the I.Q.

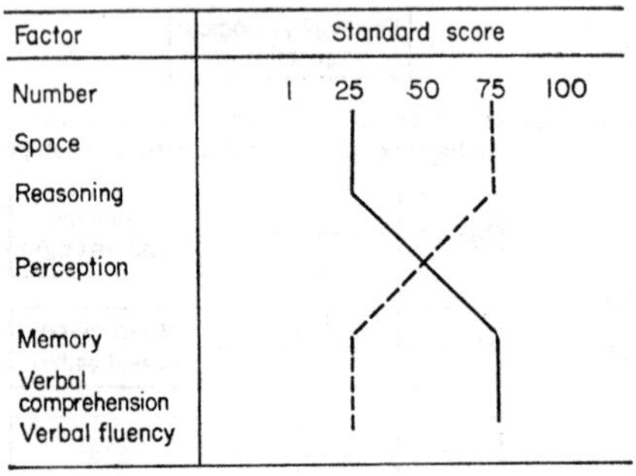

Factor	Standard score
Number	1 25 50 75 100
Space	
Reasoning	
Perception	
Memory	
Verbal comprehension	
Verbal fluency	

Fig. 23. Showing two persons, A (solid line) and B (dotted line) with the same I.Q., but with opposite mental ability profiles (Royce, 1957).

was the only information available, we would conclude that these two individuals are intellectually identical. It is obvious, however, that they are identical only in their performance on the perception factor. Otherwise person A is essentially quantitative in his intellectual strength whereas person B is essentially verbal. These high and low peaks of mental ability profiles are, of course, well established in the psychological literature.

However, only a beginning has been made in providing genetic correlate evidence for such factorially determined components. In addition to the Horn-Cattell fluid factors, evidence on human intelligence comes from four studies (Thurstone, Thurstone, and Strandskov, 1955; Blewett, 1954; and Vandenberg, 1962, 1967) involving monozygotic and dizygotic twins and the Primary Mental Abilities. These findings are briefly summarized in Table IV. The interpretation is that the first four factors, word fluency, verbal, space, and number manifest a strong hereditary determination. The implication is that the performance of single-egg twins is more alike on these four factors (which reveal significant chi square values) than is the case for two-egg or fraternal twins; hence, the importance of the genotype. The trouble is that, in spite of the impressive convergence on these four factors, the available data on human populations is very minimal, and furthermore,

Table IV. F Ratios of DZ and MZ Within-Pair Variance on 6 Subtests of the Primary Mental Abilities Test (From Vandenberg, 1967)

Name of PMA Subtest		Blewett (1954)	Thurstone, *et al.* (1955)	Vandenberg (Michigan) (1966)	Vandenberg (Louisville) (1966)
Word Fluency (3 parts)	*W*	2·78†	2·47†	2·57†	2·24†
Verbal (based on 31 parts)	*V*	3·13†	2·81†	2·65†	1·74*
Space (3 parts)	*S*	2·04*	4·19†	1·77*	3·51†
Number (3 parts)	*N*	1·07	1·52	2·58†	2·26†
Reasoning (3 parts)	*R*	2·78†	1·35	1·40	1·10
Memory (2 parts)	*M*	not used	1·62	1·26	not used
Number of DZ pairs		26	53	37	36
Number of MZ pairs		26	45	45	76

* $p<0{\cdot}05$ † $p<0{\cdot}01$

it is, in general, contradictory. The situation is even less satisfactory in the area of human temperament. Although over a dozen studies have been reported during the last decade, there is little agreement on just which temperament factors are inherited. Vandenberg has summarized the major findings in Table V below. Putting aside the serious factor invariance issues, the shortcomings of questionnaire data, and the massive inadequacies regarding experimental controls when doing behavior genetics research on humans, we can say there is a hereditary contribution in the case of three temperament factors. Vandenberg designates these as: (1) a general level of sustained activity (our first order activity level factor?), (2) open, healthy expression of emotions in interpersonal relations (our second order introversion-extroversion factor?), and (3) long-range planning and thoughtfulness as opposed to responding primarily to momentary stimuli (our first order critical thinking factor?). Furthermore, he indicates the overall evidence is most convincing in the case of the second factor, which we judge to be the same as our second order introversion-extroversion factor (e.g. see the several introversion and outward going social entries in the 0·01 and 0·05 column of Table V. Of course, some of these may relate to our first order factor of sociability). Eysenck (1957, 1967) has also argued for high heritability of this dimension. Furthermore, Eysenck puts forth similar claims for his neuroticism factor (i.e. emotional reactivity in our model), but inspection of Table V actually shows more entries in the "not significant" column than it does in the two "significant" columns.

It is my opinion that the question of factor-gene correlates is more likely to receive a convincing answer from animal research. Significant

Table V. Summary of Findings from Twin Studies of Personality Questionnaires (from Vandenberg, 1969, p. 148)

Author-year N_{DZ} / N_{MZ} questionnaire	Significance level of the increased DZ concordance ·01	·05	Not significant	$r_{MZ} < r_{DZ}$
Carter 1935 44/55 Bernreuter	Self-sufficiency Dominance Self-confidence	Neuroticism	Introversion Sociability	
Vandenberg 1962 35/45 Thurstone	Active Vigorous	Impulsive Sociable	Dominant Stable Reflective	
Cattell 1955 Vandenberg 1962 Gottesman 1963 102/137 HSPQ	Surgency Neuroticism Energetic conformity	Adventurous cyclothymia vs. schizothymia Will control	Cyclothymia Dominance Tender-tough minded Nervous tension Socialized morale	Impatient dominance
Gottesman 1963 Gottesman 1965 Reznikoff and Honeyman 1966 132/120 MMPI	Social introversion Depression Psychasthenia	Psychopathic deviate Schizophrenia	Paranoia Hysteria Hypochondriasis Hypomania Masculinity-femininity	
Wilde 1964 42/88 Amsterdam biographical quest	Psychoneurotic complaints Psychosomatic complaints	Masculinity-femininity	Introversion Test taking attitude	
Vandenberg 1967 27/40		Introversion		Thinking-feeling Judgment-perception Sensing-intuition

Stern Activity Index Factors		Closeness Sensuousness	Applied interests Orderliness Expressiveness-constraint Egoism-diffidence Educability	Motivation Submissiveness Friendliness	
Vandenberg, *et al.* 90 — 111 Comrey	1968	Achievement need Shyness	Compulsion Religious attitudes	Dependence Self-control Empathy Welfare state attitude Punitive attitude Neuroticism	Hostility Ascendance
Scarr 28 — 24 Gouch ACL Fels behaviour list	1966	Need for affiliation Friendliness Social apprehension Likeableness	Counseling readiness		
Gottesman 68 — 79 C.P.I.	1966	Dominance Sociability Self-acceptance Originality	Social presence Good impression Socialization Psychological minded	Status capacity Sense of well being Self-control Tolerance Communality Responsibility Achievement via independence Intellectual efficiency Femininity Flexibility Psychoneurotic	Achievement via conformance
Bruun 189 — 159 Special questionnaire and interview	1966	Sociability Frequency of drinking Average consumption		Need for achievement Neuroticism Aggressiveness Lack of control	Not reported

advances have been made during the past decade in non-factorial behavior genetics, particularly with the availability of highly inbred strains of mice (see Fuller and Thompson, 1960; Hirsch, 1967; Manosevitz, Lindzey and Thiessen, 1969; Lindzey and Thiessen, 1970). And a convincing factorial beginning was made some years ago by Wherry (1941) in his analysis of Tryon's bright and dull strains of rats. He found the same three factors he had previously isolated—forward going, food pointing, and goal gradient. But he reported the additional finding that dull animals make greater use of the food-pointing factor (i.e. relatively stimulus bound) and less use of the forward-going factor, whereas the bright animals clearly outclass the dull ones in the extent to which the goal gradient (or insight) factor is involved in maze learning. These striking results are brought out in Figs. 24 and 25. These findings are convincing, for they involve over 500 animals in

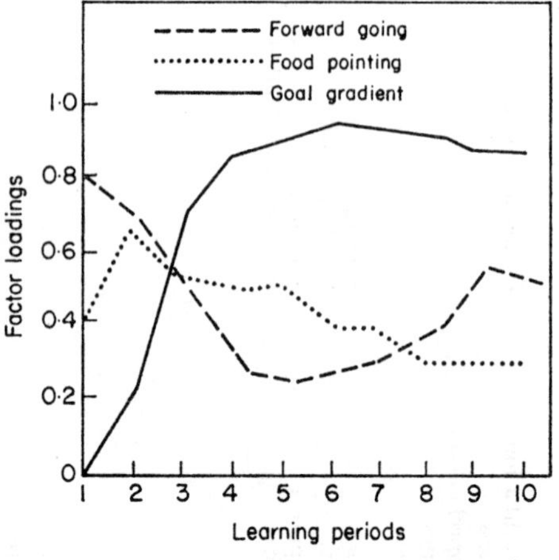

Fig. 24. Bright strain factors obtained from Tryon's maze data (Royce, 1950).

each strain, and the data were based on Tryon's 20-year selective breeding program. Furthermore, there is very strong likelihood of a tie-up with Krech's non-factorial findings to the effect that bright rats make greater use of spatial (i.e. goal gradient factor) "hypotheses", while the dull rats are more likely to involve visual (i.e. forward going factor) "hypotheses". There is mild evidence that these data can be related to recent biochemical correlate studies (e.g. Marx, 1948, 1949; Krech, *et al.*, 1954; Hughes and Zubek, 1956, 1957; King, 1960; King, Bowman and Moreland, 1961, etc.) which suggest that variations in genetically controlled biochemical processes constitute one of the

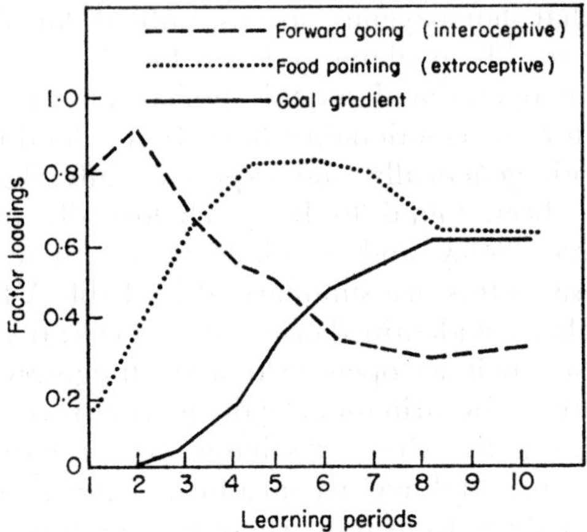

Fig. 25. Dull strain factors obtained from Tryon's maze data (Royce, 1950).

biological bases for the observed differences in factorially determined components of behavior.*

One of our research projects, involving a combination of multivariate and experimental (effects of drugs, maternal environment, litter size, stress, etc. on each factor of emotionality) strategies, at both the behavioural (factor analysis) and genetic level (diallel cross), has been conducted within the theoretical framework just reviewed. The mouse is the most appropriate species for this particular investigation because it is the mammal whose genetics is best known, and because of the

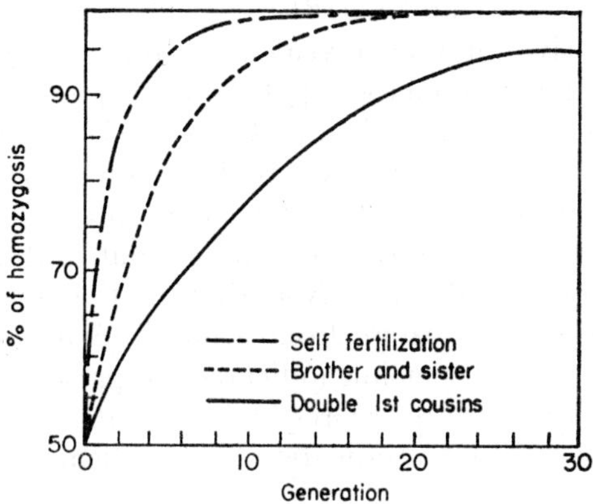

Fig. 26. The percentage of homozygosis in successive generations under three different systems of inbreeding. (From Russell, 1941.)

* This is, of course, well documented in the case of phenylketonuria, one form of mental retardation.

practical fact that homozygous strains, inbred for thirty or more generations, are readily available (refer to Fig. 26).

We have been operational on this project for approximately ten years now. Factors of emotionality have been identified, replicated, and studied, both genetically and experimentally. Eight factors, in particular, have been found to be psychologically meaningful and replicable (Royce, Poley and Yeudall, 1973a). The variables and loadings for these factors are summarized in Table VI.

Autonomic balance is identified primarily by defecation measures from a variety of tests such as open field and straightaway. Territorial marking is identified by urination loadings from several tests such as straightaway and pole. Motor discharge is a freezing factor with loadings from latency and activity measures. Tunneling 1 is identified by elimination loadings from tests where passage through a tunnel or narrow doorway is involved (pipe, cell, and hole-in-wall). Tunneling 2 loads on similar apparatus, but measures are from latency-activity and not elimination. Three experimentally dependent factors are identified as underwater swimming, audiogenic reactivity, and acrophobia.* All of these factors have reappeared in an invariance study involving separate factor analyses for pure strain, F_1, and F_2 populations (Poley and Royce, 1972).

Analyses using factor scores reveal widespread strain differences (see especially factors II and XI in Fig. 27), thereby establishing gene correlates for factors. Figure 27 also brings out the factor profile for each strain—note, for example, that the two most widely used strains, BALB (•---•) and C57BL (△———△) are highly divergent. The most pervasive finding revealed in this research is that the genetic correlate for each factor is polygenic, as postulated in the basic factor-gene model (see Fig. 22 and Royce, 1957). This conclusion is based on the degree of variability of F_1 factor scores, involving all possible pure strain crosses. Let us take Fig. 28 as a typical example. This figure shows the performance of parental and F_1 offspring on factor VIII, Autonomic Balance. Note that the F_1 entries (i.e. the small black and white circles) range from around 45 to 70 in magnitude (y axis). Such a wide dispersion indicates the presence of a polygenic system. By contrast, if the F_1 scores had concentrated at two loci, say 65 and 50, this would be an indication of a classical, Mendelian, single gene effect.

The diallel cross design also provides information concerning mode

* An activity level factor has also been partially identified. Its highest loadings are A.M. and P.M. activity, and sex. However, additional measures, such as urination from pipe and hole and pipe defecation, also load on the factor.

Table VI. Major Loadings (≥0·20) on eight factors of mouse emotionality (N=755)

	II Motor Discharge	III Acro-phobia	IV Underwater Swimming	V Tunneling 1	VI Audiogenic Reactivity	VIII Autonomic Balance	IX Terri-toriality	XI Tunneling 2
Open Field—Latency	−62							
Open Field—Activity	72							
Open Field—Penetration	53							
Open Field—Defecation						42	28	
Open Field—Urination							30	
Straightaway—Latency	−41	22						
Straightaway—Activity	43							
Straightaway—Defecation						63		
Straightaway—Urination							50	
Pole—Latency to leave top		63						
Pole—Latency to descend		45		36				
Pole—Defecation		76						
Pole—Urination							38	
Cell—Latency								39
Cell—Defecation						26		
Cell—Urination				56				
Hole-in-Wall Latency								48
Hole-in-Wall Defecation		20		31				
Hole-in-Wall—Urination				32				
Pipe—Latency to enter, Trial 1				59				20
Pipe—Latency to emerge, Trial 1								34
Pipe—Latency to emerge, Trials 2, 3 and 4		39						
Circular Activity—No bell					65			
Circular Activity—Bell					75			
Circular Activity—Defecation						26		
Underwater swimming—Latency to enter			76					
Underwater swimming—Latency to emerge			66					

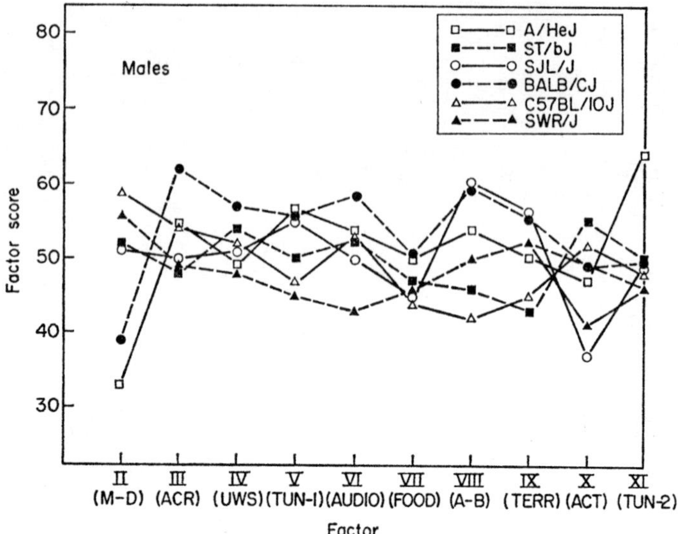

Fig. 27. Emotionality factor profile of six inbred strains of mice. (From Royce Poley and Yeudall, 1973a.)

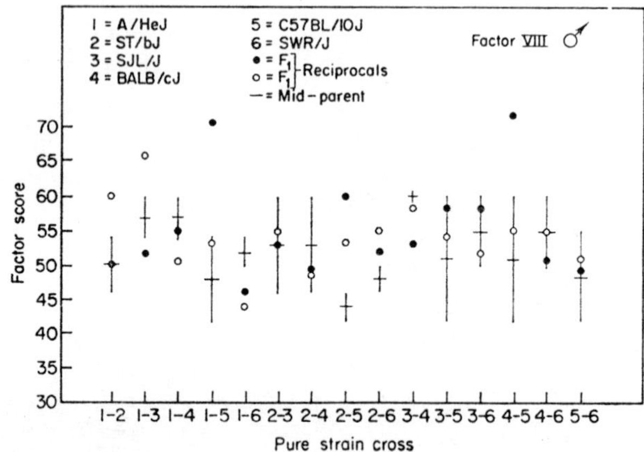

Fig. 28. Pure strain, mid-parent and F_1 factor scores for autonomic balance (pure strain scores at the ends of each line. From Royce, Poley and Yeudall, 1973a.)

of inheritance, as exemplified in Figs. 29 and 30. It is assessed by comparing the average F_1 score with the average parental score (i.e. mid-parent score). If the F_1 score is approximately equal to the mid-parent score, the inheritance is intermediate (see Fig. 29).

Five of our emotionality factors, autonomic balance, motor discharge, audiogenic reactivity, and tunneling 1 and 2, manifested an intermediate mode of inheritance. Variations of dominance effects also occur. If the F_1 score is equal to that of either parent, this is referred to

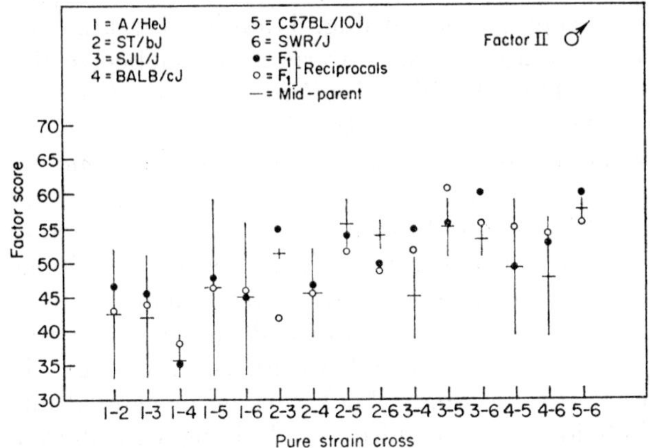

Fig. 29. Pure strain, mid-parent and F_1 factor scores for motor discharge (pure strain scores at the ends of each line. From Royce, Poley and Yeudall, 1973a).

as dominance. If the F_1 score lies between a parental score and the mid-parent score it is called partial dominance. And if the F_1 score lies outside the parental range it is referred to as overdominance. Examples of each of these are in evidence in Fig. 30.

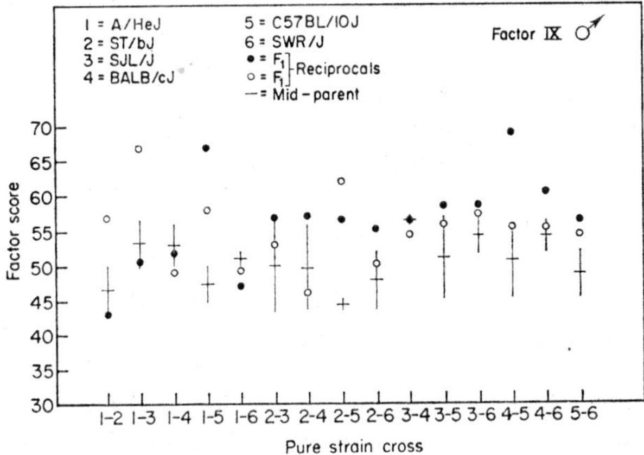

Fig. 30. Pure strain, mid-parent and F_1 factor scores for territorial marking (pure strain scores at the ends of each line. From Royce, Poley and Yeudall, 1973a).

Three of our factors, acrophobia, underwater swimming, and territorial marking are controlled by dominance effects.

Cultural-Learning Mechanisms and Factors

The key to gaining an understanding of how learning affects factors lies in how we conceive of learning. Traditional treatments of learning will not be adequate since they were not developed in the context of factor analysis. Thus, I will define *learning as any change in psychological structure due to experience (e.g. practice effects)*.

This conception of learning puts the focus on the psychological structure which underlies change in performance *per se* and it applies to all structural levels and facets, that is, mental structure, cognitive structure, affective structure (see earlier text for definitions of various structures), and all of their individual components. Thus, a change at the higher order levels of psychological and mental structure would represent shifts in style or/and world view, changes in cognitive structure relate to the usual school learning or general fund of knowledge an individual has acquired, and changes in affective structure refer to temperament and value shifts. All are manifestations of acculturation—shifts in psychological structure due to cultural learning. The implication is that different cultures and/or environments will maximize different combinations of structural components. Thus, the environmental-cultural forces of relatively "primitive" societies will reinforce those cognitive and affective components which are consistent with such activities as hunting, fishing, agriculture, and other basic survival behaviour. Similarly, so-called "developed" cultures will require that its participants learn a great deal about numbers and words, in some cases to the extent of developing "experts" in one of the knowledge specialties such as the arts or the sciences. In short, differential reinforcement is probably the learning mechanism which can best account for the acculturation process. But note one important difference between the present account and the traditional socialization account. The standard view reinforces responses; in this view it is the change in underlying psychological structure which is important. Thus, all the findings on schedules of reinforcement and the other principles of learning, such as primacy-recency, spaced versus massed trials, the effects of varying the CS-US interval and intertrial intervals, the effects of interpolated activity on acquisition and forgetting, the goal gradient principle, the effects of latent and unconscious learning, habit family hierarchy, etc. are relevant, but they must be reviewed in terms of how they affect structure rather than responses (e.g. see Buss, 1973a, b.)

Learning theorists themselves have been aware of the limitations of a purely associationistic approach, and have, in fact, recently put forward a variety of conceptualizations of a more cognitive nature.* And, while the Gestaltists have made structural units the focal point of their attention, their impact on the domain of learning has been minimal. The heretofore disparate and diffuse efforts of experts in perception and learning have recently converged, and we now have an area of study, perceptual learning, which promises to advance our understanding of the relationships between structure and learning. An important spokesman for this domain of activity, Eleanor Gibson, defines perceptual learning as "an increase in the ability to extract information from the environment as the result of experience and practice with stimulation coming from it" (Gibson, 1969, p. 3). Building on the stimulus-invariant oriented perceptual theory of J. J. Gibson, she offers a differentiation theory of perceptual development which states that there is an increase in the specificity of response to invariant stimulus inputs (i.e. a sharpening of percepts).

In the present context Eleanor Gibson's focus on structure is of special interest. However, she stresses the structure of the environment, whereas my approach puts greater importance on psychological structure. In fact, it will be recalled that I have defined learning as "any change in psychological structure due to experience" (e.g. practice). Thus, the implication is that such changes in psychological structure (learning) reflect the perceptual learning principle that there has been an increment of information (i.e. a reduction of uncertainty). More specifically, I am suggesting that changes in factor performances required for specified learning tasks be seen as manifestations of how the underlying psychological structure (primarily cognitive structure) is processing information (i.e. taking in stimulus invariants).

There has been relatively little direct commerce between the factor analytic and the experimental learning literature. The earliest steps in this direction were taken by Woodrow (1938) in the area of human learning and by Wherry (1941) when he factored Tryon's maze data. These were the first demonstrations of change in another aspect of structure (i.e. not psychological structure; see first footnote on page 313), task structure, at different stages of learning. These findings were

* See, for example, Hilgard and Bower (1966), and Miller, Galanter and Pribram (1960). It is also possible that current developments in structural learning (e.g. see Scandura, 1970) are germane. And, although there are formal similarities (e.g. hierarchical structure of rules), I am presently unable to see any *direct* implication of this approach for what is being put forward in this paper. The *indirect* implication could be that there are relationships between the multidimensional structure herein elaborated and the hierarchical rule structure described by Scandura. It is my impression that the implications of the concept of "rule governed" behavior for the advancement of theoretical psychology have not yet been adequately explored. In any event, their implications for the present position are not clear.

followed by a scattering of similar studies with both human and animal subjects, and Ferguson's (1954, 1956, 1959) sophisticated theoretical formulation in terms of transfer effects. But the most complete extension of the learning-factor approach occurs in the work of Fleishman (1967), one of Wherry's students. The essence of what is involved here can be captured by referring to Fig. 31 where we see a progressive

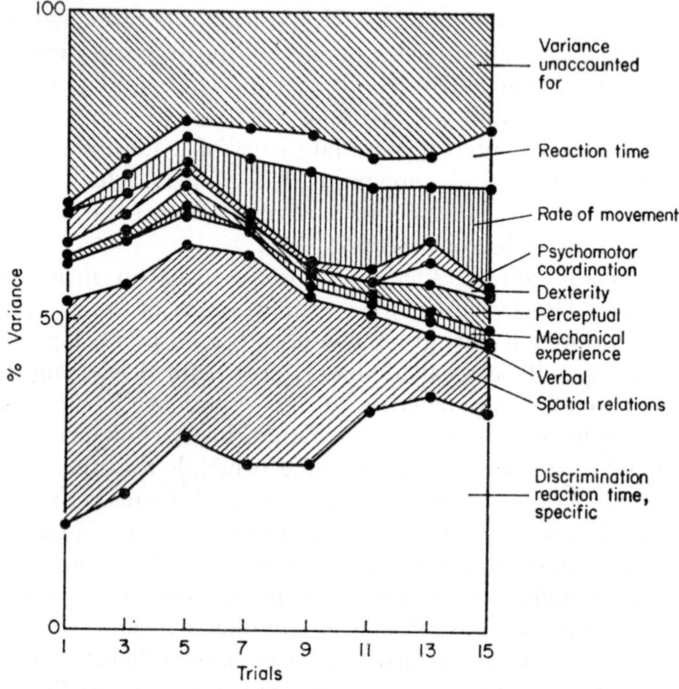

Fig. 31. Percentage of variance represented by each factor at different stages of practice on the Discrimination Reaction Time Task. (Percentage of variance is represented by the area shaded in for each factor.) (After Fleishman and Hempel, 1955.)

change in the contributions of various factors to total variance in a task involving the acquisition of a skill. Fleishman reports a systematic decrease in the contribution of non-motor factors (with increase in practice), with an attendant systematic increase in the contribution of motor factors.

Fleishman's work is illuminating as an indication of how we may observe systematic changes in task factor structure as a result of experience, but it is unfortunate that this approach has not received either adequate conceptual development nor sufficient application to other domains (e.g. affect). There have been some recent papers, however, which may mark the beginning of a movement toward further research and more adequate theory. Tucker (1966) and Cattell (1966, 1971) have proposed methods whereby one may analyze a learning curve into its component curves which may be described as a function of the same trials as the original plot (i.e. a kind of Fourier-factor analysis). Cattell's theoretical conception of learning is similar to the present one inasmuch as he views it in terms of both a change in response to a stimulus from one occasion to another, and as a change in process as well.

It should be noted that in Fleishman's methodology a task factor structure is assessed at various points in the learning situation, but that the structure to be so assessed is determined *a priori* via the standard strategy of "marker" variables. The Tucker and Cattell procedures, on the other hand, start with measurements on variables rather than factors, and use factor analysis to identify component processes which are identified *a posteriori*. A recent study by Dunham, Guilford, and Hoepfner (1968) has utilized a methodology which is similar to Fleishman's. These researchers analyzed performance on a series of concept learning tasks in terms of factors selected from cells of the Guilford structure of intellect model. The factor analyses included performance on the concept learning tasks and tests representing the posited factors, and the results allowed for an analysis of the contributions of the various factors throughout the learning trials.

A more general conceptual analysis of the relationships between various structure-of-intellect factors and Gagné's eight types of learning, presented by Merrifield, is reproduced here as Table VII. Merrifield's major point is that all the Gagné learning types can be theoretically interpreted in terms of specifiable dimensions of Guilford's cube of intellectual factors and, conversely, that all dimensions of this model contribute to at least one class of learning. The "concept category" (i.e. concept learning) has already received empirical scrutiny by Dunham, *et al.* (1968), and the problem solving category has been investigated by Merrifield, *et al.* (1962), but the remaining relationships remain to be examined. Analyses such as Merrifield's are important because they present much needed conceptual linkages between cognition and the several kinds of learning (e.g. see Butcher, 1968). This viewpoint emphasizes both the individual differences among individual learners and "factor-learning category" interactions, thereby elaborating on the multivariate nature of the learning process.

While there are important differences represented among the above methodologies, they reflect important convergences which are relevant

Table VII. Hypothesized relations among types of learning and parameters of ability (from Merrifield, 1966)

Structure-of-Intellect Parameters	Gagné's Types of Learning Signal (1)	S–R (2)	Chain (3)	Verbal Association (4)	Multiple Discrimination (5)	Concept (6)	Principle (7)	Problem Solving (8)
Operations								
Cognitive (C)			X			X	X	X
Memorative (M)	X			X	X			
Productive								
Divergent (D)				X				X
Convergent (N)		X	X	X		X		X
Evaluative (E)	X	X		X	X	X		X
Contents								
Figural (F)	X	X	X	X	X			X
Symbolic (S)			X	X	X		X	X
Semantic (M)		X	X	X	X	X	X	X
Behavioral (B)					X			
Products								
System (S)			X		X	X	X	X
Class (C)					X	X		
Unit (U)	X			X			X	X
Relation (R)		X		X	X	X	X	
Transformation (T)				X				X
Implication (I)	X	X					X	X
Selected Abilities								
Potential covariants in learning studies	MFI EFI MFU EFU	NFR NFI NMR NMI EFR EFI EMR EMI	CFS CSS CMS NFS NSS NMS	MMR MSR DMR DMT NFU EFR EMR	MSR EFC EFR EMR EMR EMS EBC	CMC CMR CMS NMC NMR NMS EMS	CSI CMS CMU CMI CMR	CMT DMT NMT CMI EMI NMI DFT

to the present conception of learning. All of them are attempting to take the traditional performance curve and to analyze changes in contributions of various components to performance over time. And all of them can be conceptualized as attempts to map out changes in psychological structure as a result of experience.

Neural Mechanisms of Individuality

In the usual S-O-R paradigm a theory of individual differences focuses its concern on the *O* variables which intervene between *S* inputs and *R* outputs. Thus, traits, factors, or dimensions are seen as constructs within *O* which determine response outputs under the condition of standardized *S* inputs. Since *O* variables are essentially characteristics of the organism, it is reasonable to assume that a *complete* understanding of such constructs must *eventually* involve getting at underlying biological mechanisms. However, it is unfortunately true that the relatively undeveloped theoretical structure of differential psychology is matched by ignorance of its underlying biology. In spite of this state of affairs, some facts and concepts have accumulated, and a beginning has been made in attempts to understand the biological foundations of individuality. However, there is very little that has been established securely, particularly as direct correlates of factorially identified constructs.

Thus, this introduction is partially by way of a disclaimer, for although we will attempt to synthesize what is available, it must be noted that the evidence, in general, is meager, and the theoretical notions are speculative. However, we feel that a theory of individuality would simply be incomplete unless it includes a statement on biological correlates. Although there is relevant evidence of a biochemical, pharmacological, hormonal, and metabolic nature, we will confine ourselves to neural correlates.

Brain Function and Cognitive Abilities

We will now consider the neural basis for factors of cognition. Let us initiate the inquiry from the perspective of the basic factor analytic model in the hope it will provide leverage on the problem of neural correlates. The factor analytic approach focuses on identifying behavioral functional unities. If we carry this notion over into brain function, it implies the existence of neural functional unities—this means the organization of subsets of neural cells as the counterparts of psychological functions. This view receives support from no less a figure than Lashley who, some three decades ago, suggested that factors

> "do seem, however, to *correspond to functions which may be independently lost as a result of localized brain injury*. Certain types of apraxia are marked by difficulty in dealing with spatial relations; the function represented by manipulation of isolated symbols resembles the ability which suffers in verbal aphasia as defined by Henry Head, and there are other less clear correspondences.
>
> "Psychology has still to discover how the various factors revealed by such analysis interplay to produce organized thought. Neurology likewise still has much to do in the investigations of the *interaction of cortical fields which are associated with diverse functions*. Nevertheless the discovery that the various capacities which independently contribute to intellectual performance do correspond to the spatial distribution of cerebral mechanisms represents a step toward the recognition of similar organization in neurological and mental events." (Lashley, 1941, pp. 468–469; italics mine.)

A decade or so later, Hebb (1949), a student of Lashley's, came up with the concept of cell assembly as the neural functional units for psychological processes.

> "This assembly is a closed system in which activity can 'reverberate' and thus continue after the sensory event which started it has ceased. Also, one assembly

will form connections with others, and it may therefore be made active by one of them in the total absence of the adequate stimulus."

And, he defines phase sequence as "a temporally integrated series of assembly activities" (Hebb, 1959, pp. 628–629).

The recent research by Hubel (1959, 1960, 1963) and Hubel and Wiesel (1959, 1961, 1962) takes the concept of neural functional unities one step further by showing that different kinds of neural units respond selectively to stimuli. That is, they function as "feature analyzers"—some neural units responding to a particular feature of stimulus input, and other units responding to a different input feature. As in the case with other differentiated units of the organism, it is believed that these neural "feature analyzers" are "wired in", or genetically determined.*

If we now put these conceptually relevant strands in the context of the massive clinical and experimental research on brain damage, it seems reasonable to suggest that when a particular neural correlate of a psychological process occurs entirely within a known anatomical unit we speak of localization of function. To the extent a particular neural correlate of a psychological process occurs across known anatomical units we regard such functioning as relatively non-localized. And while it is true that investigation of the neural basis of factors has barely gotten off the ground, we do have some empirical evidence on the brain correlates of factors. The most convincing evidence on localization of cognitive factors comes from Halstead (1947). And the most convincing of his four factors are the *C* factor (a memory factor) and the abstraction factor (*A*). The evidence is that the memory factor (Halstead's *C*) is more dependent on the functioning of the left hemisphere than the right hemisphere, and that his abstraction factor (A) is primarily localized in the frontal lobes. However, a recent study of my own (Royce and Yeudall, 1973), involving a large battery of "brain damage" tests, points to two relatively localized factors and four "across anatomical area" factors. The relatively localized factors are labeled auditory-verbal comprehension and spatial orientation. The former seems to be localized in the temporal region of the left hemisphere and the latter in the parietal region of the right hemisphere. The other four factors seem to have a broader representation in the brain. For example, perceptual

* The writer recognizes the incompleteness of the present coverage of relevant neuropsychological conceptualizing. And, while it is beyond the purposes of the present paper to review the present status of theory in physiological psychology, it is important that relevant concepts from brain research are brought into the context of this paper. Thus, in the expanded version of this paper we plan to include additional conceptualizations. It will include, for example, Pribram's work on the neural hologram, Konorski's concept of gnostic units and Luria's functional approach to brain processes.

organization and perceptual-motor speed correlate with damage in the right hemisphere (i.e. frontal, temporal, and parietal areas). Finally, our evidence is that abstraction splits into two factors, Halstead Abstraction I and II, and further, that the former is correlated with damage to the frontal, temporal, and parietal areas of the right hemisphere as well as the occipital area of the left hemisphere, whereas the latter correlated with the frontal and parietal areas of the right hemisphere. Although the focus of their research was not on factors *per se*, Teuber and Weinstein (1954), Chapman and Wolff (1959), and others confirm the interpretation that ability to abstract is not confined to the frontal lobes. Thus, the factor-brain correlate findings are consistent with the general body of neuropsychological knowledge. An obvious example is the localization of the spatial orientation factor in the parietal region of the right hemisphere. It should also be noted that auditory-verbal comprehension and spatial orientation are essentially sensory-motor in nature, and, as such, it makes good neurological sense for such factors to be highly localized. Three of the other four factors, perceptual organization, Halstead Abstraction I, and Halstead Abstraction II, are clearly more cognitive in nature, and it is consistent with extant knowledge of brain function for such factors to be relatively non-localized.*

In addition to the first order correlates already described, it is reasonable to anticipate finding neural-factor correlates at all levels of organization. For example, it can be argued that a second order visual factor should be at least partially defined by virtue of neuroanatomy. That is, the neural functional unities which underlie first order visual factors are probably localized within the anatomical limits of the visual system—i.e. the occipital lobes of the brain and the peripheral portion of the optical system. The implication is that any observable intercorrelations between such factors would reflect, in part, interactions between subsets of visual cells. It would seem reasonable, therefore, to anticipate finding at least one comparable higher order factor for each of the sensory modalities.

At a more complex level of organization, such as the perceptual and intellectual domains, which cut across sense modalities, we can anticipate a similar cross-anatomical involvement of neural units. Thus, such cognitive factors, especially those at the higher order, should involve various subsets of neural cells which are not localizable within a highly

* Since this brief summary of our brain damage project precedes the final analysis of the data, a word of caution is in order. All factor interpretations are tentative and subject to modification. Furthermore, magnitudes of correlations have not been reported because we are not yet certain of their total range. However, those available to date average around 0·30.

circumscribed anatomical unit. Potential examples of this are any of our higher order cognitive factors (see Fig. 4), the Horn-Cattell fluid intelligence factor (G_f), and "general intelligence". While the evidence is not strong in any one study, the cumulative effect of recent reports by Ertl (1968a, b, c), and Shucard and Horn (1971) suggests that latency of evoked potentials has a low, positive correlation with G_f. There is also evidence that quantity of acetylcholine (implies neural conductivity) present in rat brains correlates with rat "brightness" (Krech, Rosenzweig and Bennett, 1962). And there are low, negative correlations between cognitive dimensions and adult age. (Implies an increment in brain damage regardless of locus. See Birren, 1952; Aftanas and Royce, 1969; Horn, 1970.)

*The Neurology of Affective Traits**

The concept of neural functional unities as a biological counterpart for behavioral functional unities (or factors) is, of course, just as relevant to our understanding of affect as it is to cognition. However, the sites of the most relevant affective neural functional unities are primarily at the sub-cortical levels. There has been awareness of the importance of subcortical centers for emotional expression for a long time, particularly in the work of Cannon (1927) and Hess (1936, 1954; Hess and Akert, 1955). However, recent work on the physiology of arousal (e.g. Moruzzi and Magoun, 1949; Nauta, 1958) has stimulated psychologists to explore its implications for behavior (e.g. Lindsley, *et al.* 1950; Olds, 1958). And more directly relevant to the concerns of this paper, there have been parallel attempts to provide linkages between the physiology of the nervous system and affective traits or factors. Such attempts are summarized in a book by Duffy (1962) and a recent review chapter by Royce (1966). However, the most extensive and important conceptualizing along these lines has been put forward by Eysenck (1967),

* The material summarized in this section should be regarded as a point of departure for what will eventually be elaborated into a theory of emotionality. There are important omissions at both the psychological and physiological levels. For example, the section on evaluative factors has not yet been summarized. And the full complexity of the relevant biology has not been presented. This includes complete omission of endocrine functioning and temporary omission of various parts of the nervous system with known involvement in emotion (e.g. the frontal lobes). Furthermore, we are aware of the fact that we have not presented an adequate picture of Eysenck's views and, perhaps more importantly, we have not taken account of subsequent modifications or/and elaborations of those views (e.g. Claridge, 1967, and Gray, 1965, 1971). The author decided to present this section in spite of such inadequacies for heuristic purposes—i.e. in order to point to the kind of theoretical structure we're trying to produce on the one hand, and to elicit constructive, critical feedback on the other hand.

although these efforts have been limited to the two higher order factors of introversion-extroversion and neuroticism (i.e. anxiety in Fig. 6).

Before taking a closer look at the relevance of Eysenck's work for our affective model, it is necessary that we briefly describe the most relevant neurological mechanisms, namely, the reticular activitating system and the limbic system. An overview of the central nervous structures relevant to emotionality, with focus on the reticular formation, is shown in Fig. 32. The implication is that neural inputs (e.g. sensory and

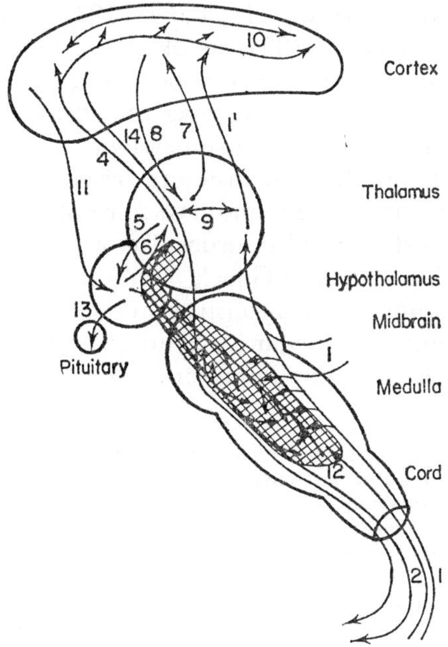

Fig. 32. The reticular formation and emotionality structures. (From Lindsley, 1951.)

visceral), "organized" (i.e. processed, modulated) via the reticular formation, are fed into the thalamus and hypothalamus, and subsequently distributed via the complexities of cortico-thalamic and hypothalamic-pituitary interconnections. In particular, such "modulation" alters the general level of electrical activity of the cortex (e.g. the EEG). Low arousal levels are characterized by slow, high-amplitude (alpha) activity, as in the case of sleep. Arousal states (e.g. waking, thinking, emotion) are characterized by fast, low-amplitude wave patterns (desynchrony).

Let us now focus our attention on that (upper) portion of Fig. 32 where the reticular formation (crosshatched area) makes contact with the thalamus and hypothalamus. This area contains the limbic system, an interconnected group of structures located in both cortical and sub-cortical regions of the brain. The following anatomical areas are included: olfactory tubercle, uncus, diagonal band of Broca, hippocampal formation, subcallosal gyrus, cingulate and retrosplenial area, orbito-frontal cortex, frontotemporal cortex, septal area, hypothalamus, anterior nucleus of the thalamus, amygdala, and midbrain tegmentum (see Fig. 33 for a simplified diagram).

These limbic structures have been implicated by various investigators (Broca, 1878; Herrick, 1933; Papez, 1937; Bard, 1939; Klüver and Bucy, 1939; MacLean, 1954) as playing a dominant role in the integration and expression of affective behavior, but no single, unified theory has been arrived at which gives an adequate account of the various interrelated mechanisms of this system.* †

Let us now examine affective structure (refer to Fig. 7) within the present neurological framework, and note some of the implications that follow. Consider first the third order factor of cortical excitation-inhibition. Eysenck (1967) and Gooch (1963) have postulated that the biological underpinnings of this construct reside in the reticular formation. Both excitatory (Reticular Activating System) and inhibitory (Reticular Inhibitory System) impulses are thought to originate from

* Since there are obvious anatomical relationships (e.g. the limbic system is an implicit part of Fig. 32) between the reticular activating system and the limbic system, it is probable there are functional relationships as well. In fact, Routtenberg (1968, 1971) has recently explored this possibility. However, since he was not focused on affect, we will leave the relevance of Routtenberg's conceptualizing for a future revision or/and extension of our model. Such an extension begins by postulating two arousal systems: (1) cortical arousal, mediated via the reticular activating system, and (2) autonomic arousal, mediated via the limbic system. One would then have to explore the implications, if any, of Routtenberg's theory for a multi-factor theory of emotionality.

† There are several ambiguities regarding the limbic system which need not concern us at this time, but which should be mentioned in passing. These include at least the following three problems: (1) which structures should be included as part of the system, (2) which portions of certain structures are cortical and which are sub-cortical, (3) exactly what roie does a given structure play in affective behavior. Brief comments on each of these points follow. In regard to (1), we have compromised by including structures claimed by various investigators (e.g. Pribram and Kruger, 1954; Nauta, 1958; McCleary and Moore, 1965; and Grossman, 1967), but presenting a highly simplified diagram (Fig. 33) for immediate purposes of exposition and communication. On point (2) we shall merely indicate that most of the limbic system is sub-cortical, but that portions of it are cortical (e.g. the cingulate gyrus and the hippocampus), and some areas contain both cortical and sub-cortical components (e.g. the amygdala and septal areas). Point (3) is the most crucial one, the one we must eventually answer. Gray (1971), for example, suggests a three emotion system, and implicates the hypothalamus for "approach" behavior, the septal and hippocampal areas for "stop" or inhibitory phenomena, and the amygdala for the fight/flight system. We look forward to more detailed study of Gray's conceptualizing in the hope it may clarify the physiological substrate of affective traits.

the reticular formation and travel upwards to the cerebral cortex. Individual differences in cortical excitation-inhibition balance have

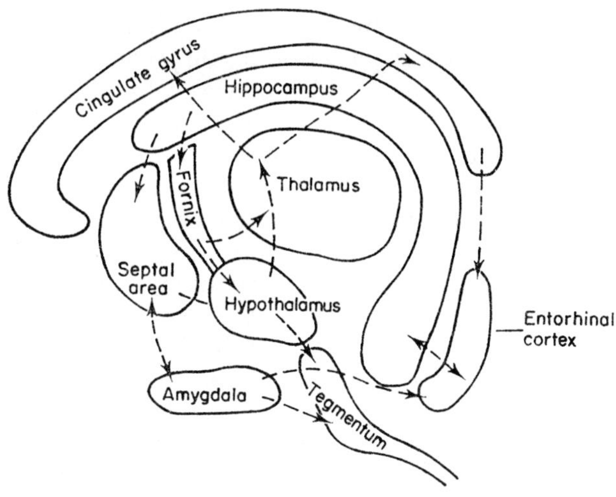

Fig. 33. A simplified, schematic diagram of the limbic system (modified version of McCleary and Moore, 1965).

direct consequences for the second order factors of motor reactivity, introversion-extroversion, and superego. Considering motor reactivity, Eysenck would predict that individuals who are characterized by high excitation will show less motor performance decrement since less inhibition will build up. This prediction has been confirmed by Ray (1959), Spielman (1963), and Eysenck (1964). Individual differences in introversion-extroversion are thought to be directly related to differences in cortical excitation-inhibition balance. It is hypothesized that introverts have an excess of cortical excitation, whereas extroverts are dominated by cortical inhibition. Thus, under identical stimulating conditions, introverts would be operating in a relatively higher state of cortical arousal than extroverts. This excitatory imbalance in introverts produces a constraint on their overt behavior, since they are in a high arousal state, and thus do not seek out additional external stimulation. Keeping this in mind, and moving to the first order factors defining introversion-extroversion, we would expect those individuals who are high on excitation (introverts) to have low scores on affectothymia, rhathymia, impulsivity, and sociability, and those individuals who are high on inhibition (extroverts) to show the opposite pattern. Individual differences on the cortical excitation-inhibition balance factor should also have a direct bearing on our second order superego factor. The reasoning is that those individuals who are characterized by high cortical excitation are predicted to condition better than those individuals who are dominated by cortical inhibition (Eysenck, 1962; Franks, 1956, 1957). A consequence of this differential conditionability is that those individuals who are high on cortical inhibition will fail to take on the conditioned responses that underlie socialization, and hence, will evidence low superego scores.

The other third order factor in Fig. 7 is emotional reactivity. If we conceptually equate this higher order factor with Eysenck's higher order emotionality factor (i.e. neuroticism), we can postulate that the limbic system is the major biological mechanism underlying this factor. This implies that individual differences in emotional reactivity are contingent upon differential thresholds of the limbic system. The second order factors of anxiety and motor reactivity are seen as providing two modes of emotional expression. First, the anxious mode. The theory is that individuals who are high on anxiety have an excess lability of their sympathetic nervous system as a possible consequence of a low threshold of arousal in portions of the limbic system. The behavioral significance of such differences is to predispose the individual to respond autonomically with greater intensity, slower recovery rate, and more quickly to intense, painful, or sudden stimuli impinging upon the sensory receptors. Translated into autonomic indicants, high level performance on the anxiety factor provides a picture of sympathetic dominance (note the first order factor of autonomic balance in Fig. 7); namely, high scores on such measures as galvanic skin response (GSR), peripheral vasoconstriction (plethysmogram), blood pressure, and heart rate, and low scores on finger temperature and salivary output. Although the details differ, several investigators provide empirical confirmation for this theoretical claim (e.g. Wenger, 1941, 1942, 1943, 1949; Cattell, *et al.*, 1947, 1950, 1957; Royce, 1955, 1966). Additional implications of first order manifestations of the anxiety factor suggest that sympathetic dominance is correlated with irritability or hypersensitivity (excitability-calmness factor), and that parasympathetic dominance is correlated with moodiness or cyclic emotional expression (cycloid disposition factor) and uncooperativeness (trust versus suspiciousness factor). This profile is claimed to be characteristic of persons classified as neurotics.

Psychiatric and physiological speculations can also be offered for the second order factor of motor reactivity.* This factor subsumes such

* Figure 7 shows motor reactivity as influenced by both third order factors; hence, the relevance of both the reticular activating system and the limbic system.

first order factors as motor discharge, acrophobia, activity level, and audiogenic reactivity. It seems reasonable to hypothesize that profiles with high values on such dimensions as motor discharge and activity level would be characteristic of manics, and that the inverse profile would characterize depressives. Furthermore, we could look to such systems as the reticular activating system, the limbic system, and variations of hormone output as the biological basis of activity factors. (Regarding the latter, the empirical evidence linking thyroxin output with activity level is quite convincing. See, for example, Overall and Williams, 1961.)

Summary and Conclusions

Briefly recapitulating, what I have tried to do is provide a first approximation of a general theory of individual differences. The proposed theory takes its point of departure from the conceptually neutral skeletal framework of factor analysis as the best way to answer the question of taxonomic structure. A review of the relevant literature suggests that a hierarchical taxonomy best accommodates the extant literature in the sub-domains of cognition, affect, and style (i.e. cognitive-affective linkages).

In the second half of the paper I deal with process—that is, how factors behave over the life span, hereditary and environmental sources of factor variation, and the neural mechanisms of cognitive and affective dimensions. Considerable synthesis is achieved by posing the problem in terms of a typical growth curve with four parameters: K_1, the y intercept, indicating the extent of prenatal development; K_2, indicating a theoretical upper limit of performance at maturity, K_3, indicating the onset of factor decline; and K_4, indicating pre-death performance level. The heredity-environment issue is dealt with in terms of the concepts of heredity dominant and environment dominant developmental factors. These concepts are operationalized in terms of observable departures from genetic base line developmental curves. That is, those performances with relatively large variations from the genotypic curve as a result of attempts to induce environmental effects are regarded as environment dominant factors, while those performances which manifest relatively small variations from the genotypic curves are defined as heredity dominant factors. The theory maintains that both hereditary and environmental sources of variation affect all dimensions of individuality, and that the modal case is neither heredity nor environment dominant.

All change, whether it is due to gene correlates, biological maturation, or cultural-learning effects, is viewed in terms of changes in psychological structure; more specifically, changes in cognitive structure, affective structure, and style structure. These changes occur at all hierarchical levels, and involve shifts in a given factor as well as shifts in overall factor organization.

The question of neural correlates of individuality dimensions will remain speculative until there is more certainty regarding taxonomic structure and factor invariance on the one hand, and until there is more knowledge of brain function on the other hand. In spite of these limitations, some headway has been made in identifying neural correlates of individuality factors. The basic conception is that there is a functional isomorphism (i.e. not literal or point for point) between the functional unities (i.e. factors) of behavior and neural functional unities (i.e. subsets of neural cells). These neural correlates may be relatively circumscribed (i.e. highly localized in a given anatomical locus), or they may involve cross anatomical areas (e.g. hemispheric localizations, or cross lobes and cross hemispheric). It is hypothesized that the neural correlates of higher-order cognitive factors are likely to involve subsets of neural cells which cut across anatomical units. More specific hypotheses are put forward in the case of neural correlates of affective factors—namely, that the limbic structures mediate the third order factor of emotional reactivity (and therefore, the second order factors of anxiety and motor reactivity, and their first order factors), and that the reticular activating system mediates the third order factor of cortical excitation-inhibition (and, therefore, the second order factors of introversion-extroversion, motor reactivity, and superego, and their first order factors). At present the rationale for neural correlates of individuality factors is clearer and more convincing in the emotionality domain than it is in the cognitive domain. It has also been subjected to more stringent experimental checks than is the case for cognitive factors.

In addition to the need for extending present efforts to include important omissions, and the need to continuously revise our efforts to date (e.g. style structure, the ontogeny of factors, etc.), the most obvious, and possibly the most important, work which remains to be done is to elaborate on principles and mechanisms of personality integration. It is anticipated that the conceptual-synthesizing value of both higher-order and stylistic (e.g. epistemological, cognitive, and affective) factors will become more apparent at that time. It is also anticipated that extra-factorial concepts derived from areas such as perception (i.e. Gestalt-like principles of organization) and learning (i.e. to account for changes in psychological structure) will be relevant.

Appendix A. Brief Definitions of Cognitive Factors

First Order Intelligence Factors

S: Spatial Relations (CFS). Ability to put together by visual imagination parts that are out of a customary place in a visual pattern and to identify such "out of place" percepts.

P: Perceptual Speed (EFU). Speed in identifying specified, small elements of a visual pattern.

I: Induction (CSS and CSC). Ability in forming and testing hypotheses directed at finding a principle of relationship among elements and applying the principle to identify an element fitting the relationship.

N: Number (MSI and NSI). Speed and accuracy in doing the basic operations of arithmetic.

V: Verbal Comprehension (CMU). Facility in understanding of English words, sentences, and paragraphs.

Fw: Word Fluency (DSU). Facility in producing words in accordance with structural restrictions but without regard to meaning.

Ma: Associative Memory (MSI). Upon presentation of one part of previously associated but otherwise unrelated material, ability to recall another part.

Cs: Speed of Closure (CFU). Ability to "take in" a perceptual field as a whole, to "fill in" unseen portions with likely material and thus to coalesce somewhat disparate parts of a visual percept.

Cf: Flexibility of Closure (NFT). Ability to "hold in mind" a particular visual percept (configuration) and find it embedded in distracting material.

Vi: Visualization (CFT). Ability to manipulate visual percepts (to imagine change in forms) and thus to "see" how things would look under altered conditions.

Fi: Ideational Fluency (DMU). Ability to quickly produce ideas and exemplars of an idea about a stated condition or object.

Fe: Expressional Fluency (DMS). Facility in finding an appropriate word or set of words to make a proper English expression.

Fa: Associational Fluency (DMR). Facility in producing (English) words having somewhat similar meanings.

R: General Reasoning (CMS). Ability in organizing the relevant aspects of problems having an algebraic quality and reasoning through to find solutions for the problems.

Xa: Figural Adaptive Flexibility (DFT). Ability to try out in imagination various possible arrangements of the elements of a visual pattern and thus to converge on one arrangement which satisfies several stated criteria.

D: Deduction (EMR+EMI). Reasoning from the general to the specific; the ability to test the correctness of a meaningful conclusion by applying general principles to the individual case.

Ss: Spatial Scanning (EFI). Ability to quickly survey a complex field to find a particular configuration representing a pathway through the field.

Re: Semantic Redefinition (NMT). Ability to imagine different functions for objects or parts of objects and thus to use them in novel ways to accomplish stated purposes.

Rs: Syllogistic Reasoning (NMT). Ability in formal reasoning from stated premises to rule out nonpermissible combinations and thus to arrive at necessary conclusions.

Sep: Sensitivity to Problems (CMI). Ability to imagine problems associated with function or change of function of objects and to suggest ways to deal with these problems.

Xs: Spontaneous Flexibility (DMC). Facility in imagining diverse functions and classifications for objects.

O: Originality (DMT). Facility in conceptualizing phenomena in ways that in our culture are judged to be unusual and clever.

Ms: Memory Span (MSS). Capacity in number of distinct elements that can be maintained within the span of immediate awareness.

First Order Psychomotor Factors

Speed of Arm Movements—Rate of arm movement after it has been initiated.

Wrist Finger Speed—Speed of simple movements of the wrist and/or fingers particularly repetitive movements which involve little, if any, eye–hand coordination.

Reaction Time—Speed of simple reaction to auditory or visual stimuli.

Aiming—Ability to execute quick and precise hand–finger movements with emphasis on good eye–hand coordination.

Articulation Speed—Rate of reading and speed of repeatedly articulating the same consonant.

Ambidexterity—Ability to use the non-preferred hand.

Psychomotor Coordination—Ability to achieve degree of adjustment of limb (finger, hand or foot) motions in response to visual stimuli.

Manual Dexterity—Speed and coordination of arm–hand movements in skillful manipulation of objects.

Finger Dexterity—Speed and accuracy in manipulating small objects with the fingers.

Steadiness—Ability to perform very precise arm–hand movements with little to no emphasis on speed.

Tempo of Large Movements—Natural speed with which motor activities of limbs and trunk are carried out.

Tempo of Fast Movements—Natural speed with which quick motor activities are carried out.

Tempo of Hand Movements—Natural speed with which hand movements are carried out.

Second Order Intelligence Factors

Memory—Ability to recall previously associated related or unrelated material that is meaningful or nonmeaningful, verbal or nonverbal.

Intellectual Speed—The speed with which each correct item is solved, length of time devoted to each abandoned item (persistence or continuance) and the number of wrong items and time spent on each.

Reasoning—Ability to organize a divergent or convergent problem that presents itself in a symbolic or nonsymbolic form.

Fluency—Facility in retrieving language elements, i.e. words or ideas, from long-term storage to immediate awareness.

Verbal—A facileness in acquiring and utilizing meaning.

Visualization—Ability to imagine the way objects change as they move in space, maintain spatial orientation, perceive the Gestalt in a field of elements, maintain flexibility in perception concerning structuring and re-structuring elements in space.

Second Order Psychomotor Factors

Motor Speed—Rate of initial bodily movement or movement after it has been initiated.
Motor Precision—Ability to hold the body in static positions or a prescribed sequence of movements as defined by a task.
Motor Tempo—The natural speed with which motor activities are carried out.

Third Order Cognitive Integrative Factors

General Verbal—Ability to acquire and utilize language elements, i.e. words, symbols, ideas, meanings, etc.
General Nonverbal—Ability to interact and structure nonverbal elements of the environment within the context of a defined problem or goal.
General Speed—Ability to respond quickly and efficiently to the demands of a task.
General Psychomotor Coordination—Ability to coordinate movement of parts of the body to overt or covert visual stimuli.
General Sensory Integration—Ability to integrate impinging stimuli across sensory modalities.

Fourth Order Cognitive Integrative Factor

"*g*"—A broad, diffuse, integrative capacity to sense, cognize, and manipulate stimuli. Not the same as Spearman's "g" since that factor is postulated as one which is common to *all* measures of intelligence.

Appendix B. Brief Definitions of Affective Factors

First Order Affective Factors

Acrophobia—Emotional reactivity where the stressful stimulus involves height.
Activity Level—Locomotion in a variety of situations where the external stimulus is not particularly stressful and internal stimuli are major contributors (e.g. hormone influence).
Affectothymia—Warmhearted, outgoing, easygoing, participating.
Audiogenic Reactivity—Emotional reactivity where the stressful stimulus is of an auditory nature.
Autonomic Balance—A response pattern under stressful stimulation where a major role is attributed to gland and smooth muscle functioning. A typical manifestation in rodents is "emotional elimination."
Conscientiousness—Persistent, moralistic, responsible, dominated by a sense of duty.
Considerateness—Quiet, non-aggressive, socially retiring, considerate of the feelings of others.
Critical Thinking—Reflective, meditating.
Cycloid Disposition—Moody, moods or energy level shift suddenly and without apparent reason.
Dominance—Assertive, outspoken, socially aggressive.
Excitability—Easily given to emotionality or worry, as opposed to calm, emotionally mature.

General Arousal—Tempo with which individual engages in an activity, stamina.
Impulsivity—Tendency toward acting without stopping to think about the consequences; acting on the spur of the moment.
Masculinity–Femininity—Unsentimental, self-reliant, tough-minded, practical; as opposed to sensitive, dependent, tender-minded.
Motor Discharge—A more specialized variety of emotional reactivity, describing response patterns under stress involving primarily skeletal muscles. This pattern in rodents is typically referred to as "freezing".
Rhathymia—Carefreeness, happy-go-lucky disposition.
Sociability—Enjoyment of social contacts, a preference for much social activity.
Trust–Suspiciousness—Accepting of behaviour of others and of events, unsuspecting of hostility; as opposed to jealous, suspicious of interference.

Second Order Affective Factors

Anxiety—Feelings of discomfort, emotionality, and troubledness, often accompanied by feelings of inferiority; mood swings, lack of concentration, etc.
Introversion–Extraversion—Retiring from social contacts, preference toward relative solitude; as opposed to seeking out contacts with people, enjoying being the "life of the party", leading an active life.
Motor Reactivity—Any response or set of responses involving the skeletal muscle system; of a more voluntary nature than elicited responses involving glands and smooth muscles.
Superego—Conscientiousness as a second order factor.

Third Order Affective Factors

Emotional Reactivity—Any response or set of responses to a stressful stimulus. The response may be elicited (e.g. *UCR*) or it may be of a more voluntary nature (e.g. escape–avoidance).
Cortical Excitation–Inhibition—A gross, molar influence stemming from the reticular activating system which either facilitates (excitation) or suppresses (inhibition) certain cognitive and affective processes.

Appendix C. Definitions of Styles

Field Articulation—An analytical, in contrast to a global, way of perceiving; entails a tendency to experience items as discrete from their backgrounds, and reflects ability to overcome the influence of an embedding context (Witkin, *et al.*, 1962, pp. 57, 58).
Extensiveness of Scanning—Extensive scanning describes a relatively stable disposition to attend to tasks intensely and in a focused manner, yet with extensive coverage of relatively incidental aspects of the field (Holzman, 1966, p. 835).
Conceptual Differentiation—"In contrast to category-width tests, in which each item assesses the limits of one conceptual realm, free sorting tests require the spontaneous differentiation of heterogeneous items into a complex of more or less related groups" (Gardner and Schoen, 1962, p. 3). Thus, this style refers to differentiation between concepts, while category width (or equivalence range) refers to distinctions made within a concept's dimensionality.

Leveling versus Sharpening—A tendency to be hypersensitive to minutiae, to respond excessively to fine nuances and small differences, to exaggerate change, and to keep adjacent or successive stimuli from fusing and losing identity (Klein, 1951, p. 332). Levelers are characterized by maximal assimilation effects, and by memory organizations in which the fine shades of distinctions among individual elements are lost (Gardner, *et al.*, 1959, p. 219).

Tolerance for the Unconventional—Acceptance of experiences which do not agree with what one knows to be true (Gardner, *et al.*, 1959, p. 31). Reflected on the Rorschach in reluctance to project or fantasize, in refusals to attribute to the blots qualities that were known not to be there, and in difficulty in adopting an "as if" attitude . . . in the apparent movement test (Klein, 1970, p. 148).

Constricted versus Flexible Control—Terms . . . to describe differing reactions to stimulus fields containing contradictory or intrusive cues . . . constricted-control subjects resorted to counteractive measures in their attempts to overcome the disruptive effect of intrusive cues . . . Flexible-control subjects seemed relatively comfortable in situations that involved contradictory or intrusive cues (Gardner, *et al.*, 1959, p. 53).

Category Width or Equivalence Range—The degree to which subjects are impelled to act on or ignore an awareness of differences. A narrow equivalence range seemed to imply detailed categorization of certain aspects of experience. "Narrow-range" subjects had relatively exact standards for judging similarity. "Broad-range" subjects, on the other hand, were less finicky about fine stimulus differences, and grouped stimuli into broader categories (Gardner, *et al.*, 1959, p. 39).

Reflection versus Impulsivity—Refers to the degree to which a subject considers alternative hypotheses in contrast to reporting hypotheses with minimal consideration of their probable validity (Kagan, 1965).

Cognitive Complexity—Persons of great "cognitive complexity" presumably make more, and more complex, distinctions between persons and events . . . Conceptual differentiation in categorizing can be achieved as of an aspect of cognitive complexity (Gardner and Schoen, 1962, p. 5).

Analytic versus Relational Categorizing—Whether one forms "analytic–descriptive" concepts (based on similarity in objective elements within a stimulus complex, that were part of the total stimulus) or "inferential–categorical" concepts ("involve an inference about the stimuli grouped together") as opposed to "relational concepts" ("based on a functional relationship between or among the stimuli grouped together") (see Kagan, *et al.*, 1963, pp. 76, 77).

Compartmentalization—Measured by the number of miscellaneous objects left ungrouped in a sorting task, and identified as "a tendency to compartmentalize ideas . . . in discrete categories . . . a possible limitation in the production of diverse ideas" (Messick and Kogan, 1963).

Conceptual Integration—The relating or hooking of such parts (concepts) to each other and to previous conceptual standards (Harvey, Hunt and Schroder, 1961, p. 18).

Physiognomic versus Literal—(For the physiognomic person) percepts are often subtly suffused with emotional or expressive qualities. Inanimate objects or events seem to move, become motivated and assume expressive and "human" areas . . . All these experiences involved a preference for the dynamic and emotive rather than for the static and literal (Klein, 1970, pp. 151–152).

Abstract versus Concrete—The more concrete, the more the structure is assumed to be restricted to, or dependent upon, physical attributes of the activating stimulus

(Harvey, Hunt and Schroder, 1961, p. 3). The ability to form concepts (Gardner, *et al.*, 1962).

Contrast Reactivity—The degree to which individuals appreciate and respond to the contrast between stimuli that vary greatly (Gardner, 1970, p. 77).

COMMENT ON ROYCE'S PAPER

J. P. GUILFORD

Royce's monograph-size paper is so full of ideas that it takes considerable space to do justice to it. He has undertaken the difficult but useful task of integrating and systematizing much of what is known concerning variables of individuality, much as I attempted to do in my book on personality (Guilford, 1959), where personality was essentially equated to individuality. The outcomes in these two products are so different that I shall have to disagree with many of Royce's proposals.

There is no question regarding the great scientific value of having taxonomies as frames of reference, as the fields of chemistry and biology have long demonstrated. In psychology, comprehensive taxonomies have been woefully lacking. It seems to have been recognized only in very recent years that there have been no approaches to the search for taxonomies to rival that which employs observations of individual differences. And no better empirical method has been found than factor analysis, imperfect as its applications have been. The two of us seem to agree essentially on these propositions.

Taxonomic Issues

Our most fundamental disagreement is on the type of taxonomy to use; whether to follow the lead of chemistry, with its matrix-type or facet model, or of biology, with its hierarchical model. Royce follows in the Burt-Thurstone tradition that advocates the hierarchical type of model, whereas I have felt forced by the psychological nature of first-order factors to employ the facet type of model, which Guttman (1965) also suggests.

I have found a facet type of model to apply well not only in the domain of intelligence but also in the areas of psychomotor abilities, temperament traits, and psychopathology (Guilford, 1959). Within each facet model, there are subdivisions with logically hierarchical relationships. But in no case is there a hierarchical picture of a total domain.

What are the pros and cons with regard to the two types of models in psychology? Both have demonstrated their potentials for providing skeletons on which to organize concepts. Both have the virtue that, once constructed, broader pictures, generalized understandings, and general principles are possible. In such a manner does a body of scientific information take on significance. Both have incidental memory value, in that a single conceived structure aids in remembering a much larger number of particulars.

There is one important advantage, however, that is much more true of the facet type of model. That is its heuristic value in making predictions of factors yet to be discovered. For example, the structure of intellect (SI) model, with its three bases for cross classification of abilities, was constructed when only about 45 factorial abilities in the intellectual domain had been demonstrated. It predicted 75 additional abilities, parallel to those already known, leading pointedly to further factor-analytical investigations that have demonstrated 53 more SI abilities. Twenty-two have not yet been investigated. A hierarchical model can do this sort of thing much less well. It is too open. It is better in recording things after the fact than in predicting things to come. Ancillary to this difference is the possibility for empirical verification of the model, by deducing hypotheses and testing those hypotheses by experimental operations. In this manner, the SI model has been vindicated many times (see Guilford and Hoepfner, 1971).

On the other hand, there has been a long-standing claim of the Thurstone school, that there is an empirical procedure for demonstrating higher-order factors, in relation to lower-order factors. This procedure involves oblique rotations of the axes that represent the first-order factors so as to achieve Thurstone's criterion of simple structure. Cosines of the angles of separation of pairs of factors are taken to estimate correlations among the first-order factors, which can then be factor analyzed to find second-order factors. The latter can in turn be analyzed to find third-order factors, and so on. Thus is a hierarchy said to be established empirically.

I should say that I am not averse to the idea of correlations among first-order factors, or among those of any other order. But I have never been able to accept the orthodox procedure for finding them. Everyone familiar at all with the mathematical aspects of factor analysis, knows that the locating of axes that should represent the psychological dimensions is an indeterminate problem. The rotating of axes to find meaningful positions is an arbitrary matter. This fact has not been taken sufficiently seriously. Thurstone proposed his simple-structure criterion as a guide to solutions, but there is no assurance that it will lead to a psychologically meaningful set of factor variables. My experience with factor analysis has led to the conviction that simple structure can be a useful aid, but it is by no means a safe guide. Analytical rotations that involve mathematical definitions of simple structure will find solutions satisfying those definitions, but there is no assurance that the obtained variables conform to psychological reality. To expect them to do so is largely wishful thinking. Better ways of estimating correlations among factors must be invented.

Royce's Hierarchical Models

Let us consider next the apparent validity of Royce's models, as such. In addition to reservations concerning his general choice of form of model, there are many questions as to how well he has succeeded in the construction of his taxonomies.

First, there is the question of the wisdom of his choices of first-order factors to include. They are basic to the higher-order factors. Royce decided to limit his selection of first-order factors to those that he considered to have adequate empirical support. This procedure involves value judgments, and many who are concerned may well disagree with his standards and his selections. In developing a taxonomy, one can either treat the task as an exercise in theory construction or as a painting of an "established picture". Royce evidently chose the latter objective, which imposes upon him the responsibility for showing that the picture is accurate. It is doubtful that Royce's resultant pictures will meet with very general acceptance or will stand very long. The reasons lie in his choice of factors, his conceptions of them, and the lack of empirical evidence for their interrelationships. In addition to the questionable estimates of factor correlations, mentioned earlier, is that even such estimates are largely nonexistent or nonreplicated.

For example, in developing his taxonomy for intelligence, he gives top priority to Thurstone's primary mental abilities. Twenty years of analytical research in the Aptitudes Research Project at the University of Southern California, which covered the ground tread by Thurstone and his associates, accumulated considerable evidence concerning the nature of those variables (Guilford, 1971). Briefly, it can be said that most of the factors found by Thurstone have been found to represent confoundings each of two or more structure-of-intellect abilities. Thurstone's namings of his factors were in the direction of structure of intellect abilities, suggesting that his insights were better than his data, and later analyses by his group tended to narrow the factors in the direction of SI abilities. But interpretations, as carried over by Royce, are still not precise. For example, it has been shown that Thurstone's closure factors are by no means confined to closure tasks, and in place of his "induction" and "deduction" abilities there are several inductive and deductive abilities.

The foundation for Royce's "mental-speed" factor is weak. It is said to rest upon a factor that Thurstone called "speed and strength of closure", the Air Force psychologists' "perceptual speed", and a number of fluency factors, which have been represented by speed tests. It has been found that neither "speed and strength of closure" nor "perceptual speed" requires speed tests to measure it. That leaves fluency factors as the first-order foundation for a higher-order speed factor. Now fluency may be regarded as an identifying feature of all the 24 divergent-production abilities of the SI model, and it may be that there is a higher-order ability that embraces all of them. I would think it more likely that there are four such factors, one for each set of divergent-production abilities according to the four kinds of informational content—visual-figural, symbolic, semantic, and behavioral. A third-order fluency factor embracing all four categories is conceivable, but evidence is lacking for it, or for an even more comprehensive mental-speed factor.

Citations to empirical evidence for the hierarchical relationships within his models are very rare in Royce's paper. In fact, he admits that in connection with the model for psychomotor abilities there is no such evidence. From a logical standpoint, it is difficult to see how the kind of evidence upon which he depends can be confirmed. Since obtained oblique factor structures are primarily descriptive of particular test batteries, replications of those structures should not be expected when populations of tests and of examinees are changed, the factors being the same. It is invariance of factor structures over such changes that is needed for his purposes.

From a broader consideration, I have always been bothered logically by the fact that higher-order factors embrace representations by numerous heterogeneous test variables, some of which may correlate zero with others. This proposition is especially true of a single, all-embracing variable such as Spearman's *g* or that of "general intelligence" at the top of the hierarchy. My experience with more than 48,000 correlations among tests of intellectual abilities has shown that 18 per cent of them were below $+0{\cdot}10$ and may well be regarded as zero (Guilford and Hoepfner, 1971). If one wanted to be facetious, he could suspect that those who demand an over-all unity for intelligence are looking for the human soul, at least implicitly.

Royce's model for intelligence fails to meet another criterion that many psychologists would be inclined to apply. That is the requirement that a model should have implications for general psychological theory. The structure of intellect model achieves this value well. Even Burt's much earlier hierarchical model (Burt, 1949) does better than Royce's model in this respect.

Relations of Traits to Determiners

Royce devotes a large part of his paper, going beyond taxonomies, to consideration of relations of traits to possible determiners, in the form of physiological correlates and the influences of heredity and environment. He wisely urges that this be done applying the concepts derived from multivariate investigations of personality. I would differ from him in one respect, in that he would emphasize higher-order factors, where I should prefer the use of first-order factors. The reason for my choice is that higher-order factors involve some ambiguity, thus losing information, and that one-one relationships may be more likely to appear with the use of basic factors.

In discussing relations of factors to brain locations and functions, Royce overlooked numerous opportunities for showing associations. I have summarized such information (Guilford, 1967), pointing out, among other things, the one-one relations between reported kinds of agnosia and aphasia with particular SI abilities, and how, generally, some of the SI categories are associated with gross brain structures.

From one who is eminent in the investigations of relations of behavior to heredity, Royce's speculations concerning developmental curves should receive serious attention. Some novel predictions are proposed, for which there is as yet only scanty and questionable empirical data. In accepting the "factor-differentiation" principle, which has been known historically as the Garrett hypothesis, Royce is in all probability wrong. Even before the more directly refuting results of Stott and Ball (1963) and of C. E. Meyers and his group at the University of Southern California, the weight of the evidence was against the idea that factorial intellectual abilities develop by differentiation from a single composite ability, call it *g* or general intelligence. As many as 30 SI abilities have been found differentiated at the age of six, and many of them earlier, as far as such investigations have gone.

On the whole, we should thank Royce for bringing out taxonomic issues and problems, and for his pointing to the way in which multivariate concepts are needed in investigations of problems of development and physiological foundations. On the other hand, in doing this, he has not taken advantage of much well-founded multiple-factor information. In his emphasis upon higher-order factors, he exhibits reservations such as many multivariate psychologists have about getting to the bottom of things. Although by their choice of approach, multivariate psychologists have shown some relaxation of the urge for parsimony, there is still apparently much tension in this regard.

It is true that synthesizing is a part of a scientist's job, as well as analysis; he wants to know how things are organized, as well as knowing what things exist. Parsimony is gained by constructing taxonomic models, but a more important gain is in the form of comprehensive and systematic insights and concepts, and fruitful foundations for future investigations. When such goals are achieved, we are much better prepared to make serious efforts to relate psychological concepts to non-psychological concepts.

COMMENT ON ROYCE'S PAPER

GEORGE F. KAWASH

Contrary to the concern that Dr. Guilford has expressed, I am pleased that Dr. Royce has been willing to explore varieties of the differentiation hypothesis. I do not find the evidence presented by researchers such as Meyers and Stott and Ball so compelling as to lead to an abandoning of this conception. For example, matching factors across different ages in childhood is risky business at best and it is very difficult to ascertain whether a factor at one age corresponds to one at another age. While their research shares this problem of matching factors across ages, the work of Coan and Cattell has come to the opposite conclusion. They have found that more temperament factors appear in adolescence and young adulthood than are found in younger children. I think that the present state of research in this area still leads to a "pay your money and take your choice" conclusion.

On the other hand, I am concerned about the emphasis that Dr. Royce gives to cognitive styles as integrating mechanisms. I have been bothered for some time by the concept of styles as being different from other conceptual tools that we have, especially temperamental traits. It is quite common for definitions of temperament to include stylistic components. Writers in the area of cognitive style have argued that these style factors have differed from temperament factors in that the former manifest themselves in a much wider array of behavioral patterns, such as perceptual responses, cognition, judgment, and social behavior. However, actual research support for this contention has been scant. With the possibility of a very small number of exceptions, such as rigidity, investigations of cognitive style have been limited to one or two of these areas of behavior. One can get as much theoretical mileage from temperament concepts with greater parsimony.

COMMENT ON ROYCE'S PAPER

H. LANSDELL

When speculating about the neurophysiology of cognition, one should probably stress first the important distinction between verbal and nonverbal abilities: each set depends mainly on contributions from opposite hemispheres (Lansdell, 1969; Milner, 1971). However, a broad factor, weighted slightly more on "abstract reasoning" and perceptual speed than on other variables, has recently been shown to have symmetrical rather than asymmetrical contributions; this second order factor was obtained with Horst's method applied to scores from the Wechsler-Bellevue Intelligence Scale and the Differential Aptitude Tests (Lansdell, 1968c; 1971a; 1971b). Horst's (1965) method of computation is an attractive means of defining second order factors, and he states that the method could be adapted for higher order factors after the fashion of Schmid and Leiman's (1957) model; perhaps it could be useful in checking Royce's theorizing.

Higher order factors of this type need not turn out to be integrative functions or higher level abilities in a phylogenetic sense. Some forms of reasoning may some day be identified primarily with activity in certain cortical areas (McAdam and Whitaker, 1971), but a broad factor at the "highest" level might be related mainly to general biological features of the mammalian brain such as adequacy of blood supply (Wilkie and Eisdorfer, 1971) or other simple measures reflecting level of neurophysiological efficiency. In other words, individual differences in some integrative cerebral functions might be revealed as variation in narrow factors, and some broad factors might not clearly entail complex coordination of cerebral activity.

COMMENT ON ROYCE'S PAPER

K. PAWLIK

I read Royce's paper with very great interest indeed—which may also relate to the psychological mechanisms of reinforcement which I received from this paper since Royce's way of integrating factorial results and the kind of synopsis he arrives at is highly similar to the one

I came up with myself. I also like his separate treatment of style factors and his emphasis on biotopical representativeness in the sampling of variables. I find myself in agreement with Royce also on the importance of integrating research in the area of multivariate analysis, looking for results which are consistent across different variable or subject sampling strategies and schools of thought rather than stressing the specifics and peculiarities of a given laboratory. If multivariate personality research is to demonstrate its relevance and usefulness to the rest of the psychological community it must give priority to the former at the expense of the latter. Royce's paper is a very valuable attempt in this very direction. My only other comment would be in reference to the neuropsychological relationships suggested in Royce's paper. How much weight would you attach yourself, Professor Royce, to getting a direct neuropsychological interpretation or explanation of factors of intelligence and temperament?

COMMENT ON ROYCE'S PAPER

W. POLEY

A considerable portion of Royce's Banff paper, as well as Guilford's comments, are concerned with hierarchical models of individual differences. I would like to add some further comments on this issue. First of all, if correlations among test variables are predominantly positive, the case for higher-order analysis is quite strong. I believe this situation exists for tests of intellectual abilities. Although Guilford points out that, from his own experience, 18 per cent of the correlations among tests are below 0·10, this does not impress me as strong evidence against oblique factors or higher-order analysis. Thus, if 18 per cent of the correlations are zero, the other 82 per cent must be significantly different from zero. Guilford seems to be concerned with the fact that higher-order factors can embrace test variables which correlate zero with each other. But it is also true that first-order factors (orthogonal or oblique) can load variables which correlate zero with each other. Thus, the "problem" is not confined to higher-order analyses.

It is true that empirical support is weak for some of the higher-order relationships proposed in the Royce paper. However, I would have to defend a relaxation of empirical criteria, both in cases where there is little available research and in some cases where the data do not indicate strong correlations among factors at lower orders. In these instances, the higher-order relationships must be recognized as hypotheses and their validity depends upon the insights of the theorist.

To give a specific example of this from my own research, I have believed for some time that a unitary concept of emotionality underlies a great number of indices of temperament in the animal domain. I have held this hypothesis although the empirical evidence points to low correlations among test variables as well as first-order factors. The hypothesis is based upon a knowledge of the literature on animal temperament which indicates that many indices of emotionality co-vary under certain conditions, including stress, drugs, and lesions. Since these conditions are not available (or are at least rare) in the normal population, differentiation of emotionality is the rule and the unitary nature of emotionality is obscured. This, of course, in no way underestimates the importance of recognizing differentiation but it does point to a need to occasionally go beyond the factor analytic evidence at hand.

REJOINDER TO DISCUSSANTS' COMMENTS

JOSEPH R. ROYCE

Since I see nothing contentious in the comments of discussants Kawash, Pawlik, Lansdell, and Poley, my remarks will be directed to the commentary of Professor Guilford. In the section of my paper concerned with the Structure of Temperament it was argued as follows: "Thus, while some investigators will . . . suggest additions to the list, we see no real basis on which to argue for deletions." In the first portion of his remarks Guilford is doing just that—suggesting the addition of certain SI factors, many of which I personally believe will eventually be shown to manifest factorial invariance. Thus, to the extent we have omitted SI or other cognitive factors which meet our minimal invariance criteria, we are simply in error and will stand corrected. Furthermore, we welcome guidance on how best to deal with the invariance problem. (At the present time, not in twenty years when a more adequate quantitative index of invariance becomes available.) Of course Guilford is right when he says these decisions are value laden. However, this problem is common to all of us, including Guilford.

The Problem of a Factor Taxonomy

Professor Guilford's concern goes deeper; he has doubts about the theoretical value of a hierarchical taxonomy. My elaboration of a hierarchical taxonomy should not be construed as a negation of the theoretical potential of alternative models, such as Professor Guilford's facet model. In fact, I have stated in my paper that in the sub-domain of intellect his approach is "the most comprehensive and viable model" (see also Royce, 1968) we have at present. However, the task before us involves covering the entire range of individual differences, and in addition, the "task is difficult . . . as the data are both incomplete and contradictory". We must take seriously the stricture "to come up with both condensation and synthesis without doing violence to the data". (Royce, introduction to his paper.) Furthermore, as theorists it is extremely important that we pay serious attention to the philosophic characteristics of the algorithmic model we are working with. For example, since factor analysis is an empirico-inductive-hypothesis-generating model (Royce, 1963), and in this sense its efforts are in the logical context of scientific discovery (i.e. it is not an *a priori* or hypothetico-deductive theory-generating algorithm), the evolution of a substantive theory of individuality will be a slow, cumulative, interacting-with-the-data process. Thus, when Guilford says Royce's approach is "too open" (Guilford's comment), I not only want to confirm that claim, but go on to say that it was adopted as a very conscious and necessary strategy. Furthermore, my personal guess is that the state of the art is such that we shall have to maintain such "openness" (i.e. a non-fixed taxonomic structure) for some time to come. My commitment is not to higher order factors over first order factors, or to oblique rather than orthogonal factors, or to Thurstone's PMAs rather than Guilford's SI model, etc., but rather, my commitment is to the identification of invariant factors (whether first order or higher order), and whatever taxonomy (whether orthogonal, oblique, or both) will best accommodate the data (e.g. as stated in the opening section of "The Structure of Individuality" in my paper, it is quite possible that the factor taxonomy in certain sensory areas, such as color vision, is orthogonal). Furthermore, I also indicated that my approach does not involve an *a priori* commitment to hierarchical order. My personal guess on this matter is that all extant models, including my own, are "special cases of a particular segment of variables. Thus, some kind of hierarchy, strata, chain, simplex, or circumplex constitutes a sub-set of the more general lattice or reticule" (see section referred to above). In short, I am committed to the strategy of letting the data guide our conceptualizing rather than vice versa. Guilford, it seems to me, recommends the reverse—namely, that we let our conceptualizing guide our data gathering. Clearly, the effective doing of science involves both strategies, i.e. going from the data to theory and vice versa. But my argument is that factor analysis is uniquely potent in the early stages of theory construction, and that we can make the most of the factor model if we see it primarily in the context of discovery rather than the context of verification. This is the crucial difference between Professor Guilford and myself. It may well be, of course, that both of us are right—namely, that for my purpose of generating a general theory of individual differences it is best to sneak up on the theoretical lattice-work, and that for Guilford (he has, after all, been sneaking up on the structure of intellect for some thirty years) it is best to proceed from his facet model to further data gathering. While I see no error in this conclusion, I would, however, point out that once the theoretical structure is solidified (as in the case of Guilford's SI model), the investigator has gone beyond factor theory *per se*. My position is that while this state of affairs is desirable in principle, and in this sense it is desirable for factor analysis to do itself out of business, it is simply premature to conclude that the delineation of an adequate taxonomic structure for a general theory of individuality has, in fact, been achieved. Of course such a conclusion does not preclude the possibility of eventually achieving such a goal, nor does it preclude the existence of a useful taxonomy for a more circumscribed theory, such as Guilford's SI model.

Once we are reasonably satisfied we have established an empirically based taxonomy, or even a partial structure, we are, of course, prepared to go beyond the data in search of an appropriate, more encompassing rationale. We are, in fact, working on this in selected sub-domains such as cognition and emotionality. However, we see such efforts as clearly premature in areas such as style and motivation, for in these areas we do not even have secure handles on the components which are to be interrelated. We have, however, tried to provide a general conceptual framework for the full range of individuality by such overarching concepts as psychological structure, mental structure, cognitive structure, affective structure, and style structure on the one hand (see Part I of my paper), and to elaborate on general processes, such as the development of factors and the biological correlates of factors on the other hand (see Part II of my paper). I would agree with Guilford, however, that my taxonomic structure is fundamentally empirical, and that it thereby suffers from a kind of antiseptic non-rationality. It is my personal hope that as we move in the direction of more rational structures we will be able to bring to the theory construction task the kind of sophistication and wisdom which is consistent with the philosophic characteristics which are intrinsic to factor analysis. The point is that the logic of factor analysis (i.e. its philosophic characteristics) is simply not well understood by either the philosophers of science or the factor practitioners. However inadequately we meet that challenge there is also the business of nimbly balancing on the tight rope which stretches between one's half-baked theoretical structure at one end and the dirty and contradictory data at the other end. I presume Professor Guilford agrees that openness, both to alternative theoretical structures* and to data, is the only antidote we have to the chasm of ignorance which lurks below. (I got rather carried away by that metaphor. It may be excusable if it manages to convey something of the factor analyst's dilemma I alluded to in my introduction to this volume.) Our review of the empirical literature indicates that: (1) relatively few factors can qualify circa 1970 as invariant (so the issue eventually reduces to the criteria one follows for invariance; this is why we stated our criteria), and (2) given some invariant factors, there is empirical evidence for all kinds of factors (orthogonal, oblique, first order, higher order, narrow band width, broad band width, bipolar, etc.). In short, the tough job here is to synthesize all the data, not just selected portions of it. This includes the empirical fact of higher order factors as well as first order factors. An orthogonal (i.e. facet) model simply ignores these findings. But there are conceptual-methodological issues as well. For example, most of us probably agree with Guilford when he points out that "better ways of estimating correlations among factors must be invented". Surely, however, it does not follow from this suggestion that reality should be declared orthogonal *a priori*. In fact, Guttman (1958) has pointed out that a hierarchical formulation is implicit in the facet model and in the spirit of rapprochement, Messick has devoted a considerable segment of his Banff paper to spelling out the conceptual-substantive implications of Guttman's claim.

Biological Correlates of Factors

With regard to biological correlates, Guilford seems to think I prefer higher-order factors, and further, that I have omitted important factor-brain correlates. My reaction to this is two-fold. First, our modus operandi limited the factors I could seriously review in this paper to those we had admitted as invariant. Thus, with that constraint we are left with very few cognitive factors which are both invariant and for which there is brain function evidence. My own recent foray into the factor-brain correlate domain (Aftanas and Royce, 1969; Royce and

* It may be worth noting, in passing, that the problem of evolving viable taxonomies is by no means limited to the domain of individual differences. In fact, I would argue that there is no adequate taxonomy in any sub-domain of psychology (e.g. psychopharmacology, psychopathology, etc.), and that this inadequacy constitutes a serious commentary on the state of our discipline. The point is that empirically based taxonomies of behavior constitute an example of the kind of "low level" conceptualizing which needs to be done. For a comprehensive summary of the wide range of possible factor taxonomies see a recent paper by Cattell (1965).

Yeudall, 1973) can serve as a reminder of the value of caution in a domain as complex as this. We ask a question of great importance, when we are seeking the brain correlates of cognitive factors, and the findings to date (at both psychological and neurological levels) are simply not adequate to the task (Royce, 1966). Thus, my bias is that the requirement of dealing with invariant factors only should err in the direction of being even more stringent when looking for biological correlates. (The above can also serve as a partial answer to Professor Pawlik's query concerning neuropsychological explanation. My position is that knowledge of underlying biological mechanisms (i.e. genetic, biochemical, and neurological) is essential for full understanding of the process aspects of factors. While I fear such understanding will accrue very slowly, my bias is that these efforts are worth the candle because of the explanatory potential of the "functional unities" approach elaborated in the text of my paper.)

The second point has to do with Guilford's charge that I prefer higher order factors. Let me say quite explicitly that I see no reason to prefer higher order factors over first order factors or vice versa. The challenge, it seems to me, is to provide a theoretical structure which will accommodate factors at all levels. Since all my experimental research to date has been with first order factors (e.g. Royce, *et al.*, 1973a, b; Aftanas and Royce, 1969; Royce and Yeudall, 1973), however, I do confess that I feel more comfortable with first order factors for the simple reason that such factors lie closer to the data. However, a significant body of data has cumulated during the past two decades concerning a small number of higher order affective factors (e.g. anxiety, introversion-extroversion). Now, at this relatively early stage I would take it as basically fruitless to argue about whether such factors are really first order or higher order factors. But, what is exciting is the growing evidence (e.g. see Gray, this book, and various publications of Eysenck) that the reticular activating system and the limbic system are important neural sites for certain emotionality factors. This is the reason for my (apparent) "preference" for higher order factors in this domain. On purely conceptual grounds higher order factors do, of course, have very wide ranging synthesizing potential. If the hierarchical model proves out, we shall undoubtedly want to pay more attention to these higher order constructs. In short, I favor those invariant factors, at all levels, which demonstrate empirical-rational synthesis.

Factor Differentiation

On the issue of factor differentiation, I agree with Guilford in rejecting Garrett's specific hypothesis, but I disagree with his conclusion that we should drop the notion of factor differentiation. (N.B. My concept of factor differentiation is not the same as Garrett's; see the section of my paper "The Ontogeny of Factors"). My stance here is based primarily on the overwhelming theoretical-experimental evidence from biology (especially embryology), which clearly demonstrates that organisms develop from a relatively amorphous tissue mass at birth (i.e. the zygote) to various differentiated organic structures at maturity (i.e. specialized anatomical cells with different physiological functions). But it is also based on evidence to the effect that cultural and sub-cultural reinforcement (i.e. learning) results in progressive differentiation. For example, in a recent review article, Anastasi (1970, p. 902) says:

> "When we examine relevant research conducted since 1960 with appropriate procedures and more carefully controlled conditions, the results do in fact indicate an increasing differentiation of group factors from early childhood to late adolescence."

Even if we grant Guilford relative separation of factors in early infancy, would he then want to extrapolate such differentiation to the pre-natal period, and then all the way back to the zygote? Complete psychobiological differentiation of structure and function in the zygote just doesn't make good biological sense. (My point is that psychobiological differentiation clearly occurs, and that it is an ontogenetic process.) My own theoretical-experimental research (Royce, *et al.*, 1973a, b) indicates that the underlying genotype, which is polygenic for each factor (Royce, 1957), contains the potential for differential psychological functions, which can be, in principle, either oblique or orthogonal. Furthermore, we must not lose sight of the fact that this biological-genetic potential requires interaction with the environment before it can become manifest, even in the case of heredity dominant factors (see Royce paper, pp. 347–348). Thus, to take obvious examples, number factors or verbal factors have not become manifest prenatally. In short, full-blown, completely differentiated, adult homunculi are not to be found in the zygote.

REFERENCES

Adcock, C. J. and Townsley, G. C. (1971). A factor analytic study of interests. *Personality* **2**, 97–116.

Aftanas, M. S. and Royce, J. R. (1969). A factor analysis of brain damage tests administered to normal subjects with factor score comparisons across ages. *Multivar. behavl. Res.* **4**, 459–481.

Ahmavaara, Y. (1957). On the unified factor theory of mind. *Ann. Finnish Acad. Sci. Helsinki*, Series B, 106.

Allport, G. W., Vernon, P. E. and Lindzey, G. (1951). "Study of Values." Houghton Mifflin, Boston.

Anastasi, A. (1970). On the formation of psychological traits. *Am. Psychol.* **25,** 899–910.

Baggaley, A. R. (1955). Concept formation and its relation to cognitive variables. *J. Gen. Psychol.* **52,** 297–306.

Balinsky, B. (1941). An analysis of the mental factors of various age groups from nine to sixty. *Genet. Psychol. Monogr.* **23,** 191–234.

Bard, P. (1939). Central nervous mechanism for emotional behavior patterns in animals. *Res. Publ. Ass. Res. nerv. ment. Dis.* **19,** 190–218.

Bieri, J. and Blacker, E. (1967). The generality of cognitive complexity in the perception of people and inkblots. *In* "Problems in human assessment." (Jackson, D. N. and Messick, S. eds) McGraw-Hill, New York. (Reprinted 1956 from *J. abnorm. soc. Psychol.*)

Birren, J. E. (1952). A factor analysis of the Wechsler–Bellevue scale given to an elderly population. *J. consult. Psychol.* **16,** 399–405.

Blewett, D. B. (1954). An experimental study of the inheritance of intelligence. *J. ment. Sci.* **100,** 922–933.

Bottenberg, R. A. and Christal, R. E. (1961). An iterative technique for clustering which retains optimal predictive efficiency. Lackland AFB, Texas: Personnel Laboratory, WADD, Report No. WADD–TN–61–30, 1961.

Botzum, W. A. (1951). A factorial study of the reasoning and closure factors. *Psychometrika* **16,** 361–386.

Broca, P. (1878). Anatomie comparée des circonvolutions cerebrales. Le grand lobe limbique et la scissure limbique dans la série des mammifères. *Rev. Anthropol.* **1,** 385–498.

Broverman, D. M. (1964). Generality and behavioral correlates of cognitive styles. *J. consult. Psychol.* **28,** 487–500.

Broverman, D. M., Broverman, I. K., Vogel, W. and Palmer R. D. (1964). The automization cognitive style and physical development. *Child Dev.* **35,** 1343–1359.

Bruner, J. S., Goodnow, J. and Austin, G. A. (1956). "A Study of Thinking." Wiley and Sons, New York.

Burt, C. (1940). "The Factors of the Mind." University of London Press, London.

Burt, C. (1949). The structure of mind: A review of the results of factor analysis. *Br. J. educ. Psychol.* **19,** 100–111, 176–199.

Burt, C. L. (1960). The factor analysis of the Wechsler scale. II. *Br. J. statist. Psychol.* **13,** 82–87.

Buss, A. R. (1973a). Learning, transfer, and changes in ability factors: A multivariate model. *Psychol. Bull.*, in press.

Buss, A. R. (1973b). A conceptual framework for learning effecting the development of ability factors. *Human Dev.*, in press.

Buss, A. and Royce, J. R. (1973). "The Ontogony of Factors: A Theoretical Interpretation", (in preparation).

Butcher, H. J. (1968). "Human Intelligence." Methuen, London.

Butler, J. M. (1969). Simple structure reconsidered: Distinguishability and invariance in factor analysis. *Multivar. behavl. Res.* **4,** 5–28.

Cannon, W. E. (1927). The James–Lange theory of emotions: A critical examination and an alternative theory. *Am. J. Psychol.* **39,** 106–124.

Cattell, R. B. (1957). "Personality and motivation and structure and measurement." World Book, Yonkers-on-the-Hudson, New York.

Cattell, R. B. (1958). The dynamic calculus: A system of concepts derived from objective motivation measurement. *In* "Assessment of Human Motives." (Lindzey, G. ed.), Chapter 8. Rinehart, New York.

Cattell, R. B. (1965). Higher order factor structures and reticular versus hierarchical formulae for their interpretation. *In* "Studies in Psychology." (Banks, C. and Broadhurst, P. L. eds) University of London Press, London.

Cattell, R. B. (ed.) (1966). "Handbook of Multivariate Experimental Psychology." Rand McNally, Chicago.

Cattell, R. B. (1971). "Abilities: Their Structure, Growth, and Action." Houghton Mifflin, Boston.

Cattell, R. B. (1972). Structured learning theory, applied to personality change. *In* "Handbook of Modern Personality Theory." (Cattell, R. B. ed.) In press.

Cattell, R. B., Cattell, A. K. and Rhymer, R. M. (1947). P-technique demonstrated in determining psycho-physiological source traits in a normal individual. *Psychometrika* **12,** 267–288.

Cattell, R. B., Eber, H. W. and Tatsuoka, M. M. (1970). "Handbook for the Sixteen Personality Factor Questionnaire." Institute for Personality and Ability Testing, Champaign, Illinois.

Cattell, R. B. and Luborsky, L. B. (1950). P-technique demonstrated as a new clinical method for determining personality and symptom structure. *J. gen. Psychol.* **42,** 3–24.

Cattell, R. B. and Scheier, I. H. (1961). "The Meaning and Measurement of Neuroticism and Anxiety." Ronald Press, New York.

Chapman, L. F. and Wolff, H. B. (1959). Cerebral hemispheres and the highest integrative functions of man. *Arch. Neurol.* **1,** 357–424.

Claridge, G. S. (1967). "Personality and Arousal." Pergamon, London.

Cohen, J. (1957). The factorial structure of the WAIS between early adulthood and old age. *J. Consult. Psychol.* **21,** 451–457.

Cohen, J. (1959). The factorial structure of the WISC at ages 7–6, 10–6, and 13–6. *J. Consult. Psychol.* **23,** 285–299.

Comrey, A. L. (1961). Factored homogeneous item dimensions in personality research. *Educ. psychol. Measur.* **21,** 417–431.

Comrey, A. L. (1962). A study of 35 personality dimensions. *Educ. psychol. Measur.* **22,** 543–552.

Comrey, A. L. and Jamison, K. (1966). Verification of six personality factors. *Educ. psychol. Measur.* **26,** 945–953.

Cropley, A. J. (1964). Differentiation of abilities, socioeconomic status, and the WISC. *J. consult. Psychol.* **28**, 512–517.

Davidson, W. M. and Carroll, J. B. (1945). Speed and level components in time-limit scores: A factor analysis. *Educ. psychol. Measur.* **5,** 411–427.

Davis, P. (1956). A factor analysis of the Wechsler–Bellevue scale. *Educ. psychol. Measur.* **16,** 127–146.

Denton, J. C. and Taylor, C. W. (1955). A factor analysis of mental abilities and personality traits. *Psychometrika* **20,** 75–81.

Duffy, E. (1962). "Activation and Behaviour." Wiley, New York.

Duffy, E. and Crissy, W. J. E. (1940). Evaluative attitudes as related to vocational interests and academic achievement. *J. abnorm. soc. Psychol.* **35,** 226–245.

Dunham, J. L., Guilford, J. P. and Hoepfner, R. (1968). Multivariate approaches to discovering the intellectual components of concept learning. *Psychol. Rev.* **75,** 206–221.

Elliott, R. (1961). Interrelationships among measures of field dependence, ability and personality traits. *J. abnorm. soc. Psychol.* **63,** 27–36.

Ertl, J. P. (1968a). "Evoked potentials, neural efficiency and I.Q." (Presented at the International Symposium for Biocybernetics, Washington, D.C.)

Ertl, J. P. (1968b). Intelligence testing by brain waves. *The Mensa Journal.*

Ertl, J. P. (1968c). "Evoked potentials and human intelligence." Final Report. Project No. 6–1545, U.S. Dept. of Health, Education and Welfare.

Evans, F. J. (1967). Field dependence and the MPI. *Percept. Mot. Skills* **24,** 526.

Eysenck, H. J. (1953). "The Structure of Human Personality." Methuen, London.

Eysenck, H. J. (1957). "The Dynamics of Anxiety and Hysteria." Praeger, New York.

Eysenck, H. J. (1962). Conditioning and personality. *Br. J. Psychol.* **53,** 299–305.

Eysenck, H. J. (1964). "Crime and Personality." Routledge, Kegan Paul, London; Houghton Mifflin, Boston.

Eysenck, H. J. (1967). "The Biological Basis of Personality." Charles C. Thomas, Springfield, Illinois.

Eysenck, H. J. (1970). "The Structure of Human Personality." Methuen, London.

Eysenck, H. J. and Eysenck, S. B. J. (1969). "Personality Structure and Measurement." Routledge, Kegan Paul, London.

Falconer, D. S. (1960). "Introduction to Quantitative Genetics." Ronald Press, New York.

Feigl, H. and Scriven, M. (eds) (1956). "The Foundations of Science and the Concepts of Psychology and Psychoanalysis." University of Minnesota Press, Minneapolis.

Ferguson, G. A. (1954). On learning and human ability. *Can. J. Psychol.* **8,** 95–112.

Ferguson, G. (1956). On transfer and the abilities of man. *Can. J. Psychol.* **10,** 121–132.

Ferguson, G. A. (1959). Learning and human ability: A theoretical approach. *In* "Factor Analysis and Related Techniques in the Study of Learning." (DuBois, P. H., Manning, W. H. and Spies, C. J. eds) A report of a conference held at Washington University, St. Louis, Mo., Feb. Technical Report No. 7, Office of Naval Research Contract No. Nonr816(02).

Ferguson, L. W., Humphreys, S. G. and Strong, F. W. (1941). A factorial analysis of interests and values. *J. educ. Psychol.* **32,** 197–204.

Fleishman, E. A. (1967). Individual differences in motor learning. *In* "Learning and individual differences." (Gagné, R. M. ed.) Charles E. Merrill, Columbus, Ohio.

Fleishman, E. A. and Hempel, W. E., Jr. (1956). Factorial analysis of complex psychomotor performance and related skills. *J. appl. Psychol.* **40,** 96–104.

Franks, C. M. (1956). Conditioning and personality: A study of normal and neurotic subjects. *J. abnorm. soc. Psychol.* **52,** 143–150.

Franks, C. M. (1957). Personality factors and the rate of conditioning. *Br. J. Psychol.* **48,** 119–126.

French, J. W. (1951). "The Description of Aptitude and Achievement Tests in Terms of Rotated Factors." University of Chicago Press, Chicago.

French, J. W. (1953). "The Description of Personality Measurements in Terms of Rotated Factors." Educational Testing Service, Princeton, New Jersey.

French, J. W. (1965). The relationship of problem-giving styles to the factor composition of tests. *Educ. psychol. Measur.* **25,** 9–28.

French, J. W., Ekstrom, R. B. and Price, L. A. (1963). "Manual for Kit of Reference Tests for Cognitive Factors." Educational Testing Service, Princeton, New Jersey.

Fuller, J. L. and Thompson, W. R. (1960). "Behaviour Genetics." John Wiley and Sons, New York.

Gardner, R. W. (1953). Cognitive styles in categorizing behavior. *J. Personality* **22,** 214–233.

Gardner, R. W. (1959). Cognitive control principles and perceptual behavior. *Bull. Menninger Clinic* **23,** 241–248.

Gardner, R. W. (1961). Cognitive controls of attention deployment as determinants of visual illusions. *J. abnorm. soc. Psychol.* **22,** 120–127.

Gardner, R. W. (1970). Individuality in development. *Bull. Menninger Clinic* **34,** 71–84.

Gardner, R. W., Holzman, P. S., Klein, G. S., Linton, H. and Spence, D. P. (1959). Cognitive control: A study of individual consistencies in cognitive behavior. *Psychol. Issues* **I,** No. 4.

Gardner, R. W., Jackson, D. N. and Messick, S. J. (1960). Personality organization in cognitive controls and intellectual abilities. *Psychol. Issues* **II,** No. 4.

Gardner, R. W. and Lohrenz, L. J. (1960). Leveling–sharpening and serial reproduction of a story. *Bull. Menninger Clinic* **24,** 295–304.

Gardner, R. W. and Long, R. I. (1960a). Errors of the standard and illusion effects with the inverted-T. *Percept. Mot. Skills* **10,** 47–54.

Gardner, R. W. and Long, R. I. (1960b). Errors of the standard and illusion effects with L-shaped figures. *Percept. Mot. Skills* **10,** 107–109.

Gardner, R. W. and Long R. I. (1962a). Control, defense and the centration effect: A study of scanning behavior. *Br. J. Psychol.* **53,** 129–140.

Gardner, R. W. and Long, R. I. (1962b). Cognitive controls of attention and inhibition: A study of individual consistencies. *Br. J. Psychol.* **53,** 381–388.

Gardner, R. W. and Moriarty, A. (1968). "Personality Development at Preadolescence." University of Washington Press, Seattle.

Gardner, R. W. and Schoen, R. A. (1962). Differentiation and abstraction in concept formation. *Psycholog. Monogr.* **76,** 560.

Ghiselli, E. E. (1963). Moderating effects and differential reliability and validity. *J. appl. Psychol.* **47,** 81–86.

Gibson, E. J. (1969). "Principles of Perceptual Learning and Development." Appleton-Century-Crofts, New York.

Gooch, R. N. (1963). The influence of stimulant and depressant drugs on the central nervous system. *In* "Experiments with Drugs." (Eysenck, H. J. ed.) Pergamon, Oxford.

Gormly, T. (1971). Cognitive structure: Functional unity in verbal and mathematical performance. *J. Personality* **39,** 70–78.

Gray, J. A. (1965). "Pavlov's Typology." Pergamon Press, New York.

Grossman, S. P. (1967). "A Textbook of Physiological Psychology." John Wiley and Sons, New York.

Guilford, J. P. (1965). The structure of intellect. *Psychol. Bull.* **53,** 267–293.

Guilford, J. P. (1959). "Personality." McGraw-Hill, New York.

Guilford, J. P. (1961). Factorial angles to psychology. *Psychol. Rev.* **68,** 1–20.

Guilford, J. P. (1967). "The Nature of Human Intelligence." McGraw-Hill, New York.

Guilford, J. P. (1972). Thurstone's primary mental abilities and structure of intellect abilities. *Psychol. Bull.* **77,** 129–143.

Guilford, J. P., Christensen, P. R., Bond, N. A. and Sutton, M. A. (1954). A factor analysis study of human interests. *Psychol. Monogr.* **68** (4, Whole No. 375).

Guilford, J. P. and Hoepfner, R. (1969). Comparisons of varimax rotations and rotations to theoretical targets. *Educ. psychol. Measur.* **29,** 3–22.

Guilford, J. P. and Hoepfner, R. (1971). "The Analysis of Intelligence." McGraw-Hill, New York.

Guilford, J. P. and Zimmerman, W. S. (1956). Fourteen dimensions of temperament. *Psychol. Monogr.* **70,** Whole No. 417.

Guttman, L. (1965). The structure of interrelations among intellectual tests. *In* "Invitational Conference on Testing Problems." (Harris, C. W. ed.) Educational Testing Service, Princeton, New Jersey.

Guttman, L. (1958). What lies ahead for factor analysis? *Educ. psychol. Measur.* **18,** 497–515.

Halstead, W. C. (1947). "Brain and Intelligence." University of Chicago Press, Chicago.

Harman, H. (1967). "Modern Factor Analysis." (2nd edtn) University of Chicago Press, Chicago.

Harvey, O. S., Hunt, D. E. and Schroder, H. M. (1961). "Conceptual Systems and Personality Organization." Wiley and Sons, New York.

Hebb, D. O. (1949). "The Organization of Behavior." Wiley, New York.

Hebb, D. O. (1959). A Neuropsychological theory. *In* "Psychology: A Study of a Science." (Koch, S. ed), Vol. I. McGraw-Hill, New York.

Henry, S. (1949). Children's audiograms in relation to reading attainment. II: Analysis and interpretation. *J. gen. Psychol.* **71,** 3–48.

Herrick, C. J. (1933). The functions of the olfactory parts of the cortex. *Proc. natn. Acad. Sci. U.S.A.* **19,** 7.

Hess, W. R. (1936). Hypothalamus und die Zentren des autonomen Nervensystems: Physiologie. *Arch. Psychiat. Nervenkr.* **104,** 548–557.

Hess, W. R. (1954). "Diencephalon: Autonomic and Extrapyramidal Functions." Grune and Stratton, New York.

Hess, W. R. and Akert, K. (1955). Experimental data on role of hypothalamus in mechanisms of emotional behavior. A.M.A. *Arch. Neurol. Psychiat.* **73,** 127–129.

Hilgard, E. R. and Bower, G. H. (1966). "Theories of Learning." (3rd edtn) Appleton-Century-Crofts, New York.

Hirsch, J. (ed.) (1967). "Behavior Genetic Analysis." McGraw-Hill, New York.

Holtzman, W. H. (1965). Personality structure. *A. Rev. Psychol.* **16,** 119–156.

Holzman, P. S. (1954). The relation of assimilation tendencies in visual, auditory, and kinesthetic time-error to cognitive attitudes of leveling and sharpening. *J. Personality* **22,** 375–394.

Holzman, P. S. (1966). Scanning: A principle of reality contact. *Percept. Mot. Skills* **23,** 835–844.

Holzman, P. S. and Klein, G. S. (1956). Motive and style in reality contact. *Bull Menninger Clinic* **20,** 181–191.

Horn, J. L. (1965). Fluid and crystallized intelligence: A factor analytic and developmental study of structure among primary mental abilities. Unpublished doctoral dissertation, University of Illinois.

Horn, J. L. (1966). "Short Period Fluctuations in Intelligence." Denver Research Institute Final Project No. DRI–614, 1966. Denver, Colorado.

Horn, J. L. (1970). Organization of data on life-span development of human abilities. *In* "Life-span Developmental Psychology: Research and Theory." (Goulet, L. R. and Baltes, P. B. eds) Academic Press, New York and London.

Horn, J. L. (1971a). Personality and ability theory. *In* "Handbook of Modern Personality Theory." (Cattell, R. B. ed.).

Horn, J. L. (1971b). The structure of intellect: Primary abilities. *In* "Multivariate Personality Research: Contributions to the Understanding of Personality in Honor of Raymond B. Cattell." (Dreger, R. M. ed).

Horn, J. L. and Bramble, W. J. (1967). Second-order ability structure revealed in rights and wrongs scores. *J. educ. Psychol.* **58,** 115–122.

Horn, J. L. and Cattell, R. B. (1966). Refinement and test of the theory of fluid and crystallized intelligence. *J. educ. Psychol.* **57,** 253–270.

Horn, J. L. and Cattell, R. B. (1967). Age differences in fluid and crystallized intelligence. *Acta Psychol.* **26,** 107–129.

Horst, P. (1965). "Factor Analysis of Data Matrices." Holt, Rinehart and Winston, New York.

Howarth, E. and Browne, J. A. (1971). Investigation of personality factors in a Canadian context. I. Marker structure in personality questionnaire items. *Can. J. behavl. Sci.* **3,** 161–173.

Hubel, D. H. (1959). Single unit activity in striate cortex of unrestrained cats. *J. Physiol. Lond.* **147,** 226–238.

Hubel, D. H. (1960). Single unit activity in lateral geniculate body and optic tract of unrestrained cats. *J. Physiol. Lond.* **150,** 91–104.

Hubel, D. H. (1963). Integrative processes in ventral visual pathway of the cat. *J. Opt. Soc. Am.* **53,** 58–66.

Hubel, D. H. and Wiesel, T. N. (1959). Receptive fields of single neurons in the cats striate cortex. *J. Physiol. Lond.* **148,** 574.

Hubel, D. H. and Wiesel, T. N. (1961). Integrative action in the cats' lateral geniculate body. *J. Physiol. Lond.* **155,** 385–398.

Hubel, D. H. and Wiesel, T. N. (1962). Receptive fields, binocular interaction, and functional architecture in the cats' visual cortex. *J. Physiol. Lond.* **160,** 106–154.

Hughes, K. R. and Zubek, J. P. (1956). Effect of glutamic acid on the learning ability of bright and dull rats. I. Administration during infancy. *Can. J. Psychol.* **10,** 132–138.

Hughes, K. R. and Zubek, J. P. (1957). Effect of glutamic acid on the learning ability of bright and dull rats. II. Duration of the effect. *Can. J. Psychol.* **11,** 182–184.

Jackson, D. N. and Messick, S. (1958). Content and style in personality assessment. *Psychol. Bull.* **55,** 243–252.

Jackson, M. A. (1960). The factor analysis of the Wechsler Scale. I. *Br. J. statist. Psychol.* **73,** 79–82.

Johnson, D. M. and Reynolds, F. (1951). A factor analysis of verbal ability. *Psychol. Rec.* **4,** 183–195.

Jones, F. N. (1948). A factor analysis of visibility data. *Am. J. Psychol.* **61,** 361–369.

Kagan, J. (1965a). Individual differences in the resolution of response uncertainty. *J. Personality Soc. Psychol.* **2,** 154–160.

Kagan, J. (1965b). Impulsive and reflective children: Significance of conceptual tempo. *In* "Learning and the Educational Process." (Krumboltz, J. ed.) Rand McNally, Chicago.

Kagan, J. (1966). Reflection–impulsivity: The generality and dynamics of conceptual tempo. *J. abnorm. Psychol.* **71,** 17–24.

Kagan, J., Moss, H. A. and Sigel, I. E. (1963). Psychological significance of styles of conceptualization. *Monogr. Soc. Res. Child Dev.* **28,** 73–112.

Kagan, J., Pearson, L. and Welch, L. (1966). Conceptual impulsivity and inductive reasoning. *Child Dev.* **37,** 583–594.

Kagan, J., Rosman, B. L., Day, D., Albert, J. and Phillips, W. (1964). Information processing in the child: Significance of analytic and reflective attitudes. *Psychol. Monogr.* **78** (1, Whole No. 578).

Karlin, J. E. (1942). The factorial isolaton of the primary auditory abilities. *Psychol. Bull.* **39,** 453–454.

Karp, S. A. (1963). Field dependence and overcoming embeddedness. *Journal of Consult. Psychol.* **27,** 294–302.

Kelly, G. A. (1955). "The Psychology of Personal Constructs." Norton, New York.

King, D. P. and Norrell, G. (1964). A factorial study of the Kuder Preference Record—Occupational Form D. *Educ. psychol. Measur.* **24,** 57–64.

King, F. J. (1960). An experimental investigation of some biochemical correlates of phenylketonuria. Unpublished doctoral dissertation, University of Texas.

King, F. J., Bowman, Barbara and Moreland, H. J. (1961). Some intellectual correlates of biochemical variability. *Behavl. Sci.* **6,** 297–302.

Klein, G. S. (1951). The personal world through perception. *In* "Perception: An Approach to Personality." (Blake, R. R. and Ramsey, G. V. eds) Ronald Press, New York.

Klein, G. S. (1954). Need and regulation. *In* "Nebraska Symposium on Motivation." (Jones, M. R. ed.) University of Nebraska Press, Lincoln.

Klein, G. S. (1958). Cognitive control and motivation. *In* "Assessment of Motives." (Lindzey, G. ed.) Rinehart and Co., New York.

Klein, G. S. (1970). "Perception, Motives and Personality." Alfred A. Knopf, New York.

Klein, G. S., Barr, H. C. and Wolitzky, D. L. (1967). Personality. *A. Rev. Psychol.* **18,** 467–560.

Klein, G. S., Gardner, R. W. and Schlesinger, H. J. (1962). Tolerance for unrealistic experiences: A study of the generality of a cognitive control. *Br. J. Psychol.* **53,** 41–55.

Klüver, H. and Bucy, P. C. (1939). Preliminary analysis of functions of the temporal lobes in monkeys. *Arch. Neurol. Psychiat. Chicago* **42,** 979–1000.

Krech, D. Rosenzweig, M. R., Bennett, E. L. and Krenckel, B. (1954). Enzyme concentration in the brain and adjustive behavior patterns. *Science, N.Y.* **120,** 994–996.

Krech, D., Rosenzweig, M. R. and Bennett, E. L. (1962). Relations between brain chemistry and problem-solving among rats raised in enriched and impoverished environments. *J. comp. physiol. Psychol.* **55,** 801–807.

Kuder, G. F. (1948). "Kuder Preference Record—Vocational." Science Research Associates, Inc., Chicago, Illinois.

Langley, C. W. (1971). Differentiation and integration of systems of personal constructs. *J. Personality* **39,** 10–25.

Lansdell, H. (1968a). Effect of extent of temporal lobe ablation on two lateralized deficits. *Physiol. Behav.* **3,** 271–273.

Lansdell, H. (1968b). Effect of extent of temporal lobe surgery and neuropathology on the MMPI. *J. clin. Psychol.* **24,** 406–412.

Lansdell, H. (1968c). Evidence for a symmetrical hemispheric contribution to an intellectual function. *Proc. 76th ann. Conv. Am. Psychol. Assoc.*, pp. 337–338.

Lansdell, H. (1968d). The use of factor scores from the Wechsler–Bellevue Scale of Intelligence in assessing patients with temporal lobe removals. *Cortex* **4,** 257–268.

Lansdell, H. (1969). Verbal and nonverbal factors in right-hemisphere speech: Relation to early neurological history. *J. comp. Physiol Psychol.* **69,** 734–738.

Lansdell, H. (1971a). A general intellectual factor affected by temporal lobe dysfunction. *J. clin. Psychol.* **27,** 182–184.

Lansdell, H. (1971b). Intellectual factors and asymmetry of cerebral function. Address presented at the meeting of the American Psychological Association, Washington, D.C.

Lashley, K. S. (1941). Coalescence of neurology and psychology. *Proc. Am. phil. Soc.* **84,** 461–470.

Lindsley, D. B. (1951). Emotion. *In* "Handbook of Experimental Psychology." (Stevens, S. S. ed.) Wiley, New York.

Lindsley, D. B., Schreiner, L. H., Knowles, W. B. and Magoun, H. W. (1950). Behavioral and EEG changes following chronic brainstorm lesions in the cat. *EEG clin. Neurophysiol.* **2,** 483–498.

Lindzey, G. and Thiessen, D. D. (eds) (1970). "Contributions to Behavior Genetic Analysis: The Mouse as a Prototype." Appleton-Century-Crofts, New York.

Lurie, W. A. (1937). A study of Spranger's value-types by the method of factor analysis. *J. Soc. Psychol.* **8,** 17–37.

MacLean, P. D. (1954). The limbic system and its hippocampal formation: Studies in animals and their possible applications to man. *J. Neurosurgery* **11,** 29–44.

Manosevitz, M., Lindzey, G. and Thiessen, D. D. (eds) (1969). "Behavior Genetics: Method and Research." Appleton-Century-Crofts, New York.

Marx, M. H. (1948). Maze learning as a function of added thiamine. *J. comp. physiol. Psychol.* **41,** 364–371.

Marx, M. H. (1949). Relationship between supra-normal glutamic acid and maze learning. *J. comp. Psychol.* **42,** 320–327.

Maxwell, A. E. (1959). Statistical methods in factor analysis. *Psychol. Bull.* **56,** 141–152.

McAdam, D. W. and Whitaker, H. A. (1971). Language production: Electroencephalographic localization in the normal human brain. *Science, N.Y.* **172,** 499–502.

McCleary, R. A. and Moore, R. Y. (1965). "Subcortical Mechanisms of Behavior." Basic Books, New York.

Meredith, W. (1968). Factor analysis and the use of inbred strains. *In* "Progress in Human Behavior Genetics." (Vandenberg, S. G. ed.) The Johns Hopkins Press, Baltimore.

Merrifield, P. R. (1966). An analysis of concepts from the point of view of the structure of intellect. *In* "Analyses of Concept Learning." (Klausmeier, H. J. and Harris, C. W. eds) Academic Press, New York and London.

Merrifield, P. R., Guilford, J. P., Christensen, P. R. and Frick, J. W. (1962). The role of intellectual factors in problem solving. *Psychol. Monogr.* **76** (10, Whole No. 529).

Messick, S. (1957). Personality measurement and college performance. *In* "Problems in Human Assessment." (Jackson, D. and Messick S. eds) McGraw-Hill, New York.

Messick, S. (1965). The impact of negative affect on cognition and personality. *In*

"Affect, Cognition and Personality." (Tomkins, S. S. and Izard, C. eds) Springer, New York.

Messick, S. (1967). *In* "Problems in Human Assessment." (Jackson, D. N. and Messick, S. eds) McGraw-Hill, New York.

Messick, S. and Fritzky, F. J. (1963). Dimensions of analytic attitude in cognition and personality. *J. Personality* **31,** 346–370.

Messick, S. and Kogan, N. (1963). Differentiation and compartmentalization in object sorting measures of categorizing style. *Percept. Mot. Skills* **16,** 47–51.

Messick, S. and Kogan N. (1965). Category width and quantitative aptitude. *Percept. Mot. Skills* **20,** 493–497.

Messick, S. and Kogan N. (1967). Personality consistencies in judgment: Dimensions of role constructs. *Multivar. behav. Res.* **1,** 165–175.

Messick, S. and Ross, J. (eds) (1962). "Measurement in Personality and Cognition." Wiley and Sons, New York.

Miller, G. A., Galanter, E. H. and Pribram, K. H. (1960). "Plans and the Structure of Behavior." Holt, New York.

Milner, B. (1971). Interhemispheric differences in the localization of psychological processes in man. *Br. med. Bull.* **27,** 272–277.

Moruzzi, G. and Magoun, H. W. (1949). Brainstem reticular formation and activation of the EEG. *EEG clin. Neurophysiol.* **1,** 455.

Nauta, W. J. H. (1958). Some ascending pathways in the brain stem reticular formation. *In* "The Reticular Formation of the Brain." (Jasper, H. H., Proctor, L. D., Knighton, R. S., Noshay, W. C. and Costello, R. T. eds) Little, Brown, Boston.

O'Connor, J. P. and Kinnane, J. F. (1961). A factor analysis of work values. *J. counsell. Psychol.* **8,** 263–267.

Olds, J. (1958). Adaptive functions of the paleocortex. *In* "Biological and Biochemical Bases of Behavior." (Harlow, H. and Woolsey, C. eds) University of Wisconsin Press, Madison.

Oltman, P. K. (1964). Field dependence and arousal. *Percept. Mot. Skills* **19,** 441.

Overall, J. E. and Williams, C. M. (1961). Models for medical diagnosis. *Behavl. Sci.* **6,** 134–142.

Papez, J. W. (1937). A proposed mechanism of emotion. *Archs. Neurol. and Psychiat. Chicago* **38,** 725–743.

Paul, I. H. (1959). Studies in remembering: The reproduction of connected and extended verbal material. *Psychol. Issues* **I,** No. 2.

Pawlik, K. (1966). Concepts and calculations in human cognitive abilities. *In* "Handbook of Multivariate Experimental Psychology." (Cattell, R. B. ed.) Rand McNally, Chicago.

Pemberton, C. (1952a). The closure factors related to other cognitive processes. *Psychometrika* **17,** 267–288.

Pemberton, C. L. (1952b). The closure factors related to temperament. *J. Personality* **21,** 159–175.

Pettigrew, T. F. (1958). The measurement and correlates of category width as a cognitive variable. *J. Personality* **26,** 532–544.

Phillips, V. K. and Torrance, E. P. (1971). Divergent thinking, remote associations, and concept attainment strategies. *J. Psychol.* **77,** 223–228.

Poley, W. and Royce, J. R. (1973). Behavior genetic analysis of mouse emotionality, II: Stability of factors across mating plans, in preparation.

Poley, W. and Royce, J. R. (1973). A theory of emotionality and arousal, in preparation.

Pribram, K. (1971a). "Languages of the Brain." Prentice-Hall, Englewood Cliffs, New Jersey.

Pribram, K. (1971). Neurological notes on knowing. *In* "The Psychology of Knowing, The Second Banff Conference on Theoretical Psychology." (Royce, J. R. and Rozeboom, W. W. eds) Gordon and Breach, New York.

Pribram, K. H. and Kruger, L. (1954). Functions of the "olfactory" brain. *In Ann. N.Y. Acad. Sci.* **58,** 109–138.

Rapaport, D. (1967). Cognitive structures. *In* "The Collected Papers of David Rapaport." (Gill, M. M. ed.) Basic Books, New York.

Ray, O. S. (1959). Personality factors in motor learning and reminiscence. *J. abnorm. soc. Psychol.* **59,** 199–203.

Rimoldi, H. J. A. (1951a). The central intellective factor. *Psychometrika* **16,** 75–102.

Rimoldi, H. J. A. (1951b). Personal tempo. *J. abnorm. soc. Psychol.* **46,** 283–303.

Routtenberg, A. (1968). The two-arousal hypothesis: Reticular formation and limbic system. *Psychol. Rev.* **75,** No. 1, 51–80.

Routtenberg, A. (1971). Stimulus processing and response execution: A neurobehavioral theory. *Physiol. Behav.* **6,** 589–596.

Royce, J. R. (1950). The factorial analysis of animal behavior. *Psychol. Bull.* **47,** 235–259.

Royce, J. R. (1955). A factorial study of emotionality in the dog. *Psychol. Monogr.* **69** (22, Whole No. 407).

Royce, J. R. (1957). Factor theory and genetics. *Educ. psychol. Measur.* **17,** 361–376.

Royce, J. R. (1958). The development of factor analysis. *J. gen. Psychol.* **58,** 139–164.

Royce, J. R. (1963). Factors as theoretical constructs. *Am. psychol.* **18,** 522–528.

Royce, J. R. and Smith, W. A. S. (1964). A note on the development of the psychoepistomological profile (PEP). *Psychol. Rep.* **21,** 297–298.

Royce, J. R. (1965). A bibliography of factor analyses in fields other than psychology. Unpublished manuscript. University of Alberta.

Royce, J. R. (1966). Concepts generated in comparative and physiological psychological observations. *In* "Handbook of Multivariate Experimental Psychology." (Cattell, R. B. ed.) Rand McNally, Chicago.

Royce, J. R. (1967). Book review of J. P. Guilford, "The Nature of Human Intelligence." McGraw-Hill, New York. *In Science, N.Y.* **162,** 990–991.

Royce, J. R. (1970). "Test manual for the Psycho-Epistomological Profile." University of Alberta Printing Office.

Royce, J. R. (1973). Epistomology: a psychological approach. *In* "Handbook of Perception," (Carterette, E. C. and Friedman, M. P. eds.) Prentice Hall, New York.

Royce, J. R. (1973). "Inquiries into a Psychological Theory of Knowledge," in preparation.

Royce, J. R. and Buss, A. (1973). "The concept of psychological structure," in preparation.

Royce, J. R. and St. John, D. (1973). "An extension of the factor-gene-model," in preparation.

Royce, J. R., Poley, W. and Yeudall, L. T. (1973a). Behavior genetic analysis of mouse emotionality, I: The factor analysis. *J. comp. physiol. Psychol.* in press.

Royce, J. R., Poley, W. and Yeudall, L. T. (1973b). "Behavior genetic analysis of mouse emotionality, III: The diallel analysis," in preparation.

Royce, J. R. and Yeudall, L. T. (1973). "An analysis of brain damage tests administered to brain damage subjects. I. Factor analysis and correlations with damaged sites," *Neuro-psychologia* (in press).

Rozeboom, W. W. (1970). The art of metascience, or what should a psychological theory be? *In* "Towards Unification in Psychology. The First Banff Conference on Theoretical Psychology." (Royce, J. R. ed.) University of Toronto Press, Toronto.

Russell, W. L. (1941). Inbred and hybrid animals and their value in research. *In* "Biology of the Laboratory Mouse." (Snell, G. D. ed.) Dover, New York.

Saunders, D. R. (1959). On the dimensionality of the WAIS battery for two groups of normal males. *Psychol. Rep.* **5,** 529–541.

Scandura, J. M. (1970). Roles of rules in behavior: Toward an operational definition of what (rule) is learned. *Psychol. Rev.* **77,** 516–533.

Schlesinger, H. J. (1954). Cognitive attitudes in relation to susceptibility to interference. *J. Personality* **22,** 354–374.

Schmid, J. and Leiman, J. M. (1957). The development of hierarchical factor solutions. *Psychometrika* **22,** 53–61.

Sciortino, R. (1970). Allport–Vernon–Lindzey study of values. 1. Factor structuer for a combined sample of male and female college students. *Psychol. Rep.* **27,** 955–958.

Scott, W. A. (1966). Brief report: Measures of cognitive structure. *Multivar. Behavl. Res.* **1,** 391–395.

Scott, W. A. (1969). Structure of natural cognitions. *J. Personality soc. Psychol.* **12,** 261–278.

Sells, S. B., Demaree, R. G. and Will, D. P., Jr. (1970). Dimensions of personality. I. Conjoint factor structure of Guilford and Cattell trait markers. *Multivar. Behavl. Res.* **5,** 391–422.

Shapiro, D. (1968). "Neurotic Styles." Basic Books, New York.

Shucard, D. W. and Horn, J. L. (1971). Cortical evoked potentials and measurement of human abilities. Unpublished manuscript. University of Denver.

Sloane, H. N., Gorlow, L. and Jackson, D. N. (1963). Cognitive styles in equivalence range. *Percept. Mot. Skills* **16,** 389–404.

Smith, W. A. S., Royce, J. R., Ayers, D. and Jones, B. (1967). The development of an inventory to measure ways of knowing. *Psychol. Rep.* **21,** 529–535.

Spearman, C. E. (1923). "The Nature of 'Intelligence' and the Principle of Cognition." Macmillan, London.

Spearman, C. (1927). "The Abilities of Man." Macmillan, New York.

Spielman, J. (1963). The relation between personality and the frequency and duration of involuntary rest pauses during massed practice. Unpublished Ph.D. thesis, University of London.

Stott, L. H. and Ball, R. S. (1963). "Evaluation of Infant and Preschool Mental Tests." Merrill-Palmer, Detroit, Michigan.

Super, D. E. (1962). The structure of work values in relation to status, achievement, interests, and adjustment. *J. appl. Psychol.* **46,** 231–239.

Teuber, Hans-Lukas and Weinstein, S. (1954). "Performance on Formboard Task after Penetrating Brain Damage." *J. Psychol.* **38,** 177–190.

Thurstone, L. L. (1931). A multiple factor study of vocational interests. *Personnel J.* **10,** 198–205.

Thurstone, L. L. (1944). A factorial study of perception. *Psychometric Monogr.* No. 4.

Thurstone, L. L. and Thurstone, T. G. (1941). Factorial studies of intelligence. *Psychometric Monogr.* No. 2.

Thurstone, T. G., Thurstone, L. L. and Strandskov, H. H. (1953). A psychological study of twins. No. 4. University of North Carolina Psychometric Laboratory, Chapel Hill.

Tucker, L. R. (1966). Learning theory and multivariate experiment: Illustration by determination of generalized learning curves. *In* "Handbook of Multivariate Experimental Psychology." (Cattell, R. B. ed.) Rand McNally, Chicago.

Vandenberg, S. G. (1962). The hereditary abilities study: Hereditary components in a psychological test battery. *Am. J. hum. Genet.* **14,** 220–237.

Vandenberg, S. G. (1967). The primary mental abilities of South American students: A second comparative study of the generality of a cognitive factor structure. *Multivar. behavl. Res.* **2,** 175–198.

Vandenberg, S. G. (1969). Human behavior genetics: Present status and suggestions for future research. *Merrill–Palmer Quarterly of Behavior and Development,* **15,** No. 1, 121–154.

Vannoy, J. S. (1965). Generality of cognitive complexity–simplicity as a personality construct. *J. Personality soc. Psychol.* **2,** 385–396.

Vernon, P. E. (1950). "The Structure of Human Abilities." Methuen, London.

Vernon, P. E. (1961). "The Structure of Human Abilities." Methuen, London.

Wechsler, D. (1958). "The Measurement and Appraisal of Adult Intelligence." (4th edtn) Williams and Wilkins, Baltimore, Maryland.

Wenger, M. A. (1941). The measurement of individual differences in autonomic balance. *Psychosom. Med.* **3,** 427–434.

Wenger, M. A. (1942). The stability of measurements of autonomic balance. *Psychosomat. Med.* **4,** 94–95.

Wenger, M. A. (1943). A further note on the measurement of autonomic balance. *Psychosom. Med.* **5,** 148–151.

Wenger, M. A. (1949). Variations in autonomic balance under nine drugs. *Am. Psychol.* **4,** 233.

Wherry, R. J. (1941). Determination of the specific components of maze ability for Tryon's bright and dull rats by factorial analysis. *J. comp. Psychol.* **32,** 237–252.

Wiggins, J. S. (1968). Personality structure. *A. Rev. Psychol.* **19,** 293–350.

Wilkie, F. and Eisdorfer, C. (1971). Intelligence and blood pressure in the aged. *Science, N.Y.* **172,** 959–962.

Witkin, H. A., Dyk, R. B., Faterson, H. F., Goodenough, D. R. and Karp, S. A. (1962). "Psychological Differentiation." Wiley and Sons, New York.

Woodrow, H. (1938). The relationship between abilities and improvement with practice. *J. educ. Psychol.* **29,** 215–230.

Wyer, R. S. (1964). Assessment and correlates of cognitive differentiation and integration. *J. Personality* **32,** 394–509.

Yando, R. M. and Kagan, J. (1970). The effect of task complexity on reflection–impulsivity. *Cognitive Psychol.* **1,** 192–200.

Zimring, F. M. (1971). Cognitive simplicity–complexity; evidence for disparate processes. *J. Personality* **39,** 1–9.

Zuckerman, M. (1971). Dimensions of sensation seeking. *J. Consult. Clin. Psychol.* **36,** 45–52.

Causal Theories of Personality and How to Test Them*

JEFFREY A. GRAY

Oxford University

There is no need for me to inform participants in this Conference that workers in the multivariate field have succeeded in describing many consistent patterns of individual differences (CPID) of varying degrees of generality from first-order factors up. This paper is concerned, not to add to this body of research, nor to the theoretical controversies which it has generated, but rather with the possible kinds of explanation one might advance for such CPID, and with the experimental strategies one might adopt to test such explanations. In approaching this problem, I shall limit myself to those areas of individual differences which appear to relate to emotional behaviour and to clinically important disturbances in emotional behaviour, a field traditionally covered by the term "temperament".

Explanations of Personality

The natural way in which to begin a classification of kinds of explanation of CPID is at the nature-nurture boundary. However, I should like to emphasise that explanations of CPID on both sides of this boundary, and indeed explanations of any kind at all, so long as we are right in assuming that behaviour is controlled by the brain and the endocrine system, have one important feature in common (Fig. 1): to be complete, they must specify the enduring structural basis in the neuro-endocrine system (NES), on which the observed behavioural CPID must rest. Thus, it is not only possible, but necessary, to study the physiological basis of personality—whatever view we may adopt as to the relative contribution of heredity and environment to the determination of any particular CPID. In other words, questions about the organisation of personality (whose physical substrate must lie in the NES) are in principle independent of questions about the origins of

* Part of this paper was also presented at the CIBA Foundation symposium on *Physiology, Emotion and Psychosomatic Illness*, London, 1972.

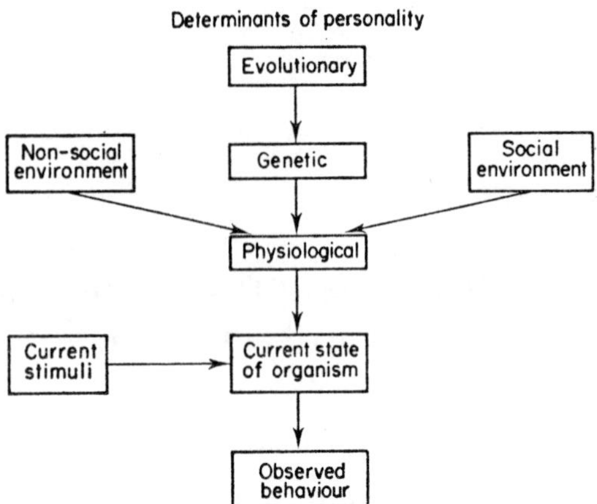

Fig. 1. Consistent patterns of individual differences (CPID), seen in the "observed behaviour" which arises in response to "current stimuli", must reflect the "current state of the organism"; and this, in turn, can produce CPID only in virtue of enduring structural differences in the neuro-endocrine system, whether such "physiological" differences have arisen from "environmental" or "genetic" factors, alone or in interaction with each other. If "genetic" factors are at work, they must be the result of the "evolutionary" pressures of natural selection.

personality. In this paper, we shall address ourselves to aspects of both sorts of question, commencing with the former.

The theorist, and even more the experimentalist, who is concerned with questions about the organization of personality at a physiological level is at once faced with a huge dilemma. Descriptions of CPID, with the exception of a few pioneering studies by workers such as Broadhurst (1960) and Bruell (1967) in the field of psychogenetics, and Royce (1966), applying factor-analytic methods to animal behaviour, are entirely concerned with our own species, and, furthermore, are heavily weighted towards a kind of behaviour for which an animal analogue is peculiarly difficult to find: the answering of questionnaires. On the other hand, our only way of studying the physiological basis of personality adequately is to use experimental animals; for otherwise, we are limited to those unfortunate natural experiments in which a patient suffers injury to the brain. (I leave aside the study of correlations between peripheral physiological variables, such as blood pressure or heart rate, and personality characteristics, for, while such experiments may undoubtedly uncover relationships of importance, it is quite wrong to suppose that change in the autonomic nervous system is any more direct an indication of what is going on in the central nervous system than is behaviour itself. Thus, the inclusion of variables describing the activity of the autonomic nervous system along with other variables describing behaviour merely amplifies our description of CPID—it does nothing to elucidate causality.)

Crossing the Gap Between Animal and Man

The result of this situation is that we are faced with an "animal–Man" gap, and this gap has to be crossed. There are three ways in principle in which we can cross it (Fig. 2). Either we must find a way of matching physiology between Man and our experimental animals, or a way of matching behaviour, or a way of matching CPID. The first is usually impossible, precisely because we have no way of studying the brain properly in Man. However, as we shall see in a later part of this paper,

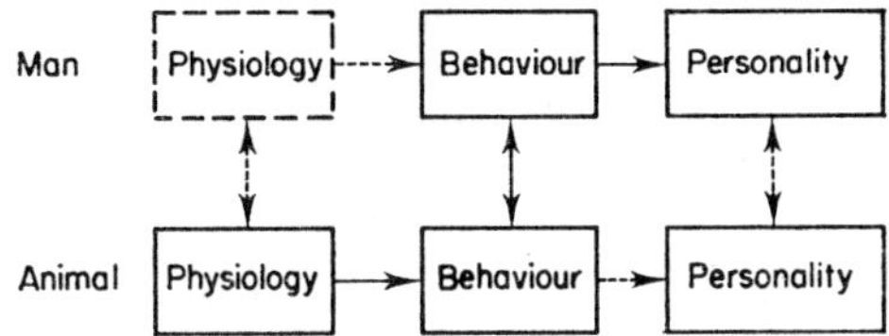

Fig. 2. Bridging the physiology–personality gap. This can rarely be done by matching physiology between Man (in whom personality is studied) and animals (in which the brain may be studied). More usually it is necessary to match behaviour between the two levels. Matching personality itself involves even more assumptions than does matching behaviour.

it is possible to make some progress along this route by the study of sex differences.

The second way of crossing the animal–Man gap, by matching behaviour, is the one which will occupy us for the first part of this paper. The general line of argument here is to suppose that, underlying a particular CPID in Man, there is inter-individual variation in a particular psychological function. This function is presumed to be performed in an essentially similar way, and to depend on essentially similar physiological mechanisms, in the animal species in which we are going to conduct physiological experiments. The psychological function will be displayed in a particular kind of behaviour. We may therefore study the personality correlates of this behaviour in Man (testing the original assumption that the CPID in question is indeed related to this kind of behaviour) and the physiological basis of this behaviour in the animal's NES. In order to do this, of course, we must be able to match behaviour patterns between animals and Man.

This second way of crossing the animal–Man gap immediately raises the issue of how we judge that Man and an animal species (or two different animal species, for that matter) are displaying "the same" behaviour: is a Man pointing a gun at another "aggressive" in the same way as a rat "boxing" with another? Answers to questions of this nature bear an irreducibly theoretical stamp: to say that behaviour pattern X is similar to behaviour pattern Y is to say that they are both executed by the same kind of mechanism and that this mechanism is operated on by the same set of variables. And, since it is precisely an understanding of the mechanisms governing behaviour which is usually lacking, we see that, at the very outset, if we are indeed to tackle the problem of the physiological basis of personality via behaviour matching, we must commit ourselves to the hazardous task of theory-building. One of the aims of the present paper is to offer the general lines of a theory which might bridge the animal–Man gap for certain kinds of emotional behaviour.

Let us be clear what kind of theory-building this is. The assumption is (Gray, 1968) that, for a given species, we may draw up a blue-print for the general form taken by the organismic machine. This machine (Fig. 3) will have various interacting sub-systems and components, each concerned with fulfilling various functions performed by the machine:

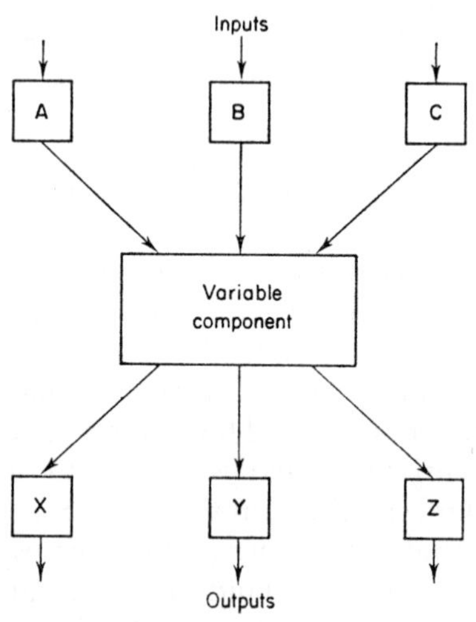

Fig. 3. Machines with "personality". The "variable component" allows the inputs, A, B and C through with varying degrees of ease in different individuals, so producing differences in the frequency or amplitude of the outputs, X, Y and Z. The correlations between the observations made on X, Y and Z will form a "consistent pattern of individual differences".

e.g. eating, sexual behaviour, fearful behaviour, etc. CPID will then be explained as systematic variation in parameters of the various subsystems and components: sensitivity to inputs, speed of initiation of activity, etc. in subsystems 1, 2, 3, etc. will vary systematically among the set of machines (i.e. among the individual members of the species). Thus, each CPID will relate to a particular subsystem within the general machine. Our general blue-print is, in other words, a design for a "conceptual nervous system" (CNS: Hebb, 1955). It is based on behavioural facts, which it attempts to explain. But, in the long run (since in fact it can only exist in the NES), it must be in agreement with what we eventually discover about the real brain. Thus, implicitly, it is a theory about how the real brain is organized; and, if it is a correct theory, there must be components and subsystems in the real brain to match the ones in the blue-print. There is then room for a further set of hypotheses co-ordinating the blue-print with anatomically and/or physiologically specified subsystems in the NES: e.g. a hypothesis stating that the component regulating the general level of arousal is the ascending reticular activating system of the midbrain, or that behavioural inhibition is mediated by the septal area and the hippocampus. Finally, in making our attempt to use behaviour-matching to cross the animal–Man gap, we make one further assumption: that the general form of the machine for the kinds of behaviour which interest us is, both functionally (i.e. at the level of the CNS) and anatomico-physiologically (at the level of the NES), the same in the animal species investigated and in Man. This chain of hypothesis formation is illustrated in Fig. 4.

Faced with such a very long line of assumptions, the tougher-minded empiricists among our number will have every reason to throw up their hands in horror and look for alternatives. Unfortunately, I do not

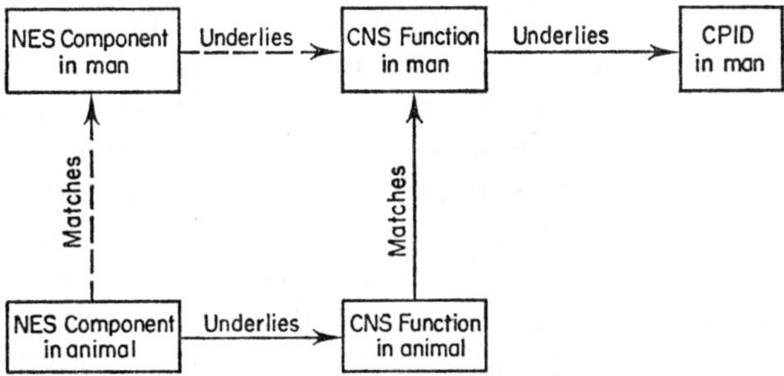

Fig. 4. Chain of hypotheses involved in behaviour matching. Solid arrows indicate links relatively accessible to experimental investigation, dashed arrows those relatively inaccessible. Compare Fig. 2.

believe that any simpler alternatives exist. Many as our assumptions are, they are one less than the assumptions needed if we try to match, not behaviour, but CPID themselves between animal and Man. For this strategy demands that, as well as a similarity between the general form of the machine for the animal species and our own, the CPID themselves are essentially similar at the two levels. Yet this seems a very strong assumption. It seems reasonable to suppose that the changing selection pressures at work on different species, as well as changing patterns of environmental influences during ontogenetic development, will be able to alter CPID between species very much more quickly than they are able to alter the general way in which a group of related species (e.g. the mammals) solve problems facing them all, such as how to learn to approach rewards, how to keep away from danger, etc. Given this argument, and the fact that most of our data on human CPID come from questionnaire responses, I think we would do well to prefer behaviour-matching to personality-matching as the first strategy to try; and given the general impossibility of matching via physiology (with the exception of the study of sex differences), it is, indeed, the only strategy to try. The assumptions on which it is based may be false; in which case the attempt will fail. But the alternative, it seems, is not to make the attempt at all.

In any case, at least some of our assumptions are probably less far-fetched than might at first sight seem, especially if our concern is with emotional behaviour. If all else fails, we can always abandon the rat and move closer along the phylogenetic scale to our own species, eventually reaching the chimpanzee, as we are counselled to do by Drewe, Ettlinger, Milner and Passingham (1970). Given the recency with which we and the chimpanzees reached the parting of the ways—estimates vary from four to twenty million years (Simons, 1969), which is as nothing in the eyes of natural selection—it is extremely implausible that we and they do not still share many behavioural mechanisms. But even if we confine ourselves to the rat and other favourite laboratory animals, including even the pigeon, it is abundantly clear that many behavioural processes originally observed in these species can be found at work in Man; we shall see an example of this later, when we consider some of Nicholson's experiments on peak shift in children (Nicholson and Gray, 1972; Gray and Nicholson, 1971). Emotional mechanisms, in particular, appear to possess considerable phylogenetic longevity. It is clear that, for the most part, they are anatomically located in the mid-brain and the limbic forebrain, rather than in the neocortex, and the basic anatomy of these structures is essentially similar throughout the mammalian phylum (Brodal, 1969). Behaviourally, also, it seems reasonable to suppose that we are more likely to find something in common between, say, rat, cat, monkey and Man if we consider emotional behaviour than if we consider problem-solving behaviour. For example, in the case of aggressive behaviour, the difference between the sexes (males showing much more intra-specific aggression than females) is common to all the species mentioned, and many more (Gray, 1971b).

There is another advantage attached to the choice of emotional behaviour for the behaviour-matching strategy outlined above. As I have said, it is essential in answering questions of similarity about behaviour to start from a theory. The theories which have in fact been employed for this task by others who have speculated about the physiological basis of personality (e.g. Pavlov, as described by Teplov, 1964; Eysenck, 1957, 1967; Nebylitsyn, 1972) have invariably been chosen from the field of animal learning (Gray, 1972a). Now, animal learning theory is often dismissed as being of no relevance to human learning. And, if the human learning concerned is, say, the learning of language, or mathematics, or painting, or playing the piano, I believe this dismissal is probably correct. For what animal learning theory is really about, is the learning of emotional responses and of behaviour which is instrumental in regulating the occurrence of emotion-provoking stimuli (e.g. Mowrer, 1960). Applied, then, to these same kinds of learning in Man, we may hope to find that animal learning theory is much more relevant. I have tried to show elsewhere (Gray, 1971a) that this is indeed so for the area of fearful behaviour.

I have so far spoken of the problem of the physiological organization of personality as though it were totally separate from that of the origins of personality. Although this is true in principle, in practice the divorce is of course harder to make. It will be clear from the foregoing that, in order to use the behaviour-matching strategy, we must choose behaviour which is phylogenetically old and essentially unchanged along that pathway of mammalian evolution which connects our experimental animals to ourselves. Clearly, the general control of behaviour which meets this specification is likely to be largely genetic in our own species. It is, of course, logically possible that, even though the general laws of the behaviour concerned are entirely genetic, individual variation in the application of these laws is entirely environmentally determined; so that the difference in principle between the organisation and the origins of personality still stands. But in practice it is likely that behaviour which is so heavily under genetic control from the standpoint of general mechanisms is also going to display a large inherited component in its CPID. It would seem wise, therefore, to choose for one's first forays into the problem of untangling the physiological organization of personality CPID which depend to an important extent on genetic determination.

With these preliminaries of a very general nature behind us, we are in a position to consider the criteria by which we would choose CPID and behaviour to fit our needs. First, we would want to choose rather broad CPID which, at the human level, appear to affect emotional behaviour in important ways. Second, the CPID should be likely to reflect individual variation in the functioning of behavioural mechanisms common either to most mammals or at least to most primates (if primates are available as experimental animals). Third, since we are only going to be able to answer questions of behavioural similarity in terms of a theory, we must have a theory applicable to the kinds of psychological function apparently involved. Fourth, we must have some paradigmatic situations in which we can study the relevant forms of behaviour in both animal and Man. And, finally, we must have some reasonable guesses as to the physiological control of the relevant form of behaviour in the experimental animal's NES. Given all of this, we can start on the job of exploring more fully the personality correlates of the behaviour in Man and its physiological basis in animals.

It is possible, of course, to go through this same chain of argument in reverse. The line we have just followed started with the human CPID: this is essentially the route followed by Eysenck (1957, 1967) in seeking to understand the physiological basis of introversion–extraversion and neuroticism. But one may also start with established behavioural mechanisms in animals and ask oneself what kinds of CPID one would expect to find in Man if the same behavioural mechanisms still exist in Man and if they are subject to systematic inter-individual variation. This is the route followed by Teplov (see Gray, 1964a) and Nebylitsyn (1972) in applying Pavlov's work on the dog to the problem of the organization of personality in Man (Gray, 1968). In this paper, I intend to follow both routes: for introversion–extraversion and neuroticism I shall move, in Eysenck's company, towards the animal data, but I shall arrive at somewhat different conclusions from those Eysenck has drawn; then I shall move back towards the human CPID from a consideration of animal data, drawn from both learning theory and physiological psychology, on the organization of emotional behaviour in rats, cats and monkeys.

In order to make these excursions, we shall need two maps; one of the current state of learning theory, as it affects our understanding of emotional behaviour; the other of the NES insofar as we understand how it controls emotional behaviour. In the next part of this paper I shall briefly sketch the essentials of these two maps.

The Emotions in Ordinary Language

It is not uncommon for the term "emotion" to be dismissed in our textbooks as being no more than a "chapter-heading". If so, it has usually been allotted to the wrong chapter; for, as we shall soon see, it is in the chapters on learning and physiology that a true theory of emotion has been rather stealthily ripening into maturity. Philosophers, too, have not been at all certain that there is a real area of discourse hidden behind the term "emotion" awaiting their technique of analysis; though some kind of consensus appears to have developed, and this is in entire agreement with the conclusions we shall reach in this paper—that the emotion-words have something to do with the appraisal of the objects which give rise to the emotional states as "good" or "bad" (e.g. Mischel, 1969). Given all this doubt on the part of the experts, one would expect the layman to have great difficulty in understanding what emotions are all about. Yet I doubt whether anyone normally fluent in the use of the English language would have difficulty in deciding that "fear", "disappointment", "hope" and "anger", for example, are emotions while "hunger", "thirst" or "drowsiness" are not. So somewhere there is a reasonably clear distinction being drawn between states which are or are not emotional. A look at the use of what are presumably emotional states by learning theorists will, I think, enable us to see what that distinction is.

It is clear that, from the learning theorist's point of view, both emotions and "drives" (as he would term "hunger", "thirst" and probably "drowsiness") are hypothetical internal states of the organism, i.e. states attributed to the CNS. These states have to be invented in order to account for the fact that an organism's reactions to identical environmental inputs are not themselves invariant. If they were, the radical behaviourist programme of quietly describing stimulus–response relationships without recourse to theory or neuronal physiology would be a feasible one. As it is, we have to suppose that the variability inherent in the way organisms respond to their environments (assuming it is not totally random) reflects some systematic set of internal states which they may enter. The question, then is: what differentiates those internal states we prefer to call "drives" from those we prefer to call "emotions"?

The answer, I think, is that "drives" are internal states which are principally caused by changes *internal* to the organism, while "emotions" are internal states which are principally caused by events *external* to the organism. Thus the states of hunger, thirst and drowsiness grow with the passage of time more or less independently of the environment in which the organism is placed, though it is true that they can be reversed or hindered in their development by environmental events (food, water or excessive stimulation for the three drives respectively). Fear, disappointment, hope and anger, on the other hand, are normally consequent upon the occurrence of particular kinds of environmental events. This analysis can be supported by a consideration of pathology. It is when drive states become dependent on specific environmental events, or alternatively, cease to show the usual variation with time independently of environmental inputs, that we suspect illness: as in, say, the obese individuals described by Schachter (1967) or the condition of anorexia nervosa. Conversely, it is when emotional states arise with no precipitating environmental event that we smell pathology, as in "free-floating" anxiety or "endogenous" depression. Our vocabulary is particularly instructive in the case of erotic internal states. Sexual behaviour, from the point of view of the internal–external control distinction, is a borderline case: it is about equally dependent on the internal milieu (hormonal status, in particular) and on appropriate external stimuli (optimally, those associated with a willing and attractive member of the opposite sex). In line with the distinction between internal and external causation of the typical drives and emotions, we do not, I think, regard "feeling sexy" where the emphasis is on internal causation as an emotion, while we do so regard "being in love" where the emphasis is on a particular object in the environment.

Excursions into linguistic philosophy of this kind normally do no more than elucidate the use made of language; the distinctions uncovered need not correspond to distinctions which exist in reality, and only the latter are of interest to the behavioural scientist. However, in this case, the distinctions apparently made in ordinary language turn out to correspond rather well both to distinctions which have arisen in the theory of learning and to lines of demarcation within the neuroendocrine system. Moreover, as I shall claim later on in this paper, it is precisely individual differences in modes of emotional reaction to external stimuli which underlie the major dimensions of temperament and the major psychiatric syndromes. It is necessary, therefore, to obtain some idea of what distinguishes the emotional states from others, and ordinary language, on this occasion, appears to be based on some useful insights.

The Emotions as Deduced from the Study of Learning

If the emotions are internal states elicited by external stimuli, what kinds of stimuli are these? The answer to this question is contained in the theory of the emotions which has grown out of the study of learning. This theory can trace its origin to a number of sources: Hull's (1952) and Spence's (1956) notions of the goal-gradient and incentive motivation; Estes and Skinner's (1942) work on the "conditioned emotional response"; Miller's (1951) and Mowrer's (1946) work on the role of fear in avoidance learning; Amsel's (1958) treatment of nonreward as eliciting "frustration"; all culminating in Mowrer's (1960) important textbook. With this body of work behind us, it is possible to give a moderately simple definition of the emotions as "those (hypothetical) states in the CNS which are produced by reinforcing events or by stimuli which have in the subject's previous experience been followed by reinforcing events". Thus, "fear", in Miller's and Mowrer's use, is a hypothetical state in the CNS elicited by stimuli previously followed by unconditioned punishing events; "conditioned frustration", in Amsel's use, is the state produced by stimuli previously followed by frustrative nonreward (i.e. by the nondelivery of anticipated reward); and so on. Most of the theorists who have been responsible for developing this kind of approach to the emotions have espoused some kind of "two-process learning theory" (e.g. Rescorla and Solomon, 1967). In this kind of theory the emotional states are either innately elicited by unconditioned reinforcing events or may come to be elicited, as a result of classical Pavlovian conditioning by contiguity, by previously neutral stimuli. As a result of such classical conditioning, stimuli in the subject's environment acquire secondary reinforcing properties, either of an appetitive kind (eliciting approach behaviour) or of an aversive kind (eliciting withdrawal behaviour), and thus control the subject's instrumental behaviour by way of some kind of reinforcement principle. The details in which this general theoretical form is clothed vary somewhat from author to author; representative samples can be found in Mowrer's (1960) book, in Amsel's (1962) well-known paper in the *Psychological Review*, or in my own recent review of research on fear (Gray, 1971a). For our present purposes, the important information to abstract from this theoretical approach and from the experimental work to which it has given rise concerns the number of distinguishable emotional states there are, and the way in which each of them is organised.

The first half of this question can be converted into the related question: how many distinguishable classes of reinforcing events and conditioned signals of reinforcing events are there? If we first consider the maximum possible number of such classes, on logical grounds, and then determine whether any of these classes ought, on empirical grounds, to be collapsed, we should be left with the number of actual distinguishable classes of reinforcing events, i.e. of distinguishable emotional states.

In general terms, it would seem that reinforcing events can be first divided into the conditioned and the unconditioned variety; and that each of these can be divided into appetitive or aversive; and that each of these can either be presented (contingently upon some response or other) or withheld. This leads to the classification set out in Table I.

Table I

	Unconditioned		Conditioned	
Presentation	R	P	R	P
Omission or Termination	$\bar{R}$	$\bar{P}$	$\bar{R}$	$\bar{P}$

Classification of reinforcing events:
R = reward; P = punishment.

There are grounds for believing, however, that this logical classification can indeed be reduced on empirical grounds. There is very good evidence, from both purely behavioural experiments and from experiments in physiological psychology, that the effects of signals of punishment and those of signals of frustrative nonreward are functionally identical and work through the same system in the NES (Miller, 1964; Wagner, 1966; Gray, 1967, 1971a). There is much less evidence, though there is some (Olds and Olds, 1965; Gray, 1971a; Bull, 1970; Grossen, Kostansek and Bolles, 1969), in favour of a second simplifying hypothesis first proposed by Mowrer (1960; see also Gray, 1971a, 1972a), that the effects of signals of reward and those of signals of "relieving non-punishment" (i.e. the nondelivery of anticipated punishment, involved in active avoidance behaviour) are functionally and physiologically identical. We shall, however, proceed on the assumption that this hypothesis, too, is correct. We are thus left with two basic classes of signals and reinforcing events: signals of reward (including non-punishment) and signals of punishment (including nonreward), the former eliciting approach behaviour (including active avoidance, which is construed as approach to safety signals: see Gray, 1971a) and the latter behavioural inhibition or passive avoidance behaviour.

In considering the unconditioned reinforcing stimuli, we are placed in something of a dilemma. Common sense names no emotional state as being set up by, say, food or water (as distinct from stimuli signalling the availability of food or water, which common sense, with Mowrer (1960), is prepared to regard as eliciting "hope"). Within learning theory, equally, this kind of stimulus is thought of as terminating internal states (namely, drives) rather than initiating them. Furthermore, the forms of behaviour initiated by presentation of food, water, etc. are quite diverse, depending on the particular stimulus presented (i.e. such consummatory acts as eating, drinking, copulation, etc.), again in distinction to the forms of behaviour initiated by stimuli signalling availability of positive reinforcers, which all elicit similar forms of approach behaviour independently of the actual positive reinforcers signalled. Thus one would wish to exclude the states elicited by unconditioned positive reinforcers from the list of the emotions. On the other hand, the state or states elicited by presentation of unconditioned aversive stimuli, which typically give rise to fight or flight behaviour, are ones which we would equally strongly expect to find in a list of the emotions. It seems, then, that we have to depart from the tidy logical classification set out in Table I and include these, but not the states elicited by unconditioned positive reinforcers, among the emotions.

As in the case of signals of aversive events, we may pursue simplicity by grouping together unconditioned punishment and unconditioned frustrative nonreward, for there is evidence that these events are functionally equivalent in that both elicit a state in which the probability of aggressive behaviour (Ulrich, 1967; Gallup, 1965) or escape behaviour (Adelman and Maatsch, 1954) is increased and behavioural vigour is also increased (Brown *et al.*, 1951; Wagner, 1963; Amsel and Roussel, 1952).

What we may not do, however, is to collapse the states elicited by conditioned and unconditioned aversive events, although common sense (and learning theorists) often name both of them "fear". We may not do this because the behaviour patterns produced by unconditioned aversive events and stimuli warning of these are not only different but often diametrically opposed to each other. Thus, an electric shock applied to the rat causes a great increase in mobility (jumping, running, etc.) and in vocalization (squealing). A conditioned stimulus (CS) regularly followed by such a shock, however, comes to elicit crouching and silence. Similarly, in human subjects, an electric shock produces an increase in heart rate, but a CS preceding the shock comes to elicit heart rate deceleration (Notterman *et al.*, 1952; Obrist, Wood and Perez-Reyes, 1965). Notice that this difference between the unconditioned response (UCR) to punishment and the conditioned response (CR) to signals of punishment is, as far as I know, the only exception to a weak form of the stimulus substitution theory of classical conditioning: namely, any response change which is part of the CR, unless it was elicited by the CS prior to conditioning, is also elicited as a response change in the same direction, though not necessarily of the same magnitude, by the UCS. As I have argued elsewhere (Gray, 1971a), this unusual exception to the laws of classical conditioning suggests that the rat and probably mammals in general, since similar observations may be made in many other species, comes equipped with an innate set of responses, those involved in passive avoidance behaviour, but has to learn to which stimuli it must allocate this set of responses—namely, stimuli which have been followed by unconditioned punishments. The system governing this set of responses appears to be quite distinct from the one which governs responses to the unconditioned punishments themselves.

Thus, on the aversive side, we have, it seems, two emotional states, one elicited by unconditioned punishment and frustrative nonreward, the other by signals of punishment and signals of frustrative nonreward.

Within the former state, one might have expected to be able to distinguish between, on the one hand, an internal state, corresponding to flight or unconditioned escape behaviour (as distinct from learnt escape behaviour, which, like active avoidance behaviour, appears to involve predominantly the system which controls approach behaviour—see Gray, 1971a) and, on the other hand, an internal state corresponding to aggressive behaviour, for both of these forms of behaviour may occur in response to unconditioned aversive stimuli. However, judging from the extensive work of Azrin and his associates (Ulrich, 1967; Gray, 1971a), the factor which determines whether fight or flight occurs in response to such stimuli does not lie in the nature of these stimuli themselves, but rather in other aspects of the environment in which they are presented. Roughly speaking, if escape is possible, the subject will try flight, if not, it will try fight.

It seems, then, that we should not split the emotional states elicited by aversive stimuli into more than two. Thus, *in toto*, the study of learning suggests the existence of three major emotional systems, which we may call the "approach", "stop", and "fight/flight" systems, respectively (Table II).

The Emotions as Deduced from Physiological Psychology

Given the uncertainty which many scientists have felt as to the very existence of a field of study concerned with emotion, it may seem an act of striking boldness to conclude, not only that such a field exists, but also that there are three major emotions; especially when we consider that ordinary language, from which I have sought some support, recognizes the existence of a much greater number of distinct

Table II. Three Major Emotional Systems

Emotional System	Reinforcing Stimuli	Behaviour	Neural Structures
Approach	CS for R and $\bar{P}$	Approach learning; active avoidance; skilled escape; predatory aggression	Olds' reward system especially septal area, medial forebrain bundle and lateral hypothalamus.
Stop	CS for P and $\bar{R}$	Passive avoidance; extinction.	Medial septal area, hippocampus, orbital frontal cortex, caudate nucleus.
Fight/Flight	Unconditioned P and $\bar{R}$	Unconditioned escape; defensive aggression.	Amygdala, stria terminalis, medial hypothalamus, central gray of midbrain.

emotions. It is comforting, therefore, that a survey of studies in which emotional behaviour has been investigated as a function of a variety of interventions in the brain of experimental animals leads to the same conclusion, as well as putting a solid anatomico-physiological basis beneath each of our as yet free-floating emotional states. Since there are a number of available reviews (Grossman, 1967; Deutsch and Deutsch, 1966; Gray, 1971a) of these studies, it will be sufficient here to summarise the main conclusions which can be drawn from existing data.

The first point of interest to emerge from these data is that the distinction we have drawn between, on the one hand, the emotions and, on the other, both drives and consummatory acts is matched by major differences in the anatomical location of the structures governing emotional behaviour, drives and consummatory behaviour. The structures which, as we shall see, are involved in the control of emotional behaviour lie predominantly in the forebrain, and particularly in the limbic system; the main controlling centres for drives and consummatory acts, in contrast, are predominantly located at the level of the hypothalamus and still lower in the midbrain. Some of the work reported by Olds and Olds (1965) strongly suggests that the medial hypothalamus is a kind of major meeting point at which forebrain emotional systems and hypothalamic drive mechanisms may influence each other (see Gray, 1971a).

Within the domain of emotional behaviour, available data strongly point to the existence of three separate, though interacting, neural systems.

One of these has been described in most detail by the self-stimulation technique introduced by Olds (Olds and Olds, 1965), and it is rather clearly involved in the control of approach behaviour. Electrical stimulation of this system is found rewarding, in that the animal works to obtain it by whatever means is made available. The major focus of the self-stimulation phenomenon appears to lie in the medial forebrain bundle and the lateral hypothalamus, and more rostral points in the septal area, to which the medial forebrain bundle projects, also maintain high rates of responding (Fig. 5).

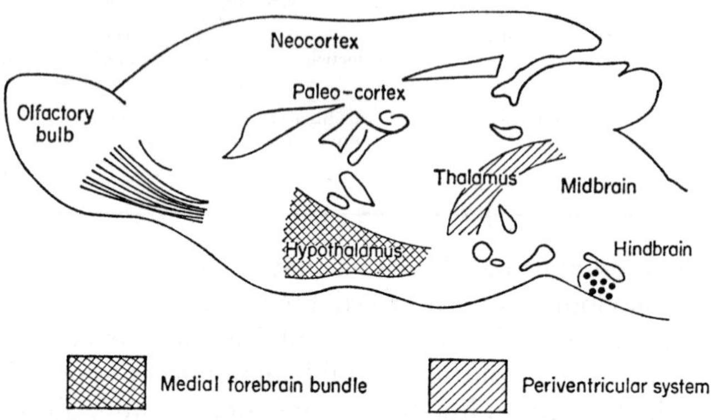

Fig. 5. The approach (medial forebrain bundle) system, as mapped by self-stimulation experiments in the rats by Olds and Olds (1965). The periventricular system consists of points at which stimulation is turned off by the rat; this area is also involved in the system mapped by Hunsperger in the cat as mediating defensive aggression (Fig. 7).

A second system is concerned with behavioural inhibition and involves a series of interconnected structures (Fig. 6) including the hippocampus, the medial septal area, the orbital frontal cortex and the

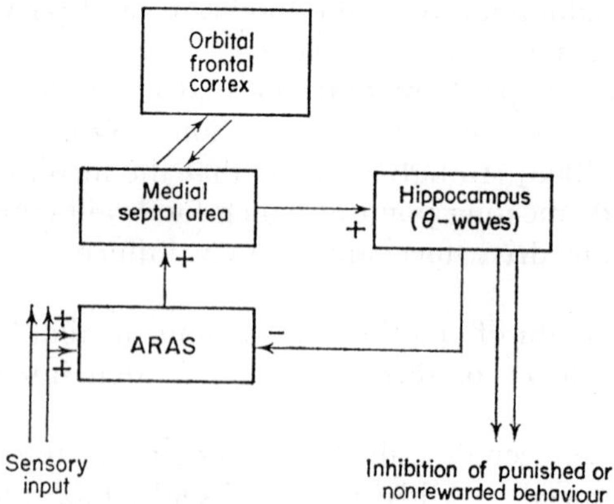

Fig. 6. The septo-hippocampal stop system. See text for further explanation, and Gray (1970a, 1972b).

caudate nucleus (McCleary, 1966; Douglas, 1967; Kimble, 1969; Gray, 1970a, 1970b; Butters and Rosvold, 1969). Lesions in this system impair not only passive avoidance of shock, but also extinction of appetitive behaviour and other behavioural responses to signals of frustrative nonreward, thus offering important support for the equation between signals of punishment and of frustrative nonreward made earlier on psychological grounds. The drug, sodium amytal, which is known to block the behavioural effects of both signals of punishment and signals of frustrative nonreward (Miller, 1964; Wagner, 1966; Gray, 1967; Ison and Rosen, 1967), has been shown by Gray and Ball (1970) probably to exert these effects by way of an alteration in the electrophysiological properties of this system. Although both this system and the Olds approach system involve neurons in the septal area, an experiment by Ball and Gray (1971), coupled with the experiments reported by Gray (1970a), show that this anatomical overlap between the two systems is not accompanied by functional interaction at this locus: the role of the septal area in the control of behavioural inhibition is exercised in virtue of its control over the theta rhythm in the hippocampus, whereas the self-stimulation phenomenon in the septal area is independent of the effects of septal stimulation on hippocampal electrical activity.

The distinction between active and passive avoidance made earlier also receives important support, and physiological underpinning, from a consideration of experiments involving these two systems. Those lesions to the behavioural inhibition system which impair passive avoidance also enhance active avoidance in the shuttlebox (McCleary, 1966; Douglas, 1967; Olton and Isaacson, 1968; Albert and Bignami, 1968), as does sodium amytal (Kamano, Martin and Powell, 1966). Conversely, electrical *stimulation* of Olds' reward system also impairs passive avoidance (more precisely, the Estes–Skinner conditioned emotional response: Brady and Conrad, 1960) and improves active avoidance (Stein, 1965). In support of the hypothesis, suggested earlier in this paper (and see Gray, 1971a, in press a), that active avoidance is learnt on the same basis as approach to rewards, Olds and Olds (1965) report that treatments (administration of chlorpromazine and cortical spreading depression) which disrupted self-stimulation also disrupted learnt escape behaviour. Furthermore, the disruption in learnt escape behaviour caused by spreading cortical depression was accompanied by reduced firing in neurons of Olds' reward system. Thus we may reasonably conclude that Olds' reward system mediates approach behaviour in response to signals of either reward or relieving nonpunishment, i.e. it is isomorphic to the approach system delineated earlier on behavioural grounds; and that the behavioural inhibition system just described mediates passive avoidance in response to signals of either punishment or frustrative nonreward, i.e. it is isomorphic to the stop system delineated on behavioural grounds.

The third system, located in the forebrain, has been described partly through a series of lesioning experiments (see Deutsch and Deutsch, 1966, for review) and partly as a result of de Molina and Hunsperger's (1962) stimulation experiments in the cat. It is involved in fight/flight behaviour, and involves structures (Fig. 7) in the amygdala, the medial

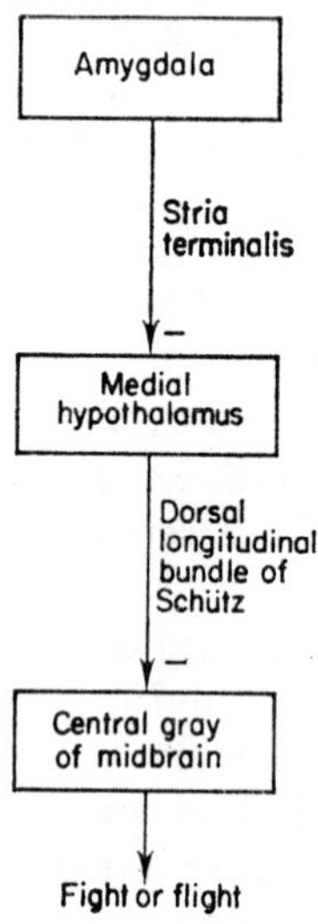

Fig. 7. The fight/flight system as mapped by Hunsperger's stimulation experiments in the cat. See text for explanation.

hypothalamus (to which the amygdala is connected by the stria terminalis) and the central gray of the midbrain (to which the medial hypothalamus is connected by way of the dorsal longitudinal bundle of Schütz). Stimulation of this system produces a cat with arched back and raised hair, which hisses and growls and will attempt to escape, if escape is possible, will learn to turn such stimulation off if such a response is available, or will attack anything suitable in its environment (the optimum stimulus for attack being another cat) if the former two courses of action are not open to it. As in the case of experiments on the intact animal (Ulrich, 1967), then, whether fight or flight occurs depends not on the eliciting stimulus, but on the environment in which the eliciting stimulus is presented. Thus, we may regard this system as isomorphic with the fight/flight system already delineated on behavioural grounds, and our Table II is complete.

An important distinction which emerges from the physiological work on the fight/flight system—and one which will be of importance to us when we consider sex differences in aggression—is that between defensive and predatory aggression. In the cat, these two forms of aggression are very distinct behaviourally in any case. Defensive aggression has already been described above, for it is this that is elicited by electrical stimulation of Hunsperger's system. Predatory aggression is typically seen when a cat is stalking a rat or a bird: the back is not arched, the hair is smooth and no vocalization occurs. This kind of aggression is never elicited from electrodes in the fight/flight system; rather, it can be elicited from electrodes located in the lateral hypothalamus, where eating behaviour is also controlled. Furthermore, whereas stimulation which elicits defensive attack is negatively reinforcing (Adams and Flynn, 1966), stimulation which elicits predatory attack is rewarding by Olds' self-stimulation test (Roberts and Kiess, 1964; Hutchinson and Renfrew, 1966). Thus the fight/flight system is concerned only with defensive attack: i.e. the kind of aggression usually elicited by a conspecific or by a threatening animal from a different species (cat–cat or cat–dog, rather than cat–rat). Predatory aggression, in contrast, appears to be mediated by the approach system.

Having delineated these three major emotional systems, it remains to say a few words about their interrelations. These are set out schematically in Fig. 8.

As already mentioned, the experiments reviewed by Olds and Olds (1965), as well as de Molina's and Hunsperger's (1962) experiments, strongly suggest that the medial hypothalamus is a nodal point in the interrelations between the approach, stop and fight/flight systems. Hunsperger's experiments on the fight/flight system in the cat have produced the clearest evidence to indicate what may be the main principle on which these interrelations are based. The results of combined lesion and stimulation experiments showed that the medial hypothalamus exerts a tonic inhibition over the final common pathway for fight/flight behaviour, the components of which are organized in the central gray of the midbrain. The amygdala (which projects to the medial hypothalamus by way of the stria terminalis) in turn, upon the receipt of appropriate environmental signals, inhibits the medial hypothalamus, thus disinhibiting the midbrain fight/flight output mechanism. The interrelations between this amygdalo–hypothalamo–midbrain fight/flight system and the septo-hippocampal stop system are indicated by a series of experiments by Kling and his collaborators and

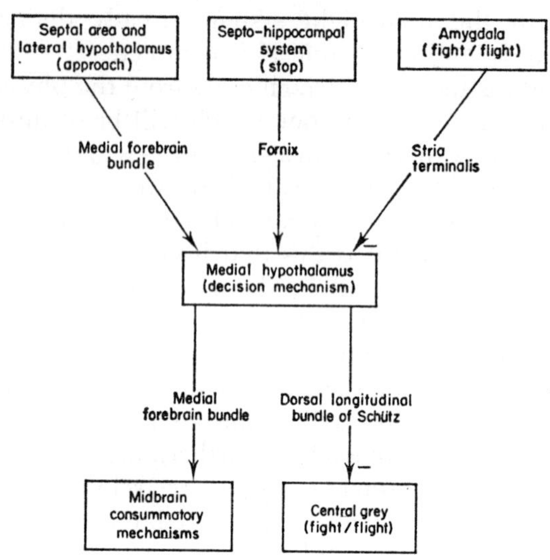

Fig. 8. Interrelations between three emotional systems. The medial hypothalamus appears to act as a nodal point in the resolution of influences proceeding downstream from limbic structures. These promote approach behaviour (from the septal area via the medial forebrain bundle) or fight/flight behaviour (from the amygdala via the stria terminalis). The medial hypothalamus may inhibit both these outcomes via its control of the final common pathways in the midbrain, and this inhibition is intensified by influences proceeding from the septo-hippocampal stop system via the fornix and mammillary bodies. From Gray (1971a).

by King and Meyer (see reviews by Deutsch and Deutsch, 1966 and Gray, 1971a) in which rats were subjected to both septal and amygdaloid lesions and the resulting "septal rage" syndrome, or its absence, was noted. These experiments suggest that the medial hypothalamic tonic inhibition of the midbrain final common pathway for fight/flight behaviour is enhanced by influences proceeding from the septal area. Thus, the outcome (fight/flight or inhibition of fight/flight) on any particular occasion depends on the balance of influences playing upon the medial hypothalamus from the amygdala and the septal area respectively. The most likely route whereby influences from the septal area reach the medial hypothalamus is via septal control of the electrical activity of the hippocampus, as suggested by Gray (1970a); the major outflow of the hippocampus, in turn, goes by way of the fornix to the mammillary bodies, situated medially at the base of the hypothalamus.

Similar principles of organization appear to be at work in the case of approach behaviour. Behavioural fragments of particular consummatory acts appear to be organized in the midbrain in a rather specific manner (Glickman and Schiff, 1967). "Drive centres", in which information concerning the current state of the internal milieu is integrated and appetitive and subsequent consummatory behaviour is initiated, are located at the hypothalamic level. For example, in the case of eating behaviour, the execution of food-seeking and ingestive behaviour is known to be mediated by the lateral hypothalamus, while the integration of information concerning the internal milieu appears to be mediated by the medial hypothalamus (specifically the ventromedial nucleus: Grossman, 1967). The medial hypothalamus exerts inhibitory control over the lateral hypothalamus (Grossman, 1967; Sclafani and Grossman, 1969), this inhibition presumably being released when appropriate messages concerning the state of the internal milieu are received by the medial hypothalamus. Little is known about the structures which mediate the effects of environmental signals concerning the availability or rewarding value of food (i.e. those which mediate Hull's "incentive motivation" or Mowrer's "hope"); but the available evidence suggests loci in the forebrain, perhaps in the septal area (e.g. Donovick, Burright and Gittelson, 1968) or more likely in the amygdala (Klüver and Bucy, 1937; Grossman, 1967). The role of the septo-hippocampal stop system in inhibiting appetitive behaviour in the face of signals of punishment or frustrative nonreward is well-known (Gray, 1970a). Presumably, this inhibition too is exercised along the pathway (fornix to mammillary bodies) described at the end of the previous paragraph.

Papez's (1937) and McLean's (1949) original intuitions that emotion is a function of the limbic structures of the forebrain, then, appear to have been good ones. The distinction which we have in our ordinary language, and which is presumably based on some kind of demarcation in our common subjective experience—between emotions and those other kinds of internal state called by psychologists "drives"—appears to correspond rather well to a distinction which, in learning theory terms, is one between internal states which arise in consequence of exposure to certain kinds of environmental influences and those which are autonomous; and which, in anatomical terms, is one between internal states mediated by structures in the limbic system—septal area, hippocampus, amygdala—and internal states mediated by structures at the level of the hypothalamus or lower. In this connection, it is worth noting that the septo-hippocampal stop system, unlike the approach and fight/flight systems, appears to have no continuation below the hypothalamus: passive avoidance behaviour does not seem to be elicited by midbrain stimulation (Glickman and Schiff, 1967). This observation fits well with the view (e.g., Voronin 1962) that behavioural inhibition is phylogenetically newer than the other behavioural functions we have been considering.

The Organization of Emotion and the Organization of Personality

We now have our two maps of the organization of emotional behaviour, one drawn from learning theory and the other from physiological psychology. And fortunately—though perhaps for no more profound reason than that the draughtsman has been the same for both—they sufficiently resemble each other for us to collapse them into one. Can they be of any use to us in interpreting the factor-analytic data on the major dimensions of personality in Man?

The universe of scientists can be rather easily dichotomized into splitters and joiners. Among the factor analysts, Thurstone, Cattell and Guilford are splitters, and Spearman, Vernon and Eysenck are joiners. In the present company, a list such as this is ample to make the distinction clear. Both learning theorists and physiological psychologists would at once recognize the curious exercise I have been engaged in so far in this paper as that of a pathological joiner. Thus it should surprise no one that I am going to take as my multivariate starting point the work of H. J. Eysenck (1967; Eysenck, H. J. and Eysenck, S. B. G. 1969).

Eysenck has claimed that, in the temperamental sphere, there are three major axes of variation in behaviour, behavioural abnormalities, laboratory test performance and questionnaire responses: introversion–extraversion (*E*), neuroticism (*N*) and psychoticism (*P*) (e.g. Eysenck, H. J. and Eysenck, S. B. G. 1969; Eysenck, S. B. G. and Eysenck, H. J. 1968, 1969). He has devoted both experimental and theoretical attention to them in degrees which correspond to the order in which I have listed them. For *E*, he has offered two major theories as to both its psychological and its physiological basis, the second (Eysenck, 1967) being a modification of the first (Eysenck, 1957), and he has reviewed a great volume of experimental work, much of it from his own laboratory, concerning each. His theoretical and experimental treatment of *N* has been much less elaborate, but still substantial; for this dimension, he has offered only one major psycho-physiological theory (Eysenck, 1967). His work on *P* is still (e.g. Eysenck, S. B. G. and Eysenck, H. J. 1968, 1969) mainly at the descriptive level, and he has not yet presented a theory concerning its psychological or physiological basis.

In the next section of this paper I wish briefly to summarize an alternative theory (Gray, 1970b) of the psycho-physiological basis of *E* and *N*, one which bears a close family resemblance to Eysenck's, but which parts company from his at one or two crucial points. I shall then offer a rash speculation concerning the psycho-physiological basis of *P*.

It is well known that factor analysis can tell you how many independent dimensions of variation there are in a given domain of data, but not where the resulting factors should be located so that they correspond to underlying causal factors, assuming that these exist. If we assume that Eysenck is correct in his conclusion that there are two major factors in the domain of data containing *E* and *N* (ignoring, for the moment, psychoticism)—and I am well aware that this conclusion is controversial (Cattell and Scheier, 1961)—we may nonetheless question the correctness of his location of the *E* and *N* axes. Precisely because factor analysis cannot itself locate the lines of causal influence, the only way in which it is possible to decide whether Eysenck's location of his *E* and *N* factors is correct is to embed these factors into a causal theory (of the kind whose general form has been discussed earlier in this paper) and then successfully to test the theory. It is very much to Eysenck's credit that he has realized that this is the only way out of the mathematical circle, with its infinity of possible solutions, in which unaided factor analysis must find itself. Indeed, his theory of *E* and *N*, and the experimental tests to which he has subjected this theory, represent easily the most sustained and successful attempt yet made to break out of this circle. Thus, while the modified theory of *E* and *N* which I wish briefly to present here suggests that Eysenck has wrongly located the main lines of causal influence within the domain of data described by *E* and *N*, both the general approach exemplified by this theory, and the particular form the theory takes, build very much on the foundations he has laid.

I have gone into the reasons which motivate this modification of Eysenck's theory of *E* and *N* elsewhere (Gray, 1970b) in some detail, so here I will do no more than indicate the nature of the modification and the main evidence requiring it. Figs. 9 and 10 set out the main features of Eysenck's theory of *E* (ignoring differences in *N*, for the moment, and assuming that we are concerned to explain the differences between groups of introverts and extroverts both of whom are high on *N*), and of the suggested modification of this theory. The modification is carried out at two levels, one psychological (i.e. in the nature of the specific function regarded as underlying individual differences in *E* in the CNS) and the other physiological (i.e. in the nature of the system in the NES regarded as exercising this function).

At the psychological level it is necessary to alter Eysenck's hypothesis that introverts are, in general, more easily conditioned than extroverts. The evidence is that introverts display greater conditionability than extroverts only under special conditions and that, under other conditions, the reverse is true (Eysenck and Levey, 1972). The special conditions which favour conditionability in the introvert, relative to the extravert, do not appear to be sufficiently wide for the postulate of

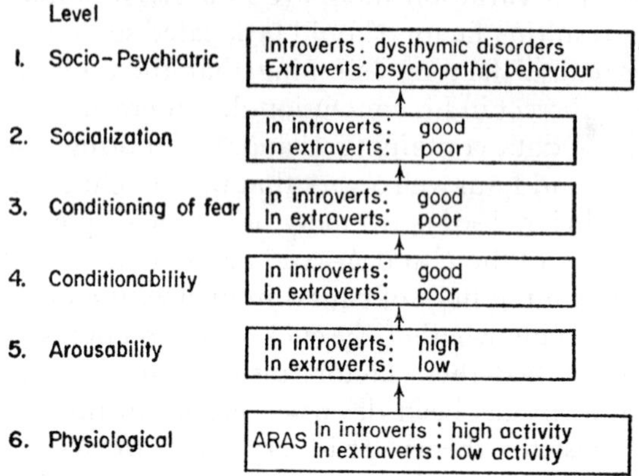

Fig. 9. Basic structure of Eysenck's theory of introversion–extraversion. Level 1 is the explicandum: the logic of explanation proceeds from level 6 upwards, the arrows signifying "therefore". From Gray (1970b).

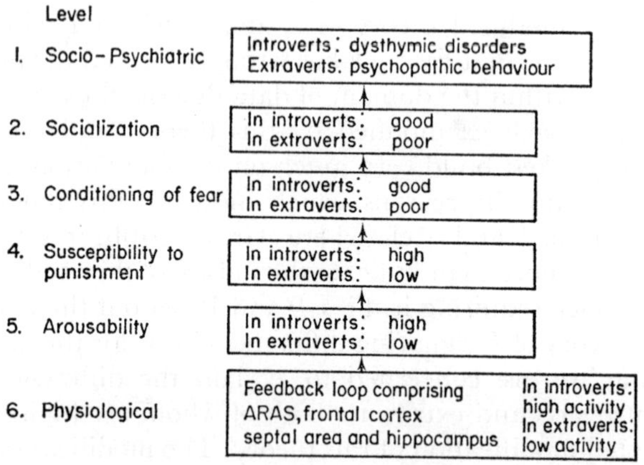

Fig. 10. Proposed modifications of Eysenck's theory of introversion–extraversion. Compare Fig. 9: alterations are made at levels 4 and 6. The physiological system at level 6 is the one shown in Fig. 6. From Gray (1970b).

greater conditionability in the introvert to continue to bear the theoretical superstructure which (Fig. 9) rests upon it (Gray, 1970b). I have suggested that it be replaced by the postulate that the introvert is, relative to the extravert, more susceptible to threats of punishment (and, via the equation between signals of punishment and signals of frustrative nonreward, more susceptible to threats of nonreward). This postulate is more consistent than the conditionability one with existing data and leads to the same general expectations regarding socialization. It is also isomorphic with the proposed physiological alteration in Eysenck's theory, though this is motivated by independent considerations.

At the physiological level, it is necessary to alter Eysenck's hypothesis that differences in *E* represent differences in the activity of the Ascending Reticular Activating System (ARAS: Magoun, 1963; Gray, 1964b). This alteration is motivated by a consideration of the physiological significance of two treatments—administration of barbiturate drugs (especially sodium amytal) or alcohol, and damage to the frontal cortex—which alter behaviour in an introverted direction (Eysenck, 1967). Gray (1970a, 1970b) has argued that these treatments are most likely to exert their effects on behaviour by disrupting the normal activity of the septo-hippocampal stop system (Fig. 6), of which the orbital frontal cortex appears to be the neocortical representation (Butters and Rosvold, 1968; Gray, 1970b; Gray and Buffery, 1971). Given the evidence, considered earlier in this paper, that the septo-hippocampal stop system mediates the behavioural inhibition which an animal displays when faced with threats of punishment or nonreward, this alteration in Eysenck's theory is isomorphic at the physiological level with the psychological alteration outlined in the preceding paragraph.

The full significance of these two alterations in Eysenck's theory for the placement of two major factors in the domain of data described by *E* and *N* is only apparent if this treatment of *E* is taken in conjunction with the writer's (Gray, 1970b) modification of Eysenck's treatment of *N*. Eysenck has always treated *N* as a dimension of general emotionality and, physiologically, he has equated emotionality with activity in the autonomic nervous system (ANS). It will be clear from the discussion of emotion earlier in this paper that, given current approaches to emotion within the theory of learning, as well as current knowledge of the physiology of emotional behaviour, such a peripheral physiological basis for a general trait of emotionality is extremely implausible. The activity of the ANS is primarily regulated at the hypothalamic level, the posterior hypothalamus being concerned in the main with control of the sympathetic nervous system and the anterior hypothalamus with the control of the parasympathetic nervous system (Gellhorn and Loofbourrow, 1963). One might therefore wish to retreat from the ANS itself into the NES, while retaining Eysenck's major hypothesis, and treat N as depending on activity in the hypothalamic controlling centres for ANS activity. However, as we have seen, the hypothalamus appears to be principally concerned with influences proceeding from the internal milieu, and perhaps with resolving the balance of influences proceeding downstream from limbic structures; but the latter are more immediately concerned with emotional behaviour proper. In any case, the significance of changes in the activity of the ANS for emotional behaviour is, to say the least, opaque. Thus, while retaining Eysenck's general notion of the neurotic as a highly emotional person, it would seem best to seek a physiological substrate for emotionality in the three limbic emotional mechanisms described above.

My own suggestion (Gray, 1970b) as to the relation of N and E to these emotional mechanisms, and to each other, is shown in Fig. 11.

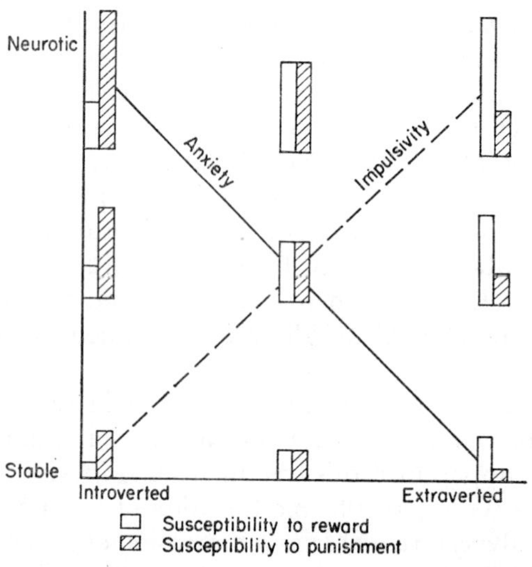

Fig. 11. Proposed relationships of (a) susceptibility to signals of reward and susceptibility to signals of punishment to (b) the dimensions of introversion–extraversion and neuroticism. The dimensions of anxiety and impulsivity (diagonals) represent the steepest rate of increase in susceptibility to signals of punishment and reward, respectively. From Gray (1970b).

The hypothesis depicted in this figure treats N as a dimension of increasing sensitivity to signals of both reward (including nonpunishment) and punishment (including nonreward); and E as a dimension of increasing relative sensitivity (in the extravert direction) to signals of reward rather than to signals of punishment. Assuming that these aspects of personality are related in a simple manner to the emotional mechanisms outlined earlier in this paper, it is immediately apparent from Fig. 11 that the major lines of causal influence are not likely to lie along the *E* and *N* axes, but rather along the two diagonals: the diagonal from stable extravert to neurotic introvert, roughly corresponding to the location of the trait of susceptibility to Anxiety as measured by the Manifest Anxiety Scale (Spence and Spence, 1966), and indicating the degree of activity in the orbitofrontal–septo-hippocampal stop system (Fig. 6); and the diagonal from stable introvert to neurotic extravert, roughly corresponding to the trait of Impulsivity (Eysenck, H. J., and Eysenck, S. B. G., 1969), and indicating the degree of activity in the approach system (Fig. 5).

This conclusion is in good agreement with the major clusterings of socio-psychiatric phenomena which Eysenck's theory (Fig. 9) set out to explain. These clusterings include, above all, the dysthymic symptoms (phobias, obsessions, anxiety states and reactive depression) found among neurotic introverts, and the anti-social behaviour found among neurotic extraverts (Eysenck, 1967, 1969; Eysenck, S. B. G., and Eysenck, H. J., 1970, 1971; Burgess, 1972). Eysenck's own theory treats these clusterings as arising out of the interaction between two causal influences acting along the dimensions of *E* and *N*. The present proposal is simpler, in that it treats each of these clusters as arising from one causal influence, acting directly along the axis on which the cluster lies, and corresponding to a single mechanism in the CNS/NES. The evidence from the behavioural changes produced by frontal leucotomy is particularly instructive in this respect. This operation, which severs the orbital frontal cortex from the rest of the septo-hippocampal stop system, is effective against the typical dysthymic symptoms, obsessions, agoraphobia, anxiety states and depression (Willett, 1960; Marks, 1969). As far as the effects of the operation on measures of personality are concerned, it appears to reduce both introversion and neuroticism. Thus, to account for its effects in Eysenck's theory, we have to suppose that the frontal cortex forms part of two separate mechanisms, one promoting high introversion, the other promoting high neuroticism. Parsimony can be simply purchased, by arguing, as has been done here, that the frontal cortex forms part of but one mechanism, the septo-hippocampal stop system, and that activity in this mechanism provides the line of causal influence, acting along the Anxiety diagonal (Fig. 11).

I have presented other arguments in favour of the present theory elsewhere (Gray, 1970b, 1971a, 1972b). Here I wish rather to devote some space to a consideration of the way in which one might, in general, decide between two theories, such as Eysenck's and the writer's, which lead to different views of the optimum location of the independent factors in a known factor space. It is clear that any resolution of an issue such as this must be based on a theory which ranges beyond factor analytic procedures themselves. What is needed is an experiment in which personality factors are rotated to give the best possible correlations with a behavioural test, or a factor derived from behavioural tests, chosen on theoretical grounds. As argued earlier in this paper, moreover, such tests will be of particular value if they can also be applied to an animal population so that their physiological basis can be studied as well. H. J. Eysenck and S. B. G. Eysenck (1969) have in fact used essentially this approach in an elegant study in which they compared the predictability of individual differences on a simple test of arousability (Corcoran's "lemon test": Corcoran, 1964), using, respectively, loadings on the unitary *E* factor, or on the two subfactors, Impulsivity and Sociability, which together compose *E*. Eysenck and Levey (1972) have applied a similar technique to the predictability of eyeblink conditioning scores. Both these studies, however, have compared factors with their subfactors, rather than considering the problem of rotation of factors.

The sort of study which would be required to resolve the issue between Eysenck's theory of *E* and *N* and the one depicted in Fig. 11 might take the following form. Behavioural tests of sensitivity to reward, punishment, nonreward and nonpunishment would be administered. The results of these tests would first themselves be factored. On Eysenck's theory, there should be a single factor of conditionability running through all these tests, whereas the writer's theory would predict that tests of sensitivity to reward and nonpunishment (active avoidance learning) would go together and be independent of tests of sensitivity to punishment (passive avoidance) and nonreward, which in turn would go together. If the single factor of conditionability were found (and the evidence to date strongly suggests that it would not: Lovibond, 1964) it should, on Eysenck's theory, be most closely correlated with the factor of extraversion as measured by questionnaires. If the two factors of sensitivity to reward and sensitivity to punishment, on the other hand, proved to be in the data, they should, on the writer's theory, correlate most closely with rotations of the *E* and *N* factors into the Impulsivity and Anxiety diagonals, respectively. In either case, one is doing more than looking for harmony within the factor analytic results themselves: the criterion for rotation of the personality factors is chosen on theoretical grounds; though, of course, the theory itself must be open to disproof (including disproof on factor analytic grounds, as in the example given above) and must survive experimental test.

An Experimental Test of Sensitivity to Nonreward in Children

Eysenck's approach to the construction of a causal theory of personality has been to start with the descriptions of CPID at the human level, and then to seek in the theory of learning and in related physiological data for a way of explaining these CPID. The Russian approach, as evidenced by the work of Teplov (Gray, 1964a) and Nebylitsyn (1972) has been rather the reverse: they have taken a theory of learning (Pavlov's) and looked for the patterns of CPID they might expect if the mechanisms in this theory were subject to systematic individual variation in activity. So far, we have been looking a little in both directions, but essentially following Eysenck's route. Recently, however, we (Nicholson and Gray, 1972; Gray and Nicholson, 1971) have completed some experiments which attacked the problem the Russian way around.

These experiments were based on a model for discrimination learning which was proposed by Gray and Smith (1969). This model (Fig. 12) incorporates the main features of the theory of learning and emotion which have been summarized in an earlier section of this paper. It is a two-process theory, with two basic classes of classically conditioned reinforcing events which control instrumental behaviour: signals of reward (and of the equivalent event, relieving nonpunishment) controlling approach behaviour; and signals of punishment (and of the equivalent frustrative nonreward) controlling passive avoidance. The model is equipped with a mathematical apparatus which is part control theory and part signal–detection theory. With this apparatus it is capable of predicting the main lines of a number of phenomena encountered in discrimination learning and partial reinforcement experiments using rats and pigeons, such as the partial reinforcement acquisition effect (Goodrich, 1959; Haggard, 1959), behavioural contrast (Reynolds, 1961; Terrace, 1966), peak shift (Hanson, 1959; Terrace, 1966) and transposition (Hebert and Krantz, 1965). By means of the co-ordinating hypotheses already used in this paper, it can be proposed that the mechanism which mediates the behavioural effects of signals of reward and nonpunishment in this model (the "reward mechanism", Fig. 12) is Olds' approach mechanism (Fig. 5), and that the mechanism which mediates the behavioural effects of signals of punishment and nonreward in the model (the "punishment mechanism," Fig. 12) is the septo-hippocampal stop system (Fig. 6). A further set of co-ordinating hypotheses links individual differences in sensitivity to reward/nonpunishment to the Impulsivity diagonal in Fig. 11, and individual differences in sensitivity to punishment/nonreward to the Anxiety diagonal in that figure. We are thus in the position which was diagrammed as desirable in Fig. 4: we are in possession of a theory

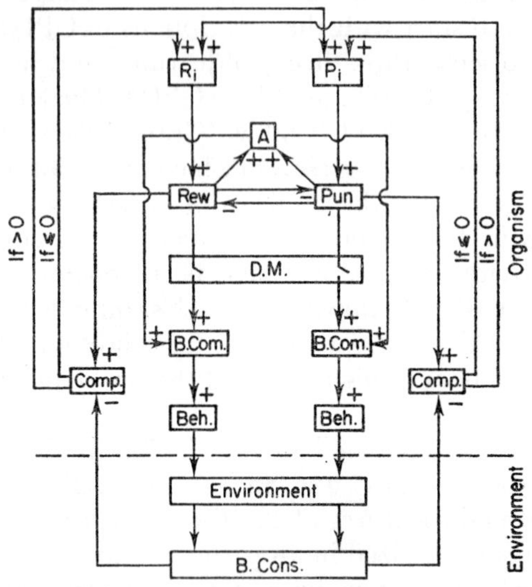

Fig. 12. Block diagram of the arousal–decision model. R_i and P_i: inputs to the reward and punishment mechanisms. Rew and Pun. D.M.: the decision mechanism. A: the arousal mechanism. B.Com.: behaviour command to "approach" (on the reward side) or to "passively avoid" (on the punishment side). Beh: the observed motor behaviour. B.Cons.: the consequences (rewarding or punishing) of the behaviour that occurs. Comp.: comparator mechanisms which compare the actual consequences of behaviour with the expected consequences and make appropriate reward or punishment inputs. If the actual reward is less than the expected reward, there is an input to the punishment mechanism (the "fear-frustration hypothesis"); if the actual punishment is less than the expected punishment, there is an input to the reward mechanism (the "hope-relief hypothesis"). From Gray and Smith (1969).

which should allow us: (a) to match behaviour between Man and experimental animals; (b) to look for personality correlates of the behaviour in Man; and (c) to look at the physiological basis of the behaviour in our experimental animals.

With this set of linked theories in mind, therefore, we set out to look for behavioural equivalents in Man of some of the behaviour the model is capable of explaining in animals. As a first choice, we tried to establish in children the phenomena of behavioural contrast and peak shift, reported in pigeons (Reynolds, 1961; Hanson, 1959), rats (Scull, Davies and Amsel, 1970; Pierrel and Sherman, 1960) and goldfish (Ames and Yarczower, 1965).

Behavioural contrast consists in a rise in response rate, in an operant conditioning situation, in the presence of the positive stimulus (i.e. the stimulus signalling that reward is available for responding) after exposure to a negative stimulus (signalling no reward or less reward for responding) compared to the rate obtaining when the positive stimulus is the only one to which the animal is exposed. Peak shift is observed under similar conditions if the positive and negative stimuli belong to the same stimulus continuum (e.g. hue or orientation of line) and generalization testing is carried out after the discrimination between the positive and negative stimuli has been established: it is found that peak response rate, instead of occurring in the presence of the positive stimulus, as it does when no such intra-dimensional discrimination training is conducted, is shifted along the stimulus continuum away from the positive stimulus in the direction opposite to the negative stimulus. Both these phenomena are treated in the Gray and Smith (1969) model as arising in consequence of the emotional effects of the frustrative nonreward occurring in the presence of the negative stimulus. These effects consist in a decrease in the probability that the subject will engage in the rewarded behaviour, coupled with an increase in the vigour with which this behaviour is carried out when he does engage in it. The detailed interactions between this decreased probability and increased vigour of the rewarded behaviour, by which both behavioural contrast and peak shift are predicted, are the heart of the mathematics of the model; for these the reader is referred to the original Gray and Smith (1969) paper.

As reported by Nicholson and Gray (1971, 1972), the attempt to find behavioural contrast and peak shift in children, using essentially similar techniques to those employed in experiments on rats and pigeons (the child presses a lever and this response is sometimes rewarded when a picture of a space rocket at a particular angle of orientation is projected on a screen, but never rewarded when a picture of a space rocket at a different angle of orientation is projected), has been entirely successful (Figs. 13 and 14). Thus these phenomena are phylogenetically of extraordinary longevity, being present in fish, birds, rats and our own species. Furthermore, since we deliberately set out to replicate at the human level a phenomenon found in these other species, and deliberately mimicked the techniques employed in the animal experiments, we need have no real doubt about the reality of our behaviour-matching programme; though, to be sure, it will be necessary to test this assumption in the future by carrying out parametric studies to verify that the same variables which are known to affect behavioural contrast and peak shift in pigeons (e.g. the size of the discrepancy between the rewards obtained in the positive and negative stimuli, the schedules of reinforcement on which these are delivered, the discriminability of the positive and negative stimuli, etc., see Gray and

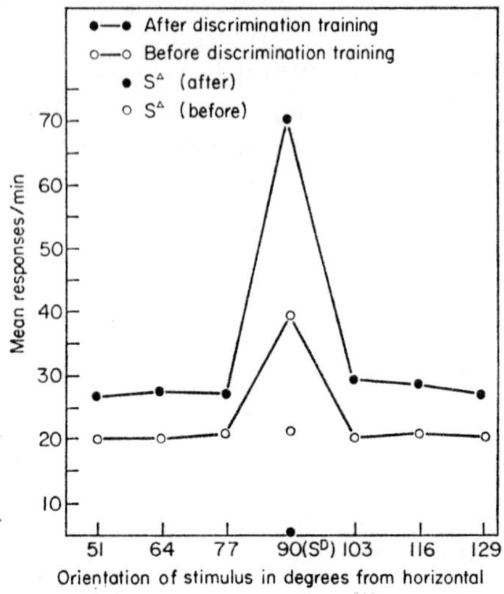

Fig. 13. Average results from four children who learnt a discrimination between presence of a vertically oriented picture of a rocket (S^D) signalling availability of reward and its absence (S^Δ) signalling non-availability of reward. Note the great increase in response rate in the presence of S^D (behavioural contrast) and the symmetry of the generalization curve around S^D. From Nicholson and Gray (1971).

Smith, 1969, and Terrace, 1966) also affect these phenomena in the same way in children.

The next step in our research programme was to look for personality correlates of these phenomena in children. Since the Gray and Smith (1969) model treats behavioural contrast and peak shift as resulting from the emotional effects of frustrative nonreward, it follows (Gray, 1972a) that, if all individuals are tested under identical conditions, individual differences in the magnitudes of these phenomena should reflect individual differences in susceptibility to these emotional effects. Reference to Fig. 11 will show that, on Gray's (1970b) theory of the psychological nature of E and N, susceptibility to frustration should grow with increasing N and decreasing E, i.e. with increasing Anxiety. These are precisely the results found by Nicholson and Gray (1972; Gray and Nicholson, 1971), though only the correlations of measures of peak shift with N and E were significant, those involving measures of behavioural contrast being in the predicted direction but not attaining statistical significance. It was also possible, in these experiments, to obtain a measure of sensitivity to reward, in the form of an estimate of the degree to which the child generalized his expectation of

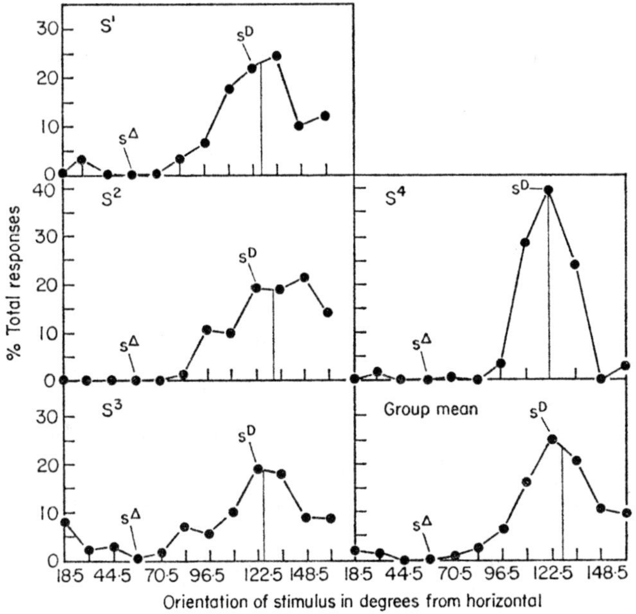

Fig. 14. Generalization curves for same four children (S^1 to S^4) whose results are shown in Fig. 13, but after further discrimination training between different angles of orientation of rocket (S^D signalling availability of reward, S^{Δ} signalling non-availability). The vertical lines indicate the means of distributions of responses at S^D and at three stimuli on either side of S^D. Note displacement of symmetry of curve away from S^{Δ} (peak shift) and compare Fig. 13. From Nicholson and Gray (1971).

reward to stimuli resembling the positive training stimuli. On Gray's (1970b) theory, such a measure of sensitivity to reward would be expected to grow with increasing neuroticism and increasing extraversion, that is, along the Impulsivity diagonal of Fig. 11. These are the results, at a statistically significant level for both dimensions, obtained by Nicholson and Gray (1972).

Thus the Russian approach, starting with learning theory and looking for appropriate CPID, has so far, in our hands, provided very promising results. We hope to pursue further the personality correlates of peak shift, behavioural contrast, and related measures of susceptibility to frustrative nonreward in Man. At the same time, we are pursuing parallel experiments on the physiological basis of responses to nonreward in the rat. These have already provided good support for the hypothesis that these responses are mediated by the septo-hippocampal stop system (Gray, 1970a; Gray and Ball, 1970; Gray, 1972c), although as yet we have been concerned with the effects of partial reinforcement rather than behavioural contrast and peak shift. Thus the strategy of behaviour matching via a conceptual nervous system has put us in a position where we can reasonably hope to carry out a relatively direct exploration of the physiological basis of susceptibility to frustration (and perhaps, therefore, of the major dimension of Anxiety) over the next few years.

Sex Differences in the Study of Personality

As we have seen, the data from both animal learning studies and physiological psychology suggest the existence of three separate, major emotional mechanisms. We have, as it were, used up two of them in attempting to account for the dimension of E and N, or perhaps we should now say Anxiety and Impulsivity. We are left with the fight/flight system. Assuming this system still exists in Man, and assuming that it is subject to systematic individual variation, what pattern of CPID might it create?

An examination of sex differences in aggressive behaviour in animals and Man makes it rather clear, not only that this system does still exist in Man, but also that it is still subject to the same pattern of sex differences as exists in nearly all other mammals, and, indeed, nearly all other vertebrate species (Collias, 1944). Furthermore, the study of sex differences throws an interesting light on the nature of the behaviour controlled by the fight/flight system, as well as on the nature of the behaviour controlled by the stop system.

I have sung the praises of sex differences, as an unrivalled clue to the biological and physiological bases of human personality and social behaviour elsewhere (Gray, 1971b; Gray and Buffery, 1971; Buffery and Gray, 1972). In the context of the present argument, their value can be most briefly put by saying that they offer, perhaps uniquely, the opportunity to match CPID themselves in a relatively direct manner, between animals and Man. For, at least if we confine ourselves to the mammals, we are never in much doubt how to match male with male and female with female in two different species, even when these species differ considerably from each other in many other ways. Thus, if we find at the human level a CPID which differentiates the two sexes, and if the same kind of CPID differentiates the sexes in a similar manner in a sufficiently large number of related mammalian species, the probability is high that this CPID is biological in origin, i.e. that it is specified in the gene pool of our species. It is true, of course, that we still have the problem of knowing what kind of CPID in an animal species is "the same" as the CPID in Man; so that the study of sex differences will not necessarily obviate the need for theory which I have previously stressed in this paper. However, occasionally the pattern of sex differences emerges sufficiently clearly, and in a behavioural form which is sufficiently amenable to simple interpretation, for us to be relatively sure that the animal CPID and the human one are indeed "the same"; and, of course, the argument does not suffer by being reversed—the very similarity of the sex differences at the two levels is evidence that the behaviour involved in the CPID is the same, i.e. a function of the same mechanism in the CNS/NES.

Such a situation appears to exist in the case of intra-specific aggressive behaviour. In mammals generally—indeed, in vertebrates generally (Collias, 1944)—the male is more likely to engage in intra-specific aggressive behaviour than the female (Gray, 1971b), the hamster providing a lonely, though not perhaps unique, exception (Payne and Swanson, 1971). It requires no special documentation to assert that the same sex difference is found in our own species, judging from the criminal statistics on murder and mayhem all over the world. There is, furthermore, good evidence from both animal (rodents and primates) and human studies that this sex difference is dependent on the action of androgens on a brain which has differentiated, as a result of early exposure to male hormone under the control of a male chromosomal constitution, as a male one (Gray, 1971b). Thus, it is reasonable to assert that the human sex difference in aggressiveness forms part of a CPID which is, in our own species as in other mammalian species, under strong genetic control, and which must therefore reflect the action of some powerful, ubiquitous and long-lasting selection pressure (Fig. 1). A consideration (Gray and Buffery, 1971) of the likely reasons for this sex difference—and of the features of the social organization of mammalian species to which it appears to relate—is able to throw some light on the nature of this selection pressure, while at the same time making it clearer what kind of aggressive behaviour we are dealing with.

As shown elsewhere (Gray, 1971b; Gray and Buffery, 1971), the sex difference in aggressiveness is confined to intra-specific aggression, that is, to aggressive behaviour which typically occurs when two individuals of the same species first meet, and which may be intensified by various experimental manipulations, such as prior isolation, overcrowding or the administration of a punishing electric shock; there are apparently no consistent sex differences when competition over food or predatory aggression is investigated (Gray, 1971b). Corresponding to this sex difference in social behaviour, there is a widespread feature of mammalian social organization: dominance hierarchies are either exclusively the concern of males as in rodents, or, when they are the concern of both sexes, as in primates, the male is, on average, dominant over the female (Gray and Buffery, 1971). Thus it would seem reasonable to conclude that the difference between the sexes lies in a greater male specialization for the kind of social interaction which is involved in the struggle for status in a social system (Wynne-Edwards, 1962).

As Wynne-Edwards (1962; see also Gray, 1971a) has shown, there is a general tendency for males to be the "epideictic" sex, that is, to be particularly concerned with a number of forms of behaviour whose function, according to his theory of population density control, is to signal to other members of the species the current population density and thereby to activate various "intrinsic" mechanisms of restraint on further population increase or even actual reduction of population density. The struggle for rank in a social hierarchy is, according to Wynne-Edwards, one such form of behaviour. Thus, the sex difference in intra-specific aggressiveness is part of a still wider pattern of greater male involvement in those aspects of social interaction (and if Wynne-Edwards is correct, these are extraordinarily diverse and wide-ranging) which are concerned with the regulation of population density. At the human level, too, and again there is hardly any need for special documentation, the sex difference in aggressiveness appears to be part of a wider pattern of sex differences in the propensity to engage in competitive social interaction. In Cattell's (1965, p. 260) factor-analytic work, this sex difference is very clearly displayed in the form of a much higher male score on the Dominance factor, *E*.

The argument may finally be pushed home to its conclusion, prefigured in the highest box in Fig. 1, labelled "evolutionary". As Wynne-Edwards (1962) points out, though there are occasional reversals of sex role in competitive behaviour, with the female becoming the epideictic sex, these are sufficiently rare for it to be probable that there are evolutionary disadvantages attached to such a reversal. Moreover, they appear to be particularly rare in our own group of species, the mammals. We must therefore ask what adaptive value attaches to the specialization of the male as the epideictic sex?

This question has been put and answered (albeit in a speculative manner) by Wynne-Edwards (1962). We (Gray and Buffery, 1971) have summarized his views as follows:

"Females undertake a much larger burden in reproductive behaviour than males. In contrast to the male's 'stripped down' spermatozoa, mobile, light, and easily produced, the female's contribution to reproduction consists of ova 'loaded with valuable nutrients, and consequently far less expendable and greatly restricted in number'. If she were also to undertake the major role in epideictic behaviour, her task would become excessively burdensome. In those cases where the female does in fact display epideictic behaviour, the male tends to undertake a greater role in caring for the young than is usual, indicating that an equitable sharing of the labour of parental and epideictic functions between the sexes has some adaptive value. The majority of the cases of reversal of epideictic and parental roles between the sexes which Wynne-Edwards quotes, however, occur in birds, and this is made possible in these species because hatching of the eggs after they are laid and feeding of the young once they are hatched are functions which either sex can perform. However, 'by virtue of the fact that the characteristic feature of mammals is the possession of mammary glands, the mother-family is mandatory since the young derive their nourishment from the female' (Eisenberg, 1966, p. 248). Thus, in mammals, the only sharing possible is for females to undertake primary responsibility for parental behaviour and for males to undertake primary responsibility for epideictic behaviour; and this, according to Wynne-Edwards' review, is indeed what happens among mammalian species."

In the case of the sex difference in aggressive behaviour, then, we have at least the lines of a possible causal theory which extends all the way from the evolutionary pressure displayed at the top of Fig. 1; through the genes carried on the X and Y chromosomes and through the action of hormones, controlled by these genes, which differentiate the developing nervous system into a male or female one (Harris, 1964); and up to the organization of the adult nervous system, which determines the nature of the CPID which distinguishes males from females. Such an outline, of course, in no way precludes the possibility of modification of these genetically controlled physiological influences on the development of personality by influences proceeding from the environment, whether in its social or non-social form. Indeed, Gray, Lean and Keynes (1969) have reported precisely such an interaction between the hormonal differentiation of the sex of the brain and the early social environment in an experiment on the rat's emotional behaviour; and similar observations have been made with regard to the development of sex differences in visuo-spatial ability in Man (Masica, Money, Ehrhardt and Lewis, 1969; Buffery and Gray, 1972).

A key link in this outline which is missing, but which it is now well within our grasp to fill in, concerns the precise neural structures which are responsible for the sex difference in intra-specific aggressive behaviour. It seems clear that the differentiation of the brain into male or female for the control of sexual behaviour and endocrinology critically involves the action of testosterone on the developing hypothalamus, particularly in the pre-optic area and the arcuate–ventromedial nuclear region (Barraclough, 1967). As we have seen, the hypothalamus also forms part of the fight/flight system described in an earlier part of this paper. However, the critical importance of stimuli of social interaction in determining the different degree of aggressive behaviour displayed by the two sexes strongly suggests that higher centres must be involved in the neural control of this sex difference. The most likely site for such control is undoubtedly in the amygdala. This, as we have seen, is the highest level of the fight/flight system (de Molina and Hunsperger, 1962). Furthermore, there is good evidence that, in primates, the amygdala is of vital importance in the integration of social dominance behaviour; rhesus monkeys which have been subjected to lesions in this structure are unable to maintain their status in a dominance hierarchy (Rosvold, Mirsky and Pribram, 1954). It is not, therefore, rash to suggest that the differentiation by testosterone of the developing mammalian nervous system into a male or a female brain for the control of intra-specific aggressive behaviour (Gray, 1971b) is due to an action of the hormone on the amygdala. As far as I am aware, data relevant to this hypothesis are not yet available.

A consideration of sex differences in another form of emotional behaviour, fearfulness, also throws a rather new light on the functions of the septo-hippocampal stop system, which, as I have suggested earlier, underlies individual differences in Anxiety (one diagonal of Fig. 11).

As reviewed elsewhere (Gray, 1971b; Gray and Buffery, 1971), the sex difference in fearfulness may also be related to the social behaviour involved in the establishment of status hierarchies and similar competitional activities; though the position is much more complex than it is in the case of aggressive behaviour, because the direction of the sex difference is different in rodents (females less fearful) from what it is in Man and possibly other primates (females more fearful). At the human level, the sex difference in fearfulness appears as greater female scores on measures of Neuroticism, Introversion and Manifest Anxiety (Gray, 1971b; Silverman, 1970), and greater incidence among females of the maladies neurotic introversion brings—especially agoraphobia (the most common and crippling phobic disorder) and reactive depression (Gray, 1971b; Marks, 1969; Mayer-Gross, Slater and Roth, 1969). Gray and Buffery (1971) have argued that, biologically, this human sex difference arises from the tendency (1) for primate females to take part in social dominance interactions (unlike rodent females, which do not), but (2) for females, on average, to lose such encounters if their opponents are males; and that physiologically, the neural structures which underlie this sex difference include the frontal cortex, the ventral aspect of which, in rhesus monkeys, appears to serve as the highest cortical representation of the septo-hippocampal stop system (Butters and Rosvold, 1968; Johnson, Rosvold and Mishkin, 1968; Gray, 1970b), and the severance of which from the rest of the brain, in Man, by the operation of frontal leucotomy, selectively relieves neurotic introvert psychiatric symptoms (Willett, 1960; Marks, 1969).

If these views are correct, it appears that the frontal cortex–septo-hippocampal stop system is concerned at the human level with the integration of submissive behaviour during social interaction, just as the amygdaloid fight/flight system is concerned with the integration of dominance behaviour. It is in accord with this view that the most important class of stimuli for elicitation of the human dysthymic syndromes consists undoubtedly in stimuli of social interaction: witness the importance of agoraphobia and social phobias amid the phobic disorders, as well as the significance of social stress in producing reactive depression (Marks, 1969; Mayer-Gross, Slater and Roth, 1969). The typical age of onset of the dysthymic disorders in late adolescence and early adulthood (Marks, 1969), that is, just at the time when competitional activities start becoming serious, is also in agreement with this view. However, it should not be thought that the importance of social stimuli in eliciting fearful behaviour is a new phenomenon appearing at the human or even primate level: stimuli of social interaction form one of the most important classes of fear-inducing stimuli in animals in general (Gray, 1971a), this being the obverse of the wide prevalance of social dominance activities noted in the animal kingdom by Wynne-Edwards (1962).

On this view of the nature of the dysthymic neuroses, then, the typical neurotic introvert has, by the time he enters adulthood, developed a stop system (or inherited one, to an extent which is reflected by about half the variance in questionnaire measures of N and E: Eysenck, 1967, in press) which makes him particularly likely to inhibit behaviour leading to signals of impending punishment or frustrative nonreward, especially if such signals arise during the course of social interaction.

Note that this view of the dysthymic neuroses leaves much less to learning than is traditionally left to it either by Freudian theories, or by views derived from learning theory and attributing, as Watson (1924) did in the dawn light of Behaviourism, most of neurosis to unfortunate episodes of classical conditioning. The early environment is very likely to be involved in the determination of the degree of sensitivity of the stop system, and such influences are well established in rodents as, for example, in Levine's (1962; and see Gray, 1971a) work on the early handling phenomenon. But the early handling phenomenon does not appear to be due to learning in the ordinary sense: instead it involves an alteration of the overall sensitivity of the NES to future stimulation, this alteration perhaps being due to a stress-induced hormonal influence on the developing brain (Levine and Mullins, 1966; Gray, 1971a). On the present view, once the sensitivity of the NES is established in this way, or as a result of genetic influences, the individual is predisposed, not only to display certain kinds of behaviour, but also to a heightened reactivity to certain kinds of stimuli. Learning may then be involved in determining the precise form of behaviour displayed (e.g. predominantly phobic or predominantly obsessional) and the precise stimuli which are prepotent in eliciting this behaviour (e.g. crowds or interviews); but these differences are relatively unimportant in comparison with the distinction between a dysthymic and a psychotic or a psychiatrically normal individual.

The Fight/Flight System and Personality

The study of sex differences, then, suggests that two of the three major emotional systems, the septo-hippocampal stop system and the amygdaloid fight/flight system, have important influences on social behaviour. We have already considered the likely reflection in the organization of human personality of individual differences in the reactivity of the stop system. What of the fight/flight system? Are there any CPID within the sexes which might correspond to an influence of this emotional mechanism?

If for no other reason than symmetry, it is tempting to suppose that individual differences in the amygdaloid fight/flight system might underlie the remaining major dimension of temperament and behaviour disorders: psychoticism (Eysenck, S. B. G., and Eysenck, H. J., 1968). This dimension is independent of the other main dimension of psychiatric disorder, neuroticism, and it differentiates both schizophrenic-type psychotics and manic-depressive type psychotics from normals, but not from each other (Eysenck, in press). Like *E* and *N*, psychoticism (*P*), too, has a strong hereditary basis; from a study of monozygotic twins living together and apart, Eysenck (in press) estimates the broad heritability of psychoticism at 0·53. Reviewing the data on the familial incidence of schizophrenia, manic-depressive psychosis, and other psychotic disorders, Eysenck (in press) concludes that these data can best be explained in terms of such a general factor of psychoticism, polygenically inherited, and predisposing the individual in greater or lesser degree to the development of some psychotic disorder or other, but not to the development of any of the specific major psychotic syndromes recognized by current psychiatric classifications. In addition, Eysenck (in press) believes there is also evidence for "more sharply demarcated subtypes" within the major psychiatric syndromes, and these may result from the action of "specific genes giving rise to special subvarieties of psychotic behaviour".

It is, of course, unlikely that the controversy over the degree to which psychosis is inherited and, if so, in how many varieties and by what genetic mechanisms, will be stilled so soon. But, in keeping with my own predilections for the joiners, let us take Eysenck's notion of a general factor of psychoticism seriously and see whether there is anything about it which could be interpreted as showing that this dimension reflects excessive or disturbed activity in an amygdaloid fight/flight system.

There are indeed one or two odd facts about the *P* scale which lend themselves to such an interpretation; and one or two facts about the psychotic disorders themselves which do so as well.

In the first place, there is the nature of the items which, on the *P* scale, have been found to discriminate well between psychotics and normals. These include a large number of questions relating to actions of an obviously aggressive, indeed cruel, nature and answers indicative of a general hostility towards other people (Eysenck, S. B. G., and Eysenck, H. J., 1968). Aggressive psychopaths score particularly high on the *P* scale (Eysenck, H. J. 1969), a fact which is of particular significance when taken in conjunction with the existence among blood relatives of schizophrenics of a particularly high incidence of criminal and psychopathic behaviour (Eysenck, in press).

Secondly, there are the sex differences which are found on the *P* scale and in the incidence of psychotic disorders. If psychoticism is to do with excessive activity in the amygdaloid system for intra-specific aggression, then we would clearly expect this trait to be particularly marked among males. In keeping with this expectation, it is found that males score much more highly than females on the *P* scale (Eysenck, S. B. G. and Eysenck, H. J., 1969), although, of course, on the *N* scale and on measures of Anxiety the direction of the sex difference is reversed (Gray, 1971b; Silverman, 1970). In looking at the sex differences in the incidence of psychosis itself, account must be taken of the age of onset of the disorder. In the case of schizophrenia, there is initially a high incidence in males, who show a particularly marked rise in first admissions between the ages of 15 and 25; females begin to catch up with males at about the age of 35 and there is a marked preponderance of females after age 45 (Mayer-Gross, Slater and Roth, 1969, p. 239). A natural implication of this pattern is that the onset of full male sexuality, and of the social interactions which entry into adulthood requires of the male, somehow facilitates the occurrence of a schizophrenic illness, while active female sexuality actually affords protection against schizophrenia, this protection being removed at the time of the menopause. With regard to depression, the psychotic form of this symptom is associated with the male sex in Kendell's (1968) factor-analytic study, in distinction to reactive depression, which is predominantly found in females (Kendell, 1968; Mayer-Gross, Slater and Roth, 1969). Direct evidence of an involvement of the sex chromosomes in the determination of psychoticism is available from a study of *P* scores in individuals with an extra Y chromosome, the XYY constitution. These individuals are "super-male" in at least two respects: they are unusually tall, and they are unusually aggressive, often needing to be housed in a maximum security prison in consequence (Court Brown, 1968). They also obtain exceptionally high scores on the *P* scale (Eysenck, in press).

There is reason to believe, therefore, that psychoticism has something to do with an excessive degree of intra-specific aggressive behaviour and it is facilitated by some aspect of male sexuality. The case would be stronger, however, if there were evidence of amygdaloid involvement in psychosis. Such evidence does not appear to be available. There is evidence, however, which implicates the temporal lobe (in which, of course, the amygdala lies buried, although along with many other structures) in psychotic behaviour. Mayer-Gross, Slater and Roth (1969, p. 470) review a number of studies which have shown associations between abnormal electrical activity in the temporal lobes and psychotic, especially schizophrenic, disorder. A more specific, and most intriguing, report has come from Flor-Henry (1969) who found that after temporal lobe epilepsy there was an increased risk of the development of psychotic disorder, and that this disorder was likely to be of a schizophrenic variety if the epilepsy had been in the left temporal lobe (which normally houses the speech centres) but of a manic-depressive variety if the epilepsy had been in the right temporal lobe.

Nature, no doubt, is not simple. But she is probably not quite so complex as she appears to us today, in the formative stages of a still confused science. Joiners are prepared to have faith in a simplicity which will one day be found hidden in the confusion. It is in this naive faith that I have offered this rash speculation on the nature of psychoticism. Three emotional mechanisms, three major dimensions of personality, three major clusters of social and psychiatric phenomena, all in one-to-one correspondence with each other: how can this be anything but unlikely? Nonetheless, it might be worth looking for. If we fail to find it, or any other simple pattern in the data, we can always go back to contemplating our state of confusion; we need never have far to look for that!

Summary

A causal theory of personality, if it is to be complete, must specify the enduring structural basis in the neuro-endocrine system on which observed consistent patterns of individual differences rest. The development of such a theory requires a comparison between personality data, obtained from human subjects, and brain and behaviour data obtained from experimental animals. The relevance of these kinds of data to each other can only be judged by theoretical considerations. A theory of the physiological basis of three major dimensions of personality (rotations of Eysenck's neuroticism and extraversion and his unrotated psychoticism) is proposed for this purpose.

This theory depends on an analysis of data from experiments both on learning and on physiological psychology, and may be regarded as a theory of the organization of emotional behaviour. It postulates three major emotional systems, individual differences in the reactivity of which are proposed to underlie each of the three dimensions of personality. The nature and neural substrates of these three emotional systems are as set out in Table II.

Some tests of the theory in experiments on children's behaviour in an operant conditioning task are described. The relevance of sex differences in emotional behaviour to the theory are also discussed.

DISCUSSANT'S COMMENT ON GRAY'S PAPER

JOSEPH R. ROYCE

Overall, my reaction to Gray's basic strategy is positive. Within the context of multivariate experimental psychology, I would describe his approach as more experimental than multivariate and, happily, more rational than most research programs currently in progress. His work can further be described as biologically oriented. He wants to get at the biological mechanisms of temperament, and the combination of a hypothetico-deductive style of thinking and his impressive experimental ingenuity have provided both insightful awareness and increments in our factual knowledge. Examples of Gray's insightful thinking include his analysis of animal learning as really dealing with "the learning of emotional responses", his argument in defense of getting at human CPIDs via the physiology of animal subjects (see Gray's Figs. 2 and 4), and his biology-to-behaviour deduction that Eysenck's two-dimensional scheme requires modification (see Fig. 11). Examples of his experimental ingenuity can be found in learning experiments on animals and humans, and a variety of neurological and drug investigations of animals. But perhaps the most impressive combination of experimental ingenuity and insightful conceptualizing is manifested in his work on sex differences, for we get pretty convincing knowledge pay-off. He takes the obvious biological–genetic differences between the sexes, embeds them within his biological–conceptual framework, and gives us a convincing experimental demonstration of a kind of "testosterone imprinting" of the hypothalamus–amygdala structures which can account for such fight/flight mammalian phenomena (i.e. across species, including Man) as greater intraspecific dominance or/and aggressiveness for males than females.

However, from the point of view of the theme of this conference, his synthesis of the evidence for a three system basis for emotionality (i.e. the hypothalamic approach system, the septo-hippocampal stop system, and the amygdala fight/flight system), involving a mutuality of data and concepts at both the behavioural and physiological levels, is clearly the most provocative aspect of Professor Gray's paper. While it is true that the relevance of the limbic system to emotional behaviour has been extensively investigated during the past two decades, it is my impression that there has been little or no parallel advance in possible theoretical linkages to differential psychology. Whatever its assets and limitations, Gray's scheme fills a void and it deserves attention for that reason alone. In my opinion, he does an outstanding job in accounting for the three systems in question, particularly at the neurological level. However, his coverage of the individual differences domain is extremely limited. While Gray's disclaimer that he is a post-Eysenckian "pathological joiner" could let him off the hook in the sense that his goals are "modest", there are various places in the text where the "simplistic pathology" of joiners gives the lie to modest goals, and at least calls for corrective commentary.

As I see it, the weakest aspect of Gray's approach is his failure to deal adequately with the multivariate nature of emotionality at the behavioral level. Surely the obvious lesson from the history of the more established differential domains such as intelligence and aptitudes is that initial, global notions such as general intelligence are too simplistic and are, therefore, superseded by more complex conceptions. In short, threeness in a domain as complex as temperament-emotionality is blatantly inadequate, whether it comes from the pen of Hans Eysenck or Jeffrey Gray. Even if we grant the possible counter argument that Gray's scheme is only meant to apply to higher-order dimensions in a manner comparable to Eysenck's theorizing in terms of *I-E*, *N* and *P*, it would still be necessary to spell out relationships between such higher order factors and lower order factors. And neither Gray nor Eysenck does this. In fact, Gray seems to suggest (see Gray's section: The Organization of Emotion and the Organization of Personality) that the dimensionality and taxonomic issue is a matter of taste!

It is, of course, not at all necessary that our factor structures be either/or—both general and group factors have been found empirically, and there is no logical incompatibility in incorporating them in the same theoretical structure. I would urge that we pay serious attention to the essentially inductive nature of factor analysis, and let the data guide us to underlying structure—whatever it may look like. This means that one does not decide in advance how many and what factors will do the job in a given area of study. In later stages of development, when a domain is well staked out factorially, "anchor variables" may be included in a test battery for the purpose of replicating factors previously identified. But the data, even then, will determine the configuration of test vectors, and it is the data which determine the rank of the matrix. The point is that factor analysis is primarily an empirico–inductive–hypothesis-generating method, and in this sense its efforts are in the logical context of scientific discovery. Thus, *a priori* postulation of dimensions (as in the case of most "joiners") in a given domain, especially when combined with early closure on the admissibility of additional dimensions, is antithetical to the basically inductive character of factor theory.

On pp. 435–43 Gray outlines a factor experiment as a way to choose between rival theories. I'm in complete agreement with the spirit of this proposal. However, it should be pointed out that a more convincing test of which theory would be more adequate involves procedures based on completely blind rotations (e.g. including no knowledge on the part of the rotator as to which set of data, theory A or theory B, is undergoing rotation). Furthermore, certain details of Gray's proposed experiment are not at all clear. For example, it looks like a 6 space may be required (i.e. for the factors of sensitivity to reward, sensitivity to punishment, impulsivity, and anxiety, in addition to *I-E* and *N*), but I get the impression Gray wants to resolve it all in a 2 space. (See especially page 436. Perhaps the material on this page could be clarified in the discussion). I had a similar reaction to Fig. 11. One possible interpretation of what is implied in that figure is that there are more dimensions in the system than two (e.g. at least anxiety and impulsivity), and further, that anxiety and impulsivity would deserve higher beta weights than the *I-E* dimension when our concern is with the prediction of neuroticism. (Note, however, that factor analysis *per se* is not concerned with prediction, although it can be used to great advantage prior to a multiple regression prediction problem.)

I should now like to bring up the question of the relationship between factors and causality. On page 431 Gray categorically states that "factor analysis cannot itself locate the lines of causal influence" because of "its infinity of possible solutions". The last part of this quote is, at the very least, misleading, and the first part, primarily an issue of scientific philosophy, has received very little serious analysis. While it is, of course, true that one can arbitrarily locate reference axes in an infinite number of loci, it does not follow that only arbitrary solutions are possible. Arbitrary positions of factors in hyper-space will surely not lead to the identification of invariant factors. And, while it is true that the theoretical–mathematical foundations of invariance remain as *the* problem in factor analysis, it is also true that invariant factors have, in fact, been identified. Such invariance probably carries causality with it, but I suspect the relevance of causality depends upon the domain in question. For example, if we are describing box sizes and we are examining the length of the diagonal from the lower left corner to the upper right corner of the frontal plane, we can "account for" that line length as a linear combination of the height and width of the box. Thus, that line length is "determined by" the two specified dimensions. But is it caused by them? It is certainly completely "accounted for" in the mathematical sense, but is that causation? Is the concept "cause" used correctly if one answers by saying that lengthening the height or width dimension will "cause" a longer diagonal length?

Let me throw further doubt on the notion of factor causality by bringing in artifactors—factors which are just as mathematically "determined" as non-artifactor factors, but which are due to one or another class of dependence. The most obvious case is that of linear dependence. In this case we can manufacture an artifactor by simply including several additional measurements which are linearly dependent upon a given measurement (e.g. the most frequent example of this in the empirical literature is to include a total test score as a separate measure, in addition to the part scores of a test). What this does is to artifactorially increase the rank of the matrix by one—that is, a measure which we will assume had only specific variance now shares its specific variance with the added linearly dependent measures, thereby mathematically creating an additional common factor. Is it correct to refer to that underlying factor as "causal"? I doubt it.

On the other hand, there are cases where I suspect factors are involved in a causal network—in the domain of psychobiology for example. The implication is that such factors are part of a sequence of biological events which results in the observed pattern of behaviour. The Overall–Williams "thyroid" factor, for example, combined with a complex "clinical thyroid" score, brings forth a canonical correlation coefficient of 0·91—a validity coefficient so unheard of that the natural reaction is to dismiss it as nonsense. Similarly, I lean toward causality when there is evidence of a decrement in factor scores associated with brain damage (in this case, causal influence exerted on the factor), or a shift in factor scores concomitant with changes in genotype.

My major point is that the scientist qua scientist focuses his energy on finding regularity or lawfulness—it is the philosopher who then wonders whether or not such lawfulness necessarily implies causality. And regardless of whether or not factor analysis can be characterized as causal, it does lead to regularity or lawfulness. Furthermore, what I have implied in the discussion above is that the question of causality is a philosophical problem for all of science, not just factor analysis. However, it is an issue which philosophically oriented factor analysts should address themselves to.

Let me conclude with two explicit questions which are put to Professor Gray in the spirit of eliciting further clarification of his position:

1. Please elaborate on what qualifies as a reliable CPID and what doesn't qualify. While the factor analyst does not wish to make monopolistic claims on the business of identifying replicable uni-dimensions of behaviour, he has put together a reasonably effective mouse trap for that task, and he is justifiably suspicious of investigators who do not spell out exactly how one identifies invariant behaviour patterns.

2. Gray's modification of Eysenck calls for a switch in the neural correlate of the *I-E* dimension from the reticular activating system to the septo-hippocampal structures of the limbic system. Isn't a third alternative possible, namely that both the RAS and the limbic systems are involved? A statement of Gray's view of the role of the RAS in emotionality is desirable.

COMMENT ON GRAY'S PAPER

H. LANSDELL

I would like to suggest that the consideration of functional differences between male and female brains be extended to include the question of asymmetry in hemispheric contributions to verbal and non-verbal abilities in the adult (Lansdell, 1964). Some differences in these asymmetrical contributions have been reported (Kimura, 1969; Lansdell, 1962; 1968b; 1968d; Lansdell and Urbach, 1965); and except for the ability to achieve visual closure (Lansdell, 1968a), there may be a stronger tendency in men than in women for lateralization of cerebral functions. Men and boys also have a higher incidence of left or right-handedness, and women and girls show more ambidexterity (Suchenwirth, 1969).

REJOINDER TO DISCUSSANTS' COMMENTS

JEFFREY A. GRAY

In clarification of some of the issues raised by Royce in his generous discussion of my paper, I would make the following points.

With regard to the factorial experiment I proposed on pp. 435–436 of my paper, it is true that I would be expecting an outcome in a two-dimensional space; but of course all the hypotheses on which this expectation is based may be wrong. I take "anxiety" and "impulsivity" to be rotations of Eysenck's neuroticism and extraversion factors through equal angles of the order of 45 degrees. My model (Gray, 1970b) then leads me to suppose that tests of sensitivity to punishment and to reward, respectively, would lie on the same factors as these two rotated Eysenckian factors.

With regard to the term "consistent patterns of individual differences (CPID)", I have deliberately chosen an expression which is not committed to any one mode of statistical description of traits. Factor-analytic procedures (though it is well-known that there are many of these, and that it is not always possible to be certain which is the most valid one to apply) are probably the best available ways of objectifying CPIDs, but I see no reason to rule out other procedures, available now or to be invented in the future.

With regard to the neural substrates of extraversion and neuroticism, I would now prefer to talk of the neural substrates of the rotations of these dimensions into the positions occupied by my "anxiety" and "impulsivity" (see above, and Fig. 11 in my paper). The neural substrate of "anxiety", according to my model, involves both the ARAS and the septo-hippocampal "stop" system joined in a negative-feedback loop (see Fig. 6 in my paper, and Gray, 1972b).

In answer to Dr. Landsell's comments, I agree fully with his assessment of the importance of studies of sex differences in asymmetry of hemispheric functions, and, indeed Buffery and Gray (1972) have discussed these studies in some detail. Although we are also in agreement with Lansdell that sex differences do exist in lateralization of function, in our view (Buffery, 1970, 1971; Buffery and Gray, 1972), it may be women rather than men who have greater lateralization of verbal and spatial functions. I do not know the Suchenwirth (1969) data, but Oldfield (1971), in a study of 1100 individuals, found greater left-handedness among men than women and a tendency for greater right-handedness among women than among men. There does not appear to be any sex difference in the proportion of ambidextrals in Oldfield's (1971) data.

ACKNOWLEDGMENTS

I am grateful to Professor H. J. Eysenck for his comments on the manuscript, and to J. N. Nicholson for many valuable discussions which helped considerably to mould its shape. My own research and that of J. N. Nicholson has received support from the Medical Research Council and the Social Science Research Council of Great Britain.

REFERENCES

Adams, D. and Flynn, J. P. (1966). Transfer of an escape response from tail shock to brain-stimulated attack behaviour. *J. exp. Analysis of Behav.* **9,** 401–408.

Adelman, H. M. and Maatsch, J. L. (1956). Learning and extinction based upon frustration, food reward, and exploratory tendency. *J. exp. Psychol.* **52,** 311–315.

Albert, Marilyn and Bignami, G. (1967). Effects of frontal median cortical and caudate lesions on two-way avoidance learning by rats. *Physiol. Behav.* **3,** 141–147.

Ames, L. L. and Yarczower, M. (1965). Some effects of wavelength discrimination on stimulus generalization in the goldfish. *Psychonom. Sci.* **3,** 311–312.

Amsel, A. (1958). The role of frustrative nonreward in noncontinuous reward situations. *Psychol. Bull.* **55,** 102–119.

Amsel, A. (1962). Frustrative nonreward in partial reinforcement and discrimination learning: Some recent history and a theoretical extension. *Psychol. Rev.* **69,** 306–328.

Amsel, A. and Roussel, J. (1952). Motivational properties of frustration: I. Effect on a running response of the addition of frustration to the motivational complex. *J. exp. Psychol.* **43,** 363–368.

Ball, G. G. and Gray, J. A. (1972). Septal self-stimulation and hippocampal activity: Separate processes. *Physiol. Behav.* **6,** 547–549.

Barraclough, C. A. (1967). Modifications in reproductive function after exposure to hormones during the prenatal and early postnatal period. *In* "Neuroendocrinology." (Martini, L. and Ganong, W. F. eds), Vol. 2. Academic Press, New York and London.

Brady, J. V. and Conrad, D. G. (1960). Some effects of limbic system self-stimulation upon conditioned emotional behaviour. *J. comp. physiol. Psychol.* **53,** 128–137.

Broadhurst, P. L. (1960). Applications of biometrical genetics to the inheritance of behaviour. *In* "Experiments in Personality." (Eysenck, H. J. ed.), Vol. 1, Psychogenetics and psychopharmacology, pp. 1–102. Routledge and Kegan Paul.

Brodal, A. (1960). "Neurological Anatomy in Relation to Clinical Medicine." (2nd edtn) Oxford University Press, New York.

Brown, J. S., Kalish, H. I. and Farber, I. E. (1951). Conditioned fear as revealed by magnitude of startle response to an auditory stimulus. *J. exp. Psychol.* **41,** 317–328.

Bruell, J. H. (1967). Behavioural heterosis. *In* "Behaviour–Genetic Analysis." (Hirsch, J. ed.) McGraw-Hill, New York.

Buffery, A. W. H. (1970). Sex differences in the development of hand preference, cerebral dominance for speech and cognitive skill. *Bull. Br. psychol. Soc.* **23,** 233.

Buffery, A. W. H. (1971). Sex differences in the development of hemispheric asymmetry of function in the human brain. *Brain Res.* **31,** 364–365.

Buffery, A. W. H. and Gray, J. A. (1972). Gender differences in the development of spatial and linguistic skills. *In* "Gender Differences: Their Ontogeny and Significance." (Ounsted, C. and Taylor, D. C. eds) Churchill, London.

Bull, J. A. (1970). An interaction between appetitive Pavlovian CSs and instrumental avoidance responding. *Learning and Motivation* **1,** 18–26.

Burgess, P. K. (1972). Eysenck's theory of criminality: A new approach. *Br. J. Crim.* **12,** 74–82.

Butters, N. and Rosvold, H. E. (1968). Effect of caudate and septal nuclei lesions on resistance to extinction and delayed alternation. *J. comp. physiol. Psychol.* **65,** 397–403.

Cattell, R. B. (1965). "The Scientific Analysis of Personality." Penguin, Harmondsworth, England.

Cattell, R. B. and Scheier, I. G. (1961). "The Meaning and Measurement of Neuroticism and Anxiety." Ronald Press, New York.

Collias, N. E. (1944). Aggressive behaviour among vertebrate animals. *Physio.. Zool.* **17,** 83–123.

Corcoran, D. W. J. (1964). The relation between introversion and salivation. *Am. J. Psychol.* **77,** 298–300.

Court Brown, W. M. (1968). The study of human sex chromosome abnormalities with particular reference to intelligence and behaviour. *Adv. Science* **24,** 390–397.

Deutsch, J. A. and Deutsch, D. (1966). "Physiological Psychology." Dorsey Press, Homewood, Illinois.

Donovick, P. J., Burright, R. G. and Gittelson, P. L. (1968). The effects of septal lesions on saccharine choice as a function of water deprivation. *Physiol. Behav.* **3,** 677–681.

Douglas R. J. (1967). The hippocampus and behavior. *Psychol. Bull.* **67,** 416–442.

Drewe, E. A., Ettlinger, G., Milner, A. D. and Passingham, R. E. (1970). A comparative review of the results of neuropsychological research on man and monkey. *Cortex* **6,** 129–163.

Eisenberg, J. F. (1966). The social organization of mammals. *Handb. Zool.*, Vol. 8, Lieferung 39, Teil 10 (7) pp. 1–92.

Estes, W. K. and Skinner, B. F. (1941). Some quantitative properties of anxiety. *J. exp. Psychol.* **29,** 390–400.

Eysenck, H. J. (1957). "The Dynamics of Anxiety and Hysteria." Praeger, New York.

Eysenck, H. J. (1967). "The Biological Basis of Personality." Charles C. Thomas, Springfield, Illinois.
Eysenck, H. J. (1970). "Crime and Personality." (2nd edtn) Granada Press, London.
Eysenck, H. J. (in press). An experimental and genetic model of schizophrenia. *In* "Genetic Factors in Schizophrenia." (Kaplan, A. R. ed.) Charles C. Thomas, Springfield, Illinois.
Eysenck, H. J. (in press). Genetic factors in criminal behaviour. *In* "Human Differences and Social Issues." (Gregor, A. J. ed.)
Eysenck, H. J. and Eysenck, S. B. G. (1969). "Personality Structure and Measurement." Routledge and Kegan Paul, London.
Eysenck, H. J. and Levey, A. (1972). Conditioning, introversion–extraversion and the strength of the nervous system. *In* "The Biological Bases of Individual Behaviour." (Nebylitsyn, V. D. and Gray, J. A. eds) Academic Press, New York and London.
Eysenck, S. B. G. and Eysenck, H. J. (1968). The measurement of psychoticism: A study of factor stability and reliability. *Br. J. Soc. Clin. Psychol.* **7,** 286–294.
Eysenck, S. B. G. and Eysenck, H. J. (1969). Scores on three personality variables as a function of age, sex and social class. *Br. J. Soc. Clin. Psychol.* **8,** 69–76.
Eysenck, S. B. G. and Eysenck, H. J. (1970). Crime and personality: An empirical study of the three-factor theory. *Br. J. Crim.* **10,** 225–239.
Eysenck, S. B. G. and Eysenck, H. J. (1971). Crime and personality: Item analysis of questionnaire responses. *Br. J. Crim.* **11,** 49–62.
Flor-Henry, P. (1969). Psychosis and temporal lobe epilepsy: A controlled investigation. *Epilepsia* **10,** 367–395.
Gallup, G. G., Jr. (1965). Aggression in rats as a function of frustrative nonreward in a straight alley. *Psychonom. Sci.* **3,** 99–100.
Gellhorn, E. and Loofbourrow, G. N. (1963). "Emotions and Emotional Disorders." Hoeber, New York.
Glickman, S. E. and Schiff, B. B. (1967). A biological theory of reinforcement. *Psychol. Rev.* **74,** 81–109.
Goodrich, K. P. (1959). Performance in different segments of an instrumental response chain as a function of reinforcement schedule. *J. exp. Psychol.* **57,** 57–63.
Gray, J. A. (1964a). Strength of the nervous system as a dimension of personality in Man: A review of work from the laboratory of P. M. Teplov. *In* "Pavlov's Typology." (Gray, J. A. ed.), pp. 152–287. Pergamon, Oxford.
Gray, J. A. (1964b). Strength of the nervous system and levels of arousal: A reinterpretation. *In* "Pavlov's Typology." (Gray, J. A. ed.), pp. 289–364. Pergamon, Oxford.
Gray, J. A. (1967). Disappointment and drugs in the rat. *Advan. Science* **23,** 595–605.
Gray, J. A. (1968). The Lister Lecture, 1967: The physiological basis of personality. *Advan. Science* **24,** 293–305.
Gray, J. A. (1970). Sodium amobarbital, the hippocampal theta rhythm and the partial reinforcement extinction effect. *Psychol. Rev.* **77,** 465–480.
Gray, J. A. (1970b). The psychophysiological basis of introversion–extraversion. *Behav. Res. Therapy* **8,** 249–266.
Gray, J. A. (1971a). "The Psychology of Fear and Stress." Weidenfeld and Nicholson, London. McGraw-Hill, New York.
Gray, J. A. (1971b). Sex differences in emotional behaviour in mammals including man: Endocrine bases. *Acta Psychol.* **35,** 29–46.
Gray, J. A. (1972a). Learning theory, the conceptual nervous system and personality.

In "The Biological Bases of Individual Behaviour." (Nebylitsyn, V. D. and Gray, J. A. eds), Academic Press, New York and London.

Gray, J. A. (1972b). The psychophysiological nature of introversion–extraversion: A modification of Eysenck's theory. *In* "The Biological Bases of Individual Behaviour." Nebylitsyn, V. D. and Gray, J. A. eds), Academic Press, New York and London.

Gray, J. A. (1972c). The effects of septal driving of the hippocampal theta rhythm on resistance to extinction of an instrumental running response in the rat. *Physiol. Behav.* **8,** 481–490.

Gray, J. A. and Ball, G. G. (1970). Frequency-specific relation between hippocampal theta rhythm, behaviour and amobarbital action. *Science* **168,** 1246–1248.

Gray, J. A. and Buffery, A. W. H. (1971). Sex differences in emotional and cognitive behaviour in mammals including man: Adaptive and neural bases. *Acta Psychol.* **35,** 89–111.

Gray, J. A., Lean, J. and Keynes, A. (1969). Infant androgen treatment and adult open field behaviour: Direct effects and effects of injections to siblings. *Physiol. Behav.* **4,** 177–181.

Gray, J. A. and Nicholson, J. N. (1971). Personality correlates of peak shift in children. Paper presented at symposium on *Inhibition and Learning*, Sussex University.

Gray, J. A. and Smith, P. T. (1969). An arousal-decision model for partial reinforcement and discrimination learning. *In* "Animal Discrimination Learning." (Gilbert, R. M. and Sutherland, N. S. eds), Academic Press, London and New York.

Grossen, N. E., Kostansek, D. J. and Bolles, R. C. (1969). Effects of appetitive discrimination stimuli on avoidance behaviour. *J. expl. Psychol.* **81,** 340–343.

Grossman, S. P. (1967). A Textbook of Physiological Psychology." Wiley, New York.

Haggard, D. F. (1959). Acquisition of a simple running response as a function of partial and continuous schedules of reinforcement. *Psychol. Rep.* **9,** 11–18.

Hanson, H. M. (1959). The effects of discrimination training on stimulus generalization. *J. expl. Psychol.* **58,** 321–334.

Harris, G. W. (1964). Sex hormones, brain development and brain function. *Endocrinology* **75,** 627–648.

Hebb, D. O. (1955). Drives and the C.N.S. (conceptual nervous system). *Psychol. Rev.* **62,** 243–254.

Hebert, J. A. and Krantz, D. L. (1965). Transposition: A reevaluation. *Psychol. Bull.* **63,** 244–257.

Horst, P. (1965). Factor Analysis of Data Matrices." Holt, Rinehart and Winston, New York.

Hull, C. L. (1952). "A Behaviour System." Yale University Press, New Haven, Connecticut.

Hutchinson, R. R. and Renfrew, J. W. (1966). Stalking attack and eating behaviour elicited from the same sites in the hypothalamus. *J. comp. physiol. Psychol.* **61,** 360–367.

Ison, J. R. and Rosen, A. J. (1967). The effects of amobarbital sodium on differential instrumental conditioning and subsequent extinction. *Psychopharmacol.* **10,** 417–425.

Johnson, T. M., Rosvold, H. E. and Mishkin, M. (1968). Projections from behaviorally-defined sectors of the prefrontal cortex to the basal ganglia, septum, and diencephalon of the monkey. *Exp. Neurol.* **21,** 20–34.

Kamano, D. K., Martin, L. K., and Powell, B. J. (1966). Avoidance response acquisition and amobarbital dosage levels. *Psychopharmacol.* **8,** 319–323.

Kendell, R. E. (1968). "The Classification of Depressive Illness." Oxford University Press, London.

Kimble, D. P. (1969). Possible inhibitory functions of the hippocampus. *Neuropsychol.* **7,** 235–244.

Kimura, D. (1969). Spatial localization in left and right visual fields. *Can. J. Psychol.* **23,** 445–458.

Klüver, H. and Bucy, P. C. (1937). "Psychic blindness" and other symptoms following bilateral temporal lobectomy in rhesus monkeys. *Am. J. Physiol.* **119,** 352–353.

Lansdell, H. (1962). A sex difference in effect of temporal-lobe neurosurgery on design preference. *Nature,* **194,** 852–854.

Lansdell, H. (1964). Sex differences in hemispheric asymmetries of the human brain. *Nature* **203,** 550.

Lansdell, H. (1968a). Effect of extent of temporal lobe ablation on two lateralized deficits. *Physiol. Behav.* **3,** 271–273.

Lansdell, H. (1968b). Effect of extent of temporal lobe surgery and neuropathology on the MMPI. *J. clin. Psychol.* **24,** 406–412.

Lansdell, H. (1968c). Evidence for a symmetrical hemispheric contribution to an intellectual function. *Proc. 76th ann. Conv. Am. Psychol. Assoc.* pp. 337–338.

Lansdell, H. (1968d). The use of factor scores from the Wechsler-Bellevue Scale of Intelligence in assessing patients with temporal lobe removals. *Cortex* **4,** 257–268.

Lansdell, H. and Urbach, N. (1965). Sex differences in personality measures related to size and side of temporal lobe ablations. *Proc. 73rd ann. Conv. Am. Psychol. Assoc.* pp. 113–114.

Levine, S. (1962). The effects of infantile experience on adult behavior. *In* "Experimental Foundations of Clinical Psychology." (Bachrach, A. J. ed.) Basic Books, New York.

Levine S. and Mullins, R. F. (1966). Hormonal influences on brain organization in infant rats. *Science* **152,** 1585–1592.

Lovibond, S. H. (1964). Personality and conditioning. *Progress in Experimental Personality Research* **1,** 115–169.

McCleary, R. A. (1966). Response-modulating functions of the limbic system: Initiation and suppression. *In* "Progress in Physiological Psychology." (Stellar, E. and Sprague, J. M. eds) Vol. 1. Academic Press, New York and London.

MacLean, P. D. (1949). Psychosomatic disease and the "visceral brain": Recent developments bearing on the Papez theory of emotion. *Psychosomatic Med.* **11,** 338–353.

Magoun, H. W. (1963). "The Waking Brain." (2nd edtn) Charles C. Thomas, Springfield, Illinois.

Marks, I. M. (1969). "Fears and Phobias." Heinemann, London.

Masica, D. N., Money, J., Ehrhardt, A. A. and Lewis, V. G. (1969). I.Q., fetal sex hormones and cognitive patterns: Studies in the testicular feminizing syndrome of androgen insensitivity. *Johns Hopkins Med. J.* **124,** 34–43.

Mayer-Gross, W., Slater, E. T. O. and Roth, M. (1969). "Clinical Psychiatry." Baillière, Tindall and Cassell, London.

Miller, N. E. (1951). Learnable drives and rewards. *In* "Handbook of Experimental Psychology." (Stevens, S. S. ed.) Wiley, New York.

Miller, N. E. (1964). The analysis of motivational effects illustrated by experiments on amylobarbitone. *In* "Animal Behaviour and Drug Action." (Steinberg, H. ed.) Churchill, London.

Mischel, T. (1969). "Human Action." Academic Press, New York and London.

de Molina, A. F. and Hunsperger, R. W. (1962). Organization of the subcortical system governing defence and flight reactions in the cat. *J. Physiol.* **160,** 200–213.

Mowrer, O. H. (1947). On the dual nature of learning: A reinterpretation of "conditioning" and "problem solving." *Harv. Educ. Rev.* **17,** 102–148.

Mowrer, O. H. (1960). "Learning Theory and Behaviour." Wiley, New York.

Nebylitsyn, V. D. (in press). "Fundamental Properties of the Human Nervous System." Plenum Press, New York.

Nicholson, J. N. and Gray, J. A. (1971). Behavioural contrast and peak shift in children. *Br. J. Psychol.* **62,** 367–373.

Nicholson, J. N. and Gray, J. A. (1972). Peak shift, behavioural contrast and stimulus generalization as related to personality and development in children. *Br. J. Psychol.* **63,** 47–62.

Notterman, J. M., Schoenfeld, W. N. and Bersh, D. J. (1952). Conditioned heart rate response in human beings during experimental anxiety. *J. comp. Physiol. Psychol.* **45,** 1–8.

Obrist, P. A., Wood, D. M. and Perez-Reyes, M. (1965). Heart rate during conditioning in humans: Effects of UCS intensity, vagal blockade and adrenergic block of vasomotor activity. *J. exp. Psychol.* **70,** 32–42.

Oldfield, R. C. (1971). The assessment and analysis of handedness: The Edinburgh inventory. *Neuropsychol.* **9,** 97–113.

Olds, J. and Olds, M. (1965). Drives, rewards and the brain. *In* "New Directions in Psychology." (Barron, F. *et al.* eds) Vol. 2. Holt, Rinehart and Winston, New York.

Olton, D. S. and Isaacson, R. L. (1968). Hippocampal lesions and active avoidance. *Physiol. Behav.* **3,** 719–724.

Papez, J. W. (1937). A proposed mechansim of emotion. *Arch. Neurol. Psychiat.* **38,** 725–743.

Payne, A. P. and Swanson, H. H. (1971). Hormonal control of aggressive dominance in the female hamster. *Physiol. Behav.* **6,** 355–358.

Pierrel, R. and Sherman, J. G. (1960). Generalization of auditory intensity following discrimination training. *J. expl. Analysis Behav.* **3,** 313–322.

Rescorla, R. A. and Solomon, R. L. (1967). Two-process learning theory: Relationships between Pavlovian conditioning and instrumental learning. *Psychol. Rev.* **74,** 151–182.

Reynolds, G. S. (1961). Behavioral contrast. *J. exp. Analysis Behav.* **4,** 57–71.

Roberts, W. W. and Kiess, H. O. (1964). Motivational properties of hypothalamic aggression in cats. *J. comp. physiol. Psychol.* **58,** 187–193.

Rosvold, H. E., Mirsky, A. F. and Pribram, K. H. (1954). Influence of amygdalectomy on social behaviour in monkeys. *J. comp. physiol. Psychol.* **47,** 173–178.

Royce, J. R. (1966). Concepts generated in comparative and physiological psychological observations. *In* "Handbook of Multivariate Experimental Psychology." (Catell, R. B. ed.) Rand McNally, Chicago.

Schachter, S. (1967). Cognitive effects on bodily functioning: Studies of obesity and eating. *In* "Neurophysiology and Emotion." (Glass, D. C. ed.) Rockefeller University Press and Russell Sage Foundation, New York.

Sclafani, A. and Grossman, S. P. (1969). Hyperphagia produced by knife cuts between the medial and lateral hypothalamus in the rat. *Physiol. Behav.* **4,** 533–537.

Scull, J., Davies, K. and Amsel, A. (1970). Behavioral contrast and frustration effect in multiple and mixed fixed-interval schedules in the rat. *J. comp. physiol. Psychol.* **71,** 478–483.

Silverman, J. (1970). Attentional styles and the study of sex differences. *In* "Attention: Contemporary Theory and Analysis." (Mostofsky, D. J. ed.) Appleton-Century-Crofts, New York.

Simons, E. L. (1969). The origin and radiation of the primates. *Ann. N. Y. Acad. Sci.* **167,** Art. 1, 319–331.

Spence, J. T. and Spence, K. W. (1966). The motivational components of manifest anxiety: Drive and drive stimuli. *In* "Anxiety and Behaviour." (Spielberger, C. D. ed.) Academic Press, New York and London.

Spence, K. W. (1956). "Behaviour Theory and Conditioning." Yale University Press, New Haven, Connecticut.

Stein, L. (1965). Facilitation of avoidance behaviour by positive brain stimulation. *J. comp. physiol. Psychol.* **60,** 9–19.

Suchenwirth, R. (1969). Bedingungen der Händigkeit und ihre Bedeutung für die Klinik der Hemisphärenprozesse. *Nervenarzt* **40,** 509–517.

Teplov, B. M. (1964). Problems in the study of general types of higher nervous activity in man and animals. *In* "Pavlov's Typology." (Gray, J. A. ed.) Pergamon Press, Oxford.

Terrace, H. S. (1966). Stimulus control. *In* "Operant Behavior: Areas of Research and Application." (Honig, W. K. ed.) Appleton-Century-Crofts, New York.

Ulrich, R. E. (1967). Pain—aggression. *In* "Foundations of Conditioning and Learning." (Kimble, G. A. ed.) Appleton-Century-Crofts, New York.

Voronin, L. G. (1962). Some results of comparative-physiological investigations of higher nervous activity. *Psychol. Bull.* **59,** 161–195.

Wagner, A. R. (1963). Conditioned frustration as a learned drive. *J. exp. Psychol.* **66,** 142–148.

Wagner, A. R. (1966). Frustration and punishment. *In* "Current Research on Motivation." (Haber, R. M. ed.) Holt, Rinehart and Winston, New York.

Watson, J. B. (1924). "Behaviorism." Norton, New York.

Willett, R. (1960). The effects of psychosurgical procedures on behavior. *In* "Handbook of Abnormal Psychology." (Eysenck, H. J. ed.) Pitman, London.

Wynne-Edwards, V. C. (1962). "Animal Dispersion in Relation to Social Behaviour." Oliver and Boyd, Edinburgh.

Key Issues in Motivation Theory (With Special Reference to Structured Learning and the Dynamic Calculus)

RAYMOND B. CATTELL

University of Illinois

The Definition of Motivation Measurement

No informed psychologist or philosopher will deny that few issues in psychology or philosophy, and for that matter, in sociology or economics, can be clearly handled without explicit postulates about motivation. Yet, apart from Madsen's Theories of Motivation (1961), I know of no systematic attempt to survey the main dynamic theories with due and clear formal analysis of the structure of theory. An attempt to handle so major a theme systematically in the space of this paper would be absurd. My aim is therefore to attempt such an analysis of theoretical structure in one development only—that called *the dynamic calculus*. In that area I aim also to formulate questions framing the key issues for further research.

In psychodynamics we are in a somewhat chaotic state of house refurnishing, in changing from a clinician's to an experimental psychologist's basis for dynamic theory. But the chaos is worse than it need have been because the new furniture is being moved in by two different firms—those who consider "experimental" to mean the classical bivariate experimental approach and those who have a broader vision of multivariate experimental methods. In the sophisticated audience of methodologists and experimentalists at home with multivariate methods now gathered here I do not need to go back over the arguments for the greater aptness of multivariate methods in handling the concepts and methods—concerning drives, integration, conflict, etc. essential to this area. Clinicians have already gotten on the track of these concepts by global and implicitly multivariate methods, without being able, however, to master the technical multivariate experimental procedures necessary to further advance. Bivariate experiment needs to be freely used where it is strategically appropriate, but a good total strategy in the motivational area calls for abundant and skilful use of multivariate designs especially to give meaning and measurement to concepts entering bivariate checks.

The dynamic calculus is a development largely over the last fifteen years which has produced an integrated array of concepts, practical means of measurements, and testable theories about the interaction of these concepts. I propose to remind you of the key concepts therein, and then to ask some seven questions which I believe research needs to ask next in the interests of greater advance. They carry the dynamic calculus into several areas of theory that are of general interest to this group, but perhaps most provocatively into the area of learning theory.

I may be wrong in supposing that I have only to remind you of developments up to this point; but if so, I am sure that in this audience the exposition I shall now give can be as brief as would be any mere reminiscence. The principal developments in the calculus so far consist of (1) An operational distinction of what is motivational from what is cognitive and temperamental; (2) Techniques for measuring motivation strength objectively and providing means of evaluating their validity; (3) Methods and findings concerning experimental means for exploring dynamic structure, including the concept of the dynamic lattice; (4) A mathematical vector representation of attitudes and interests, and last, and most vitally, (5) A form of calculation concerning conflict and decision-making. The key issues for further theory construction to be raised here concern the application of the dynamic calculus to (a) learning, (b) perception, (c) predicting conflict resolution, (d) defining and measuring the different qualities or components of drive strength arising respectively from stimulation and from deprivation, and (e) approaching the definition of an experimentally based concept of mental energy.

As to the primary problem of defining motivation, as such, psychologists and philosophers since Plato seem to have had the happy conviction that they can distinguish three kinds of experience—cognitive, affective, and conative, which parallel three kinds of traits—abilities, temperament or general personality traits, and finally, dynamic traits, such as drives, interests, and sentiments. Since it was still impossible as recently as 1945 to find any operational basis for this distinction offered in the literature, I proposed (1946; with Warburton, 1967) to define dynamic traits as those the measures of which changed most with change of incentive; abilities as factors whose measures changed most with change of complexity; and temperament traits as changing least with either type of manipulation. The rather complex experimental measurement conditions for expressing these differences statistically must be left the reader who wishes to read Cattell and Warburton, (1967). However, you will recognize that the underlying general postulate in such a "relativity" emphasis is that any measured piece of behaviour normally derives its score from contributions of a *combination* of abilities, temperament, and dynamic traits as expressed in the familiar factor specification equation thus:*

$$a_{hijk} = \sum^{x=p} b_{hjx}A_{xi} + \sum^{y=q} b_{hjy}T_{yi} + \sum^{z=r} b_{hjz}s_{kz}D_{zi} \qquad (1)$$

where A_i, T_i and D_i are the endowments of individual i in p ability, q temperament, and r dynamic traits, respectively; b_{hjx} is a behavioral index or loading stating how much a unit increase in the trait A_x contributes to an increase in the behavior a_j as a response to the focal stimulus h; and s_{kz} is a modulating index† stating how much the ambient situation‡, k, provokes a rise in the dynamic trait D_z.

The functionally unitary nature of the traits of the type A, T, and D in equation (1) is assumed experimentally established by covariance factor analysis reaching simple structure resolutions. The factor scores, here and later, we shall assume to be in real base scores, i.e. from a true,

* The simultaneous appearance and contribution of all three modalities of factor trait, when we might be aiming to measure one only, can be illustrated by intelligence testing, where motivation level and certain personality traits have been known for some time to make definite but minor contribution to variance in the test score. Under the usual classroom testing conditions, a rough estimate would be that variance from intelligence is about ten times as large as variance from effort in the test situation. Nevertheless, for exact intelligence testing, we should partial conation (effort) out of an actual intelligence test measure and do the same to remove the ability contamination from a motivation measure, and so on.

† The full meaning of the modulating index and its mode of calculation must be read up elsewhere (Cattell, 1963, 1971b). It introduces the concept, not previously present in the factor analytic specification equation, of the situation actually modifying the level of the state or trait factor, by an index s, before the factor operates on the behavior, by the behavioral index b. The modulating index, s_k, has a subscript k particular to the ambient situation, k—the background to the focal stimulus, h—and it is this ambient stimulus situation which modifies the factor level. s_k states how much the modulatable basis of the state or trait—a state proneness or a dynamic trait, D_x—is changed for the average person. It thus changes both the mean level and the dispersion of the group, since highly "prone" individuals change more under modulation than persons of low state proneness.

‡ The focal stimulus, h, is that to which the individual is consciously or deliberately and pointedly responding. It is the classical stimulus in "stimulus-response" psychology. The ambient stimulus, k, as already briefly indicated is what is in the background. It is the conditions, present and reverberating from the immediate past, which affect the attitudes that will appear in the subject in his response to the focal stimulus, h. Thus k might be anything from a room temperature, or the presence of a second observer, to a test instruction, or the cue to adopt a particular role. It is the total environmental situation minus the focal stimulus.

not an arbitrary zero. This permits factors to escape from an arbitrary sigma of unity and thus to differ in absolute size and potency. In real base factoring the variables are in universal standardized "raw" scores (Cattell, 1972a).

So much for the definition of a motivational trait and its due setting in the general behavior prediction equation, as a modulatable factor. The discovery of a valid measure of motivation strength is a matter for experiment. Consequently, the concept of the essence of such a valid measure has been approached iteratively, as in all scientific definition, and as was done, for example, in approaching the definition of intelligence as "*g*" or relation-perceiving capacity. The strategy has been to take a hundred or more devices which psychologists declared "intuitively" to be manifestations of motivation strength, i.e. which fell in the agreed semantic domain of motivation or interest, and to factor them for an underlying unitary factor or factors. This yielded seven or eight primary and two or three secondary factors retaining their patterns of expression regardless of the nature of the interest content.

The Riddle of the Motivation Components

The meaning of the primaries is still, after twenty years, a matter for some debate; but the use of integrated (I) and unintegrated (U), to designate the two main secondaries, implies a theory fitting most of what is known about them. By continually trying out new objective devices, the factors have been checked and steadily refined, at least as stable empirical patterns regardless of conceptual questions remaining open. Thus, the validity of any single device can, wherever desired, be determined by its loading on the factor, e.g. the integrated or the unintegrated, which it is designed to measure. For example, the unintegrated motivational component, which has the wishful, undisciplined, and half-unconscious qualities that Freud assigned to the unconscious id, is most validly measured by the devices called autism, distortion of perception, projection, GSR magnitude, and the speed of blood pressure changes, whereas the devices of highest validity for the integrated motivational component in any interest are word association and volume of information on the given topic.

It is obvious from this already repeatedly checked work that the applied psychologist has been wrong to speak of the strength of a motive or interest as if it were some unitary measure. At best he is permitted to throw the seven or eight primaries together into two secondaries, which are virtually uncorrelated, and to speak of two distinct qualities of motive in every attitude, erg, or sentiment.

But what are the differences of quality between these two necessary measured components in any motive? It is now beginning to appear that the I or integrated component has a magnitude of stability coefficient which indicates that it is like a trait rather than a state, whereas the U component responds more sensitively, changing in relation to experimental stimulation or deprivation. It is known also that a high U value relative to I values goes with clinical and other evidence (Cattell and Sweney, 1964; Krug, 1971; Williams, 1959) of degree of conflict in the area. Further, we know from several school studies that integrated interest is a significant positive predictor of school achievement, whereas the corresponding U components tend to have zero or negative correlation, depending on the drive involved (Cattell and Butcher, 1968; Barton, Cattell and Dielman, 1972).

Theories concerning the nature of both the seven primaries and the U and I secondaries based on criterion evidence of this kind, have taken three main directions: First, a clinical and psychoanalytic direction identifying them with or relating them to distinct ego, id, and super ego contributions to any interest; and, second, a mathematical model development in which the components are assigned different properties in various equations, not necessarily connecting with existing theory in classical dynamics. This supposes that the simpler model in equation (1) above, in which ability and dynamic traits are directly additive, is not enough. Instead, it is hypothesized that dynamic strength measures multiply ability terms, and that this occurs differently for U and I components. Thus, in analysis of variance terms, there would be *interaction* of ability and motivation effects. If this occurs a most likely consequence when a factor analysis applies its additive framework to the data would be that the motivation components would appear with the same patterns as the original ability factors. That is to say, in as much as motivation increase would only enhance the magnitude of skills already depicted as ability factors there would be a tending of motivation components to appear as factors "cooperative" to ability factors, i.e. with the same patterns. This possibility is now being investigated by De Young and Burdsal, with specially designed experiments.

Yet a third direction of interpretation of the different patterns among motivation components—and such distinct state-like components in the final motivation level as arousal, physiological need level, anxiety, and so on, as has been hypothesized in the formula (Cattell, 1957):

$$E = (S+k)\,[C+H+(P-G_1)a] - bG_2 \qquad (2)$$

where ergic tension level or motive strength, E is the product of stimulus strength S ($+k$, a constant) and various components, of which current level of gratification G is one; H, a personal history component (the Freudian fixation theory); C, a constitutional component, and P, a physiological condition are instances while a and b are constants. The satisfaction or gratification here is assumed to act differently according as it is physiological, G_1 or psychological, G_2.

Without pursuing this sketch of the concepts developing around motivation component structure any further, I shall now point out that it leads up to the first major question needing to be answered for the sake of a more complete motivation theory, namely, "What theoretical properties are to be assigned to these indubitably distinct components which repeat themselves in the measures of strength of any interest, no matter what the environmental content of that interest?"

The Measurement of Conflict and the Prediction of Decision

The second area leading to provocative issues is the clinical field, specifically the area of conflict and decision. For experimental purposes one must distinguish between the phenomena of active, current conflict and those of stabilized settled (or buried)* conflict. In the former, we have two courses of action, j and p, in response to the same stimulus situation defined by the focal stimulus h and the ambient stimulus k. Since we are not concerned with how well the courses of action a_j or a_p will be carried out, but only with which the individual will choose to do, as the process of conflict moves to a decision, we can drop all but the dynamic terms (the abilities and temperament qualities) from the general behavioral equation (1) above. The behavioral response a_{hijk} then needs to be measured in an experimental situation designed to ignore the proficiency and style components, and becomes that of pressing a button, right or left, or making a check mark. We can then write the prediction equations for the strength (and therefore the probability) of the two responses as:

$$a_{hijk} = b_{hje} s_{ke} D_{ei} + \dots + b_{hjr} s_{kr} D_{ri} \tag{3a}$$

$$a_{hipk} = b_{hpe} s_{ke} D_{ei} + \dots + b_{hpr} s_{kr} D_{ri} \tag{3b}$$

If we have already experimentally determined what the behavioral index and modulator values are for these two courses of action, a

* The expression "buried" is less satisfactory than "settled" because it implies all kinds of Freudian qualities (unconsciousness) and mechanisms (defenses). By settled, we mean a dynamic adjustment which the individual has reached as the best compromise he can find in the given situation. So long as the situation endures, he builds up tolerably stable habit systems fitting equation (5).

comparison of the two values estimated will estimate which direction the decision will go in any given individual, according to what we are now calling the dynamic calculus. This is done, of course, by substituting in the equation (1) the dynamic trait strengths of the individual and (2) the general b and s indices found from previous experiment for these courses of action. But, before this decision is made, we may expect a moment of conflict; and the severity of that conflict can be hypothesized to be a function positively of the absolute magnitude of a_j and a_p, and negatively of the size of the difference between them. Initial alternative formulations, using, respectively, additive and multiplicative functions, would be:

$$(a)^c{}_{hik}(j.p) = (a_{hijk} + a_{hipk}) - x(a_{hijk} - a_{hipk})^2 \tag{4a}$$

or:

$$(a)^c{}_{hik}(j.p) = \frac{(a_{hijk} + a_{hipk})}{y(a_{hijk} - a_{hipk})^2 + z} \tag{4b}$$

where $(a)^c$ is the intensity of *active* (hence prefix (a)) conflict; and x, y and z are constants scaling the relative contribution of the *absolute* level of the forces in conflict (the sum) and of the embarrassment from their being nearly equal (the difference).

The problem in experiment with the above has been, first, to discover some second or "criterion" measure of degree of conflict with which to compare the value reached by (4) in either form. Here, as in seeking the signs of motivation strength, Sweney and I (Cattell and Sweney, 1964) turned to the chief signs of conflict accepted by clinicians, such as heightened muscle tension, hesitation in decision, repression of associated ideas, pugnacity, slips of tongue and pen, etc. We then factored a representative thirty of them taken over several of what we defined as *loci* and *foci* of conflict. The agreement from two population samples on the nature of the seven or eight factorial components found in conflict expressions was excellent, and the psychological meaning of the components was tolerably clear. But the coincidence presented by the appearance of seven conflict factors and seven motivation strength factors was sufficient to evoke suspicion. Krug has recently (1971) taken a major step toward testing this suspicion by factoring marker variables from the two domains—motivation and conflict—together on three sets of children. His results definitely indicate that some of the motivation and conflict factors are really the same. But surely this should not surprise us. In the first place, merely to have an unrequited desire is itself to be in conflict, as Buddhism recognizes. A drive which remains at a substantial tension level, unsatisfied, must do so because of external frustration and internal conflict. Any high undischarged drive implies the existence of conflict. The line between motivation strength and conflict intensity in fact, would thus, in any actual conflict, not be easy to draw. The reason for this is clear in equations (4) and (5) above and below which obviously require that the strength of conflict manifestations should be partly a product of motivation strength.

Thus we would expect any actual expression of conflict used directly to measure *6* in equation (4) above to require for its prediction both the motivation measures already in equation (4) and certain further terms which determine what we may call the ultimate conflict product. This involves both the dynamic conflict level and certain susceptibility or proneness terms. Presumably what we are saying here is that certain personalities and certain situations will cause the same amount of motivational conflict to result in more suffering or signs of conflict. Such a model requires the phenomena to be analyzed in two stages as follows:

$$c_{hijk} = \sum^{p=k} b_{jp} s_{kp} D_{pc} + \sum^{q=l} b_{jq} s_{kq} C_{qi} \tag{5}$$

Here it is supposed that there are k dynamic, motivation factors (D's) and l conflict effect magnifying factors (C's). The b's, behavioral indices, and s's, modulators, have the usual meaning in representing the specificity of the situation. The first term (right) is to be taken not as a simple sum of dynamic strengths as in (3), but as the disparity function of their strengths given (for a specific interest) in equation (6). The second term, of course, is the susceptibility to expressing motivational disparities in signs of conflict, and is dependent on the individual's endowment in conflict proneness factors—C's, and the quality of the situation for modulating such proneness—the s's. Thus (5) says signs of conflict are jointly an expression of conflict and liability to conflict products, and for simplicity it makes these additive rather than multiplicative. This model certainly fits Krug's results in which conflict expression is shown to be resolvable into both motivation strength factors and conflict manifestation factors.

The Extra-Motivational Determiners of Conflict

In making an entirely fresh attack on the manifestations of conflict, Sweney deliberately ignored the existing biases of the clinician in order to make a clean experimental start. But the fact emerges that the main product of conflict the clinician talks about—anxiety, has duly appeared as one of the conflict manifestation products. Since I have given a full development in a chapter elsewhere (Cattell, 1972b) of the model relating anxiety to strength of dynamic traits and their conflict I shall not pursue this aspect of active conflict further here. Suffice it, however, that as stated above, the best treatment of the problem experimentally seems to be to take two stages: (1) That in which individual conflict product expressions are analyzed, as in (5) above, into strengths of motive and into conflict product factors (defense devices, anxiety, etc.) and (2) That in which the conflict product factors are analyzed into their sources in personality structure and the nature of the situation (loci of conflict). The loadings of the second order anxiety state factor on ego weakness ($C-$), guilt proneness (O), and poorly integrated self sentiment (Q_3-) (Cattell, 1957; Cattell and Nichols, 1972) show clearly what roots in personality structure we may expect to operate to determine the conflict product factors, when dynamic disparities arise. The best way to formulate the next crucial questions here we will leave until stabilized conflict has been discussed.

Practically every adjustment challenge in life ends in the individual accepting some compromise, the end result of what we have called integration learning, in which the chief drive at issue settles for a compromise expression. That is to say, a settled, habitual mode of expression is reached (at least as long as that life situation endures) in which the joint expression of several drives is maximized as far as that individual is able to achieve maximization. The consequence is that in the typical behavioral equation, as in (1) above, there will be b's with negative values, though there will be a predominance of positive values. That is to say, in order to achieve positive satisfaction for ergs E_1, E_2 and E_3 by a certain course of action the individual has to accept a denial of erg E_4. The more he follows course of action a_{hjk} the more he satisfies E_1, E_2 and E_3, and the more he is diverted from satisfaction of E_4. A ratio (or other expression) of the b values for $E_1+E_2+E_3$, and that for E_4 will therefore be a statement of the degree of unavoidable, built-in conflict, or *mutual cancellation of purposes* or *possible satisfactions* existing in the given course of action. A formula for the degree of stabilized, persisting conflict in an adopted course of action a_{hjk} would therefore be:

$$c(S)_{hijk} = \sum^{x=k} \bar{b}_{hjx} s_{kx} D_{xi} \qquad (6a)$$

where $\bar{b}_{hjx}$ means the value of any b that has a negative loading. (The (s) subscript to c is for stabilized conflict). If we prefer to express this amount of conflict as a percentage or fraction of the dynamic investment in the given course of action instead of as an absolute amount then we can use the alternative form:*

$$c(S)_{hijk} = \frac{\sum^{x=k_-} b_{hjx} s_{kx} D_{xi}}{\sum^{x=r} \bar{b}_{hjx} s_{kx} D_{xi}} \tag{6b}$$

where r is the total of dynamic factors involved including k; $\bar{b}_{hjx}$ has its sign ignored; and k is the total of factors with negative loadings.

Although (6) applies to a single course of action, a_j in a single situation hk, it can be summed for a whole sentiment structure or a whole personality. In the last instance, theory would require this sum to relate to indices of individual adjustment, and Williams' demonstration (1959) that psychotics significantly exceed normals on this c index (calculated on P-technique data, of course) supports the theory.

One wonders to what extent some of the general personality factors found in factoring general (not motivational) behavior may turn out to be higher level abstractions, as in c above (across the total dynamic realm) governing the style and manner of control of dynamic traits. For example, could ego strength (C in the questionnaire series) or such factors as *U.I.* 16, *U.I.* 20, *U.I.* 28, etc. in the objective behavior personality factors in the O-A batteries, be measurable also as abstractions at a generalized action level from motivation measurement data? Theoretically, one might state such a generalized dynamic trait—the capacity to control impulse—as something to be measured by the capacity to inhibit undesirable acts and to augment desirable acts. "Desirable" has to be defined here for the purpose of ego strength, C, or self sentiment, Q_3, in terms of utility for the individual's long range plans, not of social ethics and super ego values as in the super ego, G factor. In personality as measured by questionnaire, the ego strength factor, C, and the self sentiment strength factor, Q_3, are found most operative in such long-circuiting impulse control. Starting in the field of dynamic measurement, let us consider the specification equation for a useful, desirable course of action a_d, and for an undesirable act a_u.

* In this and other formulae here, the factor analyst will ask for more explicit clarification of why we use a rate of increase expression, in the form of the tangent value, which is b, rather than an expression for absolute level. The answer, at least in ordinary factor analysis, is that we have no expression for the average level of factor x as it affects the average level of variable a_j. However, if we go to covariance factoring and accept the assumption in Real Base True Zero Factor Analysis (Cattell, 1972a), then we reach the conclusion that the absolute level of factor x in contribution to the absolute level of a_j is also represented by b_{jx}. That is to say, the absolute amount of drive E_p relative to drive E_q, satisfied in the course of action a_{hjk} is correctly represented by the b_{jp} and b_{jq} values.

In these equations we shall consider all dynamic traits as ergs (concentrating on the basic origins in the dynamic system) and the outcome there will be a contribution $\sum^{x=k} b_{hux}s_{kx}E_{xi}$ in favour of performing this "instinct satisfying" act, a_{hux}, which happens to be undesirable. The degree of inhibition that a given individual can exercise on this act by ego strength, and the foresight of the self sentiment, will be represented by the second and third terms in equation (7a). Similarly the augmentation of a good act (which he only moderately desires to do) by C and Q_3 is shown by positive b loadings in equation (7b). (These loadings are determined by the culture, and one's education therein.)

$$a_{hiuk} = \Sigma b_{hux}s_{kx}E_{xi} - b_{huc}s_{kc}T_{Ci} - b_{huq}s_{kq}T_{Q3i} \quad (7a)$$

$$a_{hidk} = \Sigma b_{hdx}s_{kx}E_{xi} + b_{hdc}s_{kc}T_{Ci} + b_{hdq}s_{kq}T_{Q3i} \quad (7b)$$

where T_C and T_{Q3} are scores on the C and Q_3 factors (see Cattell, 1957), and E_x is any ergic tension of character x. In a society where the highest levels of control reached are good, the level of behavioral indices will be large on T_C and T_{Q3}, relative to those on ergs, for only thus will they outweigh the effect of the E's; and, of course, the individual of higher control will have larger scores on T_C and T_{Q3} (or *U.I.* 16 and *U.I.* 19 in the objective personality test series).

Concerning new trails from this dynamic calculus formulation of conflict, there are two main theoretical questions which experiment now needs to ask. First, "How correct in detail is our model which accounts for the magnitude of a manifestation of conflict, e.g. anxiety, by (a) motivation strength factors, U and I, (b) factors specifically of conflict expression, and (c) general personality integration factors (expressing themselves in T_C and T_{Q3} in (7b))?" Second, "How far are certain well known source traits, now encountered as general personality factors, to be re-interpreted as essentially dynamic structure factors that have been summed across the totality of dynamic expression?" For example, are factors such as *U.I.* 23, *U.I.* 24 and *U.I.* 35 simply the magnitude of total conflict, or the proneness to certain conflict manifestations, such as anxiety, or total capacity to control?

The possibility of raising and answering such questions experimentally has appeared only recently, and has been bestowed on us primarily as a result of the achievement of meaningful measurement in the motivation area. For the last ten years has made available instruments (such as the MAT and SMAT) and concepts for objective measurement, i.e. devices not dependent on a subject's self-estimation, and has been able to shape these measures to demonstrated unitary motivational components and dynamic structures. From the standpoint of practical aid to research, the relating of these measures to clinical criteria has been facilitated, as the incoming results show, by the provision of standardized batteries, such as the Motivation Analysis Test (the MAT) and the School Motivation Analysis Test (the SMAT). Through the work done on these by Burdsal, Horn, Krug, Radcliffe, Sweney, and others, the clinician does not have to pore over the details of test or apparatus construction in remote research articles before addressing himself to research on such questions of theory as are raised here.

The Introduction of Three Classes of Measurable Predictors in Learning Theory

The provision of objective unitary trait measurement, making possible direct ergic tension measurements, also enables us to achieve new penetrations in a third area—that of testing theory in regard to human and animal learning. In so far as motivation strength and tension reduction have been seriously introduced as terms in learning equations, they have had to rest on verbal self-estimate in humans, or on measures of hours of food deprivation, or strength of electric shock in animals. Anderson (1938) and Haverland (1954) showed, some years ago, that factoring of motivational behaviour in rats did, in fact, yield the unitary ergic tension patterns, such as hunger and thirst, which had commonly been assumed at a crude observational level, to exist as unitary tensions. The recent work of Cattell, Schneewind and Dielman (in press) supports the Anderson and Haverland indications on larger samples. But these studies also show that the usual measures employed by "brass instrument" psychologists for hunger strength as an independent variable in animal learning, e.g. hours of food deprivation, were, as single variables, relatively poor estimates of the total ergic tension present in the hunger factor. The recent work of Cattell, Schneewind and Dielman (in press) on different breeds of rats supports this, and shows very clearly that there are several distinct motivation components to be taken into account in the total motivation strength of the rat, precisely as in the α through ζ components in humans (Cattell and Dielman, in press).

Our new capacity to measure ergic tension levels in animals or men directly, as a unitary state, at a given time, instead of depending on the rather dimly related supposed causes of these tension levels, residing in food deprivation, etc. opens up new possibilities of testing more exact formulations in learning theory. Naturally, the conservative experimenter will await some further demonstration that the new measures are related consistently to the other criteria, e.g. rate of learning, to which he is accustomed. Such evidence, I would repeat, is available in some abundance in the above mentioned studies of Cattell, Schneewind, and Dielman on rats, and is very clear in the human manipulative studies on hunger, fear, and sex by Cattell, Kawash and DeYoung (in press) and Dielman, Cattell and Kawash (1971).

These studies in which hunger, sex and security-seeking (fear) have been variously stimulated and deprived bring out clearly two important facts: (a) that the objectively measured motivational component strengths change in strength in response to these objective criteria of stimulation and deprivation much as our formulation requires (equation (2)), and (b) that the U and I motivational components have interesting differentials. Indeed, one must point out, in passing, that, both in this matter and in others, it is evidently desirable to consider the likelihood that the U and I motivational components will behave differently in every one of the seven formulae above. Hypotheses exist anticipating that, both in the formulae above and in the learning formulae we are now about to consider, the different constants and laws for the two main forms of motivation will take certain forms.

The phenomena of learning with which motivation measurement and theory especially need to be concerned are of the usual two kinds in the learning domain. First, there is the domain of deliberate memorizing and the acquisition of cognitive skills; and, second, the domain of what one may call emotional learning or personality development. In regard to the first, which is less complex, a formula has been suggested (Cattell, 1970 (a), 1971 (b)), which takes into account as predictors not only (a) the abilities and other fixed traits of the individual, commonly omitted from learning equations, but also both (b) the absolute level of ergic tension under which the learning takes place, (c) the magnitude of reward, which is represented as the fall in drive tension as a result of the learning behavior, and (d) the level of general psychological states. Its essential form is thus as follows, with four main classes of terms.

$$(a_{ijt2} - a_{ijt1}) = \sum^{x=p} b_{jx}T_{xi} + \sum^{y=q} b_{jy}S_{yi} + \sum^{z=r} b_{jz}E_{zi} + \sum^{z=r} b_{jz(a-b)}\frac{(E_{zai}-E_{zbi})}{f(t_b-t_a+k)} \qquad (8)$$

Here, the term on the left is the gain in skill after one learning experience—between a measure at t_1 and a retest at t_2; the T's are the p abilities, etc. relevant to such learning; the S's are levels on the nine states so far demonstrated by P-technique (anxiety, arousal, depression, etc.); the E's are the r diverse ergic tension factors now recognized, e.gs hunger, sex, fear, gregariousness; the E_{za} and E_{zb} terms are the value.

of the ergic tension E_z (a) at the beginning of learning and (b) immediately after reward for the appropriate or relatively appropriate action; t_a and t_b are the times of making the correct response and receiving the reward for it; and f and k are constants.

The first check on this formulation has been made in regard to classroom learning studies by Cattell and Barton (in press). Although the other three terms in (8) are traditional or have at least been previously suggested the introduction of the term for states of a general nature (non-motivational)—the *S*'s—is a new hypothesis for investigation. However, preliminary research in our laboratory (Cattell and Scheier, 1961) as well as the work of Spence and Spence (1966) on anxiety show that these general state levels are, indeed, necessary terms in cognitive learning. In fact, some significant variance is contributed by all four types of terms above, according to recent research, suggesting that this model for cognitive learning is essentially sound. Nevertheless, there is scope for appreciable variation in theoretical invention regarding the form of the reward term (the fourth expression). For the time being we have taken it to a weight-constant, $b_{jz(b-a)}$ for the given behavior a_j, the ergic tensions, z, and the time interval between stimulus and reward, $b-a$, applied to a measure of the tension reduction achieved $(E_{zai}-E_{zbi})$ for the given individual, i, and divided by a function (constant k) of the time lapse between correct response and reward (t_b-t_a).

However, it is in the realm of emotional learning that the greatest challenges and the finest opportunities for developing motivation theory now arise. Under "emotional learning" must be included such classes of phenomena as the attachment of new and different emotional responses to a given situation, the building up of new control systems over previous primary ergic responses, the changing of attitudes under experience or persuasion, and what has been called confluence or integration learning (Cattell, 1950). The latter includes the change in structure which occurs when an act becomes performed for a different end—usually to obtain a different combination of goal satisfactions. This modification of an act, or even the use of the same act for different goals is a form of learning change missed in classical formulations. Integration or confluence learning also includes the discovery of new modes of behavior which more successfully manage simultaneously to satisfy several drives.

The Comprehensive, Tri-Vector Description of Learning—Including Emotional Learning

The sheer description and representation of such modes of change in these domains of emotional learning, quite apart from the setting up of a most likely theoretical model to account for the learning involved—taxes the present conceptual resources of psychology to the utmost. We simply have not developed either in clinical psychology or in learning theory anything beyond "an increment in a variable" to describe the actually much more complex changes that go on in response to a learning situation. The line between description and conceptual analysis is always impossible to draw exactly and in this case new conceptions enter in from the beginning, even in the new systematic descriptions of learning change that are proposed. In case the reader is not already familiar with the new elements in this description such as modulation, the behavioral index vector, and the dynamic lattice, let us briefly define these necessary elements in the description of learning change.

First let us consider the concept of modulation, which, as briefly introduced already above, means that a total situation (actually through the ambient situation part of it) always modifies an individual's level on a particular state (or even trait, if it has any diurnal variance) according to an index characteristic of that situation and that state. (In the R-technique model this s_{kx} value will have to be the same for all individuals, but in the P-technique model it can adjust to the experience of the given individual.) Thus, formally, in modulation, any ambient situation, k, changes the level of any ergic tension, E_x, or emotional state, S_y, by a fraction or amount which can be represented by a modulation index, written s_{kx} and s_{ky} in the various formulae here and elsewhere. Such an index has been used in equations (1), (3), (5), and (6) above because action of this kind is unquestionably part of the phenomena concerned. Incidentally, to accommodate to this the factor analyses have to be covariance factor analyses or, ideally, real base (Cattell, 1972a) since ordinary factors do not change in sigma or mean. It will be evident that a change in this index can represent emotional learning, for it indicates that the object or situation is evoking more affection, or fear, or other ergic tension than it did before. Thus, a single vector of such s's can be written to represent the emotional quality of the total change—the change in emotional interest and involvement.

A second concept for describing change is the dynamic lattice, as shown, with some concrete references, in Fig. 1, and concerning which, since it is twenty years old, I trust I am reminding the reader rather than expounding. The dynamic lattice contains the postulate that all reward is through innate ergs—broadly conceived, as our factor analytic evidence shows, to include not only sex, security (fear), hunger, etc. but also less popularly conceived drives such as need for temperature homeostasis, need for rest, etc. Consequently, to use Murray's term, all courses of action (attitudes, singly, sentiments as organized attitude

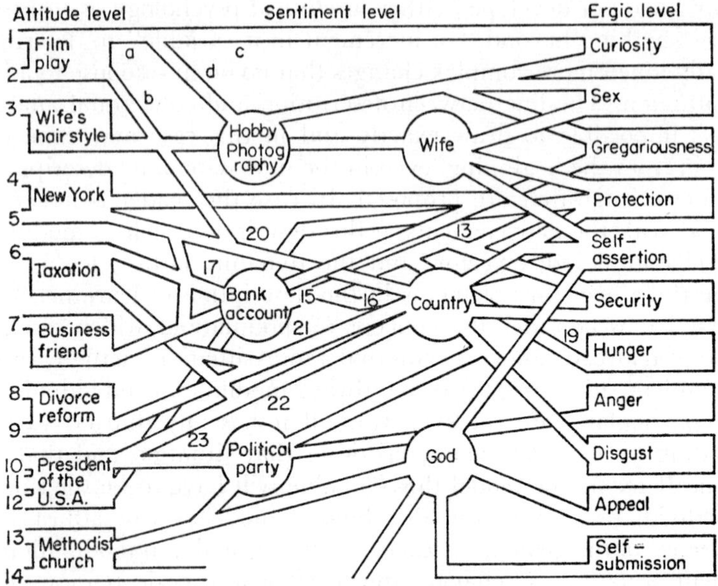

Fig. 1. The Dynamic Lattice.

systems) *subsidiate*, as shown by paths in Fig. 1, to one or (more usually) several ergic goal satisfactions.

As it stands in Fig. 1 this is a non-quantitative statement, though the lattice is normally derived from quantitative investigation, as described elsewhere, namely (a) factor analysis at various cross sections from left to right of the diagram, and (b) manipulative studies in which various paths of subsidiation are opened or blocked. The quantitative values that would be added to such a map are the b's and s's of the specification equations above (as they would affect the dynamic traits only). The b's would be attached to the pathways, which represent courses of action. For example, a_j would represent "Now that my bank account is in a healthy state (situation) I am going to join the P club (course of action) where I can get good company (gregarious erg satisfaction)." Such a number might be represented also by making the pathway a certain diameter (hydraulic analogy). The s's would attach themselves as numbers to the stimulus situations, commonly subgoals, shown by circles. (Parenthetically, the dynamic lattice, like the internal anatomy of the human body, is difficult to represent in two dimensions.) The numbers at left in Fig. 1 identify attitudes, as described elsewhere, but all in the format: "In these circumstances I want so much to do this with that."

The dynamic lattice has its initial value as a teaching and research planning "map", representing either the common structure in our culture or the structure for an individual. However, as our means of measurement become more sensitive the topological, reticular representation can actually suggest new modes of calculation (as a physicist calculates in electrical, hydraulic and other networks), various possible equilibria and change effects. One can represent in the dynamic lattice not only the subsidiations to particular ergic goals, but also the intermediate plexuses (sub-goals) which have been called acquired sentiment structures. These are objects or situations which are simultaneously involved with several attitudes (and as such cannot be represented by a single point in such a two-dimensional diagram). Calculations as to "investments" in these subjects (Cattell, 1960) can be clinically very important. However, a representation of the tangled skein of motives which constitutes the dynamic life of the average poorly integrated human being, in this spatial form can be useful only so far and might be seen as forbiddingly complex by some clinical psychologists. At some point one must shift to the translation into matrix algebra. This again may not please the average clinician, but, as a former chemist, I cannot help observing that the clinical psychologist's tolerance for complexity seems to be less than that of the stereochemist, or the molecular geneticist unravelling the double helix! That tolerance for and willingness to respond mathematically to complexity has to increase among psychologists if we are to gain serious scientific control rather than merely play with the field, deceiving the general public as to our "professional" know-how. Indeed, it is high time (the lattice having been proposed nearly twenty years ago) that some clinicians used it actually to explore the dynamics and conflicts of some typical cases, and used it to guide that emotional learning which we call therapy. The truly constructive uses that I know of are limited to a few active researchers, as in the Cartwrights' recent (1971) analyses of individual cases by a skillful use of the adjustment process analysis design which is cognate with the dynamic lattice, and Williams' (1954) and Cross's (1951) classical studies.

As will be evident from the statement that the quantitative values in the lattice are the b's and s's from the behavioral specification equation ((3) above) the factor analysis of an array of attitudes is the primary experimental approach for exploring the lattice. The second, as indicated above, is by manipulation of stimuli and satisfactions aimed at testing hypotheses about connections in particular parts of the structure. This approach might be designated the dynamic equivalents method since by increasing or decreasing satisfactions through one path it aims to produce changes in others that are considered equivalents. For example, a blocking of *b* in Fig. 1 above should cause an increase in a, d, and c. Although dynamic calculus research now needs to develop this method with precision, in conjunction with and as a check on analysis of structure by factoring, we cannot pursue it further here. It should be noted, however, that even though the lattice requires these values which can be put in matrix form, there is additional information in the lattice which is not contained in any one matrix, and it remains an indispensable element of description.

At this point, having touched on the principal elements—*b*'s, *s*'s, *D*'s, *E*'s and lattice subsidiations, in quantitatively describing the dynamic adjustment in a system of habits, we are ready to formulate the change in such a system for which structured learning theory needs to account. For so far we have only set out a learning formulation which accounts for an increase in a specific variable, and though we have done so more comprehensively than in most reflexological learning formulations, equation (7) is so far better called an interactive learning model than the full structured learning theory.

The theoretical model for what has thus been called structured learning theory no longer represents the learning change to be analyzed merely as an increase in a single performance, as in equation (7) above, and as in most classical learning theory, but by a change in all the elements needed to describe the pre-learning structure. Most of this (all but the subsidiations as depicted in the lattice) can be encompassed by referring to three vectors abstracted from the "developed" specification equation) as follows:

$$\text{A vector of change in trait level } (T_{c1}, T_{c2} \ldots T_{c(p+q+r)}) \tag{9a}$$

where the subscript *c* stands for a change measurement, so that:

$$T_{cl} = (T_{lt2} - T_{lt1})$$

$$\text{A vector of change in behavioral indices } (b_{cl}, b_{c2} \ldots b_{c(p+q+r)}) \tag{9b}$$

$$\text{A vector of change in modulation indices } (s_{c1}, s_{c2} \ldots s_{c(q+r)}) \tag{9c}$$

(Note the *s*'s would be considered to change only on the *S*'s, the states and the dynamic traits—the *D*'s—not necessarily on the *T*'s.)

Concerning the means by which these change values are obtained from the factoring of the before-learning and after-learning covariance matrices we need not bother at the present time. (The reader will be familiar with joint matrix factoring capable of giving b_c alone or T_c alone, and a special approach is needed (Cattell, 1971(b)) to give both at once.) The important point for the present is that structured learning theory describes change in all of three vectors, whereas classical reflexology, in either instrumental or classical conditioning, gives only a gross description in a scalar quantity representing change in a single variable. This is not just a mathematical difference for, as we shall see in a moment, these vectors have psychological meaning.

The psychological meaning of the vector of change in traits is, of course, simple, and not different in general nature from difference in a scalar. However, it has two differences from reflexological learning formulations in that (a) it deals with change on an important unitary trait rather than some restricted specific—one of innumerable possible specifics, and (b) it recognizes that a single kind of learning experience is not restricted in its effects to the variable the experimenter chooses to measure, but must be encompassed by a whole profile.

As to the change in the vector of behavioral indices, *b*'s, we are saying thereby that the people's traits, after the learning experience, have become differently involved and operative in regard to the same kind of behavior as before. Such significant changes in involvement are not hypothetical but have been clearly demonstrated by Hempel and Fleishman (1955) for abilities and by Hendricks (Hendricks, 1971; Cattell and Hendricks, in press) in emotional learning. It may help clarify this emotional re-adjustment learning if we take time for a concrete illustration.

Hendricks determined in the opening classes of an introductory psychology course the specification (*b* values) of the attitude, "I want to learn more about psychology." Using the ten factors of the Motivation Analysis Test, he showed that the roots of this attitude, i.e. the ergic goals to which it subsidiated, were mainly two ergs—curiosity and self-assertion, and two sentiments, those to a career and to the self. A re-analysis of the factor structure made later in the semester, after the freshmen's experience of taking the course showed a significant alteration in the vector of *b* values on career and on the security-seeking (fear) erg. As the difficult nature of the subject had become more apparent to them, the students' interest in it from the standpoint of his career sentiment became less involved, i.e. most had decided that this subject was not one in which they could easily make a career. As to the manifested increasing dependence of interest in the course upon security seeking or apprehension, as shown by higher loading in the fear erg and also upon the self-sentiment, we must realistically but regretfully conclude that the first innocent interest in the subject, at least the part springing from natural curiosity, gradually gets supplanted by the motives of competition. The loadings by the second testing suggest that fear of poor grades and the desire to do better than the next man have become more predominant.

Other studies now in progress indicate that the theory that the significant changes will occur through learning in the behavioral index vector is correct. Comparatively short learning experiences of a month or so seem to suffice to demonstrate this, but we shall probably have to wait some time for evidence of change in the third vector—the modulation vector, since good experiment in this domain requires a design using a formidable array of groups. That change occurs in the vector of trait scores, on the other hand, is so well known as scarcely to require reference to specific studies. However, I would mention as particularly interesting Graffam's (1967) demonstration that the vector of primary personality factors on the 16 *P.F.* alters differently in young people going to college and those going straight from school into jobs, and the finding of Hunt *et al.* (1959) of increases on ego strength and dominance factors (*C* and *E* on the 16 *P.F.*) in patients under therapy compared to controls. Considering therapy as organized emotional learning there are now indeed several studies showing change of a vector of source trait scores. Of particular interest is the study of Rickels, *et al.* (1966) because of the use of objective batteries to measure *U.I.* 23 (Regression) and *U.I.* 24 (Anxiety). A socially interesting instance is the finding (Cattell and Barton, 1972) of a characteristic vector of personality factor changes on the 16 *P.F.* in young people after three years of marriage compared to those who do not marry, as well as one of change under promotion in a job (Barton and Cattell, 1972, in press). Thus, we can say that the reality of the tri-vector representation of learning change in structured learning theory is supported already as to two vectors; and there is no reason to doubt that in due course the significance of changes on the modulation vector will also be practically demonstrated.

Principles in Structured Learning Theory

With this model of comprehensive (tri-vector) learning description, as we have called it, duly verified, we are required to complete the theory of structured learning by setting out the model governing the origins of these described changes. While one can set out a general model for this, as in Table I, equation (10)—a sort of catch-all for whatever specific laws may appear—nothing but experiment can guide us toward more specifically adapted models. As far as the general model is concerned one needs to enter experiment and analyze experiment in terms of a matrix formulation as in Table I, equation (10). Though this may look complex, at a glance, it is nothing but equation (8) shifted

Table 1
Matrix Arrangements for Analysis of Trait Change Vectors

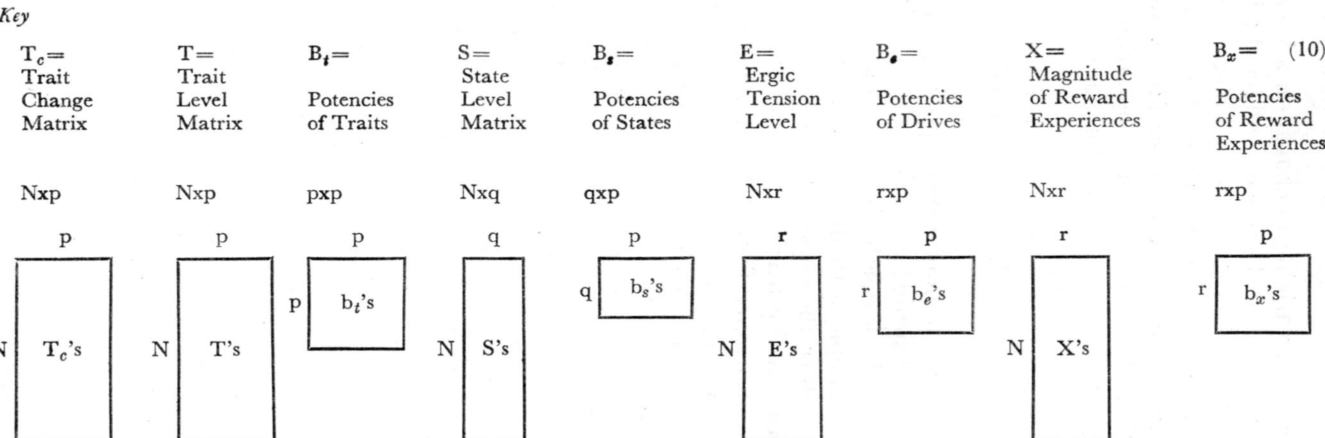

from change in a variable to change in a vector of factor scores, and set out in matrix form. Here we consider the learning of N people on p traits, the determiners being the absolute levels on the same p traits, the levels on q states at the time of learning, the level on r ergic tensions during learning, and a learning experience function, which we will call x, which depends on tension reductions and time relations, and of which there are r contributors for each individual. (This last is the last term in equation (8).)

A parallel matrix can be set up for the changes of the N people on the other two vectors—the behavioral indices (b's) and the modulators (s's).

One may well wonder which species of psychologist, the animal (reflexological) learning specialist, the educational psychometrist or the personality theorist, is likely to have the equipment and the imagination first to grapple with the problems of structured learning theory. One may venture the guess that the pioneering research is less likely to be carried out by learning theorists than by personality theorists. This is partly surmised from the continuing lack of a coherent over-all strategy among the former. On the one hand, the educational psychologist and the psychometrist are accustomed to taking some skill or memorizing task and taking as a dependent variable in learning some measured increase upon it, as in equation (7) above. On the other, the animal learning experimenter, viewing learning as instrumental conditioning, looks for some entirely new behavior development in one and the same stimulus situation. Meanwhile in other areas, such as psychotherapeutic learning, the emphasis is all on motivation, whereas in classical conditioning the emotional state is completely ignored. Only in Hull (1943) and in Tolman (1932, 1949) does one find an approach to the drive and other predictor variables used in our equation (7), and these drive and anticipation concepts are bereft of substantive foundation and form. By contrast the E's and S's in equation (7) are real entities, arising from experiments on the number and nature of drives and psychological states. The validity of measures for them has been very extensively examined and has given rise to the new concepts of motivational components, discussed above. These distinct motivational components have also been found (Cattell and Dielman, in press) in animal motivation strength measures.

Thus, learning experiment in the framework of structured learning theory is ready to go ahead both in human and animal learning, with the necessary motivation strength and psychological state measures available as independent variables and the comprehensive, vector description of change as the dependent variables. This experiment can go ahead either in a relatively blind, exploratory fashion, withholding theory development until some significant relations of b's, s's and T's to the experience parameters have begun to appear, or on a set of theoretical expectations. Since serendipity plays an important part in science, the former approach is not to be despised, but I have ventured to suggest elsewhere (Cattell, 1970a, 1972a) both some general theory and some specific hypotheses.

As to the T's the appearance of increments simultaneously in the several behaviors loaded on a given source trait could arise either from the existence of a common reinforcement schedule in the social environment, or from the action of a pre-existing unitary trait structure, which, by loading on every element, conduces simultaneously to gains in every element of the pattern. Formulae for relating T change to learning experience have been explored elsewhere (Cattell, 1971(a)). As to changes in the b's, much may be due to the performances depending more on certain factors than others as new ranges, stages and levels of performance are reached, as shown in the pioneer work of Hempel and Fleishman (1955) and Tucker (1966). As to changes in the third vector, the modulators, we are in psychological terms, seeking to explain here the fact that a situation stirs up an emotional state, or raises an ergic tension level response where previously it did not do so. Both classical conditioning or coexcitation, as I prefer to call it, and instrumental, operant conditioning or means–end learning already offer us formulations to account for such changes.

A special development of the formulation of the latter becomes necessary, however, for we have to account for an increase in a drive tension being rewarded (in the case of means–end learning). Situation k has to cause an increase in ergic tension on E in order that E may in the end be more fully satisfied than if ultimate tension reduction began from a lower level, since it is important for the attainment of the final goal that response be made to some focal stimulus j which would not be so readily reacted to (and learnt) if E were not raised to a higher tension level. (This special form of means–end learning we may call goal-rewarded tension modulation or the bow-string effect. It is a motivational instance of "reculer pour mieux sauter".) If we wish to represent the effects that are possible from both coexcitation learning and means–end learning (as goal-rewarded tension modulation) (compare Tolman, 1949) in the same equation for accounting for a modulation index change then we can write:

$$(s_{kx2} - s_{kx1}) = f\,(D_{1xk1}\,C_{kk1}) + g(D_{xa} - D_{xb}) \qquad (11)$$

Here f and g are constants, 1 and 2 are two successive learning occasions, a and *b* are respectively the time on the first occasion when the response of augmenting the ergic tension is made and the final reward is given. D^1_{xk1} is the strength of a D_x response made at ambient situation *k* to some ulterior (unconditioned) stimulus, k^1, occurring at the same time, and C_{kk1} is a measure of the degree of contiguity, in terms of efficacy for classical conditioning effects, of *k* and k_1. Thus, the augmentation of the modulation effect on the dynamic trait, D_x, when the situation *k* is met on occasion 2 is viewed as an internal response partly due to classical conditioning (if those conditions obtain) and otherwise due to reward, as represented by the tension reduction $(D_{xa} - D_{xb})$.

The growth of learning theory from its present state to a new level of prediction and control presented by structured learning theory is not going to take place easily. It calls for acceptance of a more complex model and for attainment of a more disciplined mathematical approach. In regard to the latter it requires, for example, that learning theorists become adept in matrix algebra. And in the execution of experiments themselves, since a multivariate approach is now demanded, it calls for more elaborate planning than is now customary. This was brought home to Dielman, Schneewind and myself (Cattell, Schneewind and Dielman, in press) in our experiments with rats, where the mazes themselves, the recording systems, and the reward procedures had to become decidedly more complicated than those in the usual reflexological research plans. However, in human learning in everyday life the complication is there anyway, and the multivariate approach is more adaptive to a pre-existing reality.

The demands which the introduction of structured learning theory (born largely of advances in the dynamic calculus) make upon the new experimenter, fall onerously also on the developers of the dynamic calculus themselves. It is now possible to measure ergic tension reductions directly, and to score changes in unitary psychological states, but only with appreciable testing time and with devices of only moderate validity. As with the Wright brothers' airplane, the principles have become clear, but the instrumentation is poor. Frankly, we are not yet able in the MAT (Cattell, *et al.* 1964), the SMAT and in the instrumentation for measuring states of arousal, stress and anxiety, to offer measures sufficiently brief and undisturbing to meet the needs of all types of learning experiment. We shall formulate in a moment, below, the key issues which now seem to arise in the learning area, as in the other areas, but as practical scientists let us recognize that one key issue concerns further advance in the sheer technical measurement batteries so far developed.

The Concept of Mental Energy and the Relation of Arousal to Primary Dynamic State Measures

In an exposition here at the Center for Advanced Theoretical Psychology, where more widely ranging theory is welcomed, I am tempted to take off finally into a more speculative aspect of this work than would be acceptable among experimental psychologists, who like to keep close to proven findings. Indeed, I propose to take up the concepts of mental energy and arousal which have been bandied around for a considerable time without achieving any psychometric precision or negotiability in the field of behavioral measurement.

The notion of mental energy has been freely used by such eminent writers as William James (1890), McDougall (1932) and Freud (1923), but except among physiological psychologists, where it has the same meaning as chemical energy and fits into the schema of the physical sciences, which is something quite different, psychologists have avoided it. If they ever use it, they will naturally require that it be given some operational definition as precise as the analogous $mv^2/2$ in the world of the physicist. A first issue to be raised, in psychometric terms, is whether we are dealing with a state or a trait. The former comes near to the concept of arousal; the latter is used when we talk of a "man of high energy".

A major problem in going from any set of behavioral activity measures, by any formula, to an energy concept is that whatever primary energy we can conceive is always modified and masked by inhibition, necessary to well-directed activity. Since even inhibition requires regard for objects and ideas my hunch is that the direction in which to look for an operational energy concept is at the total number of stimuli over which the individual maintains awareness, as shown by making some response to them. It may be objected that this is more like an index of awareness than of energy, and perhaps awareness would be a better term, but at least it is a beginning in an operational approach to a concept with the general semantic quality of energy, and it has the value of including inhibitory as well as excitation types of response. The obvious defect in any immediate, literal measurement of this kind is that it must involve and be substantially correlated with intelligence. To a person who intelligently understands a piece of machinery there are, cognitively, far more elements to which reaction could be attached than for a person to whom it is just an undifferentiated mass. However, it is equally clear that between a fatigued and an unfatigued person of the same understanding the former will fail to show any reaction to elements that will bring responses from the latter. We can preserve our distinct energy concept simply by agreeing to partial out intelligence.

Now the means for measuring response are available to us in the general "strength of interest measures" in the motivational component scores in the dynamic calculus. One does not have actually to measure physical activity "in situ". The memory, G.S.R., perceptual distortion, projection, fluency, etc. measures will cover both the excitatory and inhibitory response potentials. A philosopher or mathematician sitting empty handed by the hour, and registering zero energy by any overt behavior, will show the breadth and depth of his interests, i.e. of his mental energy, by these motivational–interest–symbolic response measures. Incidentally, whether we actually use the simple score just proposed above, the number of stimuli to which more than an agreed insignificant level of response is made, or some more complex function of magnitude and number, does not need to be pursued at this stage.

The state and trait issue, on the other hand, is more fundamental, because we may need to make distinctions here analogous to those which the physical scientist makes in the hierarchy of force, energy or work, and power. Measures of a state of arousal are analogous to force, because at the moment of measurement we have ascertained nothing about how that arousal would fall off with fatigue when a load is applied. The work–energy equivalent is surely the product of the arousal level and some distance through which a task is carried on, for example, a fluency level multiplied by the number of domains in which it is exercised to a given completeness of product. Hoping for a continuation of this analogy with physical science concepts, we would then define the power of an individual as the rate at which he can do work, as just defined. (Actually, what in popular terms is called an "energetic man" would be in these more organized times a man with a powerful mind.)

Since the trait concept, that of power, has to be derived from the state concept—that of force, equated to arousal level, has to be derived by time and accomplishment functions applied to the state measures—our attention to basic definition has to turn to the state measurement. For brevity we have talked of one state, that of "arousal", or "activation" (Duffy, 1962; Malmo, 1959), popular among physiological and animal psychologists. But the multivariate experimental study of psychological states in man looks with justifiable sophisticated doubt upon that concept as used currently in animal psychology. Where is the proof that it is a unitary dimension in the domain of states? How do we know that the neurological reticular system and other associations said to be characteristic of arousal (Berlyne, 1962) are not in fact just as much associated with anxiety, stress, elation and other dimensions.

The fact is that by 1957 the work of Williams (1954), Haverland (1953) and others had demonstrated a unitary state pattern, characterized by low electric skin resistance, high blood glucose and low ataxia, etc. which I indexed as *P.U.I.* 1 (1957) and which in the work of Barton and others since (Cattell and Barton, 1972) has clearly emerged as the reliable core of state response in the descriptions of an arousal pattern. Its relations to anxiety, stress, etc. have been explored for some time at the second order (Cattell, 1960) and confirmed (Cattell and Barton, 1972) as positively involved with stress and the adrenergic response and negatively related to withdrawal and anxiety.

But the relations so often speculated about concerning the role of arousal in motivation have long remained at the level of hunches (see Berlyne, 1962; Duffy, 1962). According to one theory in the dynamic calculus, arousal would be expected (a) to coincide with one component among the motivation component factors—both *U* and epsilon would be candidates for such identification—and (b) to appear as a general second or third order factor of "generalized motivation strength" running through all the primary drive strengths. So far (see Cattell, 1957, p. 566) no such comprehensive second order factor has been found, and if it is to emerge it will probably be at the third order level.

However, the higher order exploration so far has been with individual difference measures and the structure we are now discussing would be expected to appear more clearly in states. A substantial P-technique research combining for the first time *U* and *I* measures on ten dynamic factors and measures on arousal and other states (Cattell and Bolz, in press) should at last give definite evidence one way or the other on the identity or functional relationship of dynamic, motivational tension measures to the general states of arousal, anxiety, etc.

Summary of Needed Experimental Clarifications—in Seven Questions

Let us conclude, as promised, by putting in the form of crucial questions the key issues for research suggested by a close scrutiny of the present state of motivation theory, as embodied in the checked model of the dynamic calculus:

(1) The fact that diverse strength of motivation measures, no matter what the interest content, yield seven or eight primary and two or three secondary components, has been amply verified in human and in animal measures. But, although the patterns are clear, we still lack a decision on their theoretical nature, opinions on which spread from (a) stimulation and deprivation components, to (b) ability patterns multiplied

by motivation, (c) state components, e.g. arousal, anxiety, and (d) structural theories of integrated and unintegrated motivation. What crucial experiments can now decide among these?

(2) The measurement of conflict has been successfully pursued up to a certain level by two distinct formulations: (a) as a function of relations among dynamic measures, and (b) by factoring signs and symptoms of conflict, which seems to lead to personal susceptibility to conflict factors, of which low ego strength may be a typical cause. Which of the several models suggested for predicting these conflict manifestations is best?

(3) Is it possible that some of the general personality factors, found in diverse objective behavioral measures and indexed by *U.I.* numbers, are really generalized dynamic factors, i.e. factors obtainable in motivational measures alone by neglecting the specific interest measure as such and abstracting generalized ways or styles, e.g. control, conflict in interaction of dynamic elements?

(4) *Comprehensive learning description* requires a *tri-vector representation. Structured learning theory* aims to relate changes in these three vectors of dependent variables to independent variables comprehending traits, states and experiences of reward. The experimental exploration of structured learning theory can now begin because we have the tools: batteries for objective measurement of general states, ergic tension levels, and reward as tension reduction, as well as the matrix models for analysis of data. The questions posed here are: "Can the objective measures be made brief and convenient enough for the demands of reasonably practical experiment?" And "Will the global approach relating all dependent to all independent variables through matrices lead quickly enough, despite the linear additive approximation, to the more specific and functional hypotheses for learning?"

(5) Dynamic adjustment, and the "emotional learning" registered through change therein, are most completely described by the dynamic lattice, which has in it the tri-vector values and additional information on intermediate subsidiation relations. In investigating the lattice and its changes the main question which arises concerns the potency of experimental designs. "Do the distinct methods of factor analysis and dynamic equivalence experiment converge on the same result?"

(6) Recent research fully supports the hypothesis that two of the three vectors will change as expected in our learning theory. (It also gives tentative support to the coordinated change in elements of a trait pattern being the result of coordinated reinforcement schedules in the environment.) But evidence on change in the modulation vector is lacking. Two ways in which this change could arise are hypothesized:

(1) By the co-excitation (classical conditioning) principle, and (2) By the goal-rewarded tension modulation (a form of means–end learning) principle. The question now needing to be asked by experiment is "Do these principles account for the modulation of the third vector and are they sufficient to account for it?"

(7) Psychologists have been unable either to define the concept of "energy" or to give it up. If it is to be given an operational basis, that basis is most likely to be found in the framework of the dynamic calculus. Analogues to the physical scientist's force, energy and power are examined and the most promising beginning would seem to be relating force to a momentary state, arousal. There is, indeed, already a hypothesis that a general factor will be found at a higher order in measures of the strengths of all dynamic primary factors which will prove to be identical with the arousal pattern, P.U.I. 1, defined factor analytically. Exploring this experimentally is part of the answer to a more general question: "What is the relation of the general psychological states—arousal, stress, anxiety, elation, etc. to the dynamic structure factors, especially in the integrated and unintegrated scores for the chief ergic tensions?"

COMMENT ON CATTELL'S PAPER

K. PAWLIK

Dr. Cattell aims at liberating multivariate personality research from the confines of static cross-sectional data collection designs (*R* analysis), suggesting a generalized frame of reference for multivariate process and motivation analysis. In so doing he strikes a most important and promising vein and reminds us of the fact that studying personality without due reference to longitudinal processes would lead us away from psychological reality. I am in agreement with him on these general grounds and with respect to a number of the specifics. However, at the same time, there are many points in Cattell's paper on which I either cannot agree in a strict methodological sense or would like to see some clarification. I shall briefly pick the ones which to me seem to be of a more general nature.

1. Several of the equations in Cattell's paper (e.g. equations no. 1, 2, 3, 4, 7, and 9) are of a hypothetical kind; their heuristic status is that of models of behavior. The difficulty I had with some of these models relates to my failure to see how they could be tested empirically. How can one tell whether or not man functions according to equation (3) or (7), for example? In addition, problems of parameter estimation come

up frequently. For example: how would one estimate the parameter a_{kd} (modulating index) in equation (1) independently of the estimate of the *b*-loadings? I have the impression that in Cattell's system of equations the number of unknowns may already exceed the number of knowns.

2. In his theoretical reflection, Cattell seems to take the morphological validity of (at least some of) these models for granted, such as in his section "The Extra Motivational Determiners of Conflict" where he says ". . . its essential form is as follows . . .". Incidentally, equation (7) following this sentence seems incompatible with equation (1), since, without further assumptions, taking a difference on the left-hand side in equation (1) cannot produce a quotient on the right-hand side within the framework set by a linear model.

3. I wonder whether the three-vector description of learning in equation (8), let alone its solvability, is in fact superior to a straightforward and direct factoring of practice data, e.g. via *T* factor analysis or, for the case of more than one dependent measure of the learning process, three-mode factor analysis or multivariate analysis of variance. From my own work on factorization of practice data more than one "change vector" (see Cattell, The Introduction of three classes of Measurable Predictors in learning theory) would seem to be the rule.

4. One further point. In the section just referred to Cattell sets out what he calls a "structural learning theory". Expressed in standard factor analytic terminology, in this theory he presupposes that learning will have an effect on both the factor loadings of the behavior variables *and* the factor endowment of the subjects. If X_1 is the score matrix prior to learning and X_2 is the corresponding matrix after learning, this amounts to stating that for

$$X_1 = A_1F_1 \qquad\qquad X_2 = A_2F_2 \tag{1}$$

the inequalities

$$A_1 \neq A_2 \qquad\qquad F_1 \neq F_2 \tag{2}$$

will hold (assuming that learning will not effect the number of factors in question as, I think, Cattell does too). Notice though that these assumptions get us into at least three problems:

(i) Because of the inequalities in equation (2) the parameters in equation (1) cannot be solved for in any unique way. Presumably one could say the factor structure for matrix X_1 should exhibit simple structure, but would a similar assumption be at all meaningful under the circumstances given for the factor structure of matrix X_2?

(ii) If equation (2) above is to hold, then, by definition, the factors cannot be identified between structure 1 and structure 2. Since both loadings *and* factor scores are expected to change, a factor matching between the 2 structures is rendered logically impossible.

(iii) There is a third drawback in this model. Equation (1) above would suggest that X_1 and X_2 be analyzed separately, i.e. submitting each set of data to a separate factor analysis. In this case, however, differences between 1 and 2 in terms of test means and test variances are cancelled out. However, in learning research it is these very differences which one would like to account and explain!

All these problems are bypassed, on the other hand, if one chooses a three-mode factor analytic or a multivariate analysis of variance model for the multivariate analysis of practice data.

There are a few minor points in Cattell's paper which struck me too. For example, the concept of "summation" over the negative behavioral indices" in equation (5) is indeterminate because the sign of a loading only reflects the direction of scoring the variable and the model does not state that there is one and only one direction of scoring which would be *the* "true" one on *a priori* grounds.

Nevertheless, there are many general points in Cattell's paper which I could fully subscribe to, and which I have indicated already in the beginning section of my comments. They relate to the general approach of stressing the need for a multivariate analysis of learning and practice data. And I could not agree more with the statement that motivational concepts resembling the notion of "mental energy" indeed "should be kept out of decent psychological discourse"!

COMMENT ON CATTELL'S PAPER

BENJAMIN FRUCHTER

In the analysis of behavior, motivation is an intuitively appealing concept, but it has been surprisingly difficult to pin down in terms of objective measurement and other criteria. One possible reason for its elusiveness may be that, basically, it is a dynamic trait, but most of the schema used in its analysis have been based on static models. Cattell is to be commended for introducing a dynamic component as well as its interactions with other major psychological concepts, and for taking into account the effect of the ambient situation and conditions under which the response occurs in his formulation of multivariate motivation theory in relation to learning and other aspects of behavior.

When dealing with dynamic traits and their variation over time a number of special methodological problems need to be considered. As has been widely recognized, dealing directly with the differences between scores as indicators of change is usually unsatisfactory, especially for measures which are highly correlated or of low reliability, since the differences are frequently less reliable than the measures from which they were derived. In general, correlational procedures, either by themselves or in combination with other analytical methods, circumvent this problem and are preferable for analyzing change or variation over time.

Cattell's formulations mostly take this consideration into account. He refers to the types of factor analysis that are appropriate for factoring over occasions and the types of results that can be expected from those analyses, such as determining the nature of the variations in the same manifest performance that occur at different points along the learning curve or with changing conditions.

REFERENCES

Anderson, E. E. (1938). The inter-relationship of drives in the male albino rat. *J. genet. Psychol.* **53,** 335–352.

Barton, K. and Cattell, R. B. (1972). Personality factors related to job promotion and turnover, *J. consult. Psychol.* **19,** 430–435.

Barton, K., Cattell, R. B., and Dielman, T. E. (1972). Personality and I.Q. measures predictors of school achievement. *J. educ. Psychol.*, **63,** 398–404.

Berlyne, D. E. (1962). New directions in motivation theory. *In* "Anthropology and Human Behaviour." (Gladwin, T. ed.) pp. 150–173. Anthropology Society of Washington.

Cartwright, D. S., and Cartwright, C. I. (1971). "Psychological Adjustment: Behavior and the Inner World." Rand McNally, Chicago.

Cattell, R. B. (1946). "The Description and Measurement of Personality." Harcourt, Brace and World, New York.

Cattell, R. B. (1950). "Personality: A Systematic Theoretical and Factural Study." McGraw-Hill, New York.

Cattell, R. B. (1957). "Personality and Motivation Structure and Measurement." World Book, New York.

Cattell, R. B. (1960). The dimensional measurement of anxiety excitement, effort stress, and other mood reaction patterns. *In* "Drugs and Behaviour." (Uhr, L. and Miller, J. G. eds) pp. 438–462. Wiley, New York.

Cattell, R. B. (1963). Personality, role, mood, and situation-perception: A unifying theory of modulators. *Psychol. Rev.* **70,** 1–18.

Cattell, R. B. (1966). Evaluating therapy as total personality change: Theory and available instruments. *Am. J. Psychother.* **20,** 69–88.

Cattell, R. B. (1966). The principles of experimental design and analysis in relation to theory building. *In* "Handbook of Multivariate Experimental Psychology." (Cattell, R. B. ed.) Rand McNally, Chicago.

Cattell, R. B. (1969). Personality theory and learning theory. *Proc. XIXth Int. Congr. Psychol., London Symposium,* London.

Cattell, R. B. (1970). Structured learning theory. Laboratory of Personality and Group Analysis Advance Publication No. 13. University of Illinois, Champaign, Illinois.

Cattell, R. B. (1970b). The isopodic and equipotent principles for comparing factor scores across different populations. *Br. J. math. statist. Psychol.* **23,** 1, 23–41.

Cattell, R. B. (1971). "Abilities: Their Structure, Growth and Action." Houghton Mifflin, Boston.

Cattell, R. B. (1971b). Estimating modulator indices and state liabilities. *Multivar. behavl. Res.* **6,** 7–33.

Cattell, R. B. (1972a). "Real Base True Zero Factor Analysis." *Multivar. behavl. Res. Monogr.* No. 72–1, Texas C.U., Fort Worth.

Cattell, R. B. (1972b). The nature and genesis of mood states: A theoretical model, with experimental measurements concerning anxiety, depression, arousal, etc. *In* "Anxiety: Current Trends in Theory and Research." (Spielberger, C. D. ed.). Acad. Press, N.Y.

Cattell, R. B., and Barton, K. (1973). A check by P-technique on the number and nature of the principal psychological state dimensions: Arousal, anxiety, etc. Instit. Res. on Moral. and Adjust. Advance Publication No. 11. University of Illinois, Champaign, Illinois.

Cattell, R. B. and Barton, K. (in press). The Effect of Ergic Tension Level and Reduction by Reward on Learning Rates in Class.

Cattell, R. B., and Bolz, C. (1973). "The relation of specific ergic tension levels to levels on arousal, anxiety, and other general psychological states." Instit. Res. on Moral. and Adjust. Advance Publication No. 12. University of Illinois, Champaign, Illinois.

Cattell, R. B., and Butcher, H. J. (1968). The Prediction of Achievement and Creativity. Bobbs-Merrill, Indianapolis, Indiana.

Cattell, R. B., and DeYoung, G. E. (in preparation). "Response of the Hunger erg to Deprivation."

Cattell, R. B., and Dielman, T. E. (in press). The structure of motivational manifestations in the laboratory rat: An examination of motivational component theory. *Personality; An International Journal.*

Cattell, R. B., and Hendricks, B. The sensitivity of the dynamic calculus to short-term change in interest structure. Instit. Res. on Moral. and Adjust. Advanced Publication No. 2.

Cattell, R. B., Horn, J. L., Radcliffe, J. R., and Sweney, A. B. (1964). The Motivation Analysis Test (MAT). Institute for Personality and Ability Testing, Champaign, Illinois.

Cattell, R. B., Kawash, G. F., and DeYoung, G. E. (in press). Validation of objective measures of ergic tension: Response of the sex erg to visual stimulation. *J. Expl. Res. Personality.*

Cattell, R. B., and Nichols, K. E. (1972 in preparation). Personality change associated with the first years of marriage.

Cattell, R. B., Radcliffe, J. R., and Sweney, A. B. (1963). The nature and measurement of components of motivation. *Genet. Psychol. Monogr.* **68,** 49–211.

Cattell, R. B., and Scheier, I. H. (1961). "The Meaning and Measurement of Neuroticism and Anxiety." Ronald Press, New York.

Cattell, R. B., Schneewind, K. A., and Dielman, T. E. (in press). Factor analytic evidence on the ergic structure of the rat.

Cattell, R. B., and Sweney, A. B. (1964). Components measurable in manifestations of mental conflicts. *J. abnorm. soc. Psychol.* **68,** 479–490.

Cattell, R. B., and Warburton, F. W. (1967). "Objective Personality and Motivation Tests. A Theoretical Introduction and Practical Compendium." University of Illinois Press, Champaign, Illinois.

Cross, K. Patricia. (1951). "Determination of Ergic Structure of Common Attitudes by P-technique." Unpublished master's thesis, University of Illinois.

Dielman, T. E., Cattell, R. B., and Kawash, G. F. (1971). "Three studies of the manipulation of the fear erg." Laboratory of Personality and Group Analysis Advance Publication No. 14. University of Illinois, Champaign, Illinois.

Duffy, E. (1962). "Activation and Behavior." Wiley, New York.

Freud, S. (1962—first published 1923). The Ego and the Id. Norton, New York.

Graffam, D. T. (1967). Dickinson College changes personality. *Dickinson Alumnus* **44,** 2–7.

Haverland, E. M. (1953). An experimental analysis by P-technique of some functionally unitary varieties of fatigue. Unpublished master's thesis, University of Illinois.

Haverland, E. M. (1954). "The application of an analytical solution for proportional profiles rotation to a box problem and to the drive structure in rats." Unpublished doctoral dissertation, University of Illinois.

Hempel, W. E., and Fleishman, E. A. (1955). A factor analysis of physical proficiency and manipulative skill. *J. appl. Psychol.* **39,** 12–16.

Hendricks, B. (1971). "The sensitivity of the dynamic calculus to short term change and interest structure." Unpublished master's thesis, University of Illinois.

Hull, C. L. (1943). "Principles of Behavior." Appleton, New York.

Hunt. J. McV., Ewing, T. N., Laforge, R., and Gilbert, W. M. (1959). An integrated approach to research on therapeutic counseling with samples of results. *J. counsel. Psychol.* **6,** 46–54.

James, W. (1890). "Principles of Psychology." Holt, New York.

Krug, S. E. (1971). "An examination of experimentally induced changes in ergic tension levels." Unpublished doctoral dissertation, University of Illinois.

Madsen, K. B. (1961). "Theories of Motivation." Howard Allen, Cleveland.

Malmo, R. B. (1959). Activation: a neuropsychological dimension. *Psychol. Rev.* **66,** 367–386.

McDougall, W. (1932). "Energies of Man." Methuen, London.

Rickels, K., *et al.* (1966). The effects of psychotherapy on measured anxiety and regression. *Am. J. Psychother.* **20,** 261–269.

Spence, J. T., and Spence, K. W. (1966). The motivational components of manifest anxiety. *In* "Anxiety and Behavior." pp. 291–324. (Spielberger, C. D. ed.) Academic Press, New York and London.

Spence, K. W. (1956). "Behavior Theory and Conditioning." Yale University Press, New Haven.

Tolman, E. C. (1932). "Purposive Behavior in Animals and Men." Appleton, New York.

Tolman, E. C. (1949). There is more than one kind of learning. *Psychol. Rev.* **56,** 144–155.

Tucker, L. R. (1966). Learning theory and multivariate experiment: Illustration by determination of generalized learning curves. *In* "Handbook of Multivariate Experimental Psychology." (Cattell, R. B. ed.) Chapter 16. Rand McNally, Chicago.

Williams, H. V. (1954). A determination of psychosomatic functional unities in personality by means of P-technique. *J. soc. Psychol.* **36,** 39–50.

Williams, J. R. (1959). A test of the validity of the P-technique in the measurement of internal conflict. *J. Personality* **27,** 418–437.

A Multidimensional Theory of Depression*

T. WECKOWICZ

The Center for Advanced Study in Theoretical Psychology
University of Alberta

Introduction

The purpose of this paper is to show how multivariate concepts and methods could be useful in clarifying some theoretical and practical issues in the field of psychopathology. Since the topic of this symposium is not psychopathology but multivariate theory in general, the substantive issues touched upon are not important in themselves in the present context. However, they will be presented as an example of a case where traditional classificatory schema and the conventional univariate approach had failed, and where the multivariate approach holds definite promise.

Formulation of the Problem

The ambiguity of the concept of depression has always been a stumbling block in the investigation of the etiology, progress and treatment of this condition. The concept of depression is sometimes used to describe the mood of the patient and at other times as a nosological entity. Depression as a mood and depression as a nosological entity (disease entity) are concepts belonging to different locations on the empirical (observation data)—theoretical continuum. While the first refers to the data of more or less immediate observation, the other is deep in the nomological network of more or less explicit theoretical conceptualizations. As a result of this conceptual confusion, not always realized by various authors, the phenomena referred to as "depression"

* This theoretical paper is based on depression research carried out by the author and his associates at the Department of Psychiatry of the University of Alberta. The author wishes to acknowledge the financial support by Canadian Government National Health grants and also to express gratitude to K. A. Yonge, the chairman of the Department, for his help and encouragement.

are conspicuous for their heterogeneity. Mendelson (1959), who reviewed the literature concerned with the classification of the concept of depression, pointed out that the reason why various authors have arrived at different psychopathological interpretations of depression was the heterogeneity of their clinical samples. Different clinical syndromes with different outcomes tend to be labelled by a single term: "depression". For example, the type of depression characterized by sadness, guilt, and retardation is very different from the type of depression characterized by extreme agitation with hypochondriacal and nihilistic delusions. Both of these in turn differ markedly from the state of depression encountered in late adolescent patients. Such cases are characterized by apathy, inability to enjoy oneself, lack of interest in people and things, and inability to establish significant relations with other people. The lack of agreement and objectivity with respect to conceptual formulations regarding the symptoms of depression has prevented the establishment of criteria both for prognosis and for choosing the different kinds of therapies most suitable for different kinds of depression. Moreover, this lack of agreement and objectivity regarding the descriptive framework thwarted most of the research into the etiology of depressive states—research concerned with genetic, biochemical, and experiental determinants. Previous attempts at conceptual formulations followed traditional medical models stressing univariate relations, or followed intuitive multivariate formulations without the benefit of modern mathematical tools. The most prominent and the earliest of the descriptions and classifications of the depressive phenomena is the medical model of the "disease entity". Let me add that the "disease entity" model is not the only medical model. Alongside of it, throughout the ages, there has existed at least another medical model, which I like to call the "Hippocratic-Galenic" model. This second model is implicitly a multivariate-constitutional model. It postulates the existence of certain constitutional parameters ("humors"). An individual's constitution, temperament, and also his state of health and disease, depend on the values of these parameters characteristic for him, either permanently or temporarily. However, the more influential model in medical thinking, particularly in modern times, has been the model of "disease entity". The metaphysical implications of this model will be stated briefly. The conceptual roots of the "disease entity" model are in Aristotelian philosophy. It is assumed that the observed phenomena (symptoms) are separable into neat, clearly defined classes (syndromes), and that these classes are manifestations of essences (entities) called disease. One can discern two levels in this model: the observational one, which includes "syndromes" and "symptoms", and the theoretical one, "disease". In modern times doctors have not talked explicitly about essences. The latter were replaced by such notions as "pathogenic factors", "bacteria", "pathological mechanisms", and so on; however, an implicit metaphysical presupposition is still there. This presupposition is quite obvious in psychiatric nosology where, in a great majority of cases, "pathogenic factors" or "pathological mechanisms" are unknown and only speculated about. "Schizophrenia", "manic-depressive psychosis" and "paranoia" are often regarded as real essences behind phenomena by a traditional psychiatrist when he is ignorant of the causal mechanisms.

The inadequacy of the "disease entity" model in psychiatry has been pointed out many times before (Costello, 1970), so it does not need to be referred to here again. It suffices to say that one of the main drawbacks detracting from the heuristic value of the traditional psychiatric nosology is the fact that the categories of patients with symptoms corresponding to various disease entities are very poorly delineated. Very few cases present a disease picture in a pure culture. Most cases present mixed symptomatology. This state of affairs prompted some clinicians to postulate, *ad hoc*, certain dimensions along which patients varied, with "disease entities" representing the extremes of distributions. Thus, in schizophrenia the dimension of "reactive-process" and in depression various dimensions, such as "endogenous-exogenous (reactive)", "psychotic-neurotic", and "retarded-agitated", have been postulated in recent years. These dimensions have been used in various quasi-experimental studies following the univariate paradigm. An attempt is often made to treat such a dimension as an independent or dependent variable in relation to another one; for example, performance on certain tests, behavior in an experimental situation, reaction to medication, certain antecedent events in childhood, and so on. The nature of these relations is predicted by a hypothesis. The results of such studies are by and large ambiguous and contradictory (Costello, 1970; Buss, 1966; Beck, 1967). It is obvious that patients, similar to healthy individuals, vary on more than one dimension. The problem is to find a suitable mathematical model to represent most usefully and reliably the dimensionality and, thereby, the important parameters of the phenomena under investigation. There are many available mathematical models: principle component analysis, factor analysis, various scaling techniques such as Guttman's facet model (Guttman, 1965), Coombs' unfolding technique (Coombs, 1964), Lazarsfeld's latent structure analysis (Lazarsfeld, 1950), to mention only the better known ones.

Each method has its advantages and disadvantages. However, the present author feels that, provided some assumptions are met, carefully planned factor-analytical studies, discriminant function studies and multiple regression analyses, followed by hypothesis testing experiments using multivariate analysis of variance methods, appear to be the most promising approach.

Multivariate Studies of Depression

The depression research is perhaps the most striking example in the field of psychopathology where the univariate methods have failed. In view of the subjectivity of the description and classification of depressive illness prevalent in clinical psychiatry, some attempts have, in recent years, been made to develop more objective methods. One method involves the use of inventories of depressive symptoms and rating scales of various aspects of depression. The literature on this subject, which is considerable, has been reviewed by Lorr (1954), and Cutler and Kurland (1961). Another method involves objective tests, such as psychomotor retardation (Cropley and Weckowicz, 1965; Weckowicz, *et al.*, 1973) and various physiological measures, such as salivation (Strongin and Hinsie, 1939, a, b), reactions of blood pressure (Funkenstein, 1954; Funkenstein, Greenblatt and Solomon, 1952), and sedation threshold (Shagass, 1956). Using these methods there is a possibility, not only of a more objective assessment of depressed patients than simply on the basis of clinical impressions, but also of quantifying the observed phenomena. Once reliable measurement techniques of various symptoms and signs of depressive syndrome have been evolved, it is possible to intercorrelate these measures and to carry out factor analyses or some other multivariate technique. In fact, several factor analytic studies of patients' scores on rating scales, symptom check lists, and patients' answers on various inventories have been carried out. Since the purpose of this paper is not a literature review but a discussion of basic concepts, and since there already are in existence some reviews of the literature (Costello, 1970; Weckowicz, *et al.*, 1971), the factor analytic studies of depression will not be reviewed here in detail. Instead, some issues to which these studies address themselves and some misconceptions implicit in some of these studies will be mentioned.

Many investigators use factor analysis to confirm or deny the existence of the traditional types of depression, thereby very often implicitly equating obtained factors with disease entities and therefore with classes of patients. This has been commented upon before (e.g. Weckowicz, *et al.*, 1971), but it bears repetition, since the message does not seem to register with clinical investigators. Factors are dimensions or essential parameters of the universe of described phenomena; they are consistent with either the presence or absence of discrete types or taxonomic categories. They are equally consistent with an *n*-variate population distributed evenly in the factorial space (*n*-variate rectangular distribution) or with an *n*-variate unimodal distribution (highest density in the center with thinning out of the distribution at the periphery of the factorial space) or with a multi-modal *n*-variate distribution (a distribution with several clusters of high density of subjects situated in different parts of the factorial space). In the discovery of objectively existing clusters and multi-modal distributions of subjects the method called "taxonome", described by Cattell and Coulter (1966), is particularly useful. Only in the case of multi-modal distributions is one justified to talk about "types" or discrete disease categories. In other cases, dividing distributions into types implies quite arbitrary divisions of the population or separation of the extremes of the distributions from their central part and consideration of the extremes as representing "types" in a pure culture.

Another general criticism which can be made of some of these studies is the following one: in many of them, particularly those carried out in the United Kingdom, there is a tendency to extract too few factors, very often only two or three, leave them unrotated, and then to base various theoretical inferences on the obtained bipolar factors. This has happened in studies of Kiloh and Garside (1963); Carney, Roth and Garside (1965); Kay, Garside, Beamish and Roy (1969a); Hamilton and White (1959). In all these studies a bipolar factor separating "endogenous" from "neurotic" depressives was found, and an argument was made on the basis of this finding for the validity of the traditional categories of "endogenous" and "neurotic" depressions.

The last problem I would like to mention in connection with the discussion of factor analytic studies of depression is the problem of homogeneity versus heterogeneity of the samples of subjects. In order to obtain factors variation of test measures which are to be factor analyzed is required. The wider the range and the larger the variance the better. However, it is also true that for some measures low scores and high scores may load on different factors, and different populations may reflect different factorial structures in a given test domain. For example, given a constant test battery, homogenous samples of depressed subjects yield multiple factors of depression, while heterogenous samples consisting of depressed and non-depressed subjects very often yield only one general factor of depression (Weckowicz, *et al.*, 1967). Furthermore, how is one to distinguish between depressed and non-depressed patients if both are to be included in a sample? Obviously both the population from which the sample is to be selected and the combination of tests to be used depend on the purpose of the factor analysis. This purpose may be broadly characterized as establishing, on the basis of the principle of parsimony, the essential parameters of a set of measures considered important for a given universe of phenomena and a given population of subjects. The clinician needs to be reminded that this purpose requires at least as much care in multivariate research as in the more traditional bivariate research.

Toward a Multidimensional Theory of Depression

In this section some speculations will be presented on the form multidimensional theory of depression might take. These speculations are based on the multivariate, mainly factor analytic, studies of depression by the present author and his associates, as well as on multivariate studies of other authors. Also, some recent work on possible causation of depression will be touched upon. What follows is offered as only tentative suggestions and does not represent a firmly established and validated theory of depression.

First, a few points on two possible theoretical approaches in the field under discussion. The first approach is purely statistical and should be called empirical or theoretical in the "weak" sense of theoretical. It is concerned with prediction of certain outcomes. A set of factor scores is obtained from a battery of tests, rating scales, inventories and so on. These factor scores are then used in a multiple regression or a discriminant function to obtain a best prediction of the outcome of different kinds of therapies and of general prognosis of the patients. Examples of such studies are the study of Weckowicz, *et al.* (1971) on objective therapy predictors in depression and the study of Kay, *et al.* (1969b) involving a five to seven year follow-up of 104 cases of "endogenous" and "neurotic" depression. The second multivariate approach is in the "strong" sense of theoretical and is concerned with the identification of the discovered factors or other parameters as related to some causal mechanisms. This cannot be done directly; factors as such are not "causes". However, a parameter of covariation of certain variables may serve as a clue as to a possible biochemical or some other causal mechanism. A hunch as to what is involved is then tested by a series of experiments. Since multiple mechanisms are usually involved, preferable designs for testing the hypotheses are factorial designs with multiple independent and multiple dependent variables requiring multivariate analysis of variance techniques. The independent variables may be organismic variables measured in factor scores (groups of individuals defined by certain factor scores) or biochemical variables manipulated by administration of pharmacological agents or some other method. There are very few studies of this nature concerned with depression. Studies by Weckowicz, *et al.* (1971), Weckowicz, *et al.*, (1973) are pioneering attempts moving in this direction.

An interesting early theoretical formulation which may be useful for the modern multivariate studies is that of the Heidelberg School of Psychiatry (Schneider, 1958; Jaspers, 1963). A distinction was made by this school between "personality development" and "disease process". These two aspects were regarded as largely independent of one another. Comments have already been made on the shortcomings of the concept of disease in psychiatric nosology. Nevertheless, the "Heidelbergers" pointed to a useful distinction between permanent personality traits and states more transient than personality traits but lasting longer than states (such as mood or fatigue). These states of medium duration were called "disease processes". This distinction is particularly relevant to so-called "depressive illnesses" which run time limited courses, usually of a few months duration, and change over time. Different sets of factors may be required to describe permanent personality traits and temporary depressive states (Delhees and Cattell, 1971). Also, it may be that different and independent causal mechanisms are involved in "personality development" and "disease processes".

In a recent study of 170 depressed subjects, Weckowicz, *et al.* (1971) found 20 rather "narrow" first-order factors and six second-order factors. This factor analysis implied a hypothetical hierarchical model of depression which is presented in Fig. 1. The first second-order factor, accounting roughly for 20% of the common factor variance, was identified by measures of insomnia, psychomotor retardation, withdrawal, somatic complaints, and age; it received low loadings from measures of general anxiety, autonomic reactivity, and salivation. This factor was named by the authors "somatic factor of retarded depression". (See Fig. 1.) Although patients scoring high on this factor were more severely ill, they had better prognoses and responded well to ECT (electric shock treatment). Thus, the patients' scores on this factor helped to differentiate what is commonly known as psychotic from neurotic depression. However, the latter classification is not satisfactory and should be replaced by that of "retarded" and "non-retarded" depression (Colbert and Harrow, 1967; Kay, Garside, Roy and Beamish, 1969b). These results agree with those of Kay, *et al.* (1969b), who found that retarded, more severely depressed, older patients have a better prognosis than non-retarded, initially less severely depressed patients. In the study of

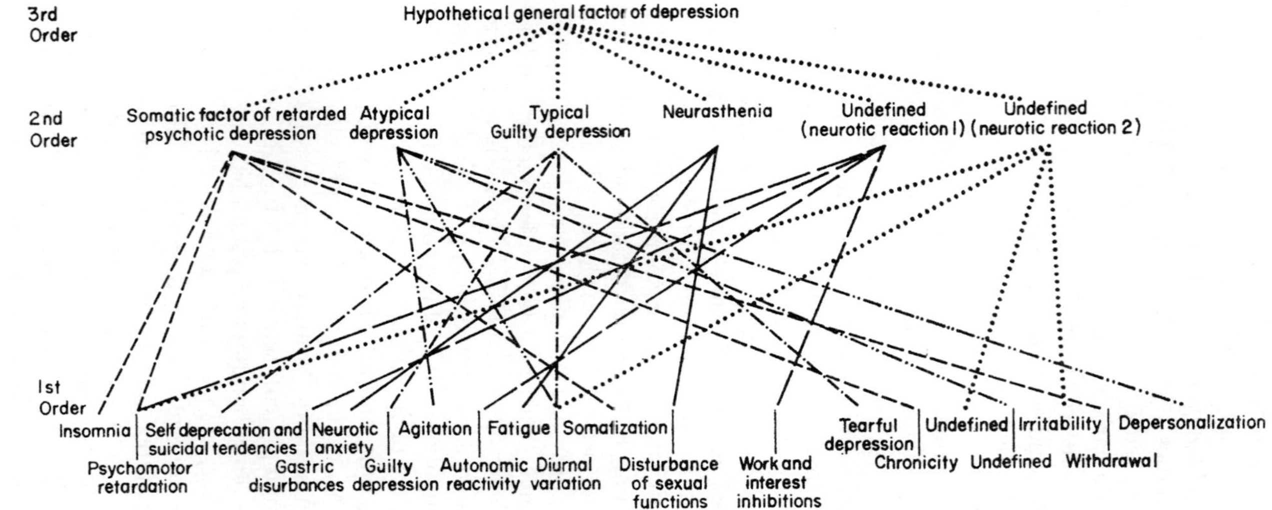

Fig. 1. Hierarchical Model of Depression.

Weckowicz, *et al.* (1971) age loaded highly on the first second-order factor. Thus, older patients are more severely ill, more retarded, subject to insomnia; however, they have a better prognosis and respond better to ECT than younger patients. Kay, *et al.* (1969b) controlled their sample for age, but still found a relationship between retardation, on the one hand, and patients' prognosis and response to ECT on the other. Similar factors, loading high on subjective feelings of retardation and incapacity or objective indices of retardation, were found in other studies (Weckowicz, Muir, and Cropley, 1967; Cropley and Weckowicz, 1966; Hamilton and White, 1959; Grinker, *et al.*, 1961; Overall, 1962; Friedman, *et al.*, 1963; Kiloh and Garside, 1963; Carney, Roth and Garside, 1965; Rosenthal and Klerman, 1966). Coppen (1967) has suggested that "retarded depression" (which may be most profitably defined in terms of high scores on a factor of retardation) is a useful criterion for biochemical research. There is some indication that metabolic abnormalities are more likely to be present in severely depressed patients with retardation than in patients without it (Board, *et al.*, 1957; Rosenblatt and Chanley, 1965; Anderson and Dawson, 1962, 1963; Anderson, 1968). Also, there is some evidence that retarded depressed subjects are deficient in dopamine and respond favorably to L-DOPA treatment (McClure, 1971; Bunney, Janowsky, and Goodwin, 1969; Bunney, Murphy and Brodie, 1970). The theoretical significance of this finding will be discussed later on.

Speed of performance on various cognitive and psychomotor tests has been investigated independently from the context of depressive illness (Babcock, 1940, 1941; Furneaux, 1961). Several of these studies were factor analytic (Payne and Hewlett, 1960; Payne, 1961, 1970; Horn and Cattell, 1966, 1967). Some evidence exists to the effect that there is more than one speed factor and that the speeds of motor, perceptual, and complex cognitive functions are relatively independent from one another and are controlled by different mechanisms (Rimoldi, 1951; Shapiro and Nelson, 1955; Payne, 1961, 1970). In a recent article Hicks and Birren (1970) reviewed the whole field of psychomotor slowing as related to aging, brain damage, and the relevant neurophysiological research. They have postulated two possible mechanisms: one accounts for speed of perception as related to "attention", "alertness" and "vigilance" and is associated with the functions of the mesencephalic ascending reticular activating system and the diffuse thalamic projective system; the other mechanisms account for the speed of voluntary movements and is associated with the function of the basal ganglia (*Caudate Nucleus*, *Globus Pallidus*, *Substantia Nigra* and the extral pyramidal system). The latter mechanism provides the optimal posturaadjustment and muscular readiness for initiating and executing movements. To quote the authors, "Heightened vigilance permits optimal detection of the stimulus, while optimal background postural and muscular adjustments provide the basis for initiating and executing movements rapidly" (Hicks and Birren, 1970, p. 391). A gross failure of this system produces Parkinson's disease or other forms of Parkinsonism. However, less severe malfunctioning will produce motor retardation; that is, difficulty in initiating and carrying out voluntary movements which often can only be detected by specific tests of psychomotor functioning. It is now well established that dopamine plays an important role in the function of the basal ganglia, very likely being the synaptic transmitter substance of the neurons of the ganglia. L-DOPA, a metabolic precursor of dopamine which, in contrast to the latter, passes the blood-brain barrier, is now widely used for treatment of Parkinson's disease (Cotzias, *et al.*, 1967). This disease is now considered to be caused by a deficiency of dopamine in the basal ganglia. Also, it has been reported that L-DOPA administration increased speed of performance on a psychomotor test (Meier and Martin, 1970). Another possible brain mechanism related to initiation of voluntary movements has been suggested by Vanderwolf (1971), at least for the rodent brain, on the basis of electro-physiological studies. This involves an ascending pathway from the diencephalon to the hippocampus and the neo-cortex which serves as a triggering-off mechanism for the organismic drive centers in the diencephalon to start voluntary actions pre-programmed in the hippocampus and the neo-cortex. This mechanism could be responsible for initiating motivated voluntary acts. Blocking this mechanism could produce an inhibition of the expression of instinctive activity and could explain some of the symptoms of depression. Thus, there are three possible mechanisms: the basal ganglia extrapyramidal system controlling motor speed, the ascending reticular activating system controlling vigilance, and Vanderwolf's diencephalic-limbic mechanism responsible for triggering voluntary actions. All three could be involved, in varying degrees, in different cases of depression. However, the basal ganglia-extrapyramidal system controlling motor speed is more likely to be associated with the factor of psychomotor retardation established in several factor analytical studies of depression. Depressed patients scoring high on this factor are probably those who respond to L-DOPA treatment. In a recent study (Weckowicz, Nutter, Cruise, and Yonge, 1972; Weckowicz, Cairns, Nutter and Cruise, 1973), a 2×3 factorial design was used involving two factors, depressed patients versus non-depressed normals, and three levels of age. Several psychomotor, perceptual information processing, speed, and also a few power, tests were used as dependent variables. Multivariate analysis of variance and covariance indicated that tests measuring psychomotor speed were most strongly associated with the diagnosis of depression. The effect of depressive illness on psychomotor speed was stronger than that of age. Also some of the tests of psychomotor speed, e.g. simple reaction time, were particularly affected by the depressive illness and less so, or not at all, by age. An alpha factor analysis of the dependent variable measures followed by Varimax rotation established (in both depressed and non-depressed normal groups, combined, and in each group separately) a factor of psychomotor speed, while measures of the speed of other functions (e.g. perceptual speed) loaded on other factors. The movements found to be slowed down in depressed patients were voluntary movements, since the speed of acquisition and latencies of classically conditioned eyelid reflexes were not affected. These findings suggest that the speed regulating mechanism which is mainly affected in depression is that associated with the rich in dopamine, basal ganglia-extrapyramidal system. The functioning of this mechanism is measured by factor scores on the "somatic factor of retarded depression" (Weckowicz, *et al.*, 1971). The loadings on this factor indicated that psychomotor retardation co-varied with insomnia and low reactivity of the autonomic nervous system. It would seem, therefore, that the functioning of other physiological systems is measured also by this factor and that the functioning of these systems co-vary with that of the basal ganglia system. The sleep disturbances in depression are caused primarily by decreased slow waves ("delta") (Iskander and Kaelbling, 1970) and, therefore, may be associated with a deficiency in serotonin (Jouvet, 1968). Whether the low reactivity of the autonomic nervous system is associated with a deficiency in the production of free noradrenaline in the hypothalamus and other diencephalic areas in depressed patients, as suggested by Schildkrout (1965), is very difficult to affirm with any degree of certainty in the present state of our knowledge. The three different mechanisms regulating psychomotor speed, sleep and autonomic nervous system reactivity were represented by the loadings of their measures on the first second-order factor (Weckowicz, *et al.*, 1971). However, each of them also yielded rather specific separate first-order factors. Thus, these data suggest a hierarchical system with the three mechanisms in question being to a certain extent independent and autonomous, but, at the same time, being regulated by a common higher center. This would explain the intercorrelations of the first-order factors in question and the loadings on the common second-order factor.

The second second-order factor found by Weckowicz, *et al.* (1971) was a factor accounting roughly for 12% of the common factor variance. This factor was not so well defined, but it loaded high on the first-order factor of agitation and other factors representing such symptoms as paranoid ideas, depersonalization, hypochondriacal ideas, and diurnal variation. It could represent an involutional dimension accompanied by schizoid features. This factor was named "atypical depression". The mechanisms responsible for variance expressed by the second-order factor must be different from the mechanisms associated with the first second-order factor. It is impossible to state now whether these mechanisms are to be characterized as those of personality development or disease process. The non-typical in classical depression schizoid features represented by this factor may be a reflection of the fact indicated by population genetic studies that there is a stronger link between involutional depression (involutional melancholia) and schizophrenia than between the former and manic-depressive (typical) depression (Kallman, 1959). The personality type (personality development) found to be associated with this kind of depressive illness (presumably in patients having high scores on this factor) is the "anankastic" personality (Schneider, 1958), characterized by obsessionality, rigidity, and excessive sensitivity. It is difficult to make a suggestion as to what physiological mechanisms could be implicated in the symptoms measured by this factor.

The third second-order factor, accounting for approximately 10% of the common factor variance, was the factor named by Weckowicz, *et al.* (1971) as "typical guilt depression". The first-order factors representing psychological symptoms of depression, such as depressive mood, guilt, suicidal tendency, self-deprecation, and self-hate, tended to load high on this second-order factor. This configuration of symptoms is typically associated with the classical picture of depressive illness. It might be asked why this factor has accounted for only 10% of the variance. The answer to this question may be simple. Since the samples consisted only of depressed subjects, there could have been relatively little variation in these symptoms (all patients feeling sad, guilty and having suicidal tendencies). Had the sample been heterogenous, consisting of depressed as well as non-depressed subjects, this factor could have accounted for most of the variance and indeed could become "a general factor of depression". A novel and rather unexpected finding however, confirmed by two independent factor analytic studies (Cropley and Weckowicz, 1966; Weckowicz, *et al.*, 1967) is the relative independence of a cluster consisting of ideas of unworthiness, suicidal tendencies, and self-hate, and a cluster of psychomotor retardation and sleep disturbances (the two clusters of symptoms loaded on two separate second-order factors). This finding suggests relatively independent causal mechanisms responsible for the two clusters of symptoms. It is difficult to know whether the symptom cluster described by the third second-order factor is determined primarily by physiological mechanisms (disease process) or experiential influences (personality development). The mood of sadness and unhappiness loaded mainly on the third second-order factor and to a lesser extent through a first-order factor of "fearful depression" on the first second-order factor of "somatic retarded depression". Thus, depressed mood may be associated with the cognitive-attitudinal aspect of depression characteristic of such symptoms as ideas of unworthiness, delusions of sin, self-hate, and suicidal preoccupations, loading on the third second-order factor of "typical guilty depression", or it may be associated with purely somatic changes represented by the first factor.

Recently some physiological and neuro-chemical mechanisms controlling mood have been suggested. To some extent these suggestions spring from the discovery of reward centers in the brain by Olds and Milner (1954) and the hedonic theory of motivation inspired by this discovery. Depressed mood has been attributed to noradrenaline deficiency in the diencephalic reward centers (Schildkrout, 1965; Stein, 1966) or to deficiency in tryptamine or phenylethylamine (Dewhurst, 1968). Finally, serotonin (5-hydroxytryptamine) deficiency has had its proponents as the mechanism underlying depressive mood and other depressive symptoms (Coppen, 1967; Lapin and Oxenkrug, 1969).* Should biochemical mechanisms regulating mood be firmly established, there remains the question whether these mechanisms are an expression of personality development (chronic neuronal alterations resulting from prolonged learning, stress and adjustive changes) or whether they are entirely somatically determined outcomes of a "disease process" which is independent of experimental factors. Sudden and spontaneous changes of mood typical of some depressive and manic–depressive states argue against a personality development type of explanation. However, there is also strong evidence that cognition plays an important role in determining the quality of affect and mood (Schachter and

* It is not the purpose of this paper to review in detail the biochemical theories of depression. In parentheses, it can be mentioned that apart from the biogenic amines (noradrenaline, serotonin, dopamine and tryptamine), changes in the electrolytic balance at the nerve membrane and various endocrine disturbances have been suggested as causative agents in depression. Some of these agents may be implicated in the pathogenesis of depression in conjunction with one another as parts of complex, self-regulating, biochemical systems. Thus, the necessity for a multivariate approach exists also at the biochemical level. The interested reader is referred to critical reviews of the subject by Coppen (1971) and McClure (1968). More partisan theoretical formulations are presented by Schildkrout (1965) and Dewhurst (1968).

Singer, 1962). It can be suggested, therefore, that measures of the purely physiologically determined components of affect (pleasure–pain) should load on Factor I, while the cognitive component of affect should load on Factor III. However, the answer to this hypothesis cannot be given until more precise measures of the two aspects of affect (mood) are found.

Taking a leap in the dark, a tentative suggestion can be offered that the third second-order factor of "typical guilty depression" represents a personality development factor which is characteristic for depressed patients. This personality development may be described as a cognitive strategy* developed by these patients in the course of their lives. The term "cognitive strategy", rather than "ego defence" is preferable because it is more in keeping with contemporary theorizing in psychology and is not committed to the psychoanalytical theory. For example, Beck (1967) has proposed a theory along these lines which can be described as a cognitive theory of depression. He has suggested, on the basis of his own and other workers' investigations, that a depressed subject, because of a series of disappointments in life, such as a bereavement in childhood, develops a pessimistic attitude and an expectation of defeat. The expectation of defeat and failure then works as a self-fulfilling prophecy with a snowballing effect. The depressed subjects come to view the world as a hostile, disappointing place. They become sensitized to failure and come to perceive themselves and thc world in unfavorable and foreboding terms. This hypothesis is being tested currently, using experimental situations, such as betting, risk taking, reaction to frustration, aspiration level, and the locus of control (Nutter, Cruise, Andreotti, Weckowicz and Yonge, 1973).

The fourth second-order factor found by Weckowicz, *et al.* (1971) was characterized as that of "bodily fatigue and neurasthenia exhaustion". (See Fig. 1.) The fifth and sixth factors could be both characterized as factors of "somatization and hypochondriasis". Little needs to be said about these factors. They account respectively for 8·5%, 7·7%, and 6·2% of the common factor variance, are rather poorly defined, and are concerned with somatic complaints of a neurotic nature. They probably represent different cognitive strategies or ego-defences occurring in some depressive patients and belong to the category of personality development rather than disease process.

* The term "cognitive strategy" has in this context a broader denotation than that of "cognitive styles" (Gardner, *et al.*, 1959). It refers not only to the style of processing immediate information input, but also, and to a greater extent, refers to expectancies, goals, and general ethos of life. In this respect, it is more like Adler's "life of style" than "cognitive style". An alternative term, "coping strategy" can also be suggested.

Although the intercorrelations among the second order factors were rather low, there is some indication that this might be due to the limitation of the sample only to depressed patients. With a mixed patient population, there emerges a large, general factor of depression.

To summarize the main features of the multidimensional model of depression emerging from these studies: a hierarchy of first and second-order factors has been found with the first-order factors representing rather narrowly delineated traits. A tentative suggestion has been made that some second-order factors may represent the "disease process" (e.g. first factor), while other second-order factors may represent "personality development" (e.g., third, fourth, fifth, and sixth factors). A longitudinal study may indicate whether this suggestion is correct. The factor scores of the "personality development" factors should remain much more stable and change less over time than the factor scores of the "disease process" factors, since the former represent relatively permanent traits while the latter reflect more changeable states. The proposed theory has some limitations arising from the limitations of the mathematical model underlying it. The assumptions are made of additivity, linearity, and an absence of significant interactions. Particularly the latter assumption may not be justified and result in spurious factors representing interactions rather than independent agents. However, the proposed model may be a useful first approximation having some heuristic value. It is likely that more powerful mathematical multivariate models than the factor analytic model will be forthcoming in the near future. These models may be more adequate for a formulation of causal theory of depression in contrast to a descriptive one based on the factor analytic model. Be this as it may, one conclusion appears to be certain, at least to the author of this paper: univariate, unidimensional theories of depressive illness are not adequate. A conceptual model of gene causing deficiency in one enzyme, thereby leading to abnormal metabolism, although adequate for explanation of congenital metabolic diseases such as phenylpyruvic idiocy (phenylketonuria), is not adequate as an explanation of depressive illness and other functional psychoses. More complex explanatory systems are needed. The fact that these conditions have a recurrent or phasic course would suggest that more than one parameter, biochemical or behavioral or both, is required. Von Bertalanffy (1968) has pointed out that oscillations from a steady state with "false starts" and "overshoots" are typical for complex open systems. Some stochastic models ("random walks") undergoing phasic changes have also been suggested (Snell, 1965). Even if the ultimate explanation of depressive illness is to be genetic and biochemical, it probably will be polygenic in character, involving a system of enzymatic reactions, rather than one gene, one enzyme and one biogenic amine.

In conclusion, it has to be stressed once again that the intention of this paper is not to present a clearly articulated, finished theory of depression, but rather to indicate the direction in which theorizing about depression may usefully develop. The ideas suggested in this paper could at their best only serve as prologomena to a multidimensional theory of depression.

Summary and Conclusions

The traditional descriptions and categories based on a univariate approach in psychopathology are by and large found to be unsatisfactory. This is particularly striking in the case of so-called depressive phenomena or "depression". The methodological pitfalls of the multivariate approach to the investigation of depression are discussed. The necessity for careful planning of factor-analytic studies with respect to the selection of tests and subjects is stressed. A tentative descriptive multivariate theory of depression based on experimental studies of the author and the studies of other investigators is put forward. It is suggested that there may be at least three independent dimensions of depressive phenomena. The first is concerned with somatic disorders such as insomnia, loss of appetite, constipation, and psychomotor retardation. The second dimension is characterized by involutional, obsessional, and mildly paranoid symptoms. The third dimension is associated with the typical symptoms of depression such as guilt feelings, self-deprecation, suicidal tendencies, and with depressive (sad) moods. The significance of this tentative model is discussed within the framework of the "disease process"—"personality development" formulation of the Heidelberg school of psychiatry, and hypotheses regarding etiology of depression are put forward.

REFERENCES

Anderson, W. McC. (1968). "The isolation of primary affective illness." Paper read at meeting of Northern and Midland Division, R.M.P.A., April.

Anderson, W. McC. and Dawson, J. (1962). The clinical manifestations of depressive illness with abnormal acetyl methyl carbinol metabolism. *J. ment. Sci.* **108,** 80–87.

Anderson, W. McC. and Dawson, J. (1963). Verbally retarded depression and sodium metabolism. *Br. J. Psychiat.* **109,** 225–230.

Babcock, Harriet. (1940). Personality and efficiency of mental functioning. *Am. J. Orthopsychiat.* **10,** 527–531.

Babcock, Harriet. (1941). "Time and Mind." Sci-Art Pub., Cambridge, Mass.

Beck, A. T. (1967). "Depression: Clinical, Experimental and Theoretical Aspects." Harper and Row, New York.

Board, F., Wadeson, R. and Persky, H. (1957). Depressive affect and endocrine functions. *A.M.A. Archs. Neurol. Psychiat.* **78,** 612–620.

Bunney, W. E. Jr., Janowsky, D. S. and Goodwin, F. K. (1969). Effects of L-DOPA on depression. *Lancet,* (1970). **1,** 885.

Bunney, W. E. Jr., Murphy, D. L. and Brodie, H. K. H. (1970). Further studies with L-DOPA in depressed patients. *Lancet* **1,** 352.

Buss, A. H. (1960). "Psychopathology." John Wiley, New York.

Carney, M. W. P., Roth, M. and Garside, R. F. (1965). The diagnosis of depressive symptoms and the prediction of E.C.T. response. *Br. J. Psychiat.* **111,** 659–674.

Cattell, R. B. and Coulter, M.A. (1966). Principles of behavioural taxonomy and the mathematical basis of the taxonome computer program. *Br. J. math. statist. Psychol.* **19,** 237–269.

Colbert, J. and Harrow, M. (1967). Psychomotor retardation in depressive syndromes. *J. nerv. ment. Dis.* **145,** 405–419.

Coombs, C. H. (1964). "A Theory of Data." John Wiley, New York.

Coppen, A. (1967). The biochemistry of affective disorders. *Br. Psychiat.* **113,** 1237–1264.

Costello, C. G. (1970). Classification and psychopathology. *In* "Symptons of Psychopathology: A Handbook." (Costello, C. G. ed.) John Wiley, New York.

Cotzias, S. C., Van Waert, M. H. and Schiffer, L. M. (1967). Aromatic amino acids and modification of Parkinsonism. *New Engl. J. Med.* **276,** 374.

Cropley, A. J. and Weckowicz, T. E. (1965). The retardation factor in depression. *Can. Psychiat. Assoc. J.* **10,** 37–42.

Cropley, A. J. and Weckowicz, T. E. (1966). The dimensionality of clinical depression. *Aust. J. Psychol.* **18,** 18–25.

Cutler, R. P. and Kurland, H. D. (1961). Clinical classification of depressive reactions. *Archs. gen. Psychiat.* **5,** 88–93.

Delhees, K. H. and Cattell, R. B. (1971). The dimensions of pathology: Proof of their projection beyond the normal 16 PF source traits. *Personality* **2,** 149–173.

Dewhurst, W. G. (1968): New theory of cerebral amine function and its clinical applications. *Nature, Lond.* **218,** 1130–1133.

Friedman, A.S., Cowitt, B., Cohen, H. W. and Granick, S. (1963). Syndromes and themas of psychotic depression. *Archs. gen. Psychiat.* **9,** 504–509.

Funkenstein, D. H. (1954). Psychophysiological studies of depression: Some experimental work. *In* "Depression." (Hoch, P. N. and Zubin, J. eds) Grune and Stratton, New York.

Funkenstein, D. H., Greenblatt, M. and Solomon, H. C. (1952). An automatic nervous system test of prognostic significance in relation to electro shock treatment. *Psychosom. Med.* **14,** 347–362.

Furneaux, W. D. (1961). Intellectual abilities and problem solving behaviour. *In* "Handbook of Abnormal Psychology." (Eysenck, H. J. ed.) Basic Books, New York.

Gardner, R. W., Holzman, P. S., Klein, G. S., Linton, H. and Spence, D. P. (1959). Cognitive control: A study of individual consistencies in cognitive behavior. *Psychol. Issues* **1,** No. 4.

Grinker, R. R., Miller, J., Sabshin, M., Munn, R. and Nunnaly, J. C. (1961). The Phenomena of Depressions. Harper and Row, New York.

Guttman, L. (1965). A faceted definition of intelligence. *Scr. Hierosolymitana* **14,** 166–181.

Hamilton, M. and White, J. M. (1959). Clinical syndromes in depressive states. *J. ment. Sci.* **105,** 985–997.

Hicks, L. H. and Birren, J. E. (1970). Aging, brain damage and psychomotor slowing. *Psychol. Bull.* **74,** 377–396.

Horn, J. L. and Cattell, R. B., (1966). Age differences in primary mental ability factors. *J. Geront.* **21,** 210–220.

Horn, J. L. and Cattell, R. B. (1967). Age differences in fluid and crystallized intelligence. *Acta Psychol.* (*Amst.*) **26,** 107–109.

Iskander, T. N. and Kaelbling, M. K. (1970). Catecholamines, a dream sleep model and depression. *Am. J. Psychiat.* **127,** 43–50.

Jaspers, K. (1963). "General Psychopathology." Manchester University Press, Manchester, England.

Jouvet, M. (1968). Insomnia and decrease of cerebral 5-hydroxytryptamine after destruction of raphe system in the cat. *Adv. Pharmacol.* **6** (Supp.) 265–279.

Kallmann, F. J. (1959). The genetics of mental illness. *In* "American Handbook of Psychiatry." (Arietti, S. ed.) Basic Books, New York.

Kay, D. W. K., Garside, R. F., Beamish, Pamela, and Roy, J. R. (1969a). Endogenous and neurotic syndromes of depression: A factor analytic study of 104 cases: Clinical features. *Bri. J. Psychiat.* **115,** 377–388.

Kay, D. W. K., Garside, R. F., Roy, J. R., and Beamish, Pamela. (1969b). "Endogenous" and "neurotic" syndromes of depression: A 5-to-7 year follow-up of 104 cases. *Br. J. Psychiat.* **115,** 389–399.

Kiloh, L. G. and Garside, R. F. (1963). The independence of neurotic depression and endogenous depression. *Br. J. Psychiat.* **109,** 451–463.

Laplin, I. P. and Oxenkrug, G. F. (1969). Intensification of the central serotoninergic processes as a possible determinant of the thymoleptic effect. *Lancet* **1,** 132–136.

Lazarsfeld, P. F. (1950). The logic and mathematical foundation of latent structure analysis. *In* "Measurement and Prediction." (Stauffer, S. A. ed.) Princeton University Press, Princeton, N. J.

Lorr, M. (1954). Rating scales and checklists for the evaluation of psychopathology. *Psychol. Bull.* **51,** 119–127.

McClure, D. J. (1971). Biochemistry of depression. *Can. psychiat. Assoc. J.* **16,** 247–252.

Meier, M. J. and Martin, W. E. (1970). Measurement of behavioral changes in patients on L-DOPA. *Lancet* **1,** 352–353.

Mendelson, M. (1959). Depression: The use and meaning of the term. *Br. J. med. Psychol.* **32,** 183–192.

Nutter, R., Cruise, D., Andreotti, L., Weckowicz, T. E. and Yonge, K. (1973, in preparation). Cognitive strategies in depression.

Olds, J. and Milner, P. (1954). Positive reinforcement produced by electric stimulation of septal area and other regions of rat brain. *J. comp. physiol.* **47,** 419–427.

Overall, J. E. (1962). Dimensions of manifest depression. *Psychiat. Res.* **1,** 239–245.

Payne, R. W. (1961). Cognitive abnormalities. *In* "Handbook of Abnormal Psychology." (Eysenck, H. J. ed.) Basic Books, New York.

Payne, R. W. (1970). Disorders of thinking. *In* Symptons of Psychopathology—A Handbook." (Costello, C. S. ed.) John Wiley, New York.

Payne, R. W., and Hewlett, J. H. S. (1960). Thought disorder in psychotic patients. *In* "Experiments in Personality." (Eysenck, H. J. ed.) Volume 2: Psychodiagnostics and Psychodynamics. Routledge and Kegan Paul, London.

Rimoldi, H. J. A. (1951). Personal tempo. *J. abnorm. soc. Psychol.* **46,** 283–303.

Rosenblatt, S. and Chanley, J. D. (1965). Differences in the metabolism of norepinephrine in depressions. *Archs of gen. Psychiat.* **13,** 495–502.

Rosenthal, S. and Klerman, G. L. (1966). Endogenous features in depressed women. *Can. Psychiat. Assoc. J.* **11** (special supplement), 11–16.

Schachter, S. and Singer, J. E. (1962). Cognitive, social and physiological determinants of emotional state. *Psychol. Rev.* **69,** 379–399.

Schildkrout. J. J. (1965). The catecholamine hypothesis of affective disorders: A review of supportive evidence. *Am. J. Psychiat.* **122,** 509–522.

Schneider, K. (1958). "Psychopathic personalities." Charles C. Thomas, Springfield, Illinois.

Shagass, C. (1956). Sedation threshold: A neurophysiological tool for psychosomatic research. *Psychosom. Med.* **18,** 410–419.

Shapiro, M. B. and Nelson, E. H. (1955). An investigation of the nature of cognitive impairment in co-operative psychiatric patients. *Br. J. med. Psychol.* **28,** 239–256.

Snell, J. L. (1965). Stochastic processes. *In* "Handbook of Mathematical Psychology." (Luce, R. D., Bush, R. R. and Galanter, E. eds) John Wiley, New York.

Stein, L. (1966). Psychopharmacological aspects of mental depression. *Can. Psychiat. Assoc. J.* **11** (special supplement), 14–49.

Strongin, E. J. and Hinsie, L. E. (1939a). Parotid gland secretion in manic depressive patients. *Am. J. Psychiat.* **94,** 145–149.

Strongin, E. J. and Hinsie, L. E. (1939b). A method of differentiating manic-depressive depressions from other depressions by means of parotid secretions. *Psychiat. Q.* **13,** 697.

Vanderwolf, C. H. (1971). Limbic-diencephalic mechanisms of voluntary movement. *Psychol. Rev.* **78,** 83–113.

Von Bertalanffy, L. (1968). "General System Theory." George Braziller, New York.

Weckowicz, T. E., Muir, W. and Cropley, A. J. (1967). A factor analysis of the Beck Inventory of Depression. *J. consult. Psychol.* **31,** 23–28.

Weckowicz, T. E., Yonge, K. A., Cropley, A. J. and Muir, W. (1971). Objective therapy predictors in depression: A multivariate approach. *J. clinic. Psychol. Monogr. Supp.* **31,** 1–27.

Weckowicz, T. E., Nutter, R. W., Cruise, D. G. and Yonge, K. A. (1972). Speed and test performance in relation to depressive illness and age. Paper presented at the conference, Psychiatric Research at Crossroads, sponsored by the G.W.N., Montreal, October, 1970; to appear in *Can. psychiat. Assoc. J.* **17,** ss 241–ss 250.

Weckowicz, T. E., Cairns, M. and Cruise, D. G. (1973, in preparation). Performance of depressed subjects and normals on a battery of psychomotor tests: A multivariate approach.

The Psychological Structure of Peer-Group Forces in Delinquency

DESMOND S. CARTWRIGHT AND KATHERINE HOWARD

University of Colorado

Juvenile delinquency refers to a collection of behaviors which violate certain social norms, and which are engaged in by persons subject to those norms, and who are classified statutorily as children or youths. Typical acts include running away from home, breaking into school and burning up laboratory equipment, stealing an automobile, burglary, robbery, arson, buying and drinking liquor while under age, engaging in gang fights with weapons, and so on.

Both sociology and psychology have provided general theories of delinquency. In sociology the theories have typically focused upon rates (such as numbers of boys before the court, per 100,000 at risk) or other social concepts such as the development of subcultures. One example is the theory of disjunction between universal cultural goals and structural inequality of opportunity to attain the goals (Cloward and Ohlin, 1960). The essence of that particular theory is that everyone is invited to strive for great success in America; but persons at lower socioeconomic class positions find themselves having lesser access to the requisite opportunities such as education, good jobs, or appropriate connections. Blocked in their access to legitimate opportunity, such persons may turn to illegitimate opportunities if these exist locally. Thereby both the provocation to delinquency, the opportunity for particular kinds of delinquency, and even the sanction for delinquency may be given explanation, for it is argued that blame falls naturally upon that existing social order which both invites everyone to strive for success and systematically blocks the access of some citizens on a discriminatory basis.

In psychology, general theories of delinquency have focused upon the individual delinquent rather than upon rates of aggregates or social forms. They have naturally placed most emphasis upon psychological processes of development, learning, frustration and aggression, modelling, and so on. For example, Friedlander (1947) emphasized the role of deficiency in super-ego formation; Hathaway and Monachesi (1953) stressed more general features of personal pathology, such as psychopathic deviancy as measured by the Minnesota Multiphasic Personality Inventory.

Not all approaches to the study of delinquency have been guided by explicit theory. Many workers have sought evidence for differentiating conditions and characteristics which may be found in the personalities, biographies, and social conditions of delinquents as compared with nondelinquents. Sir Cyril Burt's classic work on *The Young Delinquent* (1925) provides an example of this approach. He found differentiating conditions present inside the home (such as poverty or defective discipline); and outside (such as bad companions); as well as differentiating personal characteristics (such as anomalies of physical development, educational backwardness, or general emotional instability).

Burt's analyses showed approximately 170 different conditions or characteristics bearing some association with delinquency. This is not an unusually large number. If we were to add up all the associations found by different investigators in the past century, it would likely total several hundred. The purpose of theory is partly to bring order into such wealth of observations. Another purpose is to attempt simplification, either by positing of certain associations as primary in a causal sense, or by arguing for the primacy of certain processes themselves more fundamental than the observed associations, by assuming some newly conceived entity, process, or relationship which casts all old things in a new perspective and allows for prediction of hitherto unobserved phenomena.

Burt's approach to this very problem was twofold: first, that of ordering by classification (into hereditary and environmental conditions, and further into physical, intellectual, and temperamental conditions with subheads under each major class); and second, that of determining through statistical analysis which class or subclass of conditions showed the highest association with delinquency. As a result he found that defective discipline in the home was the most important subgroup of conditions; next came a number of individual characteristics such as general emotional instability; and the next most important social condition was that of bad street companions (Burt, 1925, p. 607).

There is, of course, no guarantee that a condition found to be associated with delinquency in the statistical sense is in truth causally related to delinquency; and this fact has formed the basis for criticism of the empirical approach taken by Burt and others (compare Glueck and Glueck, 1950, for a later example). Moreover, it becomes quite clear upon brief consideration that different types of conditions must have different types of causal relations with delinquency if they indeed have any causal relation at all. For example, defective discipline in the home cannot possibly have the same kind of causal impact that would be wrought by bad companions on the street. These latter may directly provoke, suggest, or demonstrate delinquent behavior, while the former explicitly fails to provide whatever would be needed to counteract the likelihood that the person would yield to provocation or suggestion. Whereas the bad companions are a presence of something, the defective discipline is presumably an absence of something.

A prime motivation for development of the present model was precisely the need to clarify (and classify) different types of causal relations (Cartwright, Reuterman and Vandiver, 1966). A formal model of forces leading to commission of a delinquent act was developed which involved three panels: the recency of the condition, the source of the condition, and the type of causal relation the condition had with delinquency. Later theoretical considerations and statistical analysis showed the necessity for adding a fourth panel to the formal model: the social context.

In this paper we shall describe the formal model first, and then consider the important subset of forces involved in peer influences. After describing the measurement device employed to study these influences, we shall present our main results and consider their significance for psychological theory.

A Formal Model of Forces in Delinquency

In Fig. 1 we present a diagram of the formal model. The forces leading to a delinquent act may arise in any one of three social contexts: Family, School, or City. Within a context the force may arise from either Social or Individual sources: either the alters or the ego may initiate the force. The force may be exerted at a point in time closely preceding the occurrence of the act, and thereby be associated with the precipitation of the act; or it may have been initiated at some earlier time, and thereby contribute mainly to the predisposition for the act. The type of causal relation that the condition of force bears to the delinquent act may be one of five major kinds: Instigation, Facilitation, Permission, Diversion, or Prohibition. These terms are defined more fully below.

Instigation—Provide the push or impulse to action

A. Social: Direct personal initiation of delinquent act, luring to immorality, daring to steal, forcing to carry weapons, inviting the person to commit delinquency.

Indirect personal provocation, unjustly depriving, stressing, aggravating, frustrating the person to the point where some kind of retaliation against the aggressor or a substitute is likely.

Impersonal provocation, such as poverty, "an added spur to dishonesty" (Burt); overexciting movies, magazines, stimulating to violence, immorality, etc.

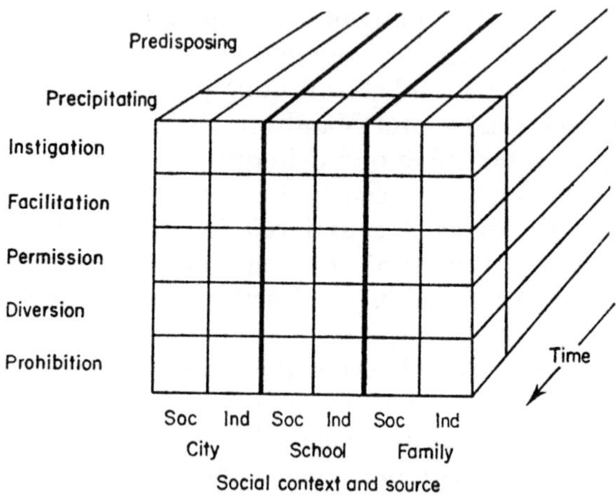

Fig. 1. The delinquency model.

B. Individual: Conscious wishes for goods, excitement, reputation, etc. fulfillment of personal ideal.

Unconscious conflict generates tension for which release is sought through delinquency; delinquency is displaced aggression or symbolic search for affection; act is compensatory for some inferiority.

Facilitation—Provide the means for carrying the impulse into actual behavior

A. Social: Assistance and opportunities. People show the person how to commit the act, or provide necessary information or tools or other means. Opportunities arise from unguarded property, left around, keys in cars, doors unlocked; dark alleys, crowded areas, places to hide, etc.

B. Individual: Physical capabilities (e.g. small enough to get through little window); skills (e.g. can make a zip gun); emotional qualities (e.g. can stay cool under pressure).

Permission—Provide sanction or tacit encouragement for an act.

A. Social: Deviant example set by parents or citizens; parents, teachers, other code-bearers lax or indifferent in discipline; people don't care or afraid to interfere in violations; friends offer protection, strengthen rationalizations, etc. enforcement inefficient or corrupted; societal anomie.

B. Individual: Personal alienation; don't-care, so-what, nothing-to-lose attitude; emotional instability, mental deficiency, ignorance of laws.

Diversion—Militate against commission of delinquent acts by preoccupying time, interest, and energy in other ways.

A. Social: Recreation programs that "keep youth off the streets" and involve them in wholesome activities; work in the usual employment sense and in the special sense of organized work programs, again designed to occupy and provide remunerative satisfaction; school and pre-employment training; special enterprises such as Big Brothers; encouragement by members of the family to engage in wholesome activities, both intra- and extra-family.

B. Individual: The personal side of involvement in work, school, or recreation; cultural interests, ability to develop sustained attention and investment of energy in constructive enterprise, hobby, sport; ability to develop trusting, admiring, affectional relationships with others, especially with persons representing stable norms of society, teachers, coaches, and so on.

Prohibition—Directly forbid, block, or threaten penalties for committing delinquent acts; or otherwise directly oppose delinquency.

A. Social: Parental supervision, control, discipline; proper supervision, counsel, and enforcement from other authorities such as teachers and police; citizen intervention; church teaching.

B. Individual: Conscience, personal scruples, disgust at violations; fear of being caught, punished, loss of social status; stake in community and sense of long-run importance to own self-image as good citizen; stake in family and complete unwillingness to risk bringing trouble.

Peer-Group Forces in Delinquency

Our primary concern in this report will be to examine the evidence relating to peer influences in delinquency. We saw above that the influence of "bad companions" was early isolated by Burt as one of the more important. The influence of peers even in ephemeral two-person groups and in gangs of increasing size and degree of organization was documented in the observational materials of Thrasher (1936). Further evidence for the strength of group forces in modifying even such apparently personal matters as performance level in baseball or bowling was provided by W. F. White (1955). The power of the street-corner group in affecting Negro adolescent behaviour in Chicago was described by Drake and Cayton (1945). Cohen (1955) made a major contribution to sociological theory in his work on the formation of subcultures among disadvantaged youth and on the role of such sub-cultural influence in the determination of delinquent behavior. Cloward and Ohlin (1960) focused attention upon the influence of different varieties of delinquent subculture in producing different kinds of delinquent behavior (such as fighting, property offenses, or drug abuse). Still within the framework of concern with gangs, Short and Strodtbeck (1964) and Cartwright, Howard, and Reuterman (1970) have shown how numerous features of group dynamics and structural characteristics affect performance of delinquent behaviors such as fighting and property offenses. Confronting also the issues of distinction between Social and Individual sources of influence, Erickson and Empey (1965) have shown that a general commitment to peers is the most highly correlated variable with general theft; next comes commitment to delinquent peer standards; third is associations with known delinquents. Similarly Lerman (1968) has shown that high reported delinquency is most likely to occur among older boys who are themselves attracted to deviant values and whose associates also support deviant values. In addition, Lerman showed that "youths who share peer values are more likely to believe that most people they know are tempted to break the law." (p. 234).

There can be little doubt then that peers exert some influence on individual delinquent behavior. There can be doubt about whether such influences are strictly and distinctly peer influences, however; for it is possible in many cases that the influences attributed to peers are really common to a wide age-range of persons within the neighborhood. Also it is not clear whether the peers in question are to be found primarily on the street corner or some other equally public place; or whether, by contrast, they are to be found in a select hideout, or perhaps in the school buildings, or even in the home. It is not clear in most cases exactly what kind of influence is strictly to be understood as exerted by peers; although it must be commonly presumed to be "bad", i.e. conducive to delinquency. Yet the concept of "bad companions" immediately suggests that there may be "good companions" too, and that the latter might exert influences which are more conducive to law-abiding behavior. There are further questions to be raised concerning the manner in which the presumed influence takes effect: by press-gang tactics including threats; or by suggestion, example, encouragement, or solicitation; or by address to existing values in the individual, either in exhortation or in attempts to control by calling into question such features as the manliness of the individual or his desirability as a member or friend.

Finally, there is the most important question of the type of social form in which the peers and the individual have commerce. Scott (1956), for example, has identified at least three major types of social forms among juvenile delinquents in London: adolescent street groups, structured gangs, and diffuse groups. These types appear to have quite different patterns of development and control over individual behavior.

In summary, peers are widely held to play an important role in influencing certain youth toward delinquent behavior. But questions abound:

Existence. Perhaps the most pressing question is whether there are so-called "peer-group influences" at all. Do they really exist? Theoretical accounts which rest upon the concept of a "delinquent subculture" have never questioned whether the subculture might in fact be "carried" by adults and "taken over" by youth from adults in the home or neighborhood. If such were exclusively the case the existence of a delinquent subculture would not at all imply that the responsible influences were really peer-group influences.

Location. If there do exist forces for delinquency which belong distinctly to peers, then where are they to be found? Most authors assume that they exist outside the home, and usually on the street. But they might exist in the home, and they might be found in the school. No systematic study has yet been made.

Source. Lay observers (such as mothers of delinquent boys) typically assume that "peer influences" mean that other people bear the responsibility for leading a youth into delinquency. But the question in fact remains open: Do peer-group influences stem primarily from manipulation of ego by alters? Or do they reside chiefly in the "commitments" of ego (to delinquent peers as persons, or to delinquent standards and values)?

Nature. Just exactly what kind of interactive influence is meant when we speak of "peer-group influence"? Several alternatives were reviewed above. At one important extreme, it is assumed that the relevant forces are toward delinquency; but there is every reason to suppose also that young people influence each other toward law-abiding behavior.

The Experience Survey

Although many different kinds of assessment can usefully provide vehicles for information concerning the categories of the model in Fig. 1, there is one method that lends itself well to representation of the forces involved. In one of his closing remarks Sir Cyril Burt asserted: "Every cause and every influence, however, no matter what its special form may be, is found to operate, and can only operate, through its inner psychological effects. Conduct and misconduct are always, in the last analysis, the outcome of mental life." (Burt, 1925, p. 608.) We have called "mental life" experience.

The Experience Survey (Cartwright, 1966, 1971) is a series of questions which ask the subject to report his experiences during a specified period of time, such as the past year. Each item begins: "During the past year, how often . . ."; and continues with its particular content, for example: ". . . have you seen adults ignore others who needed help?" The format for response has been given extensive study, and the following set of terms is currently in use:

Never	A few times	Some- times	Fairly often	Quite often	Very often indeed
0	1	2	3	4	5

It may be seen that each item asks the subject to address his memory for experiences over the given time period. In the case of "the past year" it is plausible to assume that we are dealing with predisposing conditions for or against delinquency.

Note also that the form of the item allows for the agent to be either alter or ego. In the example above, adults who ignore others are the agents. We assume that when the respondent is answering such a social item he is serving as his own ethnographer. When responding to an individual item he is assumed to be introspectively reporting his inner experience. An individual item would be, for example: ". . . how often have you felt completely bored with school?"

Consider that a particular cell in the model of Fig. 1, such as Social

School Facilitation, is unitary by fiat. The items contained within the Experience Survey representation of that cell are justified solely by judgment in the first instance. Items must then meet two criteria: test–retest reliability and external validity through positive correlation with a scale of self-reported delinquent behavior (c.f. Nye and Short, 1957, Clark and Wenninger, 1962, Smith and Cartwright, 1965). But these determinations are evidently minimal. Two further steps were taken for the present study. First, all items which had previously passed the minimal tests were subjected to examination for inter-rater agreement as to their proper cell membership within the model. Raters, familiar with the model, were required to place each item in, for example, the Social School Instigation, Individual Family Facilitation, Social City Prohibition, or other proper cell of the model. Only items that were judged with acceptable consensus ($p < 0{\cdot}05$) were retained. To fit the requirements of the research, a total of 600 items was prepared. These were arranged into six batches of 100, one batch for each of the following segments: Social City, Individual City, Social School, Individual School, Social Family, Individual Family. Within each batch there were 20 items judged to be in each of the cells (Instigation, Facilitation, Permission, Diversion, and Prohibition).

A crucial feature of each batch of 20 items within a given cell was that approximately half were phrased with adults as the agent (for social items) or referent (for individual items); approximately half were phrased with peers or friends or other children as the agent or referent. Thus it would be possible to determine whether, within a given cell, the peers stood alone as a separate class of influences, or whether their influences were mixed in with those of adults; that is, it would be possible to determine whether there exist distinctly peer influences and what they are.

Results and Implications for Theory

Data from 450 students in Colorado and Illinois public schools were studied through factor analysis.* The number of factors obtained varied between two and four across the several cells. Our first result, then, is that each cell of the model contains more than one unitary influence. On the Social side there were 50 interpretable factors; on the Individual side there were 48.

The question of existence for peer-group forces, however, rests upon whether distinct peer-group factors were found.

* Details of the research appear in the Appendix. We appreciate the collaboration of Dr. Nicholas A. Reuterman in the collection of data in Illinois. Both he and Dr. Christopher Herron played a major part in the preparation of the items for this study.

Distinct Peer Factors

By a distinct peer factor we mean a factor for which the substantial pattern coefficients all involve peers, although there may occasionally be reference to adults in a non-essential way. Twelve distinct peer factors were found. Subject to replicative confirmation, this result appears to settle the question of existence. Of the twelve distinct peer factors, eight were found in the social context of the school; four in the city; none in the home. These results provide a first answer to the question of location: peer-group influences are found outside the home; in the school more than in the city, however.

In the city, all four distinct peer factors were in the Social source category; in the school four factors each were in the Social and the Individual categories. Thus, in the city the external-agency assumption about peer-group influences appears to be substantiated; but in the school the evidence is equally in favor of forces with ego as their source. The general question of *source*, then, receives a complex answer, depending upon *location*.

As to the *nature* question about peer-group influences, the twelve distinct peer factors include at least one of every causal type of force in the model: three instigation factors, two facilitation factors, three permission factors, three diversion factors and one prohibition factor. There are other ways in which *nature* may be construed of course; and some will be taken up later. For the moment we pause to note with emphasis that some peer-group forces militate against delinquent behavior. As an example, one of two diversion factors in the city had the following pattern:*

City Peer Diversion Factor:
Peer-Initiated Constructive Activities

Item	Pattern Coefficient
has your "gang" planned any worthwhile activities (apart from things at school)?	0·62
have your friends suggested forming a group for sports activities?	0·53
have other kids in town told you about opportunities for paid part-time work?	0·46

In order to provide the reader with a second example of factor patterns in this series of data, a Social Instigation factor in the school is shown next:

* All items in this paper are taken from Cartwright, 1971.

School Peer Instigation Factor: Direct Instigation

Item	Pattern Coefficient
have other kids in school been willing to turn you on to "grass", LSD, etc.?	0·71
has someone in school told you how to get a new "kick"?	0·70
has another kid dared you to go shoplifting with him?	0·62
has another kid in school offered you a drink of beer, wine, or liquor?	0·53

Clearly in the case of delinquent behavior, the important questions are: (a) Who is providing the impetus (i.e. the source of the instigation) toward the behavior, and (b) Toward which specific forms of behavior, if any, is the individual being impelled.* In those items contributing substantially (i.e. 0·40 or higher) to *Direct Instigation*, the instigators are peers. The specific behaviors are turning on to drugs, drinking beer, etc., and going shoplifting. All three of these activities can be characterized by the phrase "getting 'kicks' ". They are not behaviors in which Cloward and Ohlin's (1960) "conflict" or "criminal" gangs would be engaged.

So that the reader may appreciate the differences in source, an Individual Instigation factor in the school is shown next:

School Peer-Oriented Instigation Factor:
Striving for "Cool" Leadership

Item	Pattern Coefficient
have you wanted to show some of the kids at school that you are just as smart as they are?	0·51
have you wanted to show the kids in school how to really get some kicks out of life?	0·49
have you felt tee'd off with the way teachers run things at school?	0·43

Striving for "Cool" Leadership is a good example of the way in which a peer-oriented individual factor involves also adults in a nonessential way. We interpret the feeling of "tee'd off with the way teachers run things" as a fretful accompaniment to the main motivation. It is as though the chief competitor for "cool" leadership is the teacher. The factor reflects a striving for status and power in school. The specific peer-related items, however, suggest that the motive is based upon deprivation in the form of feeling that others are smarter than oneself.

* An instigator can be either direct or indirect. An example of an indirect social instigator in the school is Persecution from Teachers.

For subsequent discussion of the nature of distinct peer factors it will prove convenient to list the twelve factors as in Table I.

Table I. Distinct Peer Factors in Delinquency

Segment	Factor Title
City–Social	Instigation: Aggravation Permission: Disrespect for the Police Diversion: I. Opportunities for Leisurely Entertainment Diversion: II. Peer-initiated Constructive Activities
School–Social	Instigation: Direct Instigation Facilitation: Information on Getting and Using Marijuana, etc. Permission: Negativism Toward Others Prohibition: Warnings Against Delinquency
School–Individual	Instigation: Striving for "Cool" Leadership Facilitation: Ability to Outwit Peers Permission: Felt Anonymity Among Peers Diversion: Helping Other Students

A main content of the Aggravation factor in the city is "making ego angry", "being unfair to ego", "suggesting ego is 'chicken' ". Thus it may be a direct instigator resulting in behavior aimed at the source, the peers. Or it may be an indirect instigator resulting in any form of behavior which is available and which relieves the inner tension.* From the content of the items it is not possible to predict the behavioral outcomes, but it is evident that the peers in the city can have an aggravating influence on the individual.

Two sets of peers in the city. In order to interpret these influences properly it is important to keep in mind that, for the City context in the Experience Survey, peers are forced by the instructions into two mutually exclusive groups. The peer items in the city context quite often refer to other kids "who don't go to your school". Therefore, it is likely that one group of peers in the city is either (a) from an older or younger age group than the individual, (b) not from his immediate neighborhood, or (c) not attending school at all.

The group of peers who are older or younger than the individual or who do not live in the immediate neighborhood should have less influence on his behavior than peers of the same age, school and neighborhood. Burt (1925) says: "The friendships that most commonly exert a harmful influence are friendships with others of the same age

* One dynamic model for the psychological processes involved would be that frustration leads to aggression, which under conditions of excessive threat consequent upon direct expression may be displaced upon a less threatening target.

and sex as the child himself, living outside the child's own home, but coming often from the same school and the same street, and either actively engaged in delinquency themselves, or else actively inciting and encouraging it." (p. 129.)

A second group of peers are those who go to the same school as the individual and who live in the same neighborhood. These are likely to be his close friends, and capable of influencing him more directly. Although the items which contribute substantially to the divertor, Opportunities for Leisurely Entertainment with Friends, belong to the city context, they are not phrased so as to rule out friends who attend the same school as the individual. Therefore, these peers may be close friends or simply acquaintances. Because of (a) the omission of the phrase "who don't go to your school" in the items, and (b) the kind of activities described, it seems likely that potentially positive diversion is initiated by close friends. Similarly, Peer-Initiated Constructive Activities seems to be relevant to close friends. For example, the first item, whose loading is 0·62, begins "... has your 'gang' ..." This factor, however, describes definitely constructive activities.

Two or more sets of peers in the school. While it is likely that the peers involved in diversion in the city context are also the same peers who are friends of ego in school, there are obviously other features of the peer groups at school than friendship. For example, Ability to Outwit and Felt Anonymity have an important feature in common. Each conveys a feeling of separateness from peers, a lack of community. Alerted to this characteristic it is possible to see that the "Cool" Leadership factor is also one that requires a degree of apartness from the other kids. Furthermore, the factors on the Social side in the School context can now also be seen in a similar light: Direct Instigation, Information, Negativism, and even the Warnings factors appear capable of conveyance to the child in an atmosphere of competitive presence and emotional coldness. This syndrome is reminiscent of the pluralistic ignorance which characterizes gang members (c.f. Short and Strodtbeck, 1965). Each member thinks the others really hold devil-may-care delinquent values; and each hides from the others his own tendencies to endorse non-delinquent values, not to mention his own feelings of weakness, fear, dependency, and anything else that might be counter to the professed norms of the group. A similar circumstance has been reported among some college student roommates who, despite growing inner alarm, went along with a group process of mutual stimulation which led to robbery of bank funds from a post-office (Thrasher, 1936, pp. 300–303). It seems likely also that this syndrome is related to Gordon's (1967) concept of social disability in which, among other things, inner weakness is masked by a highly competitive and hostile front presented to other gang members.

The factor Helping Other Students has items which make it clear that neither friends nor people toward whom one feels cool and distant can encompass the entire structure of peer relations at school. A salient target of help in the factor is a "younger student". Thus probably at least three subsets of peers in the school may exert influence of different kinds upon ego.

Sources and Targets. While the notion of source has entered explicitly into the formal model developed above, it has been tacitly assumed that ego is the target for Social sources. In the general understanding of peer influences it seems to be held that peers are the source and ego the target. But the several Individual factors of a distinct peer kind include some which clearly make the peers targets for ego. Striving for "Cool" Leadership is one example; Helping Other Students is another example. It is clear that pressures for and against delinquency which originate in influences associated distinctly with peers may nevertheless involve the peers in a passive rather than active way.

Sources and Channels. The notion of source in the model applies equally to all causal types of influence. However, some of the factors discovered in this research have suggested that some sources (in the formal sense) ought better be called channels (in the substantive sense). Facilitator factors offer a prime example: Information on Getting and Using Marijuana, etc., contains items referring to peers who tell where to get marijuana, where one can hide out to get intoxicated, and so on. In later discussion we shall again introduce the notion of channel in connection with factors in which both peers and adults play a role jointly.

Models. The factors Negativism Toward Others and Disrespect for the Police both contain items in which peers express anomic attitudes either verbally or in their behavior. The Negativism factor especially emphasizes the worthlessness of potential victims and of society's representatives for law enforcement. It, therefore, is a partial mirror among youthful peers at school of that wider societal state labelled Anomie by Durkheim (1951), in which, as Srole (1956) has pointed out, a central failure of interpersonal attachments is embedded in a wider breakdown of normative, socially patterned expectancies for stable successions of life experiences.

An important part of the influence of that "cold" atmosphere mentioned earlier, therefore, is apparently constituted of peers who are both demonstrating indifference themselves and reporting it (as channels) among others. In their demonstration they offer a model for ego to match.

Joint Peer–Adult Factors

In all contexts (City, School, Family) factors were found on the Social side which included both adults and peers. In previous thinking about peer influences, of course, it has always been tacitly assumed that such influences were somehow distinct from other features of the local scene. And yet it is sensible to suppose that peers and adults might share certain tendencies in a given neighborhood or society, and might also present parallel or related influences to the individual child.

In some of the joint factors the peers and the adults independently influence the individual in a simple way; in other factors peers and adults become part of a more complicated interactive process. An example of the former is provided by a factor of Devaluation by Teachers and Peers, in which such matters appear as kids putting ego down about his hair or clothes, and teachers criticizing clothes or telling ego to get a haircut. The indirect instigation is apparently carried on in a similar, parallel, but independent manner by peers and adults. An example of more complex interaction is provided by the factor Strong Controls, in which teachers are firm with the students, and kids at school mention how hard it is to get away with anything. The peer reaction here is viewed as channel for the firmness of teachers, who function as source in that respect. Both adult source and peer channel join forces in a single functional factor.

Adult influences. Strangely no one has ever focused upon adult–group influences in delinquency. The research data showed a substantial number of distinct adult factors, however. For example, in the Family Context (where there were no distinct peer factors) six distinct adult factors were found: one facilitation, three permission, and two prohibition. At the same time, ten factors in the Family Context were of the joint kind. It appears, therefore, that: either (a) the parents alone can influence the individual, and his brothers and sisters alone cannot influence him; or (b) the brothers and sisters exert influences which are the same as their parents'.

Summary

The research reported here has made possible some further developments in conceptualization of the forces in delinquency. First, the factor analyses showed that between two and four distinct forces must be posited for each one of the cells in the *a priori* structural model with which we began. Second, and more importantly for this paper, the interpretation and more detailed study of the factors involving peers enables further refinement of the conceptualization required for the general notion of "peer influences".

We have found that, quite apart from the presumably more obvious influences of gangs, there do exist distinct peer influences in the experiences of junior and senior high school students. These influences are distinct in the sense that they are not shared or interlocked with influences from adults in any obvious or essential way. Moreover, these influences are of two different kinds, namely those which are on the Social side in the sense that the peers serve as agents of experiential components impinging upon the ego, and also those which are on the Individual side, in the sense that ego is the agent of a feeling, thought, impulse, or action which is oriented toward or related to peers. However, we found also that the prevalence of these distinct peer factors varies sharply with the social context under consideration. In the School context we found both Social and Individual factors, four in each. In the City context we found only Social factors; while in the Family context we found no distinct peer factors at all.

The notion of "distinct peer influences" is to be contrasted with the notion of "joint adult–peer influences", in which both adults and peers exert influences of similar or related kinds. In order to clarify the "similar or related kinds" we have introduced the distinction between "source" and "channel" of influence. The source of an influence actually exerts and originates that influence, such as the police exert controlling influence. The channel relays to the person information concerning the existence and consequentiality of that influence, as when teachers state that police do an efficient job. Some of the joint influences of adults and peers appear to involve parallel but independent influences which are similar; they may be source influence or channel influence. Other joint factors involve related kinds of influence, as when teachers (as source) are firm with students and peers (as channel) relay the information that teachers are firm.

There is a clear need for further elaboration of these ideas through a link with the theory of persuasive communication. For example, it is known that the impact of an influence for change in attitude is a function of three attributes of the source: credibility, attractiveness, and power (McGuire, 1969). However, variables affecting the potency of the channel as a contributor to the effectiveness have been much less well explored. In the context of delinquency it seems likely that channel characteristics are quite important, since many of the factors discovered in this study are of the channel variety either entirely or in part.

We found that the topography of peer influences differs from one social context to another. For example, in the School there were both

Social and Individual distinct peer factors; while in the Family context there were only joint peer–adult factors. Within the School, the peer influences of many factors appeared to be those associated with competitive, emotionally cold relationships, probably characterized also by pluralistic ignorance of others' real feelings. In the City context two quite different groupings appeared. First, there were influences from peers who "do not go to your school". These would be older or younger, or those who have dropped out, or those who live in a different neighborhood. These peers instigate in two ways: they directly provoke aggression against themselves; and indirectly (through aggravation and ridicule) they instigate various delinquencies. By contrast there is a second group of peers in the City context, those who also perhaps do go to the same school, and whose primary function appears to be the provision of constructive diversion. We might think of these as closer school and neighborhood friendship groups, as contrasted with the first group who appear neither friendly nor close, nor even, perhaps, a group.

As we contemplate such topography from the point of view of classic distinctions between membership and reference groups, it is apparent that the Individual factors reveal membership and reference (modelling) influence from the several groups of peers. In the City the individual is a member of his friendship group which also serves as a positive reference group. In the school he is a member of the body of students, and his membership characteristics emerge strongly in such factors as Striving for Cool Leadership. Again, Ability to Outwit Peers is a factor which seems more concerned with peers as a reference group. However, the factors reveal yet another important class of relationships which should be formally recognized: peers as targets. For example, Helping other Students is a factor which most saliently relates the individual to his peers not as a member, nor in terms of reference, but as an agent to a target. Thus peers may, on the Social side, be sources; and on the Individual side, targets.

Appendix

The items in each batch of 100 were arranged on five pages, 20 items per page, with four items from each cell on each page, arranged in haphazard order. The response format was semi-forced in that respondents were requested to use the alternatives "Never" through "Very Often Indeed" (see section "The Experience Survey") with the following respective frequencies: 2, 3, 4, 4, 3, 2; and then to choose any responses for the last two. In fact, respondents only approximated this requirement.

Each batch was given to a different set of respondents. However, at any one session, all six different batches were administered: one sixth of the group received the Social City segment, for example, another sixth received the Individual Family segment, and so on. Respondents were obtained from junior and senior high schools in Adams County, Colorado, and in South East Saint Louis, Illinois. Probationer respondents were also obtained in two judicial districts of Colorado; and these subjects formed approximately one-tenth of the total sample. For each batch, usable returns were secured for between 65 and 75 subjects. Thus, for factor-analytic work on the $n=20$ items of a given cell such as Social School Prohibition, the required minimum of $3n$ subjects was always exceeded (see Cartwright, Lee and Link, 1963).

Recall that there are six separate batches; and in each batch there are five cells, of Instigation, Facilitation, etc. The design is aimed primarily at discovering the factors existing within each cell. In order to rule out the influence of dynamic connections between cells, only the items within a given cell were subjected to factor analytic study. Thus, the items entering into a factor analysis are homogeneous with respect to their classification in the model. Discovered factors, then, are assumed to reflect separate existing forces within that cell. Factors reflecting connections between cells will be studied later.

The correlation matrix of 20×20 items was factored using the principal axis method with initial estimates of communality; these estimates were the Modified Approximation B estimates of the BC TRY Executive System (Tryon and Bailey, 1970). The procedure iterates the analysis for convergence between input and obtained communalities, after once determining rank from the initial estimates. Factors were rotated to oblique positions using the Harris-Kaiser routines for independent-cluster-structure assumptions (Harris and Kaiser, 1964). This same procedure was carried out for all 30 cells of data.

COMMENT ON CARTWRIGHT AND HOWARD PAPER

S. B. SELLS

Cartwright and Howard have made a valuable contribution to theory and research on delinquency in the elegant formulation of this inquiry into the existence, location, source, and nature of peer-group forces in delinquency. While acknowledging the importance of early contributions by Burt and others, they have advanced the analysis from qualitative generalizations, such as "bad companions", to an elaborate and testable multidimensional model that articulates these forces, and through their insightful design and analysis of the Experience Survey they have carried out a productive investigation that supports their theoretical development. The factor analytic results, differentiating distinct peer factors that vary with social context, from joint adult-peer influences, demonstrate the power of multivariate analysis to pursue issues of high substantive and theoretical importance that defy laboratory and even field-experimental approaches.

This research is impressive, but, as the authors themselves have amply indicated, it represents mainly an initial step toward a remote goal. Along the road there are linkages with other developments (some of which Cartwright and Howard have mentioned) that invite serious attention, further developments of the model and of methodologies to test them, and finally integration of this model into a more comprehensive theoretical structure embracing other domains involved in the causality of delinquency. It is hoped that Professor Cartwright and his students will find the means and the opportunity to continue this excellent work.

REJOINDER TO DISCUSSANT'S COMMENT

DESMOND S. CARTWRIGHT AND KATHERINE HOWARD

We deeply appreciate Sells' thoughtful remarks about our work. Perhaps some further detail on the "remote goal" of this work will make it appear more readily attainable, however.

The present state of knowledge suggests that there are many pathways to delinquency, and our formal model of structure of forces allows for the eventual goal of finding prevalent stochastic series of force inputs into the nascent delinquent's career. A prime intermediate goal, therefore, is the determination of relevant principles of combination. For example, do forces from the individual simply add to those from the environment? Do forces from any sources build subliminally toward a threshold prior to triggering a delinquent act? How does individual instigation in the home interact with social facilitation in the city?

A still earlier subgoal is the fuller delineation of relevant environmental texture. Are there distinct adult factors in juvenile delinquency, for instance, and what are they? What are the mechanisms whereby social forces are transmitted to the individual? Here particularly, as Sells suggests, it will be necessary to integrate other theories with our present model. One very useful suggestion has just recently been given to us by Horn: namely that the modelling concepts of observational learning theory should contribute much to our understanding of how peer influences are transmitted. As another example, the recent theories of institutional labelling and limitation of access to socially desirable roles provide us with insight into the importance of a purely bureaucratic domain within the total texture of environmental forces in delinquency.

REFERENCES

Burt, Sir Cyril (1925). "The Young Delinquent." University of London Press, London.

Cartwright, D. S. (1966): E–S analysis of delinquency proneness. Unpublished manuscript, Boulder District Court Juvenile Division. Mimeo.

Cartwright, D. S., Howard, K.I. and Reuterman, N. A. (1970). Multivariate analysis of gang delinquency: II. Structural and dynamic properties of gangs. *Multivar. Behavl. Res* **5,** 303–324.

Cartwright, D. S., Lee, R. L. and Link, S. (1963). Il numero dei fattori e il numero dei soggetti. *Boll. Psicol. Appl.* Ottobre–Dicembre 1963, N. 59–60.

Cartwright, D. S., Reuterman, N. A. and Vandiver, R. I. (1966). A new multiple-factor approach to delinquency. Unpublished manuscript, Department of Psychology, University of Colorado. Mimeo.

Clark, J. P. and Wenninger, E. P. (1962). Socio-economic class and area as correlates of illegal behavior among juveniles. *Am. Soc. Rev.* **27,** 826–834.

Cloward, R. A. and Ohlin, L. E. (1960). "Delinquency and Opportunity." Free Press, Glencoe, Illinois.

Cohen, A. K. (1955). "Delinquent Boys." Free Press, New York.

Drake, St. Clair and Cayton, H. R. (1945). "Black metropolis." Harcourt Brace, New York.

Durkheim, E. (1951). "Suicide." Free Press, New York.

Erickson, M. L. and Empey, L. T. (1965). Class position, peers and delinquency. *Sociol. Soc. Res.* **49** (3), 268–282.

Friedlander, K. (1947). "The Psycho-analytical Approach to Juvenile Delinquency." Kegan Paul, London.

Glueck, S. and Glueck, E. (1950). "Unraveling Juvenile Delinquency." Harvard University Press, Cambridge, Massachusetts.

Gordon, R. A. (1967). Social level, social disability, and gang interaction. *Am. J. Sociol.* **73,** (1), 42–62.

Harris, C. W. and Kaiser, H. F. (1964). Oblique factor analytic solutions by orthogonal transformations. *Psychometrika* **29,** 347–362.

Hathaway, S. R. and Monachesi, E. (1953). "Analyzing and Predicting Juvenile Delinquency with the MMPI." University of Minnesota Press, Minneapolis.

Lerman, P. (1968). Individual values, peer values, and subcultural delinquency. *Am. sociol. Rev.* **33** (2), 219–235.

McGuire, W. J. (1969). The nature of attitudes and attitude change. *In* "The Handbook of social Psychology." (Lindzey, G. and Aronson, E. eds), (second edtn). Vol. III, pp. 136–314. Addison-Wesley, Reading, Massachusetts.

Nye, R. I. and Short, J. F., Jr., (1957). Scaling delinquent behavior. *Am. sociol. Rev.* **22,** 326–331.

Reuterman, N. A. (1968). A new multiple-factor approach to delinquency and its application to types of juvenile offenders. Unpublished Doctoral Thesis, Department of Psychology, University of Colorado.

Short, P. (1956). Gangs and delinquent groups in London. *Br. J. Delinquency* **7,** 4–26.

Short, J. F., Jr. and Strodtbeck, F. L. (1965). "Group Process and Gang Delinquency." University of Chicago Press, Chicago.

Smith, D. O. and Cartwright, D. S. (1965). Two measures of reported delinquent behavior. *Am. sociol. Rev.* **30** (4), 573–576.

Srole, L. (1965). Social integration and certain corollaries. *Am. sociol. Rev.* **21,** 709–716.

Thrasher, F. M. (1936). "The gang: A study of 1,313 gangs in Chicago." (second edn), University of Chicago Press, Chicago.

Whyte, F. W. (1955). "Street corner society." (Enl. ed.), University of Chicago Press, Chicago.

Author Index

Numbers in italics refer to the pages on which references are listed at the end of each chapter.

N

O

P

Y

Z

Subject Index